# COLLEGE ALGEBRA
# and TRIGONOMETRY

# COLLEGE
# ALGEBRA
—————————— and
# TRIGONOMETRY
## A Basic Integrated Course

**FREDERIC H. MILLER**
Professor of Mathematics, The
Cooper Union School of Engineering

*2nd Edition*

JOHN WILEY & SONS, INC., New York
CHAPMAN & HALL, LTD., London

# Preface

TO THE SECOND EDITION

All the original features of the first edition have been retained for this revision. In particular, no marked changes have been made in the content, methodology, or organization of the book.

The major innovation has been made in connection with the exercises. Nearly all of the lists have been replaced in order to provide fresh problems for the student; it will be found, however, that the new exercises are similar to the initial ones, and that the present lists are likewise well graded and comprehensive. In addition, a list entitled Supplementary Exercises has been inserted at the end of each chapter after the first elementary review chapter. These adjunct problems are intended to provide further choice, more extensive and broader review, and the stimulation of some new concepts and methods. The inclusion of these fifteen new lists brings the total number of exercises to more than 2100, an increase of about 13 per cent over the number in the first edition.

Most of the text material has been left untouched. However, Chapter I (Fundamental Algebraic Operations) and Art. 68 (Variation of Algebraic Functions) have been rewritten and somewhat expanded to provide more detailed explanations and examples. Minor changes and additions have also been inserted at various other points.

As in the first edition, necessary tables are given in the appendices and answers to all exercises have been included. A new appendix, Meanings of Symbols, has been inserted.

F. H. M.

New York, N. Y.
*May, 1955*

v

# Preface

Elementary mathematics, starting with simple arithmetic and progressing through calculus, constitutes a body of thought in which the student's understanding and absorption of new concepts and new techniques depend at each stage upon how well he has grasped his previous mathematical training. The student who has a firm foundation of arithmetic, algebra, geometry, and trigonometry will in all likelihood have no difficulty with analytic geometry and calculus; without that proper background, the latter subjects may be insurmountable obstacles.

It is largely in recognition of this fact that the subjects of algebra and trigonometry are taught in the colleges. College algebra may sometimes be studied before trigonometry; in other cases, trigonometry may become part of the student's training before college algebra; or the two subjects may be acquired together. Some of the topics usually included in college algebra have been encountered before by those students who have had secondary-school courses in advanced algebra, and at least the material relating to the solution of triangles is familiar to those students who have had high-school courses in trigonometry. But in college courses in algebra and trigonometry, the analytical aspects of these subjects, which give the student the essential background for subsequent mathematical study, require the major emphasis. Furthermore, since these two subjects are not in separate compartments, but aid each other in forming the foundation for more advanced mathematics, they can well be combined into a single preparatory course.

This book is based on the above premises. It does not consist of merely a conventional textbook on college algebra and the familiar trigonometry textbook bound together in one volume. Instead, as indicated by the subtitle, it is an attempt to give an integrated treatment of the two subjects on the college level, and to lay a suitable foundation for the study of more advanced mathematics.

The choice of material included in the book and the manner in which it is presented are both governed by these aims. Throughout, algebra and trigonometry support and complement each other, and the techniques of both subjects are applied continually. The only major topics omitted are partial fractions and infinite series; these have been ex-

cluded because it is believed that they properly belong in the course in
calculus. As regards other topics, the Table of Contents will give some
indication of the scope of the book and of its methodology. The following specific features are believed to be worthy of mention.

1. In Chapter I, the development of number systems is discussed
first, to give motivation to the adoption of the basic assumptions and
definitions of algebra.

2. In order to develop trigonometry as an analytic tool, the general
definition of an angle is used as a starting point in Chapter III, and
trigonometric functions of general angles are discussed before the special
case of an acute angle in a right triangle. The importance of the radian
as a unit angle is stressed, and radian measure is used thereafter whenever convenient so that the student will find it natural to deal with this
system in later work.

3. The integration of algebra and trigonometry is begun in Chapter
IV, on identities and conditional equations. Algebraic and trigonometric identities are discussed together, and methods for solving algebraic and trigonometric equations are likewise considered as one broad
type of problem. This chapter also includes an elementary classification of functions, for the student's difficulties with college mathematics
are often the result of his inability to identify the forms of the functions
with which he deals.

4. In connection with linear systems (Chapter V), all the necessary
theory and applications of determinants are developed. Both conti-
nuity and motivation are gained by passing directly from a consideration of second- and third-order determinants to determinants of order $n$.

5. Infinite geometric progressions afford an excellent opportunity to
introduce the prospective student of calculus to the important limit
concept and its applications, and consequently these matters are discussed in detail in Chapter X.

6. In view of the importance of inequalities in connection with the
study of functional variation, their treatment in current textbooks
seems to be too brief and incomplete. Accordingly, this topic has been
given unusually careful and detailed consideration in Chapter XI.
Both algebraic and trigonometric inequalities are treated.

7. In addition to the customary material on direct, inverse, and combined variation, Chapter XIII contains a discussion of functional variation as applied to both algebraic and trigonometric functions. This
is another topic that seldom receives adequate attention in mathematics
textbooks, but one which is quite important to the proper analysis of
functional relations in analytic geometry and calculus.

8. The variation and properties of exponential and logarithmic functions are considered in Chapter XIV, in order that the student may acquire facility in dealing with transcendental equations.

9. The method of successive approximations, rather than Horner's or Graeffe's method, is used to determine irrational roots of algebraic equations in Chapter XV. Transcendental equations are also discussed, and here the method of successive approximations is likewise employable.

10. Necessary tables for converting from sexagesimal to radian measure, tables of common logarithms, and tables of trigonometric functions and their logarithms are given in the Appendix. Answers to all exercises are also included.

I wish to express my appreciation and thanks for the aid given me by Mr. Sidney G. Roth, who carefully read the manuscript and made many helpful suggestions.

FREDERIC H. MILLER

NEW YORK, N. Y.
*January, 1945*

# Contents

FOREWORD TO THE STUDENT . . . . . . . . . 1

## I · FUNDAMENTAL ALGEBRAIC OPERATIONS

ARTICLE

1. Number Systems . . . . . . . . . . . 3
2. Assumptions and Definitions . . . . . . . . 7
3. Derived Properties of Algebraic Quantities . . . . . 9
4. Laws of Exponents . . . . . . . . . . . 14
5. Radicals . . . . . . . . . . . . . . 17
6. Factoring . . . . . . . . . . . . . 19
7. Reduction and Simplification . . . . . . . . . 22

## II · VARIABLES, FUNCTIONS, AND GRAPHS

8. Constants and Variables . . . . . . . . . . 27
9. The Function Concept . . . . . . . . . . 27
10. Functional Notations . . . . . . . . . . . 29
11. Rectangular Coordinates . . . . . . . . . . 31

## III · THE FUNDAMENTALS OF TRIGONOMETRY

12. Angles: Definitions and Representations . . . . . . 37
13. Angle Measurement . . . . . . . . . . . 38
14. Geometric Relations . . . . . . . . . . . 41
15. Functions of Angles . . . . . . . . . . . 43
16. Special Angles . . . . . . . . . . . . 47
17. Right Triangles . . . . . . . . . . . . 51
18. Functions of Large Angles . . . . . . . . . . 59
19. Polar Coordinates . . . . . . . . . . . 63

## IV · IDENTITIES AND CONDITIONAL EQUATIONS

20. Equalities . . . . . . . . . . . . . 69
21. Classification of Functions . . . . . . . . . 70
22. Trigonometric Identities . . . . . . . . . . 75
23. Transformations . . . . . . . . . . . . 78
24. Solutions of Equations . . . . . . . . . . 82

Contents

ARTICLE
25. Equivalent, Defective, and Redundant Equations . . . . . 85
26. Trigonometric Equations . . . . . . . . . . 87

## V · LINEAR EQUATIONS AND DETERMINANTS

27. Type Forms . . . . . . . . . . . . . 93
28. Systems of Linear Equations . . . . . . . . 94
29. Determinants of Second and Third Order . . . . . . 99
30. Determinants of Order $n$ . . . . . . . . . 103
31. Non-Homogeneous Systems . . . . . . . . . 112
32. Homogeneous Systems . . . . . . . . . . 114
33. Defective Systems. . . . . . . . . . . . 116
34. Redundant Systems . . . . . . . . . . . 117

## VI · FUNCTIONS OF SEVERAL ANGLES

35. Sine and Cosine of the Sum or Difference of Two Angles . . . 123
36. Tangent of the Sum or Difference of Two Angles . . . . . 129
37. Functions of Double Angles . . . . . . . . 132
38. Functions of Half Angles . . . . . . . . . . 135
39. Relations Between Sums-and Products of Functions . . . . 138
40. Sine, Cosine, and Tangent Laws . . . . . . . 141
41. Oblique Triangles . . . . . . . . . . . 144

## VII · MATHEMATICAL INDUCTION AND THE BINOMIAL THEOREM

42. Mathematical Induction . . . . . . . . . . 150
43. The Binomial Theorem . . . . . . . . . . 153

## VIII · COMPLEX NUMBERS

44. Definitions and Representations. . . . . . . . . 160
45. Operations with Complex Numbers . . . . . . . 163
46. De Moivre's Theorem . . . . . . . . . . . 167
47. Trigonometric Formulas . . . . . . . . . . 169
48. Roots of Numbers . . . . . . . . . . . 170

## IX · EQUATIONS IN QUADRATIC FORM

49. Methods of Solving Quadratic Equations . . . . . 174
50. Relations Between Coefficients and Roots . . . . . 177
51. Algebraic Equations in Quadratic Form . . . . . . 181
52. Trigonometric Equations Reducible to Quadratic Form . . . 184
53. Systems of Quadratic Equations . . . . . . . 185

# X · PROGRESSIONS

ARTICLE
54. Arithmetic Progressions . . . . . . . . . . 194
55. Geometric Progressions . . . . . . . . . . 197
56. Infinite Sequences; Limits . . . . . . . . . . 200
57. Repeating Decimals . . . . . . . . . . 204
58. Harmonic Progressions . . . . . . . . . . 205

# XI · INEQUALITIES

59. Definitions and Principles . . . . . . . . . . 209
60. Absolute Inequalities . . . . . . . . . . 211
61. Conditional Inequalities . . . . . . . . . . 212
62. Trigonometric Inequalities . . . . . . . . . . 215

# XII · INVERSE FUNCTIONS

63. Inverses of Algebraic Functions . . . . . . . . . . 219
64. Inverse Trigonometric Functions . . . . . . . . . 222
65. Trigonometric Equations . . . . . . . . . . 226

# XIII · FUNCTIONAL VARIATION

66. Direct and Inverse Variation . . . . . . . . . 229
67. Combined Variation . . . . . . . . . . 229
68. Variation of Algebraic Functions . . . . . . . . 233
69. Variation of Trigonometric Functions . . . . . . . 239

# XIV · EXPONENTIAL AND LOGARITHMIC FUNCTIONS

70. Definitions and Properties . . . . . . . . . . 245
71. Exponential Equations . . . . . . . . . . 250
72. Logarithmic Equations . . . . . . . . . . 253
73. Logarithmic Computation . . . . . . . . . . 256
74. Logarithmic Solution of Triangles . . . . . . . . 262

# XV · RATIONAL INTEGRAL EQUATIONS

75. Remainder and Factor Theorems . . . . . . . . 267
76. Synthetic Division . . . . . . . . . . 268
77. Number and Nature of Roots . . . . . . . . . 271
78. Graphs of Polynomials . . . . . . . . . . 274
79. Rule of Signs . . . . . . . . . . 278
80. Rational Roots . . . . . . . . . . 281
81. Irrational Roots . . . . . . . . . . 284

# Contents

ARTICLE

82. Relations Between Coefficients and Roots . . . . . . 288
83. Transcendental Equations . . . . . . . . . . 292

## XVI · PERMUTATIONS, COMBINATIONS, AND PROBABILITY

84. Permutations . . . . . . . . . . . . . 296
85. Combinations . . . . . . . . . . . . . 299
86. Probability . . . . . . . . . . . . . . 302

APPENDICES

A. Meanings of Symbols . . . . . . . . . . . 309
B. Greek Alphabet . . . . . . . . . . . . 310
C. Angle Conversion Tables . . . . . . . . . . 310
D. Common Logarithms . . . . . . . . . . . 311
E. Trigonometric Functions and Their Logarithms . . . . . 313

ANSWERS TO EXERCISES . . . . . . . . . . 321

INDEX . . . . . . . . . . . . . . 337

# Foreword to the Student

As the student progresses in his study of mathematics, he cannot fail to notice the manner in which each new concept or topic rests upon the firm foundation of mathematical subject matter previously encountered. Even in the mathematics first studied in primary school—arithmetic—it is apparent that the process of multiplication involves the techniques of addition, and that, in the operation of division, we make use of subtraction and multiplication.

In the same way, when the student enters the realm of college mathematics, he continually employs the tools of arithmetic, algebra, and geometry. A textbook on college mathematics—for example, analytic geometry or calculus—is therefore usually based on the supposition that the student has the more elementary material well in hand, and it builds its own superstructure on that foundation. It follows that the student can hope to master a new mathematical subject only if he has a good background of mathematical knowledge and a facility with the basic operations of arithmetic and algebra.

This book is designed to help the prospective student of analytic geometry and calculus to attain that essential background and facility. Some of the material, although perhaps already familiar to the student, has been deliberately included with the object of pointing out and emphasizing concepts and techniques of basic importance. All the subject matter has value as preparation for work with more advanced mathematics; when analytic geometry and calculus come to be studied, it will be seen that the topics from the fields of algebra and trigonometry treated in this book are utilized again and again.

In connection with each type of problem discussed in the following pages there will be found examples illustrating the concepts introduced and the possible ways of attacking the desired solutions. Although these examples can serve, to some degree, as general patterns for the student to follow, it cannot be assumed that even a complete understanding of all the steps will guarantee that the student can properly solve a like problem. There is a vast gap between the ability to follow a process of reasoning established by someone else and the creation of a logical argument by one's self. Accordingly, no amount of study of

1

illustrative examples will give the student the facility with mathematical processes that is gained by personal experience with independent problem solving.

To sum up, these are the two guidance points for the student to note particularly as he begins his study of this book: (1) algebra and trigonometry are of fundamental importance in later mathematical study—no real understanding and facility can be achieved without this basic material; (2) study of text and examples alone will not suffice—experience gained through repeated independent practice is the true road to mathematical learning.

# I ——————— Fundamental Algebraic Operations

**1. Number systems.** In the preceding foreword addressed to the student, it was pointed out that each mathematical subject, such as algebra, rests upon more elementary matters. The basis from which algebra is evolved is, of course, arithmetic. It is therefore fitting that we should begin our discussion of algebraic operations by a consideration of the numbers of arithmetic.

Our starting point will be the positive whole numbers, or **positive integers**:

$$1, 2, 3, \cdots. \qquad (1)$$

Here we are employing a symbolism frequently encountered in mathematical discussion. The first few members of the quantities under consideration are exhibited, separated by commas, and the dots are used to indicate that there are additional members in the sequence. In this instance, long familiarity with the counting numbers enables us immediately to supply as many more members of sequence (1) as may be desired. In general, when we use this sort of symbolism, the law of formation of the successive members has to be inferred; thus, we infer that each member of sequence (1), beyond the first member, is obtained by adding 1 to its predecessor. The student should early acquire the ability to discern such patterns or *forms*.

Let us now attempt to subject the members of sequence (1) to the four basic operations of arithmetic—addition, subtraction, multiplication, and division. We find from experience that the addition or multiplication of any two members of sequence (1) leads invariably to numbers of that set; that is, the sum or product of any two positive integers is again a positive integer. We say then that the set (1) is *closed* with respect to the operations of addition and multiplication.

On the other hand, subtraction and division cannot always be performed if we limit ourselves to the number system (1). Thus, although 5 may be subtracted from 11, say, to get the number 6 which is among the positive integers (1), subtraction of 11 from 5 is impossible, unless and until we extend our number system; likewise, division of 39 by 13 leads to the number 3 of the set (1), but division of 13 by 39 does not

3

yield a positive integer.  Accordingly, the system (1) of positive integers is not closed with respect to all four of the basic arithmetic operations.

Now subtraction and division are *indirect* operations, whose natures are defined in terms of the direct operations of addition and multiplication, respectively.  To find the result of subtracting an integer $n$ from an integer $m$ means to find a number $x$ such that the *sum* of $n$ and $x$ is $m$:

$$n + x = m. \tag{2}$$

Likewise, to find the result of dividing the integer $p$ by the integer $q$ means to find a number $y$ such that the *product* of $q$ and $y$ is $p$:

$$qy = p. \tag{3}$$

To make it possible to find $x$ and $y$—that is, to "solve" (2) for $x$ and (3) for $y$—we must extend our number system to the set of <u>rational numbers,</u> consisting of the positive integers (1), the negative integers $-1, -2, -3, \cdots$, the number 0, and the fractions.  All numbers of this extended system are then of the form

$$\frac{p}{q}, \tag{4}$$

where $p$ is any positive or negative integer or zero, and $q$ is any positive or negative integer.

We note particularly that, although the numerator $p$ in (4) may be the number 0, *the denominator $q$ cannot have the value 0.*  For, if $p = 0$ and $q \neq 0$,* relation (3) is satisfied by taking $y = 0$ since $q \cdot 0 = 0$; but if $p \neq 0$ and $q = 0$, $qy = 0 \cdot y = 0 \neq p$ for every number $y$, and if $p = 0$ and $q = 0$, $y$ is still not determined by (3).  Because of this impossibility of determining a unique number $y$ when $q = 0$, <u>division by zero is an excluded operation</u>—it is meaningless and therefore forbidden.

The rational number system represented by (4) suffices for all four rational arithmetic operations.  However, when we attempt the operation of root extraction, we find that we are led to the consideration of numbers not of the form (4).  Such numbers, as $\sqrt{2}$, $\sqrt[5]{17}$, etc., are called **irrational numbers.**

It is sometimes possible to show, by elementary means, that a certain number is irrational.  We shall illustrate this by proving that $\sqrt{2}$ is irrational, using the argument of "reductio ad absurdum."  The essence of this type of reasoning, which is a very powerful and frequently used method, is to suppose the statement in question to be false, and

* The symbol $\neq$ is read "is not equal to" or "is different from."

then to prove that this supposition leads to a contradiction. Accordingly, we assume that $\sqrt{2}$ is rational, and therefore of the form (4):

$$\sqrt{2} = \frac{p}{q}. \tag{5}$$

Here we may further stipulate that the fraction $p/q$ is in simplest form, that is, that the integers $p$ and $q$ have no common integral factor. For, if there were a common factor of $p$ and $q$, it could be removed from numerator and denominator, and the remaining quotient taken as $p/q$. If, now, we multiply both members of (5) by $q$ and square both members of the resulting equation, we get

$$2q^2 = p^2. \tag{6}$$

This shows us that $p^2$ contains the factor 2 (the other factor being $q^2$); or, in other words, $p^2$ is an *even* number. But that in turn implies that $p$ itself is even, since the square of an odd number is always odd. We may therefore represent $p$ by the symbol $2r$, where $r$ is an integer, whence (6) yields

$$2q^2 = (2r)^2 = 4r^2,$$

or, removing the common factor 2,

$$q^2 = 2r^2. \tag{7}$$

This relation, of the same form as (6), shows that $q^2$, and hence $q$ itself, must be even. Consequently both $p$ and $q$ have to contain the factor 2, contrary to the stipulation that they have no common factor. This is the desired contradiction, and it follows that the original supposition (5) is untenable, so that $\sqrt{2}$ is, in fact, irrational.

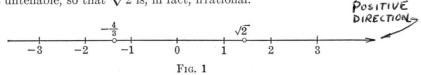

Fig. 1

All the numbers we have discussed so far—the integral and fractional rational numbers and the irrational numbers—may be represented geometrically by points on a line. For such a representation we arbitrarily choose some point to represent 0, and some length to represent unit distance. Also arbitrarily, and conventionally, we choose the points to the right of 0 to represent positive numbers; points to the left then represent negative numbers (Fig. 1). For emphasis, an arrow head is sometimes drawn toward the right to indicate the positive direction. Every number in our extended system, called the **real number system,** is represented by one and only one point on our line; and, conversely, each point on the line corresponds to a real number.

It is worth mentioning, in passing, that this one-to-one correspondence between numbers and points is more than a mildly interesting side issue; it is, in fact, the fundamental concept and basis of the powerful mathematical tool called analytic geometry, in which algebra and geometry go hand in hand.

The geometric representation of real numbers suggests the *ordering* of such numbers. We may say that a number $x$ is greater than a second number $y$ if the point corresponding to $x$ lies to the right of the $y$-point. In algebraic language, we say *

$$x > y$$

if $x - y$ is positive, and

$$x < y$$

if $x - y$ is negative. Thus, $\frac{13}{4} > 3$, $-2 < -\frac{3}{2}$, etc.

### EXERCISES

In Exercises 1–10, determine suitable values for the next three numbers in each indicated sequence.

**1.** 2, 4, 6, 8, $\cdots$.
                **2.** 1, 4, 7, 10, 13, $\cdots$.
**3.** $\frac{1}{2}, \frac{2}{3}, \frac{3}{4}, \frac{4}{5}, \cdots$.
        **4.** 1, $-3$, 5, $-7$, 9, $-11$, $\cdots$.
**5.** $\frac{1}{3}, \frac{1}{9}, \frac{1}{27}, \frac{1}{81}, \cdots$.
        **6.** 4, 16, 36, 64, 100, $\cdots$.
**7.** $\frac{1}{2}, \frac{4}{3}, \frac{9}{4}, \frac{16}{5}, \cdots$.
        **8.** $-\frac{1}{4}, 0, \frac{1}{6}, \frac{2}{7}, \frac{3}{8}, \cdots$.
**9.** 2, 3, 5, 7, 11, 13, $\cdots$.
      **10.** 1, 2, 3, 5, 8, 13, 21, $\cdots$.

**11.** We have considered three number systems: (i) the positive integers; (ii) the rational numbers; (iii) real numbers. To what system or systems do the following numbers belong?

$$29,\ -4,\ \tfrac{11}{5},\ \sqrt{729},\ \pi,\ 0.1949,\ \frac{1}{\sqrt{2}+1}.$$

**12.** Order the numbers of Exercise 11.

**13.** If $a > b$ and $b > c$, show that $a > c$.

**14.** If $a$, $b$, $c$, and $d$ are positive integers, show that $\dfrac{a}{b} > \dfrac{c}{d}$ if and only if $ad - bc$ is positive.

**15.** Show that between any two rational numbers, $x$ and $y$, there exists another rational number, $\frac{1}{2}(x + y)$.

---

* The symbol $>$ is read "is greater than"; the symbol $<$ denotes "is less than."

**2. Assumptions and definitions.**   Elementary algebra is, from one viewpoint, a generalization of arithmetic; instead of dealing with specific numbers, as we do in arithmetic, we work with algebraic quantities or symbols.   In order to treat these objects of algebra logically, suitable rules of operation must be formulated, and we naturally devise these rules in accordance with suggestions obtained from our experience with arithmetic operations.

The starting point in creating a logical algebraic structure is to state certain assumptions or *postulates.*   These postulates are fundamental in the sense that no attempt is made to "prove" them; for any proof must rest on still more basic matters.

In stating such postulates, we use words and symbols whose meanings must of course be understood.   Some of these terms can be defined, in accompanying statements, by referring to still simpler concepts; sometimes the postulates themselves furnish definitions by implication; and some of the most basic terms must remain undefined.

All assumptions and the necessary definitions may be framed at pleasure, provided merely that they be logically consistent in order to be fruitful.   Looking to arithmetic for guidance, we state here eleven postulates which we shall assume and from which additional properties may be derived.   These postulates, together with the accompanying definitions, will constitute the framework of all our subsequent developments.   The symbols $a$, $b$, $c$, etc., are the algebraic quantities with which we deal; they may be assigned any permissible values from the real number system.

I. *The sum of two quantities $a$ and $b$, denoted by $a + b$, is a definite determinate quantity $c$:*

$$a + b = c. \tag{1}$$

That is, addition is always possible and is unique.

II. *The product of two quantities $a$ and $b$, denoted by $a \times b$, $a \cdot b$, or $ab$, is a definite determinate quantity $d$:*

$$ab = d. \tag{2}$$

That is, multiplication is always possible and is unique.   We say that $a$ and $b$ are *factors* of $d$.

III. *For any two quantities $a$ and $b$, there exists one and only one quantity $x$ such that*

$$b + x = a. \tag{3}$$

*We then write*

$$x = a - b.$$

That is, subtraction of one quantity from a second is always possible and is unique.  If $a = b$, the quantity $x$ defined by this relation (3) is called *zero*, denoted by the symbol 0.  If $a = 0$, the quantity $x$ given by (3) is denoted by the symbol $-b$; when $b$ assumes a positive numerical value, $-b$ has a negative value, and when $b$ is negative, $-b$ is positive.

(IV) *For any two quantities a and b, except that b is not and cannot assume the value zero, there exists one and only one quantity y such that*

$$by = a. \tag{4}$$

*We then write*

$$y = \frac{a}{b} \quad \text{or} \quad y = a/b \quad \text{or} \quad y = a \div b.$$

Thus, division of one quantity by a *non-zero* quantity is always possible and is unique.  We call $a$ the numerator or dividend, and $b$ the denominator or divisor, and $y$ is the quotient.  If $a = b \neq 0$, the quantity $y$ obtained by division is called *unity*, denoted by 1.  Because of the uniqueness of division, when $y = 1$ we must have $a = b$; that is, $b \times 1 = b$.  If $a = 1$, the quantity $y$ found by the operation of division is $1/b$, which is called the reciprocal of $b$.  Then $b \cdot (1/b) = 1$.

(V.) *Addition is commutative; that is, for any two quantities a and b,*

$$a + b = b + a. \tag{5}$$

(VI.) *Multiplication is commutative; that is, for any two quantities a and b,*

$$ab = ba. \tag{6}$$

(VII) *Addition is associative; that is, for any three quantities a, b, and c,*

$$a + (b + c) = b + (a + c) = c + (a + b). \tag{7}$$

(VIII.) *Multiplication is associative; that is, for any three quantities a, b, and c,*

$$a(bc) = b(ac) = c(ab). \tag{8}$$

(IX.) *Multiplication is distributive with respect to addition; that is, for any three quantities a, b, and c,*

$$a(b + c) = ab + ac. \tag{9}$$

**(X.)** *If equal quantities are respectively added to equal quantities, the sums are equal; that is, if a = b and c = d, then*

$$a + c = b + d. \tag{10}$$

**(XI)** *If equal quantities are respectively multiplied by equal quantities, the products are equal; that is, if a = b and c = d, then*

$$ac = bd. \tag{11}$$

It is easy to see that these basic algebraic operations are merely generalizations of the rational arithmetic operations and, in fact, owe their existence and chosen form to our having had a previous extensive experience with numbers. It is also apparent that, although the statements of postulates I–XI are confined to relations involving two or three quantities, they may readily be broadened so as to apply to relations among a greater number of algebraic quantities.

**3. Derived properties of algebraic quantities.** We now proceed to make use of the postulates set forth in Art. 2 to obtain additional properties of algebraic quantities. The *theorems* discussed here are some, but of course not all, of the properties that may be deduced from those assumptions; the ones chosen for our presentation are among those of widest and most frequent application. Detailed proofs are given only for certain of our stated results, to illustrate the method of attacking such problems; in these proofs, the Roman numbers at the right refer to the corresponding postulates of Art. 2.

**(I.)** *The product of zero and any quantity a is zero.* For example, $0 \cdot 1 = 0$, $0(-4) = 0$, $0 \cdot 0 = 0$.

*Proof:* Let $0 \cdot a = x$. Then

$$0 \cdot a + a = x + a, \tag{X}$$

$$(0 + 1)a = x + a. \tag{IX}$$

But $0 + 1 = 1$ and $1 \cdot a = a$, so that we have

$$a = x + a,$$

and therefore $x = 0$ (III).

**(II.)** *If $b \neq 0$, $a/b = a \cdot (1/b)$.* Thus, $\frac{3}{2} = 3(\frac{1}{2})$, $4/\frac{1}{2} = 4 \cdot 2 = 8$, etc.

*Proof:* Let $x = a/b$, so that $bx = a$ (IV). Then

$$(bx) \cdot (1/b) = a \cdot (1/b). \tag{XI}$$

But we also have

$$bx \cdot \frac{1}{b} = \left(b \cdot \frac{1}{b}\right) x = x = \frac{a}{b}. \qquad \text{(VIII, IV)}$$

Combining these two relations, we get the desired result.

When $a = 0$, theorem II yields

$$\frac{0}{b} = 0 \cdot \frac{1}{b} = 0$$

by theorem I.   Hence we have the corollary:

*The quotient of zero by any non-zero quantity is zero.*

**III.** *If the product of two quantities is zero, at least one of the quantities has the value zero.*

*Proof:* Suppose that $ab = 0$.   If $a = 0$, we have our theorem immediately; if $a \neq 0$, we have

$$\frac{1}{a}(ab) = \frac{1}{a} \cdot 0, \qquad \text{(XI)}$$

and

$$\left(\frac{1}{a} \cdot a\right) b = \frac{1}{a} \cdot 0. \qquad \text{(VIII)}$$

Now the first factor on the left is unity, by postulate **IV**, and the right member is zero, by theorem I.   Hence

$$1 \cdot b = 0.$$

But

$$1 \cdot b = b \cdot 1 = b, \qquad \text{(VI, IV)}$$

and therefore

$$b = 0,$$

as was to be shown.   This is an extremely important theorem, used continually in solving equations.   Thus, if $(x - 2)(x + 3) = 0$, then either $x = 2$ or $x = -3$.

**IV.** *The operation of adding a negative quantity $(-b)$ to a quantity $a$ is equivalent to the operation of subtracting the positive quantity $b$ from $a$.*

For example, $3 + (-1) = 3 - 1 = 2$.

*Proof:* Let $x = a + (-b)$.   Then

$$a + (-b) + b = x + b. \tag{X}$$

But

$$(-b) + b = 0. \tag{III}$$

Hence

$$a + 0 = x + b.$$

Now

$$a + 0 = a,$$

and consequently

$$a = x + b,$$

or

$$a - b = x. \tag{III}$$

The desired result then follows from the two expressions for $x$:

$$a + (-b) = a - b.$$

Ⓥ *The operation of subtracting a negative quantity $(-b)$ from a quantity $a$ is equivalent to the operation of adding the positive quantity $b$ to $a$; that is,*

$$a - (-b) = a + b.$$

This may be proved in a manner similar to that employed for theorem IV. We have, for instance, $5 - (-2) = 5 + 2 = 7$, $-1 - (-1) = -1 + 1 = 0$.

Ⓥ𝐈 *The product of a quantity $a$ and a negative quantity $(-b)$ is $-ab$.*

For example, $4(-3) = -(4 \cdot 3) = -12$.

*Proof:* Let $x = a \cdot (-b)$. Then

$$a(-b) + ab = x + ab, \tag{X}$$

$$a[(-b) + b] = x + ab, \tag{IX}$$

$$a \cdot 0 = x + ab. \tag{III}$$

But $a \cdot 0 = 0$ by theorem I, and therefore $x + ab = 0$, **or**

$$x = -ab. \tag{III}$$

Combining the two expressions for $x$, we obtain the desired result:

$$a(-b) = -ab.$$

**VII.** *The product of two negative quantities, $(-a)$ and $(-b)$, is $ab$.*

The proof of this is similar to that of theorem VI. Thus, $(-2)(-3)$ $= 2 \cdot 3 = 6$, $(-\frac{1}{4})(-4) = 1$, etc.

As a consequence of theorems VI and VII, together with theorem II, we get the corollary:

*The quotient of two quantities is positive or negative according as the signs of the numerator and denominator are like or unlike.*

Accordingly, we have

$$\frac{-a}{-b} = \frac{a}{b}, \qquad \frac{-a}{b} = \frac{a}{-b} = -\frac{a}{b}, \qquad b \neq 0.$$

**VIII.** *A single pair of parentheses preceded by a positive sign may be removed without changing the signs of the individual terms within the parentheses; parentheses preceded by a negative sign may be removed if the signs of the terms within them are all changed.*

Thus we have, for instance,

$$+(a - b - c + d) = a - b - c + d,$$

$$-(a - b - c + d) = -a + b + c - d.$$

This rule follows from the concept of a negative quantity and theorems VI and VII.

**IX.** *The value of a fraction remains the same when both numerator and denominator are multiplied or divided by the same non-zero quantity; that is,*

$$\frac{a}{b} = \frac{ac}{bc} = \frac{a/d}{b/d}, \qquad b \neq 0, \qquad c \neq 0, \qquad d \neq 0.$$

This rule, which has great utility whenever fractional quantities are treated, may be established by applying postulates IV, VI, and VIII. We have, for example,

$$\frac{6}{9} = \frac{6 \cdot 2}{9 \cdot 2} = \frac{12}{18}, \qquad \frac{6}{9} = \frac{\frac{6}{3}}{\frac{9}{3}} = \frac{2}{3}.$$

**X.** *The sum (difference) of two fractions having the same denominator is a fraction whose numerator is the sum (difference) of the two numerators* *and whose denominator is the common denominator of the two given fractions; that is,*

$$\frac{a}{b} + \frac{c}{b} = \frac{a + c}{b}, \qquad \frac{a}{b} - \frac{c}{b} = \frac{a - c}{b}, \qquad b \neq 0.$$

The proof of these rules depends upon postulates IV, IX, and XI of Art. 2 and theorem II above.  Thus we have

$$\frac{5}{2} + \frac{3}{2} = \frac{5 + 3}{2} = \frac{8}{2} = 4, \qquad \frac{5}{2} - \frac{3}{2} = \frac{5 - 3}{2} = \frac{2}{2} = 1.$$

As a consequence of theorems IX and X, we get the following corollary:

*The sum and difference of two fractions are respectively given by*

$$\frac{a}{b} + \frac{c}{d} = \frac{ad + bc}{bd}, \qquad \frac{a}{b} - \frac{c}{d} = \frac{ad - bc}{bd}, \qquad b \neq 0, d \neq 0.$$

Accordingly, we have, for instance,

$$\frac{7}{2} + \frac{4}{3} = \frac{21 + 8}{6} = \frac{29}{6}, \qquad \frac{7}{2} - \frac{4}{3} = \frac{21 - 8}{6} = \frac{13}{6}.$$

**XI.** *The product of two fractions is a fraction whose numerator and denominator are respectively the products of the numerators and of the denominators of the given fractions; that is,*

$$\frac{a}{b} \cdot \frac{c}{d} = \frac{ac}{bd}, \qquad b \neq 0, d \neq 0.$$

Thus,

$$\tfrac{2}{5} \cdot \tfrac{3}{7} = \tfrac{6}{35}, \qquad \tfrac{4}{9} \cdot \tfrac{3}{2} = \tfrac{12}{18} = \tfrac{2}{3}.$$

**XII.** *The quotient of two fractions is equal to the product of the first and the reciprocal of the second; that is,*

$$\frac{\dfrac{a}{b}}{\dfrac{c}{d}} = \frac{a}{b} \cdot \frac{d}{c} = \frac{ad}{bc}, \qquad b \neq 0, c \neq 0, d \neq 0.$$

For example, we get

$$\frac{\tfrac{3}{4}}{\tfrac{8}{5}} = \frac{3}{4} \cdot \frac{5}{8} = \frac{15}{32}, \qquad \frac{\tfrac{1}{8}}{\tfrac{1}{4}} = \frac{1}{8} \cdot \frac{4}{1} = \frac{4}{8} = \frac{1}{2}.$$

## EXERCISES

**1.** Derive property V.                    **2.** Derive property VII.
**3.** Derive property VIII.                 **4.** Derive property IX.
**5.** Show that

$$\frac{-a}{b} = \frac{a}{-b} = -\frac{a}{b}, \qquad b \neq 0.$$

**6.** Derive property X.
**7.** Derive property XI.
**8.** If $a \neq 0$ and $b \neq 0$, show that the reciprocal of $a/b$ is $b/a$.
**9.** Derive property XII.
**10.** If $x = a/b$ and $x = c/d$, where $b \neq 0$ and $d \neq 0$, show that $x = (a + c)/(b + d)$ provided that $b + d \neq 0$.

**4. Laws of exponents.** When a quantity $a$ is multiplied by itself, we write, instead of $aa$, the symbol $a^2$. Similarly, the product of $a^2$ and $a$ is written $a^3$. More generally, the notation

$$a^n, \tag{1}$$

where $n$ is a positive integer, is used to denote the product of $n$ factors each equal to $a$. The symbol $a^n$ is read "the $n$th power of $a$," and $n$ is called the **exponent** or **index**.

With this notation, and by application of the laws and properties of Arts. 2–3, we may easily establish the following five laws of exponents. In these statements, $m$ and $n$ denote positive integers.

**I.** $a^m \cdot a^n = a^{m+n}$.

For example, $2^3 \cdot 2^4 = 2^7$. This is correct since $2^3 = 8$, $2^4 = 16$, $2^7 = 128$, and $8 \cdot 16 = 128$.

**II.** $(a^m)^n = a^{mn}$.

For instance, $(3^2)^3 = 3^6$; for, $3^2 = 9$, $9^3 = 729$, and $3^6 = 729$.

**III.** $(ab)^n = a^n b^n$.

Thus, $(4 \cdot 3)^2 = 4^2 \cdot 3^2$; for, $4 \cdot 3 = 12$, $12^2 = 144$, $4^2 = 16$, $3^2 = 9$, and $16 \cdot 9 = 144$.

**IV.** $\left(\dfrac{a}{b}\right)^n = \dfrac{a^n}{b^n}, \qquad b \neq 0.$

As an example, we have $\left(\dfrac{2}{3}\right)^4 = \dfrac{2^4}{3^4}$; for, $\left(\dfrac{2}{3}\right)^4 = \dfrac{16}{81}$, $2^4 = 16$, and $3^4 = 81$.

(V.) $\dfrac{a^m}{a^n} = a^{m-n}$ if $m > n$; $\dfrac{a^m}{a^n} = \dfrac{1}{a^{n-m}}$ if $m < n$.

Thus, $\dfrac{3^4}{3^3} = 3$; for, $3^4 = 81$, $3^3 = 27$, and $\frac{81}{27} = 3$.   Also, $\dfrac{2^3}{2^5} = \dfrac{1}{2^2}$ ; for, $2^3 = 8$, $2^5 = 32$, $2^2 = 4$, and $\frac{8}{32} = \frac{1}{4}$.

Simple numerical examples that may be easily checked are given here, as they were in Art. 3, in the hope that the student will follow the suggestion of checking his own algebraic manipulations in similar fashion. Many gross errors in algebra can be readily detected and corrected by means of arithmetic checks.

The foregoing five laws, verified for the case of positive integral exponents, may be taken as a basis of generalization. We are then led to the following considerations.

If, in law I, we formally set $m = \frac{1}{2}$ and $n = \frac{1}{2}$, we get $a^{\frac{1}{2}} \cdot a^{\frac{1}{2}} = a^1 = a$. Hence we *define* $a^{\frac{1}{2}}$ to be a quantity which, when multiplied by itself, yields the quantity $a$. Similarly, we define $a^{\frac{1}{p}}$, where $p$ is a positive integer, to be a quantity such that the product of $p$ such factors is $a$. Then the extension of law I to $p$ factors, and also law II with $m = 1/p$ and $n = p$, will hold.

It should be noted that we have so far merely defined $a^{\frac{1}{p}}$ as "a" quantity having a certain property, and not "the" quantity satisfying the stated condition; that is, we still have the question of uniqueness to consider. Now we know, from arithmetic, that there are *two* distinct numbers whose squares are, say, 3, namely, $+\sqrt{3}$ and $-\sqrt{3}$. Hence we do not obtain a unique quantity $a^{\frac{1}{2}}$ unless we impose further restrictions.

To avoid this lack of uniqueness and consequent ambiguity when our symbols are assigned numerical values, we therefore impose the following restrictions:

(a) When $a$ is positive and $p$ is any positive integer, $a^{\frac{1}{p}}$ is to be a positive real number.

(b) When $a$ is negative and $p$ is an odd positive integer, $a^{\frac{1}{p}}$ is to be a negative real number.

(c) When $a$ is negative and $p$ is an even positive integer, $a^{\frac{1}{p}}$ is to be undefined in our real number system.   *negative × negative = positive*
*no square root of a neg number*

Thus we have, as numerical examples: $9^{\frac{1}{2}} = 3$; $(-8)^{\frac{1}{3}} = -2$; and $(-4)^{\frac{1}{2}}$ does not exist in the real number system.

The conventions we have here adopted are important to keep in mind. We shall have frequent occasion to make use of and to refer to this set of definitions. Later (Chapter VIII) we shall extend our number system so as to give meaning to $a^{\frac{1}{p}}$ when $a$ is negative and $p$ is an even positive integer, and rules of operation with these new numbers will be formulated.

We may now easily proceed to the following definitions:

If $p$ and $q$ are positive integers, the symbol $a^{\frac{q}{p}}$ is to denote the $q$th power of $a^{\frac{1}{p}}$ (supposing $a^{\frac{1}{p}}$ to exist); that is,

$$a^{\frac{q}{p}} = (a^{\frac{1}{p}})^q.$$

This definition permits the use of the preceding laws of exponents in connection with all positive fractional powers. For example, $a^{\frac{3}{2}} \cdot a^{\frac{5}{2}} = (a^{\frac{1}{2}})^3 \cdot (a^{\frac{1}{2}})^5 = (a^{\frac{1}{2}})^{3+5} = (a^{\frac{1}{2}})^8 = a^{\frac{8}{2}} = a^4$; or, more directly, $a^{\frac{3}{2}} \cdot a^{\frac{5}{2}} = a^{\frac{3}{2}+\frac{5}{2}} = a^4$. Similarly, $a^{\frac{1}{2}}/a^{\frac{1}{3}} = (a^{\frac{1}{6}})^3/(a^{\frac{1}{6}})^2 = (a^{\frac{1}{6}})^{3-2} = a^{\frac{1}{6}}$, or $a^{\frac{1}{2}}/a^{\frac{1}{3}} = a^{\frac{1}{2}-\frac{1}{3}} = a^{\frac{1}{6}}$.

If we formally set $m = 0$ in law I, we get

$$a^0 \cdot a^n = a^{0+n} = a^n.$$

In order that this relation shall hold, we therefore define $a^0$ to be equal to unity for $a \neq 0$:

$$a^0 = 1, \qquad a \neq 0.$$

The symbol $0^0$ is not defined, for any definition would necessarily be inconsistent with previous definitions. Thus, since $a^n = 0$ when $a = 0$, whereas $a^n = 1$ when $n = 0$, these two relations are in conflict when both $a$ and $n$ are taken equal to zero.

If we formally set $n = -m$, where $m$ is a positive integer or fraction, we get from law I and the above definition of $a^0$,

$$a^m \cdot a^{-m} = a^{m-m} = a^0 = 1, \qquad a \neq 0.$$

Since $a^m \cdot (1/a^m) = 1$, we define

$$a^{-m} = \frac{1}{a^m}.$$

Thus,

$$8^{-\frac{2}{3}} = \frac{1}{8^{\frac{2}{3}}} = \frac{1}{4}.$$

The definitions given to fractional, zero, and negative powers, consistent with the laws of exponents established for positive integral powers, enable us to apply to all rational powers of quantities the properties arising from the postulates and theorems of Arts. 2–3.

*Examples.*

$$\frac{a^0 \cdot a^{\frac{5}{2}}}{a^2} = a^{0+\frac{5}{2}-2} = a^{\frac{1}{2}},$$

$$a^{\frac{1}{2}}(2a^0 - 3a^{-2}) = 2a^{\frac{1}{2}+0} - 3a^{\frac{1}{2}-2} = 2a^{\frac{1}{2}} - 3a^{-\frac{3}{2}},$$

$$(ab^2)^2 \left(\frac{a}{b}\right)^3 \left(\frac{b}{a^2}\right)^{-1} = a^2b^4 \cdot \frac{a^3}{b^3} \cdot \frac{b^{-1}}{a^{-2}} = a^{2+3-(-2)}b^{4-3-1} = a^7b^0 = a^7.$$

**5. Radicals.** Instead of writing a quantity involving a fractional power in the manner indicated in Art. 4, we sometimes use another notation, borrowed from arithmetic, namely, **radicals.** Thus, a quantity $a$ to the power $1/p$ is alternatively regarded as the $p$th *root* of $a$, and we write

$$a^{\frac{1}{p}} = \sqrt[p]{a}.$$

The radical sign $\sqrt[p]{}$ then has the same operational meaning as the fractional exponent $1/p$. The quantity $a$ affected by the radical sign is called the **radicand.**

It is important to note and remember that, just as a positive sign is understood before the symbol $a^{\frac{1}{p}}$, so a positive sign is understood before the radical in the notation $\sqrt[p]{a}$. Thus,

$$\sqrt[4]{16} = +2, \qquad \sqrt[3]{-64} = +(-4) = -4.$$

We further agree to extend the radical notation so that

$$a^{\frac{q}{p}} = (\sqrt[p]{a})^q = \sqrt[p]{a^q}.$$

Then the laws of exponents yield, in terms of radicals, the following relations:

$$\sqrt[p]{a} \cdot \sqrt[p]{b} = a^{\frac{1}{p}}b^{\frac{1}{p}} = (ab)^{\frac{1}{p}} = \sqrt[p]{ab},$$

$$\frac{\sqrt[p]{a}}{\sqrt[p]{b}} = \frac{a^{\frac{1}{p}}}{b^{\frac{1}{p}}} = \left(\frac{a}{b}\right)^{\frac{1}{p}} = \sqrt[p]{\frac{a}{b}}, \qquad b \neq 0.$$

For simplicity, the convention adopted regarding the power $\frac{1}{2}$, corresponding to the so-called square root, is to omit the index 2 in the radical symbol; that is, we write $a^{\frac{1}{2}} = \sqrt{a}$ instead of $\sqrt[2]{a}$.

## EXERCISES

Simplify each of the following expressions by performing the indicated operations. Using negative exponents where necessary, obtain results free of fractions. Check by substituting numbers for the letters involved.

**1.** $\dfrac{a^3 \cdot a^4}{a^2}$.

**2.** $\dfrac{a^2 \cdot a^4}{a^7}$.

**3.** $\dfrac{a^4 \cdot a^3 \cdot a}{a^8}$.

**4.** $\dfrac{a^4 b}{a^3 b^3}$.

**5.** $\dfrac{(ab)^3}{a^3(ab)^2}$.

**6.** $\dfrac{(-a^3)^3 b^2}{a(-b)^3}$.

**7.** $\left(\dfrac{a^3 b^2}{ab^3}\right)^2$.

**8.** $a^2 b \left(\dfrac{a^2}{b}\right)^2$.

**9.** $\dfrac{a^p b^q}{(ab^2)^2}$.

**10.** $\dfrac{a^{p+2} b^{q-1}}{a^{p-1} b^{q+2}}$.

**11.** $\dfrac{a^{2p+1} b^{p+3}}{a^{p-1} b^2}$.

**12.** $\left(\dfrac{a^p b^q}{a^4 b^2}\right)^3$.

**13.** $\dfrac{(-a^p)^2 (b^3)^p}{a^p(-b^2)^3}$.

**14.** $\dfrac{a^0 b^3}{(a^2 b)^p}$.

**15.** $\dfrac{a^{-2} b^3}{a^{-3} b^{-2}}$.

**16.** $\dfrac{(-a)^{-2} b}{a(-b)^{-2}}$.

**17.** $\dfrac{(2a)^2 b^2}{2a^2(3b)^{-2}}$.

**18.** $\dfrac{a^{\frac{1}{2}} b^{\frac{1}{3}}}{(ab)^2}$.

**19.** $\dfrac{a^{\frac{1}{2}} \cdot a^{\frac{2}{3}}}{a^{\frac{5}{6}}}$.

**20.** $\dfrac{a^{\frac{3}{2}} \cdot a^2}{b^{\frac{2}{3}} \cdot b^3}$.

**21.** $\left(\dfrac{a^2}{b^{\frac{1}{2}}}\right) \cdot \left(\dfrac{a^{\frac{1}{2}}}{b^3}\right)$.

**22.** $\dfrac{(a^{\frac{1}{2}})^p (b^p)^{\frac{1}{2}}}{(ab)^p}$.

**23.** $\dfrac{(a^{-3})^p b^{1+q}}{a^{p-1} b^{1-q}}$.

**24.** $\dfrac{(a^{-\frac{1}{2}})^{-3} b^{-3}}{(a^{\frac{1}{2}})^2 b^{-4}}$.

**25.** $\dfrac{a^3}{b^2} \div \dfrac{b^3}{a^2}$.

**26.** $\dfrac{a^{-p}}{b^{-q}} \div \dfrac{b^{q-1}}{a^p}$.

**27.** $\dfrac{a^{\frac{1}{2}} \div b^{\frac{3}{2}}}{a^{-1} \div b^{-2}}$.

**28.** $\sqrt{a^5} \cdot \sqrt[5]{a^2}$.

**29.** $\sqrt{\dfrac{a^2}{b^3}} \cdot \sqrt{\dfrac{a^3}{b^2}}$.

**30.** $\left(\dfrac{a^{-3}}{b^2}\right)^{\frac{1}{2}} \div \dfrac{\sqrt[3]{b^{-2}}}{a^2}$.

**31.** $(a^3 + 2b^0)(a^3 - 2b^0)$.

**32.** $a^{\frac{1}{2}}(q^{-\frac{1}{2}} + a^{\frac{3}{2}})$.

**33.** $(a^{-1} - b^{-2})(a^{-1} + b^{-2})$.

**34.** $(a^3 - b^3)(a^6 + a^3 b^3 + b^6)$.

**35.** $(a^{-2} + b^2)(a^2 - b^{-2})$.

**36.** $a^2 b^2 (a^{-\frac{1}{2}} - b^{-\frac{1}{2}})^2$.

**37.** $(a^p + b^{-q})(a^{-p} - b^q)$.

**38.** $\left(\dfrac{1}{a^0} + a^{\frac{1}{2}} - 2\right)\left(2 + a^{-\frac{1}{2}} - a^0\right)$.

**39.** $(a^{\frac{1}{3}} - a^{\frac{1}{4}})(a^{\frac{1}{3}} + a^{\frac{1}{4}})$.

**40.** $(a^{\frac{2}{3}} + 2b^{\frac{1}{3}})^3$.

**41.** $(a^{\frac{p}{2}} + b^{-\frac{p}{2}})(a^{-\frac{p}{2}} - b^{\frac{p}{2}})$.

**42.** $(a^{\frac{1}{2}} - 2a^{\frac{1}{4}} + a^0)(a^{\frac{1}{2}} + 2a^{\frac{1}{4}} + a^0)$.

**43.** $\sqrt{(a^2 - b)}\sqrt{a^2 - b}$.

**44.** $a^{-\frac{1}{3}} \sqrt[3]{\left(\dfrac{a}{a^{\frac{1}{2}}}\right)^2} + b^{\frac{3}{4}} \sqrt{\left(\dfrac{\sqrt{b}}{b}\right)^3}$.

**45.** $\sqrt{a^{-2} b^{-4}} - \left(\dfrac{1}{a^2 b}\right)^{\frac{1}{2}}$.

**46.** $\sqrt{(a^p b^{-p})^3} \div (a^3 b^{-3})^{\frac{p}{2}}$.

**47.** $(a^p + b^p)(a^{3p} - a^{2p}b^p + a^pb^{2p} - b^{3p})$.

**48.** $(a^{\frac{1}{2}} + b^{-2} - c^{-1})^2 - 2a^{\frac{1}{2}}b^{-2} + 2a^{\frac{1}{2}}c^{-1} + 2b^{-2}c^{-1}$.

**49.** $(a^{-4} + b^{\frac{4}{3}})(a^{-2} + b^{\frac{2}{3}})(a^{-2} - b^{\frac{2}{3}})$.

**50.** $[(a^{4p} + b^{-4q})(a^{2p} + b^{-2q})(a^{2p} - b^{-2q}) + b^{-8q}]^{-\frac{1}{2}}$.

**6. Factoring.** When simplifying and reducing an algebraic expression, a process of considerable utility is factoring, that is, finding two or more quantities whose product is equal to the given expression.

The factorable forms given here are some of the more common types.

I. An expression consisting of the sum of two or more terms may have a numerical or algebraic factor common to each term. Usually we extract only rational numerical factors, and, if each term is algebraically rational (that is, if each contains only positive integral powers), we generally seek rational algebraic factors.

*Examples.*

$$4a^2b - 2ab = 2ab(2a - 1),$$

$$9ab^2c^3 - 6a^2c + 12ac = 3ac(3b^2c^2 - 2a + 4).$$

II. An expression may sometimes be factored by grouping terms having a common factor and thus getting new terms containing a common factor. The type form for this case is $ac + bc + ad + bd$, for

$$ac + bc + ad + bd = c(a + b) + d(a + b)$$

$$= (a + b)(c + d).$$

*Examples.*

$$15ac + 6bc - 10ad - 4bd = 3c(5a + 2b) - 2d(5a + 2b)$$

$$= (5a + 2b)(3c - 2d),$$

$$3a^2c + 3a^2d^2 + 2b^2c + 2b^2d^2 = 3a^2(c + d^2) + 2b^2(c + d^2)$$

$$= (c + d^2)(3a^2 + 2b^2).$$

III. An expression may be of the form $a^2 + 2ab + b^2$, which is the square of a quantity since

$$a^2 + 2ab + b^2 = (a + b)^2.$$

*Examples.*

$$a^4 + 4a^2 + 4 = (a^2)^2 + 2 \cdot a^2 \cdot 2 + 2^2 = (a^2 + 2)^2,$$

$$9a^2 - 6ab^2 + b^4 = (3a - b^2)^2.$$

**IV.** An expression which may be regarded as the difference of two quantities each of which is the square of a quantity may be factored, for

$$a^2 - b^2 = (a + b)(a - b).$$

*Examples.*

$$4a^4 - b^6 = (2a^2)^2 - (b^3)^2$$
$$= (2a^2 + b^3)(2a^2 - b^3),$$
$$a^2 - b^2 + 2bc - c^2 = a^2 - (b^2 - 2bc + c^2) = a^2 - (b - c)^2$$
$$= (a + b - c)(a - b + c).$$

**V.** An expression may sometimes be regarded as the sum, or as the difference, of two quantities each of which is the cube of a quantity. Such expressions are factorable, for

$$a^3 + b^3 = (a + b)(a^2 - ab + b^2),$$
$$a^3 - b^3 = (a - b)(a^2 + ab + b^2);$$

or, combining these two lines into one, as we sometimes do for brevity in writing,*

$$a^3 \pm b^3 = (a \pm b)(a^2 \mp ab + b^2).$$

*Examples.*

$$8a^3 + 27b^3 = (2a)^3 + (3b)^3$$
$$= (2a + 3b)(4a^2 - 6ab + 9b^2),$$
$$512a^3 - 125b^9 = (8a - 5b^3)(64a^2 + 40ab^3 + 25b^6).$$

**VI.** Sometimes an expression of the form $ax^2 + bx + c$ is factorable rationally. The attempt to find factors, each of which is the sum of two terms, must be a tentative one, and no general rule can well be given, other than the following: The product of the first terms must be $ax^2$, the product of the second terms must be $c$, and the sum of the cross products must be $bx$.

*Examples.*

$$x^2 - 5x + 6 = (x - 2)(x - 3),$$
$$2a^2 - 7ab - 15b^2 = (2a + 3b)(a - 5b).$$

---

* The symbol $\pm$ is read "plus or minus"; similarly, $\mp$ is read "minus or plus." In a given relation containing two or more such double signs we shall understand two distinct relations: one corresponding to the upper signs, and the other to the lower signs.

Occasionally an expression may be factored in more than one way. For example, an expression which may be regarded as the difference of two sixth powers falls under both cases IV and V.  Thus,

$$a^6 - b^6 = (a^3 + b^3)(a^3 - b^3)$$

$$= (a + b)(a^2 - ab + b^2)(a - b)(a^2 + ab + b^2);$$

and also

$$a^6 - b^6 = (a^2 - b^2)(a^4 + a^2b^2 + b^4)$$

$$= (a + b)(a - b)(a^4 + a^2b^2 + b^4).$$

Now a comparison of these two results shows that we have

$$a^4 + a^2b^2 + b^4 = (a^2 - ab + b^2)(a^2 + ab + b^2),$$

which is easily checked.  This is an instance of the more general relation,

$$a^4 + ma^2b^2 + b^4 = (a^2 - \sqrt{2 - m}\, ab + b^2)(a^2 + \sqrt{2 - m}\, ab + b^2),$$

which holds with real coefficients when the number $m$ is negative, zero, or positive and not greater than 2.  This relation may be obtained as follows:

$$a^4 + ma^2b^2 + b^4 = a^4 + 2a^2b^2 + b^4 - (2 - m)a^2b^2$$

$$= (a^2 + b^2)^2 - (\sqrt{2 - m}\, ab)^2$$

$$= (a^2 + b^2 + \sqrt{2 - m}\, ab)(a^2 + b^2 - \sqrt{2 - m}\, ab).$$

To acquire facility in factoring, one must be able to recognize the intrinsic form possessed by an algebraic expression.  As has been mentioned before, it is important that the student be able to discern form; experience with factoring is one of the best ways of developing such ability.

### EXERCISES

Factor each of the following expressions.  Check by substituting numbers for the letters involved.

1. $4a^2b - 12a^3b^2$.

2. $21a^6 - 33a^4 + 45a^7$.

3. $a^4 - 9b^2$.

4. $64 - 125a^6$.

5. $8x^3 + 27y^9$.

6. $3r^2 - 48s^2$.

7. $x^6 + y^6$.

8. $9a^2 + 6ab + b^2$.

9. $3x + 9y + x^2 + 3xy$.

10. $(a - b)^2 + 4(a - b) + 4$.

11. $a^2 - 5ab + 6b^2$.

12. $x^2 + xy - 6y^2$.

13. $mn^4 - 9m^3n^2$.

14. $a^4 + 4a^2b + 3b^2$.

15. $a^8 - 8a^2b^6$.

16. $3x^3y + 24y^4$.

17. $6x^2 - 13x - 5$.

18. $ax - 2bx - 6by + 3ay$.

19. $a^2 + 4ab + 4b^2 - 3a - 6b$.

20. $r^2 - 9s^2 + 2(r + 3s)^2$.

21. $x^2 - 2xy + y^2 - 5x + 5y + 6$.

22. $3a^3 + 6a^2b + 2ac^2 + 4bc^2$.

23. $8a^3b^3 - c^6$.

24. $m^2 - 4m^2n^2 - 6mn + 9n^2$.

25. $x^2 + 4xz + 8yz - 4y^2$.

26. $4a^2 + 2ab^2 - 6b^4$.

27. $x^4 + 64$.

28. $2a^4 - 15a^2 - 27$.

29. $(2x - y)^2 - (x - 2y)^2$.

30. $(x - y)^3 - (x + 2y)^3$.

31. $(a - 2b)^3 + (b - 2a)^3$.

32. $r^8 + 16s^4$.

33. $a^4 - 8a^2b^2 + 4b^4$.

34. $x^5 - y^5 - x^3y^2 + x^2y^3$.

35. $a^8 - 81b^4$.

36. $(a + 2b)^6 - a^6$.

37. $4m^4 - 17m^2n^2 + 4n^4$.

38. $a^5 - 32b^7 + 8a^2b^3 - 4a^3b^4$.

39. $x^2 + xy - 2y^2 + 2x + y + 1$.

40. $2a^2 + 5ab - 3b^2 - a + 4b - 1$.

**7. Reduction and simplification.**  The operations and processes discussed in the preceding articles provide means of simplifying complicated algebraic expressions and reducing them to more compact or more usable forms.  We shall discuss briefly some of the common methods of reduction by application of the foregoing principles.

Expressions sometimes involve two or more pairs of parentheses or their equivalent.  To avoid confusion, it is common practice to use various symbols, such as: parentheses, $(\ )$; brackets, $[\ ]$; braces, $\{\ \}$; the vinculum, $\overline{\phantom{xxx}}$.  Theorem VII of Art. 3 may be successively applied, first to the innermost parentheses, next to the inner symbol then remaining, and so on.

*Example.*

$$3a - \{2a + 5[a - 1 - 2(a + 3 - \overline{a + 5})]\}$$

$$= 3a - \{2a + 5[a - 1 - 2(a + 3 - a - 5)]\}$$

$$= 3a - \{2a + 5[a - 1 - 2(-2)]\}$$

$$= 3a - \{2a + 5[a - 1 + 4]\}$$

$$= 3a - \{2a + 5[a + 3]\}$$

$$= 3a - \{2a + 5a + 15\}$$

$$= 3a - \{7a + 15\}$$

$$= 3a - 7a - 15 = -4a - 15.$$

When dealing with a fraction, it is sometimes possible to factor both numerator and denominator. If numerator and denominator contain a common factor, this factor may be removed by division, applying theorem IX of Art. 3.

*Example.*

$$\frac{a^3 - 8b^3}{2a^2 - 8b^2} = \frac{(a - 2b)(a^2 + 2ab + 4b^2)}{2(a + 2b)(a - 2b)}$$

$$= \frac{a^2 + 2ab + 4b^2}{2(a + 2b)}.$$

In the addition of two or more fractions, theorems IX and X of Art. 3 come into play. When the denominators are not all the same, we first find the lowest common denominator (L.C.D.), which is the expression having the following three properties: (1) each denominator is a factor of the L.C.D.; (2) every factor element of the L.C.D. is a factor of at least one denominator; (3) each factor of the L.C.D. appears to the lowest possible power consistent with the two preceding requirements. By using theorem IX we can then express each of the given fractions as an equivalent fraction having the L.C.D. as its denominator, and add in accordance with theorem X.

*Example.*

$$\frac{12b - 16a}{3a^2 - 3b^2} + \frac{5}{a + b} - \frac{1}{b - a}$$

$$= \frac{12b - 16a}{3(a + b)(a - b)} + \frac{5 \cdot 3(a - b)}{3(a + b)(a - b)} - \frac{-3(a + b)}{3(a + b)(a - b)}$$

$$= \frac{12b - 16a + 15a - 15b + 3a + 3b}{3(a + b)(a - b)} = \frac{2a}{3(a^2 - b^2)}.$$

The multiplication and division of fractions depend upon theorems XI and XII of Art. 3. Here again, factoring and the removal of common factors from numerator and denominator will sometimes materially simplify the result.

*Example.*

$$\frac{4a^2 + 4ab + b^2}{2a^3 + 16b^3} \div \frac{4a^2 - b^2}{6a + 12b} = \frac{(2a + b)(2a + b)}{2(a + 2b)(a^2 - 2ab + 4b^2)} \cdot \frac{6(a + 2b)}{(2a + b)(2a - b)}$$

$$= \frac{3(2a + b)}{(a^2 - 2ab + 4b^2)(2a - b)}.$$

A complex fraction is one in which either the numerator or the denominator (or both) involves one or more fractions. Usually the simplest and quickest way to reduce a complex fracion is to multiply numerator and denominator by the L.C.D. of all the component fractions.

*Example.*

$$\frac{\dfrac{1}{a-b}+\dfrac{1}{a+b}}{1+\dfrac{b^2}{a^2-b^2}} = \frac{a+b+a-b}{a^2-b^2+b^2} = \frac{2a}{a^2} = \frac{2}{a}.$$

## EXERCISES

Simplify each of the following expressions. Check by substituting numbers for the letters involved.

**1.** $3a^2 - (a+2)(3a-1)$.

**2.** $4a^3 - [a^3 - 2(a^3 - 3)]$.

**3.** $2xy^2 - y[xy - x(y - x)]$.

**4.** $\dfrac{5}{x} - \dfrac{7}{3x^2}$.

**5.** $\dfrac{2}{a} + \dfrac{3}{b} - \dfrac{4a}{b^2}$.

**6.** $\dfrac{1}{x-3} - \dfrac{x+2}{x^2-3x}$.

**7.** $\dfrac{3}{a-b} - \dfrac{3b(a+b)}{a^3-b^3}$.

**8.** $\dfrac{1}{2x-3} + \dfrac{2}{2x+3} - \dfrac{1+6x}{4x^2-9}$.

**9.** $\dfrac{4a^2-2ab+b^2}{8a^3+b^3} - \dfrac{1}{b-2a}$.

**10.** $\dfrac{1}{y-\sqrt{xy}} + \dfrac{1}{\sqrt{xy}+y}$.

**11.** $2a - a\left(1 - \dfrac{2b-c}{2b+c}\right)$.

**12.** $\dfrac{a+b}{a^2-b^2} - \dfrac{a(a+b)}{a^3-b^3}$.

**13.** $\dfrac{2x}{x-2} - \dfrac{x^2-5}{x^2-4x+4} - 1$.

**14.** $\left(a - \dfrac{4}{a}\right)\left(1 - \dfrac{2}{a+2}\right)$.

**15.** $\left(\dfrac{3a+b}{2a-b} - 1\right)\left(2 - \dfrac{5b}{a+2b}\right)$.

**16.** $9x^2 + 6xy + 4y^2 - \dfrac{2x^3-8y^3}{3x-2y}$.

**17.** $\left(x + \dfrac{9}{x} + 6\right)\left(x^2 + \dfrac{x-x^2}{x+3}\right)$.

**18.** $\dfrac{2}{2x-4y} - \dfrac{3}{3x+y} - \dfrac{7}{3x^2-5xy-2y^2}$.

**19.** $\dfrac{a+b}{(b-c)(a-c)} + \dfrac{b+c}{(a-b)(a-c)} - \dfrac{a+c}{(a-b)(b-c)}$.

**20.** $\dfrac{a^2-(b-c)^2}{b^2-(c+a)^2} + \dfrac{b^2-(c-a)^2}{c^2-(a+b)^2} + \dfrac{c^2-(a-b)^2}{a^2-(b+c)^2}$.

**21.** $\dfrac{2x - \dfrac{8}{x}}{x - 2}.$

**22.** $\dfrac{1 - \dfrac{y^2}{4x^2}}{\dfrac{y}{2x} - 1}.$

**23.** $\dfrac{a - \dfrac{1}{a}}{2a + \dfrac{2}{a} + 4}.$

**24.** $\dfrac{\dfrac{a}{2b} - \dfrac{2b}{a}}{\dfrac{(a + 2b)^2}{4ab} - 2}.$

**25.** $\dfrac{3x}{3 - \dfrac{2}{x}} - \dfrac{9x^2}{9x + \dfrac{4}{x} - 12}.$

**26.** $\dfrac{\dfrac{1}{2(x + h)} - \dfrac{1}{2x}}{h}.$

**27.** $\dfrac{\dfrac{3}{x + h + 1} - \dfrac{3}{x + 1}}{h}.$

**28.** $\dfrac{\dfrac{x + h}{x + h - 4} - \dfrac{x}{x - 4}}{h}.$

**29.** $\dfrac{\dfrac{3x - (2 + 3x)}{x^2}}{\dfrac{2 + 3x}{x}}.$

**30.** $\dfrac{\dfrac{2 - x - (2 + x)(-1)}{(2 - x)^2}}{\dfrac{2 + x}{2 - x}}.$

**31.** $18(1 - x)(3 + 2x)^{\frac{1}{2}} - 6(3 + 2x)^{\frac{3}{2}}.$

**32.** $(6 + 2x)(3 - 2x)^{-\frac{1}{2}} - 2(3 - 2x)^{\frac{1}{2}}.$

**33.** $\dfrac{\sqrt{1 - x^2} + \dfrac{x^2}{\sqrt{1 - x^2}}}{1 - x^2}.$

**34.** $\dfrac{1 + \dfrac{x}{\sqrt{x^2 + 4}}}{x + \sqrt{x^2 + 4}}.$

**35.** $\dfrac{\dfrac{1}{x^2}}{\sqrt{1 - \dfrac{1}{x^2}}}.$

**36.** $\dfrac{\sqrt{x^2 - 3} - \dfrac{x^2}{\sqrt{x^2 - 3}}}{x^2 - 3}.$

**37.** $\sqrt{a^2 - x^2} - \dfrac{x^2}{\sqrt{a^2 - x^2}} + \dfrac{a}{\sqrt{1 - x^2/a^2}}.$

**38.** $\dfrac{\dfrac{x^2}{\sqrt{a^2 + x^2}} - (a + \sqrt{a^2 + x^2})}{x^2(a + \sqrt{a^2 + x^2})}.$

**39.** $\dfrac{\dfrac{2x(3 + 4x^2) - 8x^3}{(3 + 4x^2)^2}}{\dfrac{x^2}{3 + 4x^2}}.$

**40.** $\dfrac{b}{2a\sqrt{a}} \sqrt{\dfrac{a}{bx - a}} \cdot \dfrac{1}{1 + \dfrac{bx - a}{a}}.$

**41.** $\dfrac{\sqrt{a^2 - x^2} + \dfrac{x^2}{\sqrt{a^2 - x^2}}}{a^2 - x^2} - \dfrac{\dfrac{1}{a}}{\sqrt{1 - x^2/a^2}}.$

**42.** $\dfrac{ax}{a + \sqrt{a^2 - x^2}} \cdot \dfrac{\dfrac{x^2}{\sqrt{a^2 - x^2}} + a + \sqrt{a^2 - x^2}}{x^2} - \dfrac{x}{\sqrt{a^2 - x^2}}.$

**43.** $a^2 \left( \sqrt{a^2 - x^2} - \dfrac{x^2}{\sqrt{a^2 - x^2}} + \dfrac{a}{\sqrt{1 - x^2/a^2}} \right) + 6x^2\sqrt{a^2 - x^2} - 2(a^2 - x^2)^{\frac{3}{2}}.$

**44.** $\dfrac{a}{\sqrt{1 - x^2/a^2}} + \dfrac{x^2}{\sqrt{a^2 - x^2}} - \sqrt{a^2 - x^2}.$

**45.** $\dfrac{\dfrac{x^2}{\sqrt{x^2 + a^2}} - \sqrt{x^2 + a^2}}{x^2 + a^2} + \dfrac{1 + \dfrac{x}{\sqrt{x^2 + a^2}}}{x + \sqrt{x^2 + a^2}}.$

**46.** $\dfrac{x^2}{\sqrt{x^2 + a^2}} + \sqrt{x^2 + a^2} + a^2 \dfrac{1 + \dfrac{x}{\sqrt{x^2 + a^2}}}{x + \sqrt{x^2 + a^2}}.$

**47.** $\dfrac{(x - a)(a - x)}{\sqrt{2ax - x^2}} + \sqrt{2ax - x^2} + \dfrac{a}{\sqrt{1 - (x - a)^2/a^2}}.$

**48.** $\dfrac{x^{n-1}(a - x)}{\sqrt{2ax - x^2}} + (n - 1)x^{n-2}\sqrt{2ax - x^2} + \dfrac{a(1 - 2n)x^{n-1}}{\sqrt{2ax - x^2}}.$

**49.** $\dfrac{\dfrac{x^n(a - x)}{\sqrt{2ax - x^2}} - nx^{n-1}\sqrt{2ax - x^2}}{x^{2n}} - \dfrac{n - 1}{x^{n-1}\sqrt{2ax - x^2}}.$

**50.** $2(a^2 - x^2)^{\frac{3}{2}} - 6x^2\sqrt{a^2 - x^2} - \dfrac{3a^2x^2}{\sqrt{a^2 - x^2}} + 3a^2\sqrt{a^2 - x^2} + \dfrac{3a^3}{\sqrt{1 - x^2/a^2}}.$

# II ———————————————— Variables, Functions, and Graphs

**8. Constants and variables.** In general, an algebraic expression involves both numbers and letter symbols. The numbers, of course, remain fixed in value. In addition, in each particular expression, we may choose to regard certain of the symbols as fixed but unspecified in value. Such fixed letters, as well as the numbers concerned, are called **constants.** On the other hand, we may wish to assign, in turn, various numerical values to certain of the symbols in the course of our discussion. The symbols that may be so treated are called **variables.**

For example, we frequently deal with an expression of the form

$$ax^2 + bx + c,$$

in which we regard the quantities $a$, $b$, and $c$ as constants and $x$ as a variable. If we can determine properties of this expression when $a$, $b$, and $c$ are unspecified constants (although perhaps restricted in some ways), the behavior of each expression having that form, such as $2x^2 - 5x + 1$ or $3 - x^2$, when $x$ is given different numerical values, can be predicted to some degree.

**9. The function concept.** We begin our discussion of the function concept, which is a broad and pervading idea in mathematics, by an examination of a particular instance.

Consider the expression

$$2x^2 - 5x + 1, \tag{1}$$

which was used as an example of the form mentioned in the preceding article. We see that when the variable $x$ is assigned any real value—positive, negative, or zero, integral or fractional, rational or irrational—we get a definite real number from expression (1). For convenience and brevity, we may denote our expression by a single letter, say $y$. Then $y$ is also a variable whose value depends upon the value given to $x$. In the following table, the value of $y = 2x^2 - 5x + 1$, corresponding to each of various values assigned to $x$, is shown:

| $x$ | 0 | 1 | $-1$ | $\frac{1}{2}$ | $-\frac{3}{2}$ | $\frac{5}{4}$ | $\sqrt{5}$ | 3 | 4 |
|---|---|---|---|---|---|---|---|---|---|
| $y$ | 1 | $-2$ | 8 | $-1$ | 13 | $-\frac{17}{8}$ | $11 - 5\sqrt{5}$ | 4 | 13 |

27

The values of $x$ tabulated were chosen more or less at random; the table could easily be extended and gaps could be filled in at pleasure.

We now frame a definition of a function of a single variable as follows: *If, to each permissible value of the variable $x$, there corresponds one or more values of a second variable $y$, then $y$ is said to be a* **function of $x$.**

The correspondence may be exhibited by having some expression involving $x$ set equal to $y$, as $y = 2x^2 - 5x + 1$; or it may be given through a table, such as that above; or in any one of other possible modes of symbolic or verbal expression. The essential thing is that there be stipulated in some way a correspondence between $x$ and $y$—some *dependence* between them—some *functional relation* connecting them.

Since $x$ may be given a value at pleasure, and the value assumed by $y$ is a consequence, we say that $x$ is the **independent variable** and $y$ the **dependent variable.**

The above definition of a function allows for more than one value of $y$ corresponding to a single value of $x$. This is to permit the possibility of a relation such as, for example, $y^2 - x^2 = 1$. For this leads to $y = \pm\sqrt{1 + x^2}$, so that there are two values of $y$ corresponding to each value of $x$.

It should be noticed that the relation $y = k$, a constant, defines $y$ as a function of $x$; for, to each value assigned to $x$, there corresponds a value of $y$ —one and the same value, $k$, for each value of $x$.

Consider next the expression

$$\frac{x}{\sqrt{x^2 + y^2}}, \tag{2}$$

involving two variables $x$ and $y$. Here both $x$ and $y$ can be given any values at will, except that the choice $x = 0$ and $y = 0$ is not allowed to us since that choice produces the illicit operation of division by zero. Evidently the value assigned to each variable is independent of the value given to the other with the one exception mentioned; hence we have here an expression in two independent variables. A table consisting of three lines of figures can readily be constructed: values assigned to $x$ will be in one line, values assigned to $y$ in a second, and the corresponding computed values of expression (2) in the third line.

We therefore have, in expression (2), an example of a function of two independent variables. Further generalization is not difficult, and a definition of a function of $n$ variables, where $n$ is any positive integer, may be framed by obvious changes in the wording of the definition of a function of one variable.

### EXERCISES

1. The volume $V$ of a sphere depends only upon the radius $r$. Express $V$ as a function of $r$.    $V = \frac{4}{3}\pi r^3$

2. Express the volume $V$ of a right circular cone as a function of its base radius $r$ and altitude $h$.    $V = \frac{1}{3}\pi r^2 h$

3. The length of a side of an equilateral triangle is $s$. Express the area $A$ of the triangle as a function of $s$.    $A = \frac{1}{4}\sqrt{3}s^2$

4. For what values of $x$ and $y$ will expression (2) of Art. 9 be (a) positive; (b) negative; (c) zero?

5. Show that, for all permissible values of $x$ and $y$, expression (2) of Art. 9 will be not less than $-1$ and not more than 1.

6. A right circular cylinder of base radius $r$ is inscribed in a sphere of radius 5. Express the volume $V$ of the cylinder as a function of $r$.

7. A right circular cone of base radius $r$ is inscribed in a sphere of radius 10. Express the volume $V$ of the cone as a function of $r$.

8. A right circular cone of base radius $r$ is circumscribed about a sphere of radius 6. Express the volume $V$ of the cone as a function of $r$.

9. Given the equation $x^2 y - x^2 - 4y = 0$. Regarding $y$ as a function of $x$, how many $y$-values correspond to each $x$-value, and what values of $x$ are permissible?

10. If, in Exercise 9, $x$ is regarded as a function of $y$, how many $x$-values correspond to each $y$-value, and what values of $y$ are permissible?

### 10. Functional notations.

For convenience and brevity, the words "function of $x$" are often represented symbolically. A common notation is $f(x)$, and other symbols frequently used are $F(x)$, $g(x)$, $\phi(x)$, etc. If two or more functions are being treated in the same discussion, different symbols may be used in order to distinguish among the several functions.

When $y$, say, is the dependent variable corresponding to the independent variable $x$, the functional relation between $x$ and $y$ may then be denoted by

$$y = f(x).$$

If we wish to speak of the value of $y$ corresponding to some particular value $a$ of $x$, we may then use the notation $f(a)$, which indicates that $x$ has been replaced by $a$ wherever it appears in the functional expression. Thus, if

$$f(x) = 2x^2 - 5x + 1,$$

then

$$f(a) = 2a^2 - 5a + 1,$$

$$f(2) = 2 \cdot 2^2 - 5 \cdot 2 + 1 = -1,$$

$$f(-\sqrt{2}) = 2(-\sqrt{2})^2 - 5(-\sqrt{2}) + 1 = 5 + 5\sqrt{2},$$

and so on.

Similarly, if $z$ is a function of two independent variables, $x$ and $y$, we express the fact by means of a notation such as

$$z = F(x, y).$$

If we have, for example,

$$F(x, y) = \frac{x}{\sqrt{x^2 + y^2}},$$

then

$$F(0, 1) = 0, \qquad F(1, 0) = 1, \qquad F(3, 4) = \tfrac{3}{5},$$

etc. It should be noted that, of the two quantities within the parentheses, separated by a comma, the first is the $x$-value and the second the $y$-value; that is, the order is that of the symbol $F(x, y)$. Accordingly, we have

$$F(y, x) = \frac{y}{\sqrt{y^2 + x^2}},$$

which is a function different from the original one.

### EXERCISES

**1.** If $f(x) = 2x - 5$, find $f(0)$, $f(3)$, $f(-2)$.

**2.** If $g(x) = \sqrt{9 + 4x^2}$, find $g(1)$, $g(-2)$, $g(\sqrt{3})$. What is the smallest value $g(x)$ may have, and to what value of $x$ does this correspond?

**3.** If $\phi(x) = \dfrac{2x}{x + 2}$, find $\phi(0)$, $\phi(2)$, $\phi(-\tfrac{1}{2})$. For what value of $x$ does $\phi(x)$ fail to exist?

**4.** If $F(x, y) = \dfrac{x - y}{x + y}$, show that $F(y, x) = -F(x, y)$. Also find $F\left(\dfrac{1}{x}, \dfrac{1}{y}\right)$ and express it in terms of $F(x, y)$.

**5.** If $G(x, y) = 2\sqrt{x} - \sqrt{y} + x^2 y$, find $G(4, 1)$, $G(x^2, y^2)$.

**6.** If $F(x, y) = \dfrac{x^2 - 4y^2}{4x^2 - y^2}$, find $F(x, x)$, $F(-x, -y)$. Also show that $F(ax, ay) = F(x, y)$ when $a \neq 0$.

**7.** If $\phi(x, y) = a^{x-y}$, show that $\phi(x, x) = 1$ and that $\phi(y, x) = 1/\phi(x, y)$.

**8.** If $F(x, y) = \dfrac{a^x - a^y}{a^x + a^y}$, show that $F(0, 0) = F(x, x)$ and that $F(-x, -y) = -F(x, y)$.

**9.** If $y = f(x) = \dfrac{4x + 5}{3x - 4}$, show that $x = f(y)$.

**10.** As a generalization of Exercise 9, let $y = f(x) = \dfrac{ax + b}{cx + d}$, where $a$, $b$, $c$, and $d$ are constants all different from zero. What relation must these constants obey in order that $x = f(y)$?

**11. Rectangular coordinates.**   In Art. 1 we briefly discussed a geometric representation of real numbers as points on a line.  We now wish
to represent, instead of a set of single numbers, a set of number pairs,
such as we have in a table of corresponding values of $x$ and $y$.

Accordingly, we extend our one-dimensional representation, involving
only a line, to two dimensions, that is, a plane.  The most common representation is that in which two mutual perpendicular lines are drawn in
a plane.  One line, along which direction the first number $x$ is measured,
is then called the **X-axis;** and the other, in which direction the second
number $y$ is measured, is called the **Y-axis.**  This procedure gives us
what is called a **rectangular coordinate system.**

We usually adopt the convention of drawing the $X$-axis horizontally
and the $Y$-axis vertically, intersecting at the point $O$ called the **origin,**
which is the zero point on each axis.  Also conventionally, we measure
$x$-distances as positive to the right and negative to the left, as in the one-
dimensional representation of Fig. 1, and we measure $y$-distances as
positive upward and negative downward from the origin $O$.

Suppose now that we wish to represent a particular number pair,
$x_1$ and $y_1$.*  We first measure $x_1$ units in the horizontal direction,
according to the scale adopted for the $X$-axis, and to the right or left of
$O$ according as $x_1$ is a positive or a negative number.  From the position
thus reached on the $X$-axis, we then measure $y_1$ units vertically, according to the $Y$-scale and upward or downward according as $y_1$ is positive
or negative.  We thus reach a point $P_1$ which geometrically represents
our number pair; the number pair or point is then said to be plotted.
We call $x_1$ and $y_1$ the **coordinates** of $P_1$, and we use the notation $P_1(x_1, y_1)$
or simply $(x_1, y_1)$ as a complete symbolic representation of the number
pair and the corresponding geometric point representation.

It should be noted that, in the symbol $P_1(x_1, y_1)$, the $x$-distance,
called the **abscissa** of the point, is written first, followed by a comma, and
the $y$-distance, called the **ordinate** of the point, is written second, the
pair being enclosed in parentheses.

Conversely, if $P_2$ is any point in the plane, its abscissa and ordinate
can be measured, and we get a number pair $(x_2, y_2)$ corresponding to the
point.  Thus in Fig. 2, the point $P_2$ has the coordinates $(3.5, -2)$.

The rectangular coordinate system therefore provides a one-to-one
correspondence between number pairs and points; that is, corresponding
to a number pair $(x_1, y_1)$ there is always one and only one point $P_1$, and
corresponding to a point $P_2$ there is one and only one number pair $(x_2,$

---

* The symbol $x_1$ is read "$x$ sub one."

$y_2$). This one-to-one correspondence is the starting point of the subject of plane analytic geometry.

The coordinate axes divide the plane into four regions, or **quadrants.** The first quadrant is taken as that in which both the abscissa and ordinate are positive, and the others are numbered consecutively in the

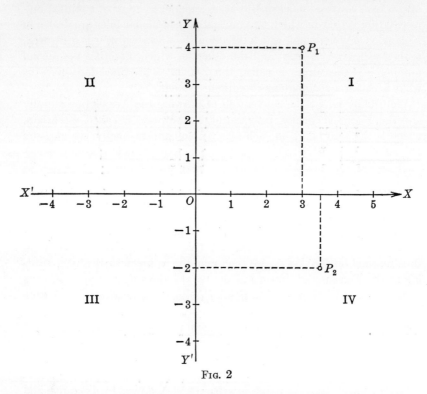

Fig. 2

counterclockwise direction, as indicated in Fig. 2. Then the signs of abscissa and ordinate in each quadrant are as follows:

| Quadrant | I | II | III | IV |
|----------|---|----|-----|-----|
| Abscissa | + | − | − | + |
| Ordinate | + | + | − | − |

The plotting of number pairs as described permits the geometric representation of a functional relation between two variables $x$ and $y$. Such a representation, called the **graph** of the function, consists of all points, and only those points, whose coordinates $x$ and $y$ are number pairs obtainable from the functional relation.

If, for example, we plot the number pairs given in the table of Art. 9, we get the points indicated by small circles in Fig. 3. As mentioned in

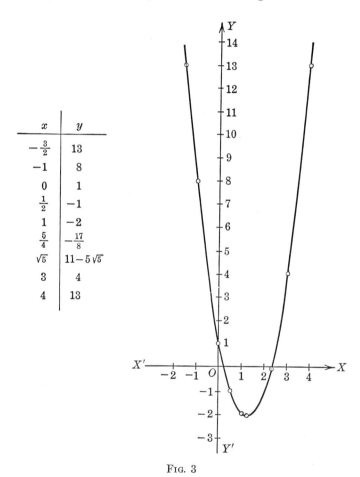

| $x$ | $y$ |
|---|---|
| $-\frac{3}{2}$ | 13 |
| $-1$ | 8 |
| 0 | 1 |
| $\frac{1}{2}$ | $-1$ |
| 1 | $-2$ |
| $\frac{5}{4}$ | $-\frac{17}{8}$ |
| $\sqrt{5}$ | $11-5\sqrt{5}$ |
| 3 | 4 |
| 4 | 13 |

Fig. 3

Art. 9, we could get additional number pairs from the functional relation $y = 2x^2 - 5x + 1$, and thus we could plot additional points. As a result, we would find the plotted points evidently ranged in a way which indicates that the full graph of the function $y = 2x^2 - 5x + 1$ consists of a smooth curve through all the points; this curve is also shown in Fig. 3.

It may be proved by more advanced methods, involving calculus, that the function $2x^2 - 5x + 1$, and indeed all functions of the form

$$a_0 x^n + a_1 x^{n-1} + \cdots + a_{n-1} x + a_n,$$

where $n$ is a positive integer and $a_0, a_1, \cdots, a_n$ are real constants, have graphs which are smooth continuous curves. We shall assume this fact in all our later work.

It should be noted, however, that when a functional relation is given through a definite number of corresponding value pairs, as in a table, the graph consists merely of the isolated points obtained from the discrete number pairs.

It will be seen from Fig. 3 that the graph crosses the $X$-axis at two points: one between 0 and 1, and the other between 2 and 3. The values of $x$ for which the function $f(x) = 2x^2 - 5x + 1$ reduces to zero may be found to any desired degree of accuracy by a process of *successive approximations*. Thus, if we estimate, from the graph, that the curve crosses the $X$-axis at $x = 0.2$ and at $x = 2.3$, we find by computation that $f(0.2) = 0.08$ and $f(2.2) = -0.32$. Since $f(0.2) > 0$ and $f(2.2) < 0$, it appears that the values of $x$ for which $f(x) = 0$, called *zeros* of the function, are slightly more than 0.2 and 2.2, respectively. By further trial, we find

$$f(0.21) = 0.0382, \qquad f(0.22) = -0.0032;$$

$$f(2.2) = -0.32, \qquad f(2.3) = 0.08.$$

Consequently the zeros of $2x^2 - 5x + 1$ are a little below 0.22 and somewhat below 2.3. This process can be continued through as many stages as desired. The zeros of our function are actually

$$\frac{5 - \sqrt{17}}{4} = 0.219 \text{ approx.}, \qquad \frac{5 + \sqrt{17}}{4} = 2.281 \text{ approx.},$$

as may easily be verified.

The problem of finding the zeros of a given function is an important one; much of our work will be connected with this type of problem. We have seen here how the graph of a function of one variable may be of aid in getting at least a first approximation to the real zeros.

It is possible to get a geometric representation of a function of two independent variables by extending the rectangular coordinate system to three-dimensional space. This is an important matter in the subject of solid analytic geometry, but it cannot be discussed here.

## EXERCISES

Plot each of the functions in Exercises 1–10 and estimate its real zeros.

**1.** $4x + 3$.                              **2.** $7 - 5x$.
**3.** $x^2 - x - 2$.                          **4.** $3x^2 + 7x + 2$.
**5.** $x^3 + x^2 - 4x - 4$.                    **6.** $x^3 - x^2 + 2x - 2$.
**7.** $x^4 - 7x^2 + 12$.                       **8.** $\sqrt{2 - x^2}$.
**9.** $-\sqrt{9 - 4x^2}$.                       **10.** $\pm\sqrt{x^2 - 1}$.

**11.** Show graphically that the function $x^2 + 4x + 5$ has no real zeros.

**12.** Show graphically that the function $\sqrt{2 + x^2}$ has no real zeros.

**13.** Where are all the points whose abscissas are 2? Draw the graph.

**14.** Where are all the points whose ordinates are $-3$? Draw the graph.

**15.** Discuss the graph of the equation $x = k$, where $k$ is (a) positive; (b) negative; (c) zero.

**16.** Discuss the graph of the equation $y = k$, where $k$ is (a) positive; (b) negative; (c) zero.

**17.** Graph on the same set of axes: $y = x$, $y = x^2$, $y = x^3$, $y = x^4$. What points do all four graphs have in common?

**18.** The functional relations of Exercise **17** are instances of $y = x^n$, where $n$ is a positive integer. In what quadrants does the graph lie whenever $n$ is (a) even; (b) odd?

**19.** Graph on the same set of axes: $xy = 1$, $x^2 y = 1$, $x^3 y = 1$. What point do all three graphs have in common?

**20.** Given $x^n y = 1$, where $n$ is a positive integer. In what quadrants does the graph lie whenever $n$ is (a) even; (b) odd?

## SUPPLEMENTARY EXERCISES

**1.** A gutter is to be made from a long rectangular piece of metal 10 in. wide by bending it longitudinally so as to get a cross section in the form of a rectangle with open top. Express the cross-sectional area of the gutter as a function of its depth $x$.

**2.** Equal squares are cut from the corners of a piece of cardboard 24 in. long and 15 in. wide, and the remaining rectangular portions along the sides are folded up to form an open box. Express the volume of the box as a function of the length $x$ of a side of a square cut out.

**3.** The two equal sides of an isosceles triangle are 8 in. long. Express the area of the triangle as a function of the length $x$ of its base.

**4.** One base and the two non-parallel sides of a trapezoid are each equal to 8 in. Express the area of the trapezoid as a function of the length $x$ of the other base.

**5.** If $f(x) = 3x^2 - 1$, find $f(2x - 1)$ and $f[f(x)]$.

**6.** If $f(x) = 2x^2 - 4x + 2$ and $g(x) = x^2 + 1$, find $f[g(x)]$ and $g[f(x)]$.

**7.** Plot the graph of the function of Exercise **1** for the permissible values of $x$ between 0 and 5. Observe that the function has zeros for $x = 0$ and $x = 5$ and is positive for all intermediate values. Estimate the value of $x$ for which the area has its largest value.

**8.** Plot the graph of the function of Exercise 2 for the permissible values of $x$ between 0 and 7.5. Observe that the function has zeros for $x = 0$ and $x = 7.5$ and is positive for all intermediate values. Estimate the value of $x$ for which the volume has its largest value.

**9.** Plot the graph of the function of Exercise 3 for the permissible values of $x$ between 0 and 16. Observe that the function has zeros for $x = 0$ and $x = 16$ and is positive for all intermediate values. Deduce the fact that the right triangle has the largest area.

**10.** Plot the graph of the function of Exercise 4 for the permissible values of $x$ between 0 and 24. Observe that the function has only one geometrically significant zero, at $x = 24$, and is positive for all other values of $x$ in the stated range. Estimate the value of $x$ for which the area has its largest value.

# III———————— The Fundamentals of Trigonometry

**12. Angles: definitions and representations.** The subject of trigo-nometry has to do with angles and relations among angles, and with quantities depending upon angles, that is, with functions of angles. It is therefore proper to begin our discussion with a precise and sufficiently general definition of an angle, so that we shall have a suitable foundation for subsequent development of the subject. (We shall regard an angle as being *generated* by the rotation about a point $O$ of a line emanating from $O$.) For definiteness, we refer to the

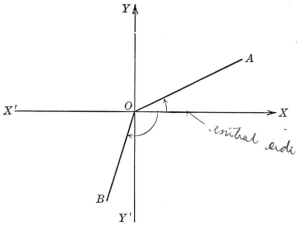

FIG. 4

rectangular coordinate system. Let the original position of the line, called the **initial side**, be along the positive $X$-axis, the point $O$ being the origin. If the line is rotated into a position $OA$ called the **terminal side**, we say that an angle $XOA$ has been generated. The direction of rotation from the initial position may be either clockwise or counterclockwise; we shall agree to adopt the convention that counterclockwise rotation shall generate a positive angle, and clockwise rotation, a negative angle. To indicate the direction of rotation, and therefore the sign attached to the angle, we sometimes use a circular arc with an arrow head on it, as in Fig. 4, where a positive angle is shown for $XOA$ and a negative angle for $XOB$.

We place no restriction on the amount of rotation possible, and consequently an angle may have any magnitude we wish. A quarter revolution generates a right angle, $XOY$; a half revolution, an angle equal to two right angles, $XOX'$; a complete revolution, an angle equal to four right angles; two revolutions, eight right angles; and so on. The zero angle is defined as one for which no rotation has taken place, the terminal side coinciding with the initial side.

An angle is said to lie in the quadrant in which its terminal side lies. Thus, $XOA$ is in the first quadrant, $XOB$ is in the third quadrant.

**13. Angle measurement.** The two common systems of angle measurement are the **sexagesimal system** and the **radian** or **circular system**.

The basic unit of the sexagesimal system is the **degree,** which is defined as $\frac{1}{360}$ part of a complete revolution. The degree is divided into 60 equal parts called **minutes,** and the minute is made up of 60 equal parts called **seconds.** Then a right angle, such as $XOY$ in Fig. 4, is equal to 90 degrees, written 90°. The prime denotes minutes, and the double prime seconds. Thus the angle whose sexagesimal measure is 13 degrees, 42 minutes, and 27 seconds is written 13° 42′ 27″. The sexagesimal system is most frequently used in computation.

The **radian** is defined as that central angle of a circle which subtends an arc whose length is equal to the radius of the circle. Thus, in Fig. 5, if the radius $OA$ is of length $r$, and arc $AB = r$, then the angle $\theta = AOB$ is 1 radian. In terms of our concept of generated angles, we may also frame the definition as follows: One radian is the positive angle generated when a point on the rotating line has moved through an arc equal in length to the radius of the circle being traced by the point.

It is apparent from elementary geometry that the radian is independent of the radius $r$ of the circle. Also, since the circumference of a circle is equal to $2\pi r$, it appears that a *complete revolution is equal to* $2\pi$ *radians.* Since a complete revolution likewise corresponds to 360° in sexagesimal measure, we have

$$2\pi \text{ radians} = 360°.$$

Therefore

$$1 \text{ radian} = \frac{360°}{2\pi} = 57.296°$$

$$= 57° \ 17′ \ 45″$$

approximately; and, conversely,

$$1° = \frac{2\pi}{360} = 0.017453 \text{ radian}$$

approximately.  Using these relations between degrees and radians, it is easy to compute the equivalent in one system of measurement of an angle given in the other system.  The table of equivalents in the Appendix to this book will be of aid in converting from one system to the other.

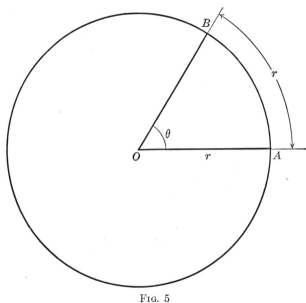

FIG. 5

The number of radians in a given angle, being expressible as the ratio of two lengths (intercepted arc length divided by length of corresponding radius), will be a pure number, that is, dimensionless, or without units.
It is usual to omit the word "radians" after a number expressing the size of an angle.  Thus, we speak of an angle $\pi/2$, the word radians being understood, when we wish to express in radian measure the right angle, 90°.

The reason for the wide use of radian measure in mathematical discussion is not easy to see at this point.  When the student studies calculus, however, he will find that radian measurement is the natural and convenient system for use in theoretical development.  The mathematical treatment of topics in engineering, physics, chemistry, and other sciences is nearly always based on the radian measure of angles. Since the student should therefore become thoroughly familiar with the circular system, we shall in this book denote angles in that system whenever it is convenient to do so.

There are other systems of angular measurement, including that often used in artillery work in which the *mil*, defined as $\frac{1}{6400}$ revolution, is the unit employed. The mil is nearly equal to 0.001 radian (actually $\pi/3200$).

In Fig. 4, the angle $XOA = \theta$, say, has its sign and magnitude indicated by the curved arrow. It is clear that the same terminal side would be reached if we were to rotate, from the positive $X$-axis as initial side, through any number of complete revolutions, in either direction, and then follow this rotation by a positive rotation through the acute angle $\theta$. Since one revolution equals $2\pi$ radians, the totality of angles with initial side $OX$ and terminal side $OA$ may be expressed as $2n\pi + \theta$, where $n$ is any positive or negative integer or zero. We can express similarly the general measure of all angles having their terminal sides in specified positions.

### EXERCISES

**1.** Express each of the following angles in radian measure as some rational number times $\pi$: $30°$, $-45°$, $120°$, $315°$, $300°$, $210°$, $-135°$, $270°$, $540°$, $600°$.

**2.** Express each of the following angles in degrees: $\pi/3$, $3\pi/2$, $5\pi/6$, $-3\pi/4$, $3\pi$, $7\pi/3$, $11\pi/6$, $9\pi/4$, $13\pi/6$, $8\pi$.

**3.** Express in radian measure in terms of $\pi$: (a) each angle of an equilateral triangle; (b) each angle of an isosceles right triangle; (c) each angle of a regular pentagon.

**4.** Express in radian measure in terms of $\pi$ the angle swept through in 3 hours and 24 minutes by (a) the hour hand, (b) the minute hand, of a clock.

**5.** Express in radian measure decimally, correct to four significant figures, each of the following angles: $67° 30'$, $105°$, $729°$, $49'$.

In Exercises 6–15, express the given angles in sexagesimal measure correct to the nearest minute.

**6.** 1.7 radians.  **7.** 4.2 radians.

**8.** 0.37 radian.  **9.** $\frac{1}{4}$ radian.

**10.** $\frac{\pi}{7}$ radian.  **11.** 0.035 radian.

**12.** 6.28 radians.  **13.** 11.5 radians.

**14.** 0.0175 radian.  **15.** 3.142 radians.

In Exercises 16–25, express the given angles in radian measure decimally, correct to four significant figures.

**16.** $24°$.  **17.** $53°$.

**18.** $37° 20'$.  **19.** $11° 5'$.

**20.** $10° 24'$.  **21.** $87° 8'$.

**22.** $57° 18'$.  **23.** $7° 27' 49''$.

**24.** $9° 14' 47''$.  **25.** $617° 19' 3''$.

**26.** Convert the angular velocity of 3650 revolutions per minute to radians per second, in terms of $\pi$.

**27.** If the angles of a triangle are in the ratio of $3:4:5$, find each angle in radian measure in terms of $\pi$.

**28.** On coordinate axes, with the positive $X$-axis as initial side, draw the terminal sides for the angles $(3n + 1)\pi/3$, where $n$ is an integer or zero.

**29.** Lines are drawn bisecting the four quadrants. Determine the general radian measure for the angles having these lines as terminal sides.

**30.** Lines are drawn trisecting the first and third quadrants. Determine the general radian measure for the angles having these lines as terminal sides.

**14. Geometric relations.** There are several useful geometric relations that can be simply expressed when the angle involved is measured in radians. We shall discuss two of these relations here, so that we shall have them for reference in later work.

Let $\theta$ denote a central angle in a circle of radius $r$, and let $s$ be the length of the intercepted arc, measured in the same units as $r$. Then, if $\theta$ is measured in radians, we have immediately from the definition of a radian

$$\theta = \frac{s}{r}. \tag{1}$$

This relation enables us to find easily any one of the quantities $\theta$, $r$, or $s$ when the other two are known.

Now let $A$ denote the area of the sector bounded by the arc of length $s$ and the two radii of length $r$. The ratio of the area $A$ to that of the entire circle, $\pi r^2$, will be equal to the ratio of the central angle $\theta$ of the sector to a complete revolution. If $\theta$ is again measured in radians, one revolution will be equal to $2\pi$ radians, and therefore we have

$$\frac{A}{\pi r^2} = \frac{\theta}{2\pi},$$

whence

$$A = \tfrac{1}{2}r^2\theta. \tag{2}$$

If any two of the three quantities $r$, $\theta$, and $A$ are known, the third may be determined from equation (2).

If we replace $\theta$ in equation (2) by its value given by (1) we find

$$A = \tfrac{1}{2}r^2 \cdot \frac{s}{r} = \tfrac{1}{2}rs.$$

This is the familiar formula for sector area given in elementary geometry.

*Example.* If the central angle of a circle of radius 5 in. is 30°, what is the length of the intercepted arc, and what is the area of the sector?

*Solution.* We first convert the given angle, 30°, to radian measure; we have

$$\frac{\theta}{2\pi} = \frac{30°}{360°},$$

$$\theta = \frac{\pi}{6}.$$

Hence equation (1) gives

$$s = r\theta = 5 \times \frac{\pi}{6} = 2.618 \text{ in., approx.,}$$

for the length of arc; and equation (2) yields for the area

$$A = \frac{1}{2} \times 5^2 \times \frac{\pi}{6} = 6.545 \text{ in.}^2 \text{ approx.}$$

### EXERCISES

**1.** If the bounding arc of a circular sector is 8 in. long and the radius is 5 in., find the area of the sector.

**2.** If the central angle of a sector is 60° and the arc is 10 in. long, find the sector area.

**3.** Using equations (1) and (2), Art. 14, obtain a formula for $s$ in terms of $\theta$ and $A$.

**4.** If the area of a sector is to be 64 in.$^2$ when the central angle is $\frac{1}{2}$ radian, what must the radius be?

**5.** A point is moving along a circle of radius 5 in. with a constant angular speed of 60 revolutions per minute. How far does the point travel in 1 second?

**6.** The outside diameter of a wagon wheel is 40 in. Find the number of revolutions per minute when the wagon is moving at the rate of 10 miles per hour.

**7.** A flywheel, 3 ft. in diameter, is rotating at the rate of 200 revolutions per minute. Find the speed, in feet per second, at which a point on the rim is moving.

**8.** If the diameter of the earth is 7920 miles, find the speed, in feet per second, of a point on the equator.

**9.** What is the length in feet of an arc of the earth's equator if the corresponding central angle is 1″? (Take the diameter of the earth as 7920 miles.)

**10.** The perimeter of a circular sector is 12 in. and its area is 9 in.$^2$ Find the length of the bounding arc.

**11.** Find the speed, in miles per second, of the earth in its motion about the sun. Assume that the motion is in a circle of radius $9.28 \times 10^7$ miles, and take 365.25 days as the time required for one revolution.

**12.** If the moon's radius is 1080 miles and the distance between its center and the surface of the earth is 238,000 miles, find the angle, to the nearest minute, subtended by the moon at an observer's eye.

**13.** The peripheral speed for a certain emery wheel is to be 120 ft./sec. Find the corresponding number of revolutions per minute of a wheel 10 in. in diameter.

**14.** A conical surface is to be formed by joining the radial edges of a sheet in the form of a circular sector. If the base radius and altitude of the cone are to be $r$ and $h$, respectively, find the central angle of the sector.

**15.** Using the result of Exercise 14, obtain a formula for the lateral surface area of a cone.

**15. Functions of angles.** Let there be given any angle $\theta$, and suppose
it to be placed on the coordinate axes as described in Art. 12. If we
choose an arbitrary point $P(x, y)$ on the terminal side, other than the
origin $O$, and drop a perpendicular $PQ$ from $P$ to the $X$-axis, we shall
form a right triangle $OPQ$ whose legs are respectively of lengths $|x|$
and $|y|$,* and whose hypotenuse $OP$, called the **distance,** is of length

$$r = |OP| = \sqrt{x^2 + y^2}.$$

In Fig. 6 are shown the four typical diagrams, the terminal side of
the angle lying in the first, second, third, or fourth quadrant.

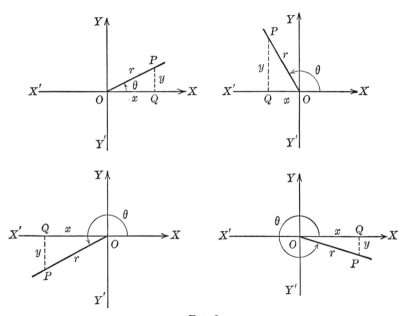

Fig. 6

Associated with each given angle $\theta$ six ratios may be expressed, each
involving two of the three quantities $x$, $y$, and $r$; they are

$$\frac{x}{y}, \quad \frac{y}{x}, \quad \frac{x}{r}, \quad \frac{r}{x}, \quad \frac{y}{r}, \quad \frac{r}{y}.$$

* The notation $|a|$ is read "the absolute value of $a$." By that is meant the
numerical value or magnitude of $a$, so that $|a|$ is never a negative number. Thus,
$|3| = 3$, $|-2| = 2$. More precisely, if $a$ is positive, $|a| = a$; and if $a$ is nega-
tive, $|a| = -a$.

Evidently the algebraic value of each of these ratios will depend upon the angle $\theta$; but, as may readily be seen by a consideration of similar triangles, each ratio will be the same for a given angle, regardless of the choice of position of the point $P$ on the terminal side. Thus, *each ratio is a function of* $\theta$; we call them **trigonometric functions** of $\theta$. For convenience in dealing with these six functions of $\theta$, each has been given a name and a specific functional symbolism, as follows:

| Name | Functional Symbol | Definition | |
|---|---|---|---|
| sine of $\theta$ | $\sin \theta$ | $\dfrac{\text{ordinate}}{\text{distance}}$ | $= \dfrac{y}{r}$ |
| cosine of $\theta$ | $\cos \theta$ | $\dfrac{\text{abscissa}}{\text{distance}}$ | $= \dfrac{x}{r}$ |
| tangent of $\theta$ | $\tan \theta$ | $\dfrac{\text{ordinate}}{\text{abscissa}}$ | $= \dfrac{y}{x}$ |
| cotangent of $\theta$ | $\cot \theta$ | $\dfrac{\text{abscissa}}{\text{ordinate}}$ | $= \dfrac{x}{y}$ |
| secant of $\theta$ | $\sec \theta$ | $\dfrac{\text{distance}}{\text{abscissa}}$ | $= \dfrac{r}{x}$ |
| cosecant of $\theta$ | $\csc \theta$ | $\dfrac{\text{distance}}{\text{ordinate}}$ | $= \dfrac{r}{y}$ |

It should be noted that, given any angle $\theta$, there is one and only one value of each trigonometric function of that angle. On the other hand, corresponding to a given value of, say, $\sin \theta$, there are indefinitely many angles. We shall consider this latter lack of uniqueness more fully in Chapter XII.

For an angle with its terminal side in any one of the four quadrants, as illustrated in Fig. 6, the abscissa and ordinate of $P$, as well as the distance $r$, will be different from zero, and consequently each trigonometric function will exist for every such angle. However, if the terminal side falls along a coordinate axis, between two quadrants, either $x$ or $y$ will be zero, and two of the six functions will fail to exist since division by zero is not a valid operation.

Since a trigonometric function is a ratio of two lengths, each is a pure number subject to the rules of operations on real numbers. Whether each such number is positive or negative will evidently depend upon the quadrant in which the angle lies. For example, $\sin \theta$ will be positive or negative according as $y$ is positive or negative, $r$ being positive by definition; consequently $\sin \theta$ is positive for $\theta$ in the first or second quadrant.

and negative when $\theta$ lies in the third or fourth quadrant. By similar means, the signs of the remaining five functions of $\theta$ mav be determined for each quadrant; we then get the following table:

| Quadrant | $\sin \theta$ | $\cos \theta$ | $\tan \theta$ | $\cot \theta$ | $\sec \theta$ | $\csc \theta$ |
|:---:|:---:|:---:|:---:|:---:|:---:|:---:|
| I | + | + | + | + | + | + |
| II | + | − | − | − | − | + |
| III | − | − | + | + | − | − |
| IV | − | + | − | − | + | − |

When dealing with the power of a trigonometric function, a simplified notation is used. Thus, instead of writing $(\sin \theta)^2$ for the square of $\sin \theta$, we write $\sin^2 \theta$. In general, the exponent is written between the functional symbol and the angle symbol, but there is one important exception: when the exponent is $-1$, we write, for example, $(\sin \theta)^{-1}$. The reason for this exception will be seen when we discuss inverse functions (Chapter XII); the notations $\sin^{-1} \theta$, $\cos^{-1} \theta$, etc., are there seen to have a special meaning.

One way to find the approximate values of the functions of a given angle is by direct measurement and computation as in the following example.

*Example.* Find the functions of 40°.
*Solution.* We first construct the angle, 40°, as accurately as possible by means of a protractor, taking the initial side along the positive $X$-axis as usual. Choose the point $P$ on the terminal side so that the distance $r = OP = 10$ units, say, according to some large convenient scale, and drop the perpendicular $PQ$ to the $X$-axis (Fig. 7). Then measure the abscissa $x = OQ$ and ordinate $y = PQ$ by means of the same scale; we find $x = 7.66$ and $y = 6.43$, approximately. Therefore, by definition, we have

$$\sin 40° = \frac{y}{r} = \frac{6.43}{10} = 0.643, \quad \cos 40° = \frac{x}{r} = \frac{7.66}{10} = 0.766,$$

$$\tan 40° = \frac{y}{x} = \frac{6.43}{7.66} = 0.839, \quad \cot 40° = \frac{x}{y} = \frac{7.66}{6.43} = 1.19,$$

$$\sec 40° = \frac{r}{x} = \frac{10}{7.66} = 1.31, \quad \csc 40° = \frac{r}{y} = \frac{10}{6.43} = 1.56,$$

as approximate values.

By more refined means, including computations based on certain series obtained by calculus, functions of numerous angles may be calculated more accurately. It is then possible to construct tables of trigonometric functions. Tables giving function values for various angles, to four

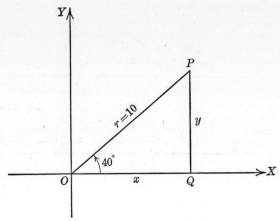

FIG. 7

decimal places, are given in the back of this book. The manner in which such tables are used is discussed in Art. 17.

## EXERCISES

In each of Exercises 1–6, determine the quadrant in which the angle $\theta$ lies when the given functions satisfy the stated conditions.

**1.** $\sin \theta > 0$, $\cos \theta < 0$.
**2.** $\cos \theta > 0$, $\tan \theta < 0$.
**3.** $\csc \theta > 0$, $\cot \theta > 0$.
**4.** $\tan \theta < 0$, $\csc \theta < 0$.
**5.** $\sec \theta > 0$, $\sin \theta > 0$.
**6.** $\cot \theta > 0$, $\sec \theta < 0$.

In Exercises 7–15, determine the sign of each trigonometric function for each given angle.

**7.** $\pi/3$.
**8.** $5\pi/6$.
**9.** $4\pi/3$.
**10.** $7\pi/3$.
**11.** $-2\pi/3$.
**12.** $-7\pi/4$.
**13.** $(12n + 1)\pi/6$.
**14.** $(6n - 1)\pi/3$.
**15.** $(8n + 3)\pi/4$.

**16.** Determine which of the six trigonometric functions fail to exist for each of the following angles: $0$, $\pi/2$, $\pi$, $3\pi/2$.

**17.** Show that neither the sine nor the cosine of an angle can ever exceed 1 and that neither is ever less than $-1$.

**18.** Show that the tangent and cotangent of an angle may be any real number.

**19.** Show that neither the secant nor the cosecant of any angle can have a value between $-1$ and 1.

**20.** Three additional functions occasionally used and tabulated are the following:

$$\text{versed sine of } \theta \text{ (vers } \theta) = 1 - \cos \theta,$$
$$\text{coversed sine of } \theta \text{ (covers } \theta) = 1 - \sin \theta,$$
$$\text{haversine } \theta \text{ (hav } \theta) = (1 - \cos \theta)/2.$$

Using the result of Exercise 17, determine the range of values that each of these functions may have.

**16. Special angles.** In the preceding article we discussed briefly the manner in which the trigonometric functions of an angle may be approximately evaluated by measurement and computation. There are also certain angles whose functions may be simply expressed in terms of rational or irrational numbers; we proceed to consider some of these special angles.

For both the isosceles right triangle, with each acute angle equal to 45° ($\pi/4$ radians), and the right triangle whose acute angles are 30° and 60° ($\pi/6$ and $\pi/3$), it is possible to express particular relations between the lengths of the sides. Accordingly, the angles $\pi/6$ and $\pi/4$, and all multiples of these angles, lead to triangles $OPQ$ (constructed as described in Art. 15) that have special properties, and we can therefore evaluate the functions of all these angles. We illustrate the method of reasoning by means of typical examples.

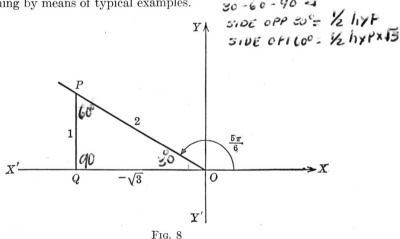

Fig. 8

*Example 1.* Find the six trigonometric functions of $5\pi/6$.

*Solution.* First construct the given angle, $5\pi/6 = 150°$, the initial side lying along the positive $X$-axis as usual, and the terminal side in the second quadrant, as shown in Fig. 8. For convenience, take the distance $r = |OP| = 2$ units, and drop the perpendicular $PQ$ to the $X$-axis. Then, from elementary geometry, since $\angle POX' = \pi/6$, we have $|PQ| = 1$ and $|OQ| = \sqrt{3}$ units, whence $x = -\sqrt{3}$ and $y = 1$. Hence, from the function definitions, we get

$$\sin \frac{5\pi}{6} = \frac{y}{r} = \frac{1}{2}, \qquad \cos \frac{5\pi}{6} = \frac{x}{r} = -\frac{\sqrt{3}}{2},$$

$$\tan \frac{5\pi}{6} = \frac{y}{x} = -\frac{1}{\sqrt{3}} = -\frac{\sqrt{3}}{3}, \qquad \cot \frac{5\pi}{6} = \frac{x}{y} = -\sqrt{3},$$

$$\sec \frac{5\pi}{6} = \frac{r}{x} = -\frac{2}{\sqrt{3}} = -\frac{2\sqrt{3}}{3}, \qquad \csc \frac{5\pi}{6} = \frac{r}{y} = 2.$$

45 - 45 - 90
Each Leg = ½ hyp
hyp = Leg × √2

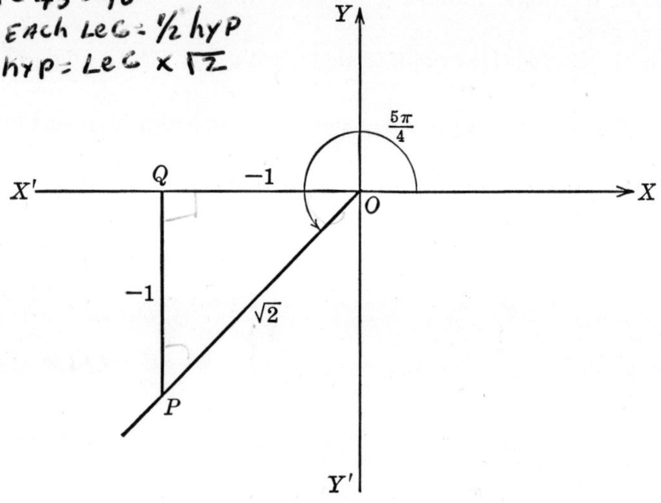

Fig. 9

*Example 2.* Find the trigonometric functions of $5\pi/4 = 225°$.

*Solution.* Construct the diagram (Fig. 9) in the customary manner, so that $\angle POX' = \pi/4$. Taking $r = |OP| = \sqrt{2}$, we find $x = -1, y = -1$. Therefore

$$\sin \frac{5\pi}{4} = \frac{y}{r} = -\frac{1}{\sqrt{2}} = -\frac{\sqrt{2}}{2}, \qquad \cos \frac{5\pi}{4} = \frac{x}{r} = -\frac{1}{\sqrt{2}} = -\frac{\sqrt{2}}{2},$$

$$\tan \frac{5\pi}{4} = \frac{y}{x} = \frac{-1}{-1} = 1, \qquad \cot \frac{5\pi}{4} = \frac{x}{y} = \frac{-1}{-1} = 1,$$

$$\sec \frac{5\pi}{4} = \frac{r}{x} = -\sqrt{2}, \qquad \csc \frac{5\pi}{4} = \frac{r}{y} = -\sqrt{2}.$$

*Example 3.* Find the trigonometric functions of 0.

*Solution.* Here the terminal side coincides with the initial side (Fig. 10), so that $|PQ| = 0$. Consequently, for any chosen distance $r = |OP|$, we have $x = r$ and $y = 0$. By definition, therefore,

$$\sin 0 = \frac{y}{r} = 0, \qquad \cos 0 = \frac{x}{r} = 1,$$

$$\tan 0 = \frac{y}{x} = \frac{0}{r} = 0, \qquad \cot 0 = \frac{x}{y} : \text{does not exist,}$$

$$\sec 0 = \frac{r}{x} = 1, \qquad \csc 0 = \frac{r}{y} : \text{does not exist.}$$

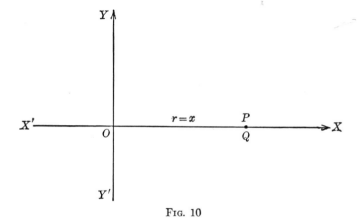

FIG. 10

In this particular case, four of the functions have simple values, whereas two functions, cotangent and cosecant, fail to exist since division by $y = 0$ is meaningless.

*Example 4.* Find the trigonometric functions of $\pi/2$.

*Solution.* The student should draw a diagram for this case, in which the terminal side lies along the positive $Y$-axis. We have then, for any choice of position for $P$, $x = 0$ and $y = r$, whence we get

$$\sin \frac{\pi}{2} = \frac{y}{r} = 1, \qquad \cos \frac{\pi}{2} = \frac{x}{r} = 0,$$

$$\tan \frac{\pi}{2} = \frac{y}{x} : \text{does not exist,} \qquad \cot \frac{\pi}{2} = \frac{x}{y} = 0,$$

$$\sec \frac{\pi}{2} = \frac{r}{x} : \text{does not exist,} \qquad \csc \frac{\pi}{2} = \frac{r}{y} = 1.$$

In a similar manner, it is possible to determine the functions of other special angles. A table giving the functions of sixteen angles, including the four already discussed, is shown below. These are all the positive angles (and 0) less than one revolution to which the described processes apply. It is to be noted that extension of the table for larger angles ($2\pi$, $13\pi/6$, etc.) merely gives us a repetition of the function values exhibited here.

| $\theta$ (radians) | $\theta$ (degrees) | $\sin\theta$ | $\cos\theta$ | $\tan\theta$ | $\cot\theta$ | $\sec\theta$ | $\csc\theta$ |
|---|---|---|---|---|---|---|---|
| 0 | 0 | 0 | 1 | 0 | .. | 1 | .. |
| $\pi/6$ | 30° | $\dfrac{1}{2}$ | $\dfrac{\sqrt{3}}{2}$ | $\dfrac{\sqrt{3}}{3}$ | $\sqrt{3}$ | $\dfrac{2\sqrt{3}}{3}$ | 2 |
| $\pi/4$ | 45° | $\dfrac{\sqrt{2}}{2}$ | $\dfrac{\sqrt{2}}{2}$ | 1 | 1 | $\sqrt{2}$ | $\sqrt{2}$ |
| $\pi/3$ | 60° | $\dfrac{\sqrt{3}}{2}$ | $\dfrac{1}{2}$ | $\sqrt{3}$ | $\dfrac{\sqrt{3}}{3}$ | 2 | $\dfrac{2\sqrt{3}}{3}$ |
| $\pi/2$ | 90° | 1 | 0 | .. | 0 | .. | 1 |
| $2\pi/3$ | 120° | $\dfrac{\sqrt{3}}{2}$ | $-\dfrac{1}{2}$ | $-\sqrt{3}$ | $-\dfrac{\sqrt{3}}{3}$ | $-2$ | $\dfrac{2\sqrt{3}}{3}$ |
| $3\pi/4$ | 135° | $\dfrac{\sqrt{2}}{2}$ | $-\dfrac{\sqrt{2}}{2}$ | $-1$ | $-1$ | $-\sqrt{2}$ | $\sqrt{2}$ |
| $5\pi/6$ | 150° | $\dfrac{1}{2}$ | $-\dfrac{\sqrt{3}}{2}$ | $-\dfrac{\sqrt{3}}{3}$ | $-\sqrt{3}$ | $-\dfrac{2\sqrt{3}}{3}$ | 2 |
| $\pi$ | 180° | 0 | $-1$ | 0 | .. | $-1$ | .. |
| $7\pi/6$ | 210° | $-\dfrac{1}{2}$ | $-\dfrac{\sqrt{3}}{2}$ | $\dfrac{\sqrt{3}}{3}$ | $\sqrt{3}$ | $-\dfrac{2\sqrt{3}}{3}$ | $-2$ |
| $5\pi/4$ | 225° | $-\dfrac{\sqrt{2}}{2}$ | $-\dfrac{\sqrt{2}}{2}$ | 1 | 1 | $-\sqrt{2}$ | $-\sqrt{2}$ |
| $4\pi/3$ | 240° | $-\dfrac{\sqrt{3}}{2}$ | $-\dfrac{1}{2}$ | $\sqrt{3}$ | $\dfrac{\sqrt{3}}{3}$ | $-2$ | $-\dfrac{2\sqrt{3}}{3}$ |
| $3\pi/2$ | 270° | $-1$ | 0 | .. | 0 | .. | $-1$ |
| $5\pi/3$ | 300° | $-\dfrac{\sqrt{3}}{2}$ | $\dfrac{1}{2}$ | $-\sqrt{3}$ | $-\dfrac{\sqrt{3}}{3}$ | 2 | $-\dfrac{2\sqrt{3}}{3}$ |
| $7\pi/4$ | 315° | $-\dfrac{\sqrt{2}}{2}$ | $\dfrac{\sqrt{2}}{2}$ | $-1$ | $-1$ | $\sqrt{2}$ | $-\sqrt{2}$ |
| $11\pi/6$ | 330° | $-\dfrac{1}{2}$ | $\dfrac{\sqrt{3}}{2}$ | $-\dfrac{\sqrt{3}}{3}$ | $-\sqrt{3}$ | $\dfrac{2\sqrt{3}}{3}$ | $-2$ |

Because of the frequent occurrence of these angles, it is important that the student be able to evaluate their functions accurately and quickly. Particular attention should be given to the algebraic sign attached to each function value.

## EXERCISES

**1–12.** Obtain the six trigonometric functions of each of the remaining twelve angles in the above table.

In Exercises 13–30, evaluate each expression given.

**13.** $2 \sin \dfrac{\pi}{3} + \sin \dfrac{\pi}{2}\cdot$

**14.** $\cos \pi - 2 \sin \dfrac{3\pi}{2}\cdot$

**15.** $\sin \pi \cos \dfrac{3\pi}{2}\cdot$

**16.** $\sin \dfrac{3\pi}{4} \cot \dfrac{\pi}{2}\cdot$

**17.** $\tan \dfrac{\pi}{3} \cot \dfrac{2\pi}{3}\cdot$

**18.** $\sin \dfrac{\pi}{6} \sec \pi.$

**19.** $\cos \dfrac{4\pi}{3} \csc \dfrac{7\pi}{6}\cdot$

**20.** $3 \cot \dfrac{7\pi}{3} \sec 0.$

**21.** $\tan \dfrac{3\pi}{4} \csc \dfrac{5\pi}{6}\cdot$

**22.** $\sec \dfrac{3\pi}{4} \tan \dfrac{5\pi}{3}\cdot$

**23.** $\sqrt{2} \sin \dfrac{5\pi}{4} \cos \pi.$

**24.** $\sqrt{6} \cot \dfrac{\pi}{6} \sin \dfrac{3\pi}{4}\cdot$

**25.** $\dfrac{\cos \dfrac{\pi}{4} \tan \dfrac{\pi}{4}}{\sin \dfrac{\pi}{4}}\cdot$

**26.** $\dfrac{\sin \dfrac{11\pi}{6}}{\cos \dfrac{11\pi}{6}} - \dfrac{\sec \dfrac{5\pi}{6}}{\csc \dfrac{5\pi}{6}}\cdot$

**27.** $\sin^2 \dfrac{3\pi}{4} + \cos^2 \dfrac{3\pi}{4}\cdot$

**28.** $\sec^2 \dfrac{4\pi}{3} - \tan^2 \dfrac{4\pi}{3}\cdot$

**29.** $\csc^2 \dfrac{7\pi}{6} - \cot^2 \dfrac{7\pi}{6}\cdot$

**30.** $\dfrac{1}{2\left(\sin \dfrac{3\pi}{4} - \cos \dfrac{4\pi}{3}\right)}\cdot$

**17. Right triangles.** The student may have noticed that the names of three of the trigonometric functions contain the prefix "co" followed by the respective names of the three other functions. The reason for this choice of labels is found upon examination of the functions of the two acute angles of a right triangle.

Let there be given any right triangle $ABC$; denote the sides opposite each vertex by the corresponding small letters $a$, $b$, and $c$. First place the triangle on the coordinate axes with the vertex $A$ at the origin and the side $b$ along the positive $X$-axis, as shown in Fig. 11($a$). Then the coordinates of vertex $B$, on the terminal side $c$ of angle $A$, are $x = b$ and $y = a$, and we get, by definition,

$$\sin A = \frac{a}{c}, \qquad \tan A = \frac{a}{b}, \qquad \sec A = \frac{c}{b},$$

$$\cos A = \frac{b}{c}, \qquad \cot A = \frac{b}{a}, \qquad \csc A = \frac{c}{a}. \tag{1}$$

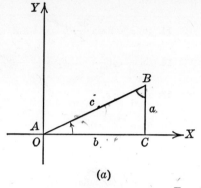 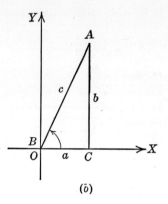

(a)          (b)

Fig. 11

Next place the vertex $B$ at the origin and the side $a$ along the positive $X$-axis. Then the coordinates of $A$ are $x = a$ and $y = b$, and we have for angle $B$,

$$\sin B = \frac{b}{c}, \qquad \tan B = \frac{b}{a}, \qquad \sec B = \frac{c}{a},$$

$$\cos B = \frac{a}{c}, \qquad \cot B = \frac{a}{b}, \qquad \csc B = \frac{c}{b}. \tag{2}$$

We then see that the functions sine, tangent, and secant, for angle $A$, are respectively equal to the corresponding *co*-functions of the *complementary* angle $B$. Of course, the former functions, for angle $B$, are then respectively equal to the corresponding co-functions of $B$'s complement, $A$. The prefix "co" may thus be regarded as a contraction of "complementary."

Since these relations between functions of complementary angles exist, it is necessary only to tabulate functions of angles from 0° to 45°. For convenience, however, tables are usually arranged so that functions of angles between 45° and 90° may be read directly, from the bottom of the page upward, just as the functions of the complementary angles are read from the top downward.

For application in subsequent computation, we now discuss the use of tables of trigonometric functions. The tables in the back of this book contain the sines, cosines, tangents, and cotangents, correct to four decimal places, of the acute angles in steps of 10'. We shall consider here only the determination of the actual values of these functions, as given in the columns headed "Func." in the tables. The columns headed "Log." contain the logarithms of the functions; these are discussed in Chapter XIV.

Angles between 0° and 45° are given in the left-hand columns, increasing downward, and the corresponding functions are found in accordance with the headings at the top of the page. Angles between 45° and 90° appear in the right-hand columns, increasing upward, and their functions are determined by referring to the titles at the bottom of the page.

When an angle is a multiple of 10', its functions can be read directly from the table. Thus we find, for example, that $\cos 24° \, 20' = 0.9112$, and $\tan 73° \, 50' = 3.4495$.

If a given angle lies between two tabulated values, we use *interpolation* to find any one of its trigonometric functions. To illustrate this process, let us find $\sin 16° \, 37'$. From the tables we get

$$\sin 16° \, 30' = 0.2840,$$

$$\sin 16° \, 40' = 0.2868.$$

We see that, when the angle increases by 10' in this range, the sine function increases by 0.0028. Now the increase in the sine function is not exactly proportional to the increase in the angle, but for small variations, such as we have here, we may assume proportionality. That is, we suppose that

$$\frac{\sin 16° \, 37' - \sin 16° \, 30'}{\sin 16° \, 40' - \sin 16° \, 30'} = \frac{16° \, 37' - 16° \, 30'}{16° \, 40' - 16° \, 30'},$$

whence

$$\frac{\sin 16° \, 37' - 0.2840}{0.2868 - 0.2840} = \frac{7}{10},$$

$$\sin 16° \, 37' = 0.2840 + \tfrac{7}{10}(0.0028)$$

$$= 0.2840 + 0.00196,$$

or, to four decimal places,

$$\sin 16° \, 37' = 0.2860.$$

These values of the angle and its sine have thereby been interpolated between tabulated values.

In practice, it is, of course, not necessary to go through all these details. Since our angle is $\frac{7}{10}$ of the way between two tabulated angles, we need merely compute $\frac{7}{10}$ of the tabular difference in the sines of the listed angles, 0.0028, and add the result to the sine of the smaller tabulated angle.

It should be noticed that the sine and tangent functions increase with the angle, but the cosine and cotangent functions decrease as the angle increases from 0° to 90°. Hence the interpolated difference must be added in the former cases, as was done above, but it must be subtracted from the tabulated value corresponding to the smaller angle for the two co-functions.

As further illustrations, we list below a few more function values obtained by interpolation. The student should examine these until the process is thoroughly familiar.

$$\cos 27° \ 52' = 0.8840,$$

$$\tan 62° \ \ 3' = 1.8847,$$

$$\cot 38° \ 17' = 1.2670,$$

$$\sin 77° \ 49' = 0.9774.$$

When sufficient data are given to determine a right triangle, that is, when there is one and only one right triangle with the stated values for the given parts, it is possible to compute the remaining parts of the triangle. A right triangle is determined either if two sides are given, or if one side and an acute angle are given. With the notation of Fig. 11 for the acute angles $A$ and $B$, the hypotenuse $c$, and the legs $a$ and $b$, we have for our use in right-triangle calculations: trigonometric relations (1) and (2) and the geometric relations

$$A + B = 90°, \tag{3}$$

$$a^2 + b^2 = c^2. \tag{4}$$

When solving a right-triangle problem, the student should organize his work neatly and systematically. The following points are worthy of note:

1. Draw a diagram, indicating all the given data and the part or parts required. If possible, construct the triangle carefully to scale, so that the computed results may be checked by measurement; in any event,

see that the proportions are nearly enough correct so that gross errors, at least, can be detected.

2. Write down those relations, from among the above equations, needed in your solution. Each .chosen relation, other than (3), must involve two quantities given, or determined at the time the relation is to be used. In practice, it is always possible to restrict ourselves to relations

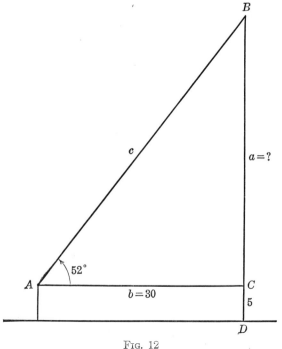

Fig. 12

involving the sine, cosine, and tangent of an acute angle, since the remaining three functions are merely the reciprocals of the three stated ones. As a consequence, trigonometric tables need contain values of only sines, cosines, and tangents.

3. After completing the computation, check by reference to your diagram or by means of additional relations among the quantities.

*Example 1.*    From a point 5 ft. above the horizontal ground, and 30 ft. from the trunk of a tree, the line of sight to the top of the tree is measured as 52° with the horizontal. Find the height of the tree.

*Solution.*    In Fig. 12, $A$ is taken at the observer's eye, $B$ is the top of the tree, and the required height is $BD = a + 5$ ft. One relation connecting the known angle $A = 52°$, the known distance $b = 30$ ft., and the unknown length $a$ is

$$\tan A = \frac{a}{b}.$$

We therefore have, with the aid of trigonometric tables,

$$a = b \tan A = 30 \tan 52°$$

$$= 30 \times 1.280 = 38.4 \text{ ft.,}$$

whence the height of the tree is

$$BD = a + 5 = 43.4 \text{ ft.}$$

This result may be checked by first finding $c$ from the relation $\cos A = b/c$, and then getting $a$ from $\sin A = a/c$.

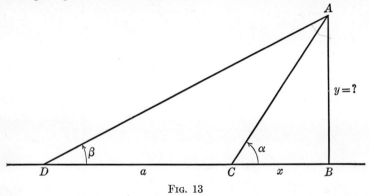

Fig. 13

*Example 2.* To find the height of an inaccessible mountain, the following procedure is adopted. Two points are chosen, on the horizontal ground on which the mountain rests, in the same vertical plane through the mountain top, and distant $a$ ft. apart. From these points, angles of elevation $\alpha$ and $\beta$ are respectively measured between the horizontal and the lines of sight to the mountain top. Obtain a formula for the height of the mountain.

*Solution.* The data are indicated in Fig. 13, where $y$ is the unknown height. From the smaller right triangle $ABC$, we see that $\tan \alpha = y/x$; from the larger right triangle $ABD$, $\tan \beta = y/(a + x)$. Equating the two expressions for $y$ obtained from these relations, we have

$$y = x \tan \alpha = (a + x) \tan \beta,$$

$$x \tan \alpha - x \tan \beta = a \tan \beta,$$

$$x = \frac{a \tan \beta}{\tan \alpha - \tan \beta}.$$

Hence
$$y = x \tan \alpha = \frac{a \tan \alpha \tan \beta}{\tan \alpha - \tan \beta}.$$

This is the desired formula.

From one point of view, Example 2 was a problem involving an oblique triangle, $ACD$, in which two angles, $\pi - \alpha$ and $\beta$, and the included side $a$ are known. By constructing an altitude to one side of an oblique triangle, such as $AB$ in the example, it is often possible to find the remaining parts of the triangle by a consideration of right triangles. Thus, if the side $AC$ of triangle $ACD$ were required, we could employ the relation $\cos \alpha = x/AC$ together with the expression for $x$ obtained above.

### EXERCISES

Exercises 1–10 refer to right triangles $ABC$ in which $C$ is the right angle and $a$, $b$, and $c$ are the sides opposite the vertices $A$, $B$, and $C$, respectively.

1. If $a = 6$ and $\sin A = \frac{3}{5}$, find $b$ and $c$.
2. If $b = 4$ and $\cos A = \frac{5}{6}$, find $a$ and $c$.
3. If $a = 5$ and $\tan A = 1.5$, find $b$ and $c$.
4. If $c = 12$ and $\sin A = \frac{2}{3}$, find $a$ and $b$.
5. If $c = 7$ and $\tan A = \frac{3}{4}$, find $a$ and $b$.
6. If $a = 11.5$ and $\csc A = 1.2$, find $b$ and $c$.
7. If $b = 3.8$ and $\sec A = 2.1$, find $a$ and $c$.
8. If $c = 7.29$ and $\cot A = 0.49$, find $a$ and $b$.
9. If $a = \sqrt{2mn}$ and $b = \sqrt{m^2 + n^2}$, find $\sin A$.
10. If $a = m^2 - n^2$ and $b = 2mn$, find $\cos A$.

In Exercises 11–15, all the angles involved are acute.

11. If $\sin 27° = \cos \theta$, find $\theta$.
12. If $\tan 2\theta = \cot 4\theta$, find $\theta$.
13. If $\sec \dfrac{\theta}{2} = \csc 4\theta$, find $\theta$.
14. If $\sin (40° - \theta) = \cos 3\theta$, find $\theta$.
15. If $\sin (70° - 2\theta) = \cos (10° + 7\theta)$, find $\theta$.

Exercises 16–25 refer to right triangles $ABC$ in which $C$ is the right angle and $a$, $b$, and $c$ are the sides opposite the vertices $A$, $B$, and $C$, respectively.

16. If $a = 8.8$ and $A = 32°$, find $b$ and $c$.
17. If $b = 32.2$ and $B = 63°$, find $a$ and $c$.
18. If $c = 5.65$ and $A = 18°$, find $a$ and $b$.
19. If $a = 0.48$ and $B = 25°$, find $b$ and $c$.
20. If $a = 176$ and $B = 42° 10'$, find $b$ and $c$.
21. If $a = 74.5$ and $A = 56° 40'$, find $b$ and $c$.
22. If $b = 3.69$ and $A = 38° 12'$, find $a$ and $c$.
23. If $a = 5.25$ and $b = 6.75$, find $A$ and $c$.
24. If $b = 447$ and $c = 632$, find $B$ and $a$.

**25.** If $a = 10.3$ and $c = 15.9$, find $A$ and $b$.

**26.** When the angle of elevation of the sun is 35°, the shadow of a certain tree is 20 ft. long. How high is the tree?

**27.** What is the angle subtended at the center of a circle 8 in. in diameter by a chord 5.5 in. long?

**28.** A stairway has steps with a tread of 9 in. and a rise of 6.5 in. What is the angle of inclination of the stairway with the horizontal?

**29.** Twelve points are equally spaced around the circumference of a circle 6 in. in diameter. Find the distance between two adjacent points.

**30.** Taking as a reference line the diameter connecting two of the points of Exercise 29, find the distance of each of the remaining points from this line.

**31.** Two streets intersect at an angle of 64°. Lots are bounded by lines perpendicular to one street and 40 ft. apart. Find the frontage of each lot on the other street.

**32.** The adjacent sides of a parallelogram are respectively 10 and 14 in. long, and the included angle is 125°. Find the area of the parallelogram.

**33.** A ladder 26 ft. long forms an angle of 20° with the vertical wall against which it rests. How far is the top of the ladder from the floor?

**34.** If the foot of the ladder of Exercise 33 is drawn away from the wall an additional foot, how far down the wall does the top of the ladder descend?

**35.** Using the notation of Exercises 1–10, show that the area $K$ of a right triangle may be expressed in each of the following ways:

$$K = \tfrac{1}{2}ac \cos A = \tfrac{1}{2}bc \sin A = \tfrac{1}{2}c^2 \sin A \cos A.$$

**36.** One side of a regular octagon is 8 in. Find the radius of the circumscribed circle.

**37.** Find the radius of the circle inscribed in the octagon of Exercise 36.

**38.** Find the area of the octagon of Exercise 36.

**39.** A segment of a circle of radius $r$ is cut off by a chord subtending a central angle $\theta$. Find the area of the segment. *Hint:* Use the formula for the area of a circular sector obtained in Art. 14.

**40.** From a point 20 ft. above the horizontal ground, the angles of elevation and depression (angles made by the lines of sight above and below the horizontal) of the top and base of a building are respectively 52° and 16°. Find the height of the building.

**41.** From a point 80 ft. above the level of a canal, and to one side, the angles of depression of a point on the near bank and a point directly opposite across the canal are respectively 42° and 36°. Find the width of the canal.

**42.** Show that the area $K$ of a regular polygon of $n$ sides, circumscribed about a circle of radius $r$, is

$$K = nr^2 \tan \frac{\pi}{n}.$$

**43.** If a regular polygon of $n$ sides is inscribed in a circle of radius $r$, show that the area $K$ of the polygon is given by

$$K = nr^2 \sin \frac{\pi}{n} \cos \frac{\pi}{n} = \frac{1}{2} nr^2 \sin \frac{2\pi}{n}.$$

**44.** A regular hexagon and a regular octagon both have perimeters of 60 in. Find the difference between their areas.

**45.** A tree stands upon the top of the mountain of Example 2. If the tree subtends an angle $\theta$ from the point $D$ of Fig. 13, find an expression for the height of the tree.

**46.** A regular square pyramid has a base $ABCD$ of side $a$ and the vertex at a point $P$ vertically above the center of the base. If one of the triangular faces, $PAB$, makes an angle $\theta$ with the base, find the volume of the pyramid.

**47.** Find the total surface area (base and four triangular faces) of the pyramid of Exercise 46.

**48.** A frustum is cut from the pyramid of Exercise 46 by a plane parallel to, and at a distance $b$ from, the base. Find the length of edge of the square upper face of the frustum.

**49.** A rectangular billboard $ABCD$ has its lower edge $AB$ on the horizontal ground. When the angle of elevation of the sun is $\alpha$, the shadow of the upper edge $CD$ is at a distance $a$ from $AB$, and the shadow of the vertical edge $BC$ makes an acute angle $\beta$ with $AB$. Find the height $BC$ of the billboard.

**50.** A vertical pole of height $h$ is braced by attaching $n$ guy wires of equal length $a$ to its top and fixing the lower ends of the wires in the horizontal ground at points equally spaced around a circle. Show that the angle between adjacent wires is $2\theta$, where $\theta$ is given by

$$\sin \theta = \frac{\sqrt{a^2 - h^2}}{a} \sin \frac{\pi}{n}.$$

**18. Functions of large angles.** In the preceding article we found certain relations between the functions of an acute angle and the func-

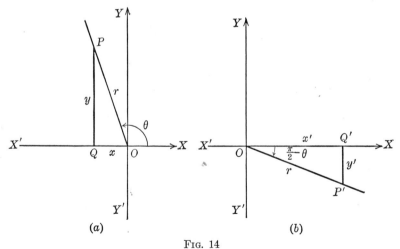

(a)                                (b)

Fig. 14

tions of the complementary angle. As a matter of fact, these same relations hold not only when the angles involved, $\theta$ and $\pi/2 - \theta$, are acute, but for any angle $\theta$; we shall show this when $\theta$ is an angle in the second quadrant

If $\theta$ is obtuse, as shown in Fig. 14($a$), then $\pi/2 - \theta$ will be negative and will have its terminal side in the fourth quadrant, as in Fig. 14($b$). Take the points $P$ and $P'$ on the respective terminal sides at the same distance $r$ from the origin, so that the triangles $OPQ$ and $OP'Q'$ are congruent. Let the coordinates of $P$ and $P'$ be denoted by $P(x, y)$ and $P'(x', y')$. Then $x$ and $y'$ are the same in length, and since they are both negative they are algebraically equal: $x = y'$. Likewise, $y$ and $x'$ are equal in length, and since both are positive we have $y = x'$. Consequently, we have

$$\sin\left(\frac{\pi}{2} - \theta\right) = \frac{y'}{r} = \frac{x}{r} = \cos\theta,$$

$$\cos\left(\frac{\pi}{2} - \theta\right) = \frac{x'}{r} = \frac{y}{r} = \sin\theta,$$

$$\tan\left(\frac{\pi}{2} - \theta\right) = \frac{y'}{x'} = \frac{x}{y} = \cot\theta,$$

$$\cot\left(\frac{\pi}{2} - \theta\right) = \frac{x'}{y'} = \frac{y}{x} = \tan\theta,$$

$$\sec\left(\frac{\pi}{2} - \theta\right) = \frac{r}{x'} = \frac{r}{y} = \csc\theta,$$

$$\csc\left(\frac{\pi}{2} - \theta\right) = \frac{r}{y'} = \frac{r}{x} = \sec\theta.$$

Thus each function of $\pi/2 - \theta$ is equal to the corresponding co-function of $\theta$.

These results suggest that functions of all angles of the form $n\pi/2 \pm \theta$, where $n$ is a positive integer, may be expressed in terms of functions of $\theta$. This inference may, in fact, be confirmed, and it is therefore possible to obtain the functions of any angle from a table listing functions of acute angles only. Moreover, the relations in question are found to be correct not only when $\theta$ is acute, but also for any value of $\theta$. Because of their general validity, these dependencies are important in theoretical, or analytic, trigonometry as well as in computation, and the student should early acquire a facility in their use.

Below are listed the relations corresponding to $n = 1, 2, 3$, and 4. For larger values of $n$, the angle $n\pi/2 \pm \theta$ will differ from one of the angles listed by one or more complete revolutions, and its functions will therefore correspond to those of one of the following groups.  Thus, if the functions of 609° are desired, we may write

$$609° = 360° + 249° = 360° + (270° - 21°)$$

$$= 2\pi + \left(\frac{3\pi}{2} - \frac{7\pi}{60}\right),$$

whence the functions of 609° are the same as those of $3\pi/2 - \theta$, where $\theta = 7\pi/60 = 21°$.  Alternatively, we may say that $249° = 180° + 69° = \pi + 23\pi/60$, and then express the functions of 609° as functions of $\pi + \theta'$, where $\theta' = 23\pi/60 = 69°$.  Evidently $\theta$ and $\theta'$ are complementary angles.

For compactness, two groups of functions are written as one by use of the double signs, $\pm$ and $\mp$.  It is understood here that the upper signs in each equation go together, and the lower signs together, in each equation in which two such double signs occur.

$$\sin\left(\frac{\pi}{2} \pm \theta\right) = \cos\theta, \qquad \cos\left(\frac{\pi}{2} \pm \theta\right) = \mp\sin\theta,$$

$$\tan\left(\frac{\pi}{2} \pm \theta\right) = \mp\cot\theta, \qquad \cot\left(\frac{\pi}{2} \pm \theta\right) = \mp\tan\theta,$$

$$\sec\left(\frac{\pi}{2} \pm \theta\right) = \mp\csc\theta, \qquad \csc\left(\frac{\pi}{2} \pm \theta\right) = \sec\theta.$$

$$\sin(\pi \pm \theta) = \mp\sin\theta, \qquad \cos(\pi \pm \theta) = -\cos\theta,$$
$$\tan(\pi \pm \theta) = \pm\tan\theta, \qquad \cot(\pi \pm \theta) = \pm\cot\theta,$$
$$\sec(\pi \pm \theta) = -\sec\theta, \qquad \csc(\pi \pm \theta) = \mp\csc\theta.$$

$$\sin\left(\frac{3\pi}{2} \pm \theta\right) = -\cos\theta, \qquad \cos\left(\frac{3\pi}{2} \pm \theta\right) = \pm\sin\theta,$$

$$\tan\left(\frac{3\pi}{2} \pm \theta\right) = \mp\cot\theta, \qquad \cot\left(\frac{3\pi}{2} \pm \theta\right) = \mp\tan\theta,$$

$$\sec\left(\frac{3\pi}{2} \pm \theta\right) = \pm\csc\theta, \qquad \csc\left(\frac{3\pi}{2} \pm \theta\right) = -\sec\theta.$$

$$\sin(2\pi \pm \theta) = \pm\sin\theta, \qquad \cos(2\pi \pm \theta) = \cos\theta,$$
$$\tan(2\pi \pm \theta) = \pm\tan\theta, \qquad \cot(2\pi \pm \theta) = \pm\cot\theta,$$
$$\sec(2\pi \pm \theta) = \sec\theta, \qquad \csc(2\pi \pm \theta) = \pm\csc\theta.$$

It should be noticed that the upper signs in the last group give us nothing essentially new, for the functions of $2\pi + \theta$ and $\theta$ must match since these angles differ by a complete revolution. The lower signs in the last group, however, yield particularly important relations: functions of a negative angle, $-\theta$, in terms of functions of the corresponding positive angle.

All the above relations may be obtained from suitable figures, as were the functions of $\pi/2 - \theta$ when $\theta$ lies in the second quadrant. As further illustration, we shall obtain the functions of $\pi + \theta$ when $\theta$ is in the third

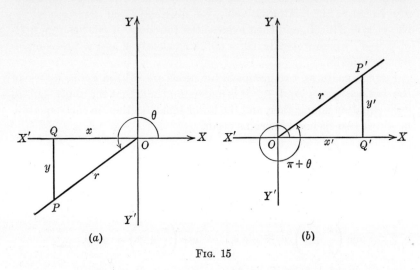

(a)                               (b)

FIG. 15

quadrant, as shown in Fig. 15(a). Then $\pi + \theta$ will be more than one revolution and will lie in the first quadrant; see Fig. 15(b). From the congruent triangles $OPQ$ and $OP'Q'$, formed as before, and again taking into account the algebraic signs of $x$, $y$, $x'$, and $y'$, we have $x = -x'$, $y = -y'$. Hence

$$\sin (\pi + \theta) = \frac{y'}{r} = -\frac{y}{r} = -\sin \theta,$$

$$\cos (\pi + \theta) = \frac{x'}{r} = -\frac{x}{r} = -\cos \theta,$$

$$\tan (\pi + \theta) = \frac{y'}{x'} = \frac{y}{x} = \tan \theta,$$

and similarly for the other three functions of $\pi + \theta$.

To illustrate the use of the above relations in analytic trigonometry, consider the following problem.

*Example.*  Simplify the expression

$$2 \sin \left(\frac{3\pi}{2} - \theta\right) - 3 \cos (\pi + \theta) - \tan (-\theta) + \cot \left(\frac{\pi}{2} + \theta\right).$$

*Solution.*  We get immediately

$$2 \sin \left(\frac{3\pi}{2} - \theta\right) - 3 \cos (\pi + \theta) - \tan (-\theta) + \cot \left(\frac{\pi}{2} + \theta\right)$$

$$= 2(- \cos \theta) - 3(- \cos \theta) - (- \tan \theta) + (- \tan \theta)$$

$$= -2 \cos \theta + 3 \cos \theta + \tan \theta - \tan \theta$$

$$= \cos \theta.$$

### EXERCISES

**1–6.** Verify the six groups of relations not treated in the text.  For each group, take $\theta$ in each of the four quadrants in turn.

Evaluate each of the functions given in Exercises 7–21.

| | | |
|---|---|---|
| **7.** $\sin 102°$. | **8.** $\cos 205°$. | **9.** $\tan 294°$. |
| **10.** $\cos (-12°)$. | **11.** $\sin 490°$. | **12.** $\cot 112°$. |
| **13.** $\sin (-140°)$. | **14.** $\sin 1955°$. | **15.** $\cos 258°$. |
| **16.** $\sin 310° \ 30'$. | **17.** $\tan 462° \ 40'$. | **18.** $\cos 749° \ 25'$. |
| **19.** $\sin 0.7$. | **20.** $\cos 1.44$. | **21.** $\sin (-1.03)$. |

Simplify each of the expressions in Exercises 22–30.

**22.** $\sin \left(\frac{\pi}{2} - \theta\right) + \cos (\pi - \theta)$.

**23.** $\tan (\pi - \theta) + \cot \left(\frac{3\pi}{2} - \theta\right)$.

**24.** $\sec (\pi + \theta) + 2 \sec (-\theta)$.

**25.** $\sin \left(\frac{\pi}{2} + \theta\right) - \sin (\pi - \theta)$.

**26.** $\sin (\pi - \theta) \cos (\pi + \theta) - \cos \theta \sin (2\pi - \theta)$.

**27.** $\cos \left(\frac{\pi}{2} + \theta\right) \cos (\pi - \theta) - \sin \left(\frac{\pi}{2} + \theta\right) \sin (\pi - \theta)$.

**28.** $\sin \left(\frac{3\pi}{2} + \theta\right) \cos \left(\frac{\pi}{2} + \theta\right) - \cos \left(\frac{3\pi}{2} + \theta\right) \sin \left(\frac{\pi}{2} + \theta\right)$.

**29.** $\cos (\pi - \theta) \cos (2\pi - \theta) + \sin (\pi + \theta) \sin (2\pi + \theta)$.

**30.** $\sin \left(\frac{5\pi}{2} - \theta\right) \cos \left(\frac{3\pi}{2} - \theta\right) - \cos \left(\frac{5\pi}{2} - \theta\right) \sin \left(\frac{3\pi}{2} - \theta\right)$.

**19. Polar coordinates.**  The rectangular coordinate system described in Art. 11 is the system most frequently used to indicate, graphically, functional relations between two variables.  However, for some purposes, the **polar coordinate system** is more convenient.

Our treatment of this new system will necessarily be brief, as was the discussion of rectangular coordinates.  In textbooks on analytic geometry the usefulness of each system is more fully revealed and the techniques of treating various types of problems by the aid of these concepts are extensively discussed.  Here we shall merely introduce the idea of polar coordinates and indicate its connection with trigonometry.

Let a fixed line $OA$, called the **polar axis,** serve as the initial side of an angle $\theta$, which we use as one of the polar coordinates.  Angles generated by a counterclockwise rotation about the point $O$ (called the **pole**) as vertex are considered positive; clockwise rotation produces a negative

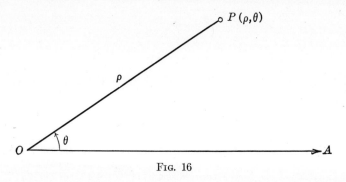

Fig. 16

angle.  This is in agreement with the convention adopted in Art. 12. Along the terminal side of the angle $\theta$, the distance $\rho$ is measured; $\rho$ is positive if on the terminal side itself, and negative if on the terminal side oppositely produced.  We call $\rho$ the **radius vector** and $\theta$ the corresponding **vectorial angle.**  These two quantities are the polar coordinates of a point $P$, designated as $P(\rho, \theta)$.

Given a pair of polar coordinates, we then may *plot* the point $P(\rho, \theta)$ as follows.  First construct the angle $\theta$, measured from the polar axis, and on its terminal side (or on its terminal side produced if $\rho$ is a negative number) measure the distance $\rho$.  This gives us a definite point $P$, as shown in Fig. 16, where $\theta$ has been taken as an acute angle and $\rho$ as a positive length.

Conversely, if a point $P$ is fixed in the plane of the polar coordinate system, we may assign to $P$ the polar coordinates obtained by taking the angle $AOP$ as $\theta$ and the distance $OP$ as $\rho$.

Starting with the polar coordinates $(\rho, \theta)$, there is evidently one and only one point $P$ corresponding to them; that is, the correspondence is unique.  On the other hand, a given point $P$ may have indefinitely many polar coordinates assigned to it.  Thus, the point $P$ in Fig. 16 may also be represented by the coordinates $(\rho, \theta + 2n\pi)$, where $n$ is any integer, or by $(-\rho, \theta + m\pi)$, where $m$ is any odd integer. To avoid this lack of uniqueness, we shall agree to assign to point $P$ a non-negative radius vector $\rho$ and a vectorial angle $\theta$ which is non-negative and less than $2\pi$:

$$\rho \geqq 0, \qquad 0 \leqq \theta < 2\pi.*$$

To facilitate plotting in the polar system, it is well to have polar co-ordinate paper on which are ruled a set of circles concentric with the pole $O$ and a set of equally spaced radial lines through $O$, say at intervals of $\pi/12 = 15°$.

*Example 1.* Plot the curve $\rho = \cos \theta$.

*Solution.* We assign to $\theta$, in turn, various values and compute the corresponding values of $\theta$, as shown in the table accompanying the graph, Fig. 17.

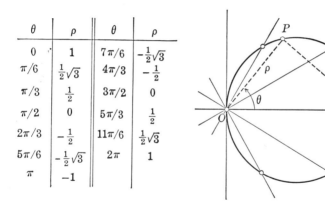

| $\theta$ | $\rho$ | $\theta$ | $\rho$ |
|---|---|---|---|
| 0 | 1 | $7\pi/6$ | $-\frac{1}{2}\sqrt{3}$ |
| $\pi/6$ | $\frac{1}{2}\sqrt{3}$ | $4\pi/3$ | $-\frac{1}{2}$ |
| $\pi/3$ | $\frac{1}{2}$ | $3\pi/2$ | 0 |
| $\pi/2$ | 0 | $5\pi/3$ | $\frac{1}{2}$ |
| $2\pi/3$ | $-\frac{1}{2}$ | $11\pi/6$ | $\frac{1}{2}\sqrt{3}$ |
| $5\pi/6$ | $-\frac{1}{2}\sqrt{3}$ | $2\pi$ | 1 |
| $\pi$ | $-1$ | | |

Fig. 17

It is seen that a closed curve is obtained as $\theta$ varies from 0 to $\pi$, and that this curve is traced again as $\theta$ varies from $\pi$ to $2\pi$. Evidently additional values assigned to $\theta$ will not contribute further to the graph.

The graph of $\rho = \cos \theta$ appears to have the form of a circle of diameter 1. If we draw a circle with its diameter $OB$, where $O$ is the pole and $B$ is the point $(1, 0)$, and take any point $P(\rho, \theta)$, other than the pole, on this circle, then, since angle $OPB$ is a right angle, we have $\rho = OB \cos \theta = \cos \theta$, which is the given equation. This confirms our guess, and the graph is, in fact, a circle.

It is sometimes desirable to change from an equation in polar coordinates to one in rectangular coordinates, and conversely. This *transfor-*

---

* The symbol $\geqq$ is read "greater than or equal to," and $\leqq$ is "less than or equal to."

*mation* of coordinates may be effected as follows. We superimpose the polar axis on the positive $X$-axis, the pole coinciding with the origin. Then any point $P$ has two sets of coordinates: $(\rho, \theta)$ and $(x, y)$. These are connected by relations easily obtained from Fig. 18; we have:

$$x = \rho \cos \theta, \qquad y = \rho \sin \theta;$$

$$\rho^2 = x^2 + y^2, \qquad \tan \theta = \frac{y}{x}.$$

By means of these relations, transformations can readily be carried out.

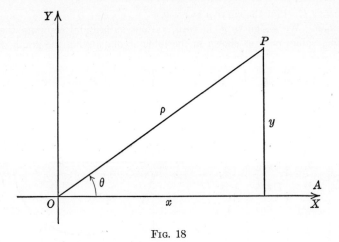

Fig. 18

*Example 2.* Transform the equation $\rho = \cos \theta$ to rectangular coordinates.

*Solution.* To make the application of the above transformation equations easy, we first multiply each member of the given equation by $\rho$. Then we have $\rho^2 = \rho \cos \theta$, and since $\rho^2 = x^2 + y^2$ and $x = \rho \cos \theta$, we get immediately the rectangular equation

$$x^2 + y^2 = x.$$

At this point in our study of trigonometry we are not in a position to effect every transformation, nor can the obtainable transformed equations always be reduced to the most convenient form. Thus, if a polar equation contains $\theta$ itself instead of a trigonometric function of $\theta$, as $\rho = \theta$, or if functions of multiples of $\theta$ are involved, as $\rho = \sin 2\theta$, the stated transformation equations do not suffice. In subsequent chapters the necessary tools for handling these and other transformation problems will be developed.

## EXERCISES

Plot the graph of each of the equations given in Exercises 1–30.

**1.** $\rho = 2$.

**2.** $\rho = 2 \sin \theta$.

**3.** $\rho = 4 \sec \theta$.

**4.** $\rho = 3 \csc \theta$.

**5.** $\rho \sin \theta + 2\rho \cos \theta = 4$.

**6.** $2\rho \cos \theta - \rho \sin \theta = 6$

**7.** $\rho = 4 + 4 \cos \theta$.

**8.** $\rho = 4 - 4 \cos \theta$.

**9.** $\rho = 1 - \sin \theta$.

**10.** $\rho = 2 + \sin \theta$.

**11.** $\rho = 4 + 2 \cos \theta$.

**12.** $\rho = 3 - 6 \cos \theta$.

**13.** $\rho = 1 + 2 \cos \theta$.

**14.** $\rho = \cos 2\theta$.

**15.** $\rho = \sin 3\theta$.

**16.** $\rho^2 = \sin 2\theta$.

**17.** $\rho^2 = 4 \cos 2\theta$.

**18.** $\rho(1 - \cos \theta) = 4$.

**19.** $\rho(3 - \cos \theta) = 6$.

**20.** $\rho(1 - 3 \cos \theta) = 6$.

**21.** $\rho(1 + \cos \theta) = 2$.

**22.** $\rho(3 + \sin \theta) = 6$.

**23.** $\rho(1 + 3 \sin \theta) = 8$.

**24.** $\rho = \cos 4\theta$.

**25.** $\rho = 2\theta$.

**26.** $\rho\theta = 2$.

**27.** $\rho = 2 \sin 4\theta$.

**28.** $\rho = \cos \dfrac{\theta}{2}$.

**29.** $\rho = 2 \sec^2 \dfrac{\theta}{2}$.

**30.** $\rho = 3 \csc^2 \dfrac{\theta}{2}$.

In Exercises 31–40, transform each equation into polar form.

**31.** $x = 2$.

**32.** $y + 4 = 0$.

**33.** $2x + y = 3$.

**34.** $2x - 4y = 1$.

**35.** $x^2 + y^2 = 9$.

**36.** $x^2 + y^2 = 4y$.

**37.** $x^2 + y^2 + 2x = 0$.

**38.** $(x - 2)^2 + (y - 1)^2 = 1$.

**39.** $y = x^2$.

**40.** $x = y^3$.

In Exercises 41–50, transform each equation into rectangular form.

**41.** $\rho = 4$.

**42.** $\rho = 3 \sin \theta$.

**43.** $\rho \cos \theta + 2 = 0$.

**44.** $\rho(\sin \theta + 3 \cos \theta) = 1$.

**45.** $\rho^2 + 4\rho \cos \theta = 5$.

**46.** $\rho^2 - 2\rho \sin \theta = 8$.

**47.** $\rho^2 - 2 \tan \theta = 3$.

**48.** $\rho(1 - \cos \theta) = 4$.

**49.** $\rho(2 + \cos \theta) = 3$.

**50.** $\rho(1 + 2 \sin \theta) = 5$.

## SUPPLEMENTARY EXERCISES

**1.** Obtain a formula for the area $A$ of a circular sector as a function of the central angle $\theta$ (radians) and the length $s$ (in.) of the bounding arc.

**2.** If the central angle and area of a circular sector are $65°$ and $5$ in.$^2$, respectively, find the length of the bounding arc.

**3.** A ring-shaped area is bounded by concentric circles of radii $6$ in. and $8$ in., respectively. Two radial lines are drawn, cutting off a ring segment of area $15$ in.$^2$ Find the perimeter of the segment.

**4.** Generalize Exercise 3 as follows. Let $r_1$ and $r_2$ respectively denote the inner and outer radii, and let $A$ be the segment area. Find the perimeter $P$ as a function of $r_1$, $r_2$, and $A$.

Evaluate each expression in Exercises 5–10

**5.** $\sin \dfrac{3\pi}{4} \csc \dfrac{3\pi}{4} - \cos \dfrac{5\pi}{3} \sec \dfrac{5\pi}{3}.$

**6.** $\tan \dfrac{7\pi}{6} \cot \dfrac{7\pi}{6} - \sin^2 \dfrac{3\pi}{2}.$

**7.** $\cos^4 \dfrac{5\pi}{4} - \sin^4 \dfrac{5\pi}{4} + 2 \sin \dfrac{3\pi}{2} \cos \dfrac{3\pi}{2}.$

**8.** $\dfrac{\sin \dfrac{\pi}{6}}{\cos \dfrac{5\pi}{6}} + \dfrac{\sin \dfrac{5\pi}{6}}{\cos \dfrac{\pi}{6}} - \sin^2 \dfrac{\pi}{6} - \cos^2 \dfrac{5\pi}{6}.$

**9.** $\sec^2 \dfrac{7\pi}{4} + \csc^2 \dfrac{7\pi}{6} - \tan^2 \dfrac{7\pi}{4} - \cot^2 \dfrac{7\pi}{6}.$

**10.** $\cos^2 \dfrac{2\pi}{3} - \tan^2 \dfrac{3\pi}{4} + \sin^2 \dfrac{2\pi}{3} + \sec^2 \dfrac{3\pi}{4}.$

**11.** A regular pentagon is inscribed in a circle 10 in. in diameter. Find the perimeter of the pentagon.

**12.** A man in a boat $B$, distant $b$ miles from the nearest point $A$ on a straight shore, wishes to reach a point $C$, $a$ miles along the shore from $A$. If he rows to a point $P$, between $A$ and $C$ on the shore, at the rate of 3 miles an hour, and then walks from $P$ to $C$ at the rate of 4 miles an hour, find his total traveling time $t$ as a function of the angle $\theta = ABP$.

**13.** A wall $a$ ft. high is $b$ ft. from a house. A ladder, making an angle $\theta$ with the horizontal ground outside the wall, leans against the house, just touching the top of the wall. Find the length $L$ of the ladder as a function of $\theta$.

**14.** If the diameter of the earth is 7920 miles, and if the length of the parallel of latitude through a certain point $P$ is also 7920 miles, find the distance of $P$ from the equator.

**15.** Find the angle between the altitude from the vertex $V$ of a regular tetrahedron and an edge through $V$.

Simplify each of the expressions in Exercises 16–19.

**16.** $\sin (\pi + \theta) \cos (\pi - \theta) + \sin (2\pi - \theta) \cos (2\pi + \theta).$

**17.** $\tan \left( \dfrac{3\pi}{2} - \theta \right) \cot \left( \dfrac{\pi}{2} + \theta \right) - \tan (\pi - \theta) \cot (\pi + \theta).$

**18.** $\cos \left( \dfrac{\pi}{2} - \theta \right) \tan \left( \dfrac{3\pi}{2} + \theta \right) - \sin (\pi - \theta) \cot (2\pi - \theta).$

**19.** $\sin (\theta - \pi) \cos (\theta - 2\pi) - \sin \left( \theta - \dfrac{\pi}{2} \right) \cos \left( \theta - \dfrac{3\pi}{2} \right).$

Plot the graph of each of the equations given in Exercises 20–25.

**20.** $\rho^2 = \sin \theta.$        **21.** $\rho = \sin^2 \theta.$

**22.** $\rho^2 = 1 - 2 \sin \theta.$        **23.** $\rho^2 = \sqrt{3} - 2 \cos \theta.$

**24.** $\rho = \sin^3 \dfrac{\theta}{3}.$        **25.** $\rho = \cos^3 \dfrac{\theta}{3}.$

# IV——— Identities and Conditional Equations

**20. Equalities.** When two expressions are equated, the equality may be either one of two possible kinds—an identity or a conditional equation.

An **identity** is a relation which holds true for every value that may permissibly be assigned to each non-numerical quantity in the relation. Thus,

$$a^3 - b^3 = (a - b)(a^2 + ab + b^2), \tag{1}$$

$$\frac{x}{x + 2} = 1 - \frac{2}{x + 2}, \tag{2}$$

$$\left(\sqrt{\frac{x}{y}} + \sqrt{\frac{y}{x}}\right)^2 = \frac{(x + y)^2}{xy}, \tag{3}$$

are all identities, for any real numbers substituted for $a$ and $b$ produce the same number in both members of (1); any $x$-value other than $-2$ (which is not a permissible value) yields the same number in the two members of (2); relation (3) holds for all permissible values of $x$ and $y$ ($x$ and $y$ must both be different from zero, and they must have the same algebraic sign if the square roots in the left member are to have meaning in the real number system).

If an equality fails to hold true for every permissible value assigned to the quantity or quantities in it, we have what is known as a **conditional equation.** Thus,

$$x^2 + x - 2 = 0, \tag{4}$$

$$3x + 4y = 12, \tag{5}$$

$$\sin \theta = \cos \theta, \tag{6}$$

are examples of conditional equations. Equation (4) holds when $x = 1$ and when $x = -2$, but no other values of $x$ yield zero when substituted in the left member; indefinitely many pairs of values $(x, y)$ satisfy (5), but when either $x$ or $y$ is specified the other is uniquely determined from this functional relation; (6) holds when $\theta = (4n + 1)\pi/4$, where $n$ is any integer or zero, but it is not true for any other value of $\theta$.

Given an equality, there is usually no doubt as to whether the relation is an identity or a conditional equation, and consequently the sign $=$ may be used in either kind of equality. However, we sometimes use the symbol $\equiv$, read "is identically equal to," for emphasis when dealing with an identity. In verbal expression, we shall, in general, say "equation" only when referring to a conditional equation, and we shall use the word "identity" whenever it applies.

In connection with identities, the principal question that arises is usually the establishing or proving of an identity. An identity is frequently established merely by *transforming* an expression into another form by application of the fundamental algebraic operations and, sometimes, by the use of other identities as well. Thus, the left member of (1) is transformed into the right member by factoring; (2) is established by dividing $x$ by $x + 2$; (3), by algebraic reduction.

On the other hand, the principal question concerning conditional equations is generally the determination of the values of the variables, or *unknowns* as they are then called, satisfying the equation or equations in hand.

We shall devote much of our subsequent treatment of algebra and trigonometry to the discussion of these two types of questions.

**21. Classification of functions.** We have so far had occasion to discuss a few different kinds of functions, to some of which we have attached names. In order to develop general methods of attacking the questions mentioned at the close of the preceding article, it is desirable to label and classify some of the types or forms of functions with which we shall be concerned.

The process of classifying functions may be effected by considering first a simple and common type, and then by augmenting this form with new types obtainable through algebraic operations. In this way, our thinking will be along lines that have their analogy in the development of number systems, as discussed in Art. 1.

Apart from constants, the simplest function of $x$ is $x$ itself. If we perform the four fundamental arithmetic operations, using two or more $x$'s and any constants as coefficients, we are led to functions of the form $cx^n$, where $n$ is an integer and $c$ a constant. This type of function is called a **rational power function** since it is a rational integral power of the variable $x$ multiplied by some coefficient $c$.

Now if the four arithmetic operations are applied to one or more power functions, we get the class of **rational algebraic functions.** An example of such a function, obtained by rational operations on $x$, is

$$\frac{4x^3 - 5x^{-2} + 9}{3x + x^{-1}}.$$

Remembering that, by definition (Art. 4), $x^{-n} = 1/x^n$, we may write an expression like that above as a single complex fraction containing only positive integral powers of $x$, and this complex fraction may be reduced to a simple fraction (Art. 7). Or, from an alternative point of view, we may obtain the desired simplification immediately by multiplying numerator and denominator by a suitable positive integral power of $x$. Thus, if we multiply numerator and denominator of the above fraction by $x^2$, we get

$$\frac{4x^5 - 5 + 9x^2}{3x^3 + x}.$$

If we have two or more rational algebraic functions, each may be reduced as indicated, so that only positive integral powers of $x$ and constants are involved, and the resulting fractions may further be combined by the four arithmetic operations to produce a single fraction of the same form. Hence every rational algebraic function may be expressed in the form

$$\frac{a_0 x^n + a_1 x^{n-1} + \cdots + a_{n-1} x + a_n}{b_0 x^m + b_1 x^{m-1} + \cdots + b_{m-1} x + b_m}, \qquad (1)$$

where $m$ and $n$ are positive integers or zero and the $a$'s and $b$'s are constants; this is the usual form for defining a rational algebraic function. For example, the function taken as an illustration above is of this type, with $m = 3$, $n = 5$, $a_0 = 4$, $a_1 = 0$, $a_2 = 0$, $a_3 = 9$, $a_4 = 0$, $a_5 = -5$; $b_0 = 3$, $b_1 = 0$, $b_2 = 1$, $b_3 = 0$.

In the general case, in which $m > 0$, the function is called a **rational fractional function;** in the special case $m = 0$ (so that the denominator function is merely a constant), we have what is called a **rational integral function** of $x$, or simply a **polynomial** in $x$. A polynomial in $x$ is therefore a function of the form

$$P(x) \equiv a_0 x^n + a_1 x^{n-1} + \cdots + a_{n-1} x + a_n, \qquad (2)$$

where $P(x)$ is a shorthand functional symbol identified with the expression given, and $n$ is a positive integer or zero.

A rational algebraic function thus is the quotient of two polynomials in $x$. If the **degree** (the highest power involved in the polynomial) of the numerator is less than that of the denominator, that is, if $n < m$ in (1), we say that (1) is a **proper fraction**; if $n \geqq m$, (1) is said to be an **improper fraction**. By performing the indicated division through a sufficient number of stages, an improper fraction may always be expressed as the sum of a polynomial in $x$ (possibly a constant) and a proper fraction. For example, we have

$$\frac{4x^3 - 8x^2 + 14x - 12}{2x^2 - 3x + 5} = 2x - 1 + \frac{x - 7}{2x^2 - 3x + 5} ;$$

here the left member is an improper fraction that is transformed by division into the sum of the polynomial $2x - 1$ and a proper fraction.

Since the four rational arithmetic operations applied to the variable $x$ lead only to rational algebraic functions, we must extend our field of operations in order to produce other types of functions. By root extractions we may obtain power functions, $x^p$, where $p$ is a fractional rational number, such as $x^{\frac{1}{2}}$ and $x^{-\frac{2}{3}}$. Combining these more general power functions arithmetically, we thus obtain **irrational algebraic functions**; examples are

$$\frac{5x^{\frac{1}{2}}}{3x - 7}, \quad \frac{1}{2x - x^{\frac{1}{3}}}, \quad 9x^2 - 3x + \frac{4}{\sqrt[5]{x}}.$$

We may formulate our ideas and definitions more precisely as follows. Consider a functional relation between two variables, $x$ and $y$, of the form

$$P_0(x)y^n + P_1(x)y^{n-1} + \cdots + P_{n-1}(x)y + P_n(x) = 0 , \qquad (3)$$

where $n$ is a positive integer, and $P_0(x), P_1(x), \cdots, P_n(x)$ are polynomials (rational integral functions), of any degrees, in $x$. Let $f(x)$ be some function of $x$; then if there exists an equation of the form (3) such that the substitution of $f(x)$ for $y$ reduces the left member to zero *identically*, then $f(x)$ is said to be an **algebraic function** of $x$.

This definition is certainly consistent with the definition of a rational algebraic function, for, if we have any rational function, $P(x)/Q(x)$, where $P(x)$ and $Q(x)$ are polynomials in $x$, then

$$Q(x)y - P(x) = 0$$

is a relation of the form (3), with $n = 1$, such that the substitution of $P(x)/Q(x)$ for $y$ gives us zero identically:

$$Q(x) \cdot \frac{P(x)}{Q(x)} - P(x) \equiv 0.$$

Moreover, irrational functions produced by root extractions will enter under the above definition. Thus, three equations of the form (3), respectively satisfied by the examples given above, are

$$(3x - 7)^2 y^2 - 25x = 0,$$

$$(8x^3 - x)y^3 - 12x^2 y^2 + 6xy - 1 = 0,$$

$$xy^5 - 5x(9x^2 - 3x)y^4 + 10x(9x^2 - 3x)^2 y^3 - 10x(9x^2 - 3x)^3 y^2$$
$$+ 5x(9x^2 - 3x)^4 y - x(9x^2 - 3x)^5 - 1024 = 0.$$

Using (3) as the basis of our broad definition of algebraic functions, and (1) for the subclass of rational algebraic functions, we now define an **irrational** algebraic function as *any* algebraic function that is *not* rational. This procedure certainly covers the ground as far as algebraic functions are concerned.

Now there are also functions that are not algebraic, such as the trigonometric functions, sin $x$, cos $x$, etc. All functions that are not algebraic are called **transcendental.** In addition to the trigonometric functions, there are other elementary transcendental functions, some of which we shall discuss in later chapters; they include inverse trigonometric functions (Chapter XII) and exponential and logarithmic functions (Chapter XIV).

All the above classes and subclasses can be exhibited in a chart such as that below, which is a kind of functional family tree:

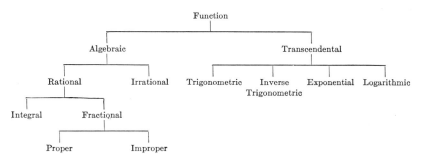

In the preceding discussion, we have restricted ourselves to functions of one variable. At this stage of the student's mathematical training, it is not feasible, nor is it necessary, to consider functions of two or more variables in any detail. Our immediate needs will be filled if we discuss briefly the class of rational algebraic functions involving more than one variable.

A **rational integral function,** or **polynomial,** in several variables may be defined as a sum of terms of the form $cx^m y^n \cdots$, where the $c$'s are constants and $m, n, \cdots$ are positive integers or zero. For example,

$$3x^2 y z^3 - 5xy^3 z + 7y^2 z^2 - \tfrac{1}{2}x + z + \sqrt{6}$$

is a rational integral function of three variables, $x$, $y$, and $z$. The total **degree** of each term $cx^m y^n \cdots$ is the sum of the exponents, $m + n + \cdots$, in that term; thus, the degrees of the successive terms in the above example are 6, 5, 4, 1, 1, and 0. The total degree of the polynomial is the highest total degree of any term in it; this is 6 in our example. Sometimes we speak of the degree in one of the variables; then the above polynomial is of degree 2 in $x$, 3 in $y$, and 3 in $z$.

If the total degree is the same in each term of a polynomial in several variables, the expression is said to be **homogeneous.** Thus, $x^2 - 2xy + 5y^2$ is a homogeneous polynomial, but $x - y + 1$ is non-homogeneous.

A **rational fractional function** of several variables is a function that may be expressed as the quotient of two rational integral functions in the variables.

In Chapter VI, concerned with trigonometric functions of several angles, we shall have occasion to treat some elementary transcendental functions of more than one variable.

### EXERCISES

In Exercises 1–10, simplify and then classify each of the given functions according to the chart above.

1. $2x^3 - 7x + 3$.

2. $6x^{-2} + 4x$.

3. $x^{-1} + 4\sqrt{x^2}$.

4. $3x - (2\sqrt[3]{x})^2$.

5. $\dfrac{x^3 + 2x^2 - 3}{1 - x}$.

6. $\dfrac{4}{3x + 1}$.

7. $2 - x - \dfrac{4}{2 + x}$.

8. $\sin \dfrac{x + 1}{x - 1}$.

9. $\cos 2\sqrt{x}$.

10. $5x - 2 \tan x^2$.

**11–13.** Verify the statement that the three examples of irrational algebraic functions of Art. 21 respectively satisfy the three given relations of form (3).

In each of Exercises 14–20, state the total degree and the degree in each variable. Which expressions are homogeneous?

14. $5x - 2y + z$.

15. $x^2 - 2xz + yz + 4z^2 + 3$.

16. $x^2 + 2y^2 - z^2$.

17. $x^2 yz + xy^2 z + xyz^2$.

**18–20.** The left members of the relations of form (3), Art. 21, satisfied by the three examples of irrational algebraic functions.

**22. Trigonometric identities.** We shall consider here a few identities, involving trigonometric functions, that are fundamental to a large part of our subsequent work in analytic trigonometry. In Chapter VI we shall obtain additional trigonometric identities.

The student will probably have noticed that, of the six trigonometric ratios, namely,

$$\sin \theta = \frac{y}{r}, \qquad \cos \theta = \frac{x}{r}, \qquad \tan \theta = \frac{y}{x},$$

$$\csc \theta = \frac{r}{y}, \qquad \sec \theta = \frac{r}{x}, \qquad \cot \theta = \frac{x}{y},$$

three are merely respective reciprocals of the remaining three. Accordingly, we have the following relations:

$$\sin \theta = \frac{1}{\csc \theta}, \quad \text{or} \quad \csc \theta = \frac{1}{\sin \theta}, \quad \text{or} \quad \sin \theta \csc \theta = 1; \qquad (1)$$

$$\cos \theta = \frac{1}{\sec \theta}, \quad \text{or} \quad \sec \theta = \frac{1}{\cos \theta}, \quad \text{or} \quad \cos \theta \sec \theta = 1; \qquad (2)$$

$$\tan \theta = \frac{1}{\cot \theta}, \quad \text{or} \quad \cot \theta = \frac{1}{\tan \theta}, \quad \text{or} \quad \tan \theta \cot \theta = 1. \qquad (3)$$

As a further consequence of the definitions, we also have

$$\tan \theta = \frac{y}{x} = \frac{\dfrac{y}{r}}{\dfrac{x}{r}}, \qquad \cot \theta = \frac{x}{y} = \frac{\dfrac{x}{r}}{\dfrac{y}{r}},$$

whence

$$\tan \theta = \frac{\sin \theta}{\cos \theta}, \qquad (4)$$

$$\cot \theta = \frac{\cos \theta}{\sin \theta}. \qquad (5)$$

Relation (5) may alternatively be obtained by combining (3) and (4).

Three additional relations are easily derived from the geometric relation (see Fig. 6)

$$x^2 + y^2 = r^2.$$

If we divide both members of this equation by $r^2$, we get

$$\frac{x^2}{r^2} + \frac{y^2}{r^2} = 1.$$

Hence, since $\sin \theta = y/r$ and $\cos \theta = x/r$,

$$\sin^2 \theta + \cos^2 \theta = 1. \tag{6}$$

Division by $x^2$ gives us

$$1 + \frac{y^2}{x^2} = \frac{r^2}{x^2},$$

and since $\tan \theta = y/x$ and $\sec \theta = r/x$, we find

$$1 + \tan^2 \theta = \sec^2 \theta. \tag{7}$$

Finally, division by $y^2$ and the definitions together yield

$$\frac{x^2}{y^2} + 1 = \frac{r^2}{y^2},$$

$$1 + \cot^2 \theta = \csc^2 \theta. \tag{8}$$

Relations $(1) - (8)$ hold no matter what the magnitude of $\theta$ may be, and for angles in all four quadrants; it is necessary merely that the functions concerned exist. Consequently these relations are identities and may be used whenever they are applicable. The uses of these identities are many, as we shall see, and therefore the student should become thoroughly familiar with them in all possible forms; he should not only recognize, for example, that $\sin^2 \sqrt{2x-1} + \cos^2 \sqrt{2x-1}$ may be replaced by unity, but the form $1 - \cos^2 (\cdots)$, whatever may be the symbol for the angle, should suggest $\sin^2 (\cdots)$.

From (6), we have

$$\sin \theta = \pm \sqrt{1 - \cos^2 \theta} \quad \text{and} \quad \cos \theta = \pm \sqrt{1 - \sin^2 \theta};$$

from (7),

$$\tan \theta = \pm \sqrt{\sec^2 \theta - 1} \quad \text{and} \quad \sec \theta = \pm \sqrt{1 + \tan^2 \theta};$$

from (8),

$$\cot \theta = \pm \sqrt{\csc^2 \theta - 1} \quad \text{and} \quad \csc \theta = \pm \sqrt{1 + \cot^2 \theta}.$$

When dealing with an unspecified angle $\theta$, the student should be careful to take into account each double sign. On the other hand, when a particular angle, or merely a particular quadrant, is concerned, the student should choose that one of the signs, before each square root, that applies to the case in hand.

*Example 1.*  Express cos θ in terms of each of the remaining five functions in turn.

*Solution.*  Using identities (2) and (6), we get directly

$$\cos \theta = \frac{1}{\sec \theta}, \tag{9}$$

$$\cos \theta = \pm \sqrt{1 - \sin^2 \theta}, \tag{10}$$

as expressions for cos θ in terms of sec θ and sin θ, respectively.  Combining (9) with (7), we also have

$$\cos \theta = \pm \frac{1}{\sqrt{1 + \tan^2 \theta}} \tag{11}$$

as the expression for cos θ in terms of tan θ.  Now if we replace sin θ in (10) by its equivalent, $1/\csc \theta$, given by (1), we find

$$\cos \theta = \pm \sqrt{1 - \frac{1}{\csc^2 \theta}} = \pm \frac{\sqrt{\csc^2 \theta - 1}}{\csc \theta}; \tag{12}$$

and, combining (11) with (3), we find

$$\cos \theta = \pm \frac{1}{\sqrt{1 + \frac{1}{\cot^2 \theta}}} = \pm \frac{\cot \theta}{\sqrt{\cot^2 \theta + 1}}. \tag{13}$$

Relations (9)–(13) are the ones desired.  The ambiguous double signs must be retained in (10)–(13) since cos θ may be either positive or negative, depending upon the quadrant in which θ lies.  If, for example, θ is in the second quadrant, only the negative signs apply in (10)–(13).

*Example 2.*  If $\cos \theta = \frac{4}{5}$ and θ is in the fourth quadrant, find the remaining five functions of θ.

*Solution.*  Since θ is in the fourth quadrant, cos θ and sec θ will be positive and the other four functions will be negative (Art. 15).  Hence we have

$$\sin \theta = -\sqrt{1 - \cos^2 \theta} = -\sqrt{1 - \tfrac{16}{25}} = -\tfrac{3}{5},$$

$$\tan \theta = \frac{\sin \theta}{\cos \theta} = -\frac{\tfrac{3}{5}}{\tfrac{4}{5}} = -\frac{3}{4},$$

$$\cot \theta = \frac{1}{\tan \theta} = -\frac{4}{3},$$

$$\sec \theta = \frac{1}{\cos \theta} = \frac{5}{4},$$

$$\csc \theta = \frac{1}{\sin \theta} = -\frac{5}{3}.$$

It will be noticed that we had merely to determine the algebraic sign of sin θ in order to use identity (6) properly; then identities (4), (3), (2), and (1) in turn automatically yielded the proper signs, as well as the magnitudes, of the remaining functions.

## EXERCISES

**1–5.** Express each of the functions $\sin\theta$, $\tan\theta$, $\cot\theta$, $\sec\theta$, and $\csc\theta$ in terms of each of the remaining five functions.

In each of Exercises 6–11, the value of one function of $\theta$ and the quadrant in which $\theta$ lies are given. Using the fundamental identities (1)–(8), find the values of the remaining functions in each exercise and check by means of a figure.

**6.** $\cos\theta = \frac{5}{13}$, $0 < \theta < \pi/2$.     **7.** $\sin\theta = \frac{1}{2}\sqrt{2}$, $\pi/2 < \theta < \pi$.

**8.** $\tan\theta = \sqrt{15}$, $\pi < \theta < 3\pi/2$.     **9.** $\cot\theta = -\frac{1}{2}$, $3\pi/2 < \theta < 2\pi$.

**10.** $\sec\theta = -\sqrt{10}$, $\pi/2 < \theta < \pi$.     **11.** $\csc\theta = -2$, $\pi < \theta < 3\pi/2$.

**12.** If $\sin^2\theta = (s-a)(s-b)/ab$, where $s = \frac{1}{2}(a+b+c)$, show that $\cos^2\theta = s(s-c)/ab$.

**13.** If $\sin^2\theta = (s-a)(s-c)/ac$, where $s = \frac{1}{2}(a+b+c)$, show that $\tan^2\theta = (s-a)(s-c)/s(s-b)$.

**14.** If $\sin\theta = \sqrt{2mn}/(m+n)$, find $\cot\theta$.

**15.** If $\tan\theta = 2mn/(m^2-n^2)$, find $\csc\theta$.

## 23. Transformations.

It was stated in Art. 20 that identities are often established by transforming one expression into a second of somewhat different form and by using additional identities. The eight fundamental identities derived in Art. 22 are powerful aids in transforming one trigonometric expression into another; simple examples are the transformations of $\cos\theta$ into equivalent forms in identities (9)–(13) of Art. 22. We now illustrate the processes of trigonometric transformations by further examples.

*Example 1.*   Prove that the relation

$$\sec^4\theta - \tan^4\theta = -1 + \frac{2}{1-\sin^2\theta} \tag{1}$$

is an identity by transforming the left member into the right member.

*Solution.*   We first notice that the left member is factorable as the difference of two squares (Art. 6):

$$\sec^4\theta - \tan^4\theta = (\sec^2\theta + \tan^2\theta)(\sec^2\theta - \tan^2\theta). \tag{2}$$

Now, since $\sec^2\theta - \tan^2\theta = 1$ [identity (7), Art. 22], we have an immediate simplification. Furthermore, the form of the desired right member of (1) suggests that we change the remaining factor in (2) to sines and cosines, using identities (2) and (4) of Art. 22. Hence we get

$$(\sec^2\theta + \tan^2\theta)(\sec^2\theta - \tan^2\theta) = \frac{1}{\cos^2\theta} + \frac{\sin^2\theta}{\cos^2\theta}$$

$$= \frac{1+\sin^2\theta}{\cos^2\theta}. \tag{3}$$

Since the final result is to involve only the sine function, we use identity (6) of Art. 22 and get

$$\frac{1 + \sin^2 \theta}{\cos^2 \theta} = \frac{1 + \sin^2 \theta}{1 - \sin^2 \theta}.$$

Finally, if we divide $\sin^2 \theta + 1$ by $- \sin^2 \theta + 1$, we have

$$\frac{1 + \sin^2 \theta}{1 - \sin^2 \theta} = -1 + \frac{2}{1 - \sin^2 \theta}, \tag{4}$$

which is the required form.

*Example 2.* By trigonometric transformations, simplify the expression

$$\frac{\sec \theta \cot \theta - \csc \theta \tan \theta}{\cos \theta - \sin \theta}. \tag{5}$$

*Solution.* When we have to simplify an expression involving several functions, it is often profitable to express each function in terms of sines and cosines. In the given expression (5), all six functions are present, and hence we proceed as follows.

$$\frac{\sec \theta \cot \theta - \csc \theta \tan \theta}{\cos \theta - \sin \theta} = \frac{\dfrac{1}{\cos \theta} \cdot \dfrac{\cos \theta}{\sin \theta} - \dfrac{1}{\sin \theta} \cdot \dfrac{\sin \theta}{\cos \theta}}{\cos \theta - \sin \theta}$$

$$= \frac{\dfrac{1}{\sin \theta} - \dfrac{1}{\cos \theta}}{\cos \theta - \sin \theta}. \tag{6}$$

This complex fraction may be simplified by multiplying numerator and denominator by $\sin \theta \cos \theta$; this yields

$$\frac{\cos \theta - \sin \theta}{\sin \theta \cos \theta (\cos \theta - \sin \theta)} = \frac{1}{\sin \theta \cos \theta}$$

$$= \csc \theta \sec \theta. \tag{7}$$

The last expression is as compact and simple in form as we can make it at this point; when additional identities have been developed (Chapter VI), we shall see that it is possible to express the result in terms of a single trigonometric function, $2 \csc 2\theta$.

If we are to treat a given trigonometric expression, whether to employ it in computation or to examine and discuss its functional characteristics, the ability to transform it into something simpler or into another form that exhibits certain properties more clearly is obviously desirable. Accordingly, facility in the manipulation of trigonometric expressions is important. Although no universal rules can well be stated, the following points will be found helpful:

1. Apply any algebraic operations that serve to simplify an expression: factoring, reducing a complex fraction to a simple fraction, expressing the sum of two or more fractions as a single fraction, performing indicated divisions when possible, etc. When simplifying a complex fraction or combining two fractions, leave the component expressions in factored form, so that possible common factors in numerator and denominator are exhibited and can be removed.

2. Look for combinations of functions appearing in the fundamental identities of Art. 22, and apply these identities to simplify the form. For example, $\sin \theta / \cos \theta$, $1 - \cos^2 \theta$, and $1 - \sec^2 \theta$ suggest the possibility of replacement by $\tan \theta$, $\sin^2 \theta$, and $-\tan^2 \theta$, respectively.

3. If possible, avoid irrational expressions, particularly those involving the ambiguous double sign. Notice that $\tan \theta$, $\cot \theta$, $\sec \theta$, and $\csc \theta$ are all expressible rationally in terms of $\sin \theta$ and $\cos \theta$, and these two functions are themselves connected by a simple identity, $\sin^2 \theta + \cos^2 \theta = 1$. Hence an expression containing several functions rationally may often be materially simplified first by a transformation to sines and cosines, as in Example 2.

The student may be tempted to prove an identity by assuming the relation to be true and deducing from the assumed equality a known relation. This procedure is dangerous, for it is possible to deduce a correct relation from an incorrect or meaningless one. Thus, suppose we are asked to show that

$$\frac{\cos \theta + 2}{\sqrt{\cos \theta - 1} + \sin \theta} = \frac{\sqrt{\cos \theta - 1} - \sin \theta}{\cos \theta - 1}. \tag{8}$$

If we assume this equality, and multiply both members by the product of the denominators, we get

$$\cos^2 \theta + \cos \theta - 2 = \cos \theta - 1 - \sin^2 \theta$$

$$= \cos \theta - 1 - (1 - \cos^2 \theta)$$

$$= \cos \theta - 1 - 1 + \cos^2 \theta$$

$$= \cos^2 \theta + \cos \theta - 2,$$

which is obviously true. But $\sqrt{\cos \theta - 1}$, appearing in both members of (8), will be a real number only when $\cos \theta = 1$, since $\cos \theta$ can never be greater than unity, and in that case (when $\theta = 0, \pm 2\pi, \pm 4\pi, \cdots$)

$\sin \theta = 0$ and $\sqrt{\cos \theta - 1} = 0$, so that both members of (8) become meaningless.

On the other hand, if we were to attempt to transform one member of (8) into the other, we might proceed to "force" the result by multiplying numerator and denominator of the left member by $\sqrt{\cos \theta - 1} - \sin \theta$. This would appear to be an application of one of the basic operations (IX, Art. 3); but here it would not be valid since the only value $\sqrt{\cos \theta - 1} - \sin \theta$ may have is zero, which is not a permissible multiplier. A critical examination of the processes employed is therefore necessary; here it is at once seen that we cannot prove the correctness of a meaningless relation.

Moreover, the conditions of a problem necessitating trigonometric transformations will usually govern the form into which the given expression is to be changed, but the specific result will not be known in advance. Consequently, in the following exercises, the student should transform one member into the other, being careful to employ only valid operations.

## EXERCISES

Prove the following identities by transforming one member into the other.

1. $\dfrac{\cos \theta \tan \theta - \sin^2 \theta}{1 - \sin \theta} = \sin \theta.$

2. $\dfrac{\csc \theta - \sin \theta}{\cos^2 \theta} = \csc \theta.$

3. $\dfrac{\sin \theta \sec^2 \theta - \sin \theta}{\cos \theta} = \tan^3 \theta.$

4. $\dfrac{2}{\sin \theta + 1} - \dfrac{2}{\sin \theta - 1} = 4 \sec^2 \theta.$

5. $(\sec \theta - 1)(\sin \theta + \sin \theta \cos \theta) = \sin^2 \theta \tan \theta.$

6. $(\cot \theta + 1)(\sin \theta - \cos \theta) - \sin \theta = - \cos \theta \cot \theta.$

7. $\dfrac{3 \cos \theta}{2 - 2 \csc \theta} + \dfrac{3 \cos \theta}{2 + 2 \csc \theta} = -3 \sin \theta \tan \theta.$

8. $(\tan \theta - \sec \theta)^2 - 1 + \dfrac{2 \sin \theta}{\cos^2 \theta} = 2 \tan^2 \theta.$

9. $(1 - \sin^4 \theta - \cos^4 \theta) \csc^2 \theta = 2 \cos^2 \theta.$

10. $\left( \dfrac{\sqrt{\cos^2 \theta}}{\sqrt{1 - \sin \theta}} + \dfrac{\sqrt{\sin^2 \theta}}{\sqrt{1 - \cos \theta}} \right) (\sqrt{1 + \sin \theta} - \sqrt{1 + \cos \theta}) = \sin \theta - \cos \theta.$

11. $\sqrt{\dfrac{1 - \sin \theta}{1 + \sin \theta}} - \sqrt{\dfrac{1 + \sin \theta}{1 - \sin \theta}} = -2\sqrt{\tan^2 \theta}.$

**12.** $\dfrac{\sin^3 \theta + \cos^3 \theta}{1 - \sin \theta \cos \theta} - \sin \theta + \cos \theta = 2 \cos \theta.$

**13.** $(\tan \theta + \cot \theta)^2 \sin^2 \theta - \tan^2 \theta = 1.$

**14.** $(\cot \theta - \csc \theta)^2 (\cos \theta + 1)^2 = \sin^2 \theta.$

**15.** $\dfrac{(\sec \theta - \tan \theta)^2 + 1}{\sec \theta \csc \theta - \tan \theta \csc \theta} = 2 \tan \theta.$

**16.** $(3 - \csc^2 \theta) \cot^4 \theta + (7 - 5 \csc^2 \theta + \csc^4 \theta) \csc^2 \theta = 3.$

**17.** $1 + 3 \tan^2 \theta + 2 \tan^4 \theta + \tan^4 \theta \sec^2 \theta = \sec^6 \theta.$

**18.** $\dfrac{\sqrt{\cot \theta} - 2}{\sqrt{\cot \theta} + 2} + 1 = \dfrac{2(1 - 2\sqrt{\tan \theta})}{1 - 4 \tan \theta}.$

**19.** $\dfrac{\cos^2 \theta \csc^2 \theta - \sin^2 \theta \cot^2 \theta}{\csc^4 \theta - 2 \cot^2 \theta - 1} = \sin^2 \theta.$

**20.** $\dfrac{\cot \theta}{1 - \cot \theta} + \dfrac{\tan \theta}{1 + \tan \theta} = \dfrac{1}{2 \sin^2 \theta - 1}.$

**21.** $\left( \dfrac{\sin \theta}{1 - \tan \theta} - \dfrac{\cos \theta}{1 - \cot \theta} \right) (\cos \theta - \sin \theta) = 2 \sin \theta \cos \theta.$

**22.** $\left( \dfrac{\cos \theta}{1 - \sin \theta} - \dfrac{\sin \theta - 1}{\cos \theta} \right) \tan \theta = 2 \sin \theta \sec^2 \theta.$

**23.** $\dfrac{\cos \alpha - \sin \beta}{\sec \alpha - \csc \beta} = - \cos \alpha \sin \beta.$

**24.** $\left( \dfrac{\csc \alpha + \csc \beta}{\cot \alpha + \cot \beta} \right) (\sin \alpha \cos \beta + \cos \alpha \sin \beta) = \sin \alpha + \sin \beta.$

**25.** $\dfrac{2 \cot^2 \alpha - 2 \cot^2 \beta}{\csc^2 \alpha - \csc^2 \beta} + \tan^2 \alpha + \tan^2 \beta = \sec^2 \alpha + \sec^2 \beta.$

**26.** $\dfrac{\sin^3 \alpha + \cos^3 \beta}{\sin^2 \alpha - \cos^2 \beta} = \sin \alpha - \cos \beta + \dfrac{\sin \alpha \cos \beta}{\sin \alpha - \cos \beta}.$

**27.** $\dfrac{\cos^6 \theta - \sin^6 \theta}{\cos^2 \theta - \sin^2 \theta} = 1 - \sin^2 \theta \cos^2 \theta.$

**28.** $\dfrac{\sin \theta - \cos^2 \theta - 1}{3 \sin \theta + 3 - \cos^2 \theta} = 1 - \dfrac{2}{\sin \theta + 1}.$

**29.** $\dfrac{2 \sec^2 \theta - \tan \theta - 5}{4 \sec^2 \theta - 8 \tan \theta - 1} = \dfrac{3}{2 - \cot \theta} - 1.$

**30.** $\dfrac{\tan^4 \theta - 4 \sec^4 \theta}{\cos^4 \theta - 2 \cos^2 \theta - 3} = \sec^4 \theta.$

**24. Solutions of equations.** In earlier discussions we have occasionally spoken of a "solution," or of an equation being "satisfied," or of processes for "solving" equations. Our purpose in this article is to make these ideas more precise.

There is no need to consider identities in this connection, since, by definition, an identity holds true for all permissible values of the quantities involved. On the other hand, conditional equations, which are relations holding only for certain values of the quantities, present the problem of determining those certain values, which are then called solutions.

For definiteness, suppose first that we have an equation (of condition) containing only one variable or unknown $x$, all the constants being numerical; we denote this equation symbolically as

$$f(x) = 0. \tag{1}$$

If $x_0$ is a number that reduces the left member to zero, that is, if

$$f(x_0) \equiv 0, \tag{2}$$

then $x = x_0$ is called a **solution** or **root** of (1), and (1) is said to be *satisfied* by $x = x_0$. Consequently a solution of $f(x) = 0$ is a **zero** of the function $f(x)$ (Art. 11). This definition of a solution gives us a definite criterion: If the number $x_0$ produces the identity (2), it is a solution of (1), and if we do not have identity (2), then $x_0$ is not a solution. Thus, if

$$f(x) \equiv 2x + 3 \cos x - \pi = 0, \tag{3}$$

then $x = \pi/2$ is a solution, but $x = \pi$ is not, since

$$f\left(\frac{\pi}{2}\right) = \pi + 3 \cdot 0 - \pi \equiv 0, \quad f(\pi) = 2\pi + 3(-1) - \pi = \pi - 3 \not\equiv 0.$$

Next suppose that we have an equation (1) containing, in addition to the variable $x$, other non-numerical quantities. Then the criterion given by (2) still holds, but now $x_0$ may or may not involve these other quantities. For example, if

$$f(x) = x^2 - (a + b^2 + 1)x + a + b^2 = 0, \tag{4}$$

then $x = 1$ is one solution and $x = a + b^2$ is another:

$$f(1) = 1^2 - (a + b^2 + 1) \cdot 1 + a + b^2$$
$$= 1 - a - b^2 - 1 + a + b^2 \equiv 0,$$
$$f(a + b^2) = (a + b^2)^2 - (a + b^2 + 1)(a + b^2) + a + b^2$$
$$= (a + b^2)(a + b^2 - a - b^2 - 1 + 1) \equiv 0.$$

The notation $f(x)$ for a function implies that $x$ is regarded as the sole variable, and that other algebraic quantities are fixed but unspecified constants. We may choose to regard $a$ and $b$, as well as $x$, as variables in equation (4), and we indicate this by writing

$$F(x, a, b) = x^2 - ax - b^2x - x + a + b^2 = 0. \tag{4'}$$

Then $x = a + b^2$ is, as was found above, a solution *for x in terms of a and b*. In addition, $a = x - b^2$ is a solution for $a$ in terms of $x$ and $b$:

$$F(x, x - b^2, b) = x^2 - (x - b^2)x - b^2x - x + (x - b^2) + b^2 \equiv 0;$$

and $b = \pm \sqrt{x - a}$ are two solutions for $b$ in terms of $x$ and $a$:

$$F(x, a, \pm \sqrt{x - a}) = x^2 - ax - (x - a)x - x + a + (x - a) \equiv 0.$$

Thus, for an equation containing two or more algebraic quantities, we may pose separate problems of solving for each variable in terms of the others.

Consider now a **system** of two or more equations, that is, a group of equations to be regarded together or **simultaneously**. As a simple illustration, let there be given two equations involving two variables:

$$3x - 2y = 8,$$

$$x + 4y = -2.$$

Each equation may be solved for either $x$ or $y$ in terms of the other variable; thus, we have from the first equation,

$$x = \frac{8 + 2y}{3} \quad \text{or} \quad y = \frac{3x - 8}{2},$$

and from the second equation,

$$x = -2 - 4y \quad \text{or} \quad y = -\frac{2 + x}{4}.$$

But the more usual problem in connection with a system of equations is to find expressions for all the variables that will satisfy all the equations simultaneously. In the above example, a solution pair is $x = 2, y = -1$, for

$$3 \cdot 2 - 2(-1) \equiv 8, \qquad 2 + 4(-1) \equiv -2;$$

it may be shown, as we shall see in the next chapter, that this is the only solution pair.

In general, for a system of $n$ equations involving the same number $n$ of variables, there will be a specific number of solution sets, but for certain systems of $n$ equations in $n$ unknowns there may be none or there may be indefinitely many solutions. Moreover, when the number of equations and the number of variables differ, any one of three situations may prevail: there may be no simultaneous solution, there may be a certain number of solutions, or there may exist indefinitely many simultaneous solutions of the system.

All these situations will be considered in various connections in our subsequent work.

**25. Equivalent, defective, and redundant equations.**   For definiteness and simplicity, we shall confine our discussion to a single equation containing only one variable,

$$f(x) = 0. \tag{1}$$

If there is a second equation,

$$g(x) = 0, \tag{2}$$

obtained either by operations performed on (1) or by independent means, such that all solutions of (2) are solutions of (1), and such that every solution of (1) also satisfies (2), then equations (1) and (2) are said to be **equivalent.**   For example,

$$f(x) = 2x^2 - 3x - 2 = 0 \quad \text{and} \quad g(x) = 4 - 4x^2 + 6x = 0$$

are equivalent since each is satisfied by $x = 2$ and by $x = -\frac{1}{2}$, but neither has any additional solutions; here it is easy to see that $g(x) = 0$ is obtainable from $f(x) = 0$ merely by multiplying both members by $-2$ and rearranging the terms in the resulting left member.

In general, if we add the same quantity to both members of (1), or if we multiply both members by the same quantity, *provided that quantity is independent of* $x$, the new equation will be equivalent to (1).*

The restriction to a quantity independent of the variable $x$ is clearly necessary.   For example, if we multiply both members of the equation $2x^2 - 3x - 2 = 0$ by, say, $x$, we get the equation $2x^3 - 3x^2 - 2x = 0$, which has the solution $x = 0$ in addition to the solutions $2$ and $-\frac{1}{2}$ of the original equation, and consequently the new equation is not equivalent to the first one.   Likewise, if we divide both members of $2x^2 - 3x - 2 = 0$ by $x - 2$, we get the new equation $2x + 1 = 0$, which, since it lacks the solution $x = 2$, is not equivalent to the original one.

If we perform certain operations on an equation (1) so as to produce a new equation lacking one or more solutions of (1), then the new equation is said to be **defective.**   Thus, when we divide both members of $2x^2 - 3x - 2 = 0$ by $x - 2$, we produce a defective equation.

If certain operations performed on (1) produce an equation possessing one or more solutions that do not satisfy (1), then the new equation is said to be **redundant.**   Thus, the equation $2x^3 - 3x^2 - 2x = 0$ is redundant with respect to the equation $2x^2 - 3x - 2 = 0$ from which it was obtained.

---

* It should be noted that subtraction, and division by a non-zero quantity, are both allowed since subtraction is merely the addition of the negative of a quantity and division is multiplication by the reciprocal of a quantity (IV and XII, Art. 3).

Defective equations are usually produced by carelessly dividing by an expression containing the variable $x$. If this expression can reduce to zero for some value of $x$, such division is in effect violating the stipulation that the divisor must be different from zero. The student should therefore guard against the possibility of producing a defective equation, by scrutinizing each division.

Redundant equations may result from the introduction of a factor involving $x$, as in the above example, and they may also come about by rationalizing processes. Consider, for example, the equation

$$x + 3 = \sqrt{3 - x}.$$

The usual manner of solving such an equation is to remove the irrationality by squaring both members. This is an application of XI, Art. 2. We then have

$$x^2 + 6x + 9 = 3 - x.$$

By adding $x - 3$ to both sides, we find the equivalent equation

$$x^2 + 7x + 6 = 0.$$

Factoring the left member, we get

$$(x + 1)(x + 6) = 0.$$

Now, if either factor is set equal to zero, this equation will be satisfied (I, Art. 3). Hence we get two solutions,

$$x = -1 \quad \text{and} \quad x = -6.$$

Applying the criterion of Art. 24, we see that only $x = -1$ satisfies the original equation:

$$-1 + 3 = \sqrt{3 - (-1)}, \qquad -6 + 3 \neq \sqrt{3 - (-6)};$$

consequently the equation obtained after rationalizing is redundant. The value $x = -6$, which is obtained from the redundant equation but which does not satisfy the original equation, is called an **extraneous** solution.

Evidently, if the original equation had been $x + 3 = -\sqrt{3 - x}$, rationalizing would have led to the same rational integral equation, $x^2 + 7x + 6 = 0$, and the solutions $x = -1$ and $x = -6$. In this event only $x = -6$ would satisfy the original equation, so that we would again have redundancy; $x = -1$ would be extraneous.

As a consequence of all that has been said, it appears that, when performing operations with equalities, one should exercise great care and should carefully examine the ostensible solutions of the equations thereby found. To avoid getting defective equations, give full consideration to factors containing the variable and removed by division; to detect possible redundancies, use the criterion of Art. 24 for each solution whenever multiplication by a factor containing the variable has been applied and whenever rationalizing has been done.

As stated at the beginning of this article, these remarks are made with reference to single equations containing one variable. Similar comments, of course, apply also to systems of equations involving several variables.

### EXERCISES

In each of Exercises 1–15, use the criterion of Art. 24 to determine whether or not the given equation is satisfied by the stated quantity.

1. $4x + 2 = 5x - 5$; $x = 7$.
2. $ax + 4b^2 = 2bx + a^2$; $x = a + 2b$.
3. $\dfrac{5 - 3x}{x} - 2x = 6$; $x = \frac{1}{2}$.
4. $\dfrac{x - a}{x + 3a} + \dfrac{x + a}{x - 3a} + 1 = 0$; $x = -a$.
5. $2x^2 + ax - 6a^2 = 0$; $x = -2a$.
6. $2ab(x^2 - 1) - (a^2 - 4b^2)x = 0$; $x = -2b/a$.
7. $2x^2 - 4x - 3 = 0$; $x = 1 + \frac{1}{2}\sqrt{10}$.
8. $x^2 - 4ax + b^2 = 0$; $x = 2a - \sqrt{4a^2 - b^2}$.
9. $x^2 + 2 \sin x + 3 \cos x = 3$; $x = 0$.
10. $4 \sin 2x + 3 \cos 5x = 0$; $x = \pi/2$.
11. $\sqrt{x^2 - 7x + 4} = x + 1$; $x = \dfrac{1}{3}$.
12. $\sqrt{3x - 2} + \sqrt{x} = 2$; $x = 9$.
13. $\sqrt{7 - x} - \sqrt{6 + x} = 1$; $x = 3$.
14. $\sqrt{5 + 2x} + \sqrt{5 - 2x} = 4$; $x = 2$.
15. $\sqrt{4 + 5x} - \sqrt{9 + 7x} = 1$; $x = 1$.

16. Show that the equation of Exercise 11 has no extraneous solutions.
17. Show that the equation of Exercise 12 has only one solution, and determine its value.
18. Show that the equation of Exercise 13 has only one solution, and determine its value.
19. Show that the equation of Exercise 14 has no extraneous solutions. Find all correct solutions.
20. Show that the equation of Exercise 15 has two extraneous solutions and no valid solutions.

### 26. Trigonometric equations.
By a trigonometric equation we shall mean a conditional equation containing trigonometric functions of the variable or unknown. In Chapter XII we shall extend the meaning of the term so as to permit the presence of inverse trigonometric functions.

At this point the trigonometric functions involved will be functions of a single quantity, which may or may not be the unknown itself. Thus, the trigonometric equation

$$\sin^2 \theta + 2 \cos \theta - 1 = 0$$

contains functions of the angle $\theta$ only, and the equation

$$2 \cos 2\theta + \cot 2\theta = 0$$

contains functions of $2\theta$ only. With the aid of additional trigonometric formulas or identities, some of which will be discussed in Chapter VI, it will be possible to transform certain equations containing functions of several angles into new equations involving functions of only one angle, such as those considered here.

The processes of solving trigonometric equations will usually entail algebraic manipulations and the application of the fundamental trigonometric identities (Art. 22). In general, we make necessary transformations and then try to solve algebraically for a function of the unknown; from the value of the function, the angle or angles may then be determined.

Since there exist indefinitely many angles having the same value for a particular trigonometric function (Art. 15), a trigonometric equation may have indefinitely many solutions. Sometimes all solutions are expressed, using general measure (Art. 13), but usually it suffices to determine all non-negative values of $\theta$ less than one revolution, $0 \leqq \theta < 2\pi$.

*Example 1.* Solve the equation

$$\sin^2 \theta + 2 \cos \theta - 1 = 0$$

for non-negative values of $\theta$ less than $2\pi$.

*Solution.* Two trigonometric functions of the unknown $\theta$ itself appear in this equation. Accordingly, we make use of the identity connecting these functions, namely, $\sin^2 \theta + \cos^2 \theta = 1$, to transform into an equation involving only one function of $\theta$. We replace $\sin^2 \theta$ by $1 - \cos^2 \theta$, since this gives us a rational integral equation in $\cos \theta$; the replacement of $\cos \theta$ by $\pm\sqrt{1 - \sin^2 \theta}$ would introduce an irrationality and the consequent needless complications. Then we get

$$1 - \cos^2 \theta + 2 \cos \theta - 1 = 0,$$

$$(\cos \theta)(2 - \cos \theta) = 0.$$

This equation will be satisfied if either factor in the left member is set equal to zero. Now there are two angles in the range $0 \leqq \theta < 2\pi$ for which $\cos \theta = 0$, namely

$$\theta = \frac{\pi}{2}, \qquad \theta = \frac{3\pi}{2}.$$

But, since a cosine of an angle can never exceed unity (Art. 15), the relation $2 - \cos \theta = 0$ does not yield a value of $\theta$. Hence we have just two solutions, as given above. It is easy to check these solutions; since $\sin \dfrac{\pi}{2} = 1$ and $\sin \dfrac{3\pi}{2} = -1$, the given equation gives us, in each case, $1 + 2 \cdot 0 - 1 \equiv 0$.

*Example 2.* Solve the equation

$$2 \cos 2\theta + \cot 2\theta = 0$$

for non-negative values of $\theta$ less than $2\pi$.

*Solution.* Here the single angle involved is $2\theta$, and we therefore solve for this quantity. Now if we are to have $0 \leqq \theta < 2\pi$, then $2\theta$ may be any non-negative number less than $4\pi$. This is an important point, which should be the first consideration when solving a trigonometric equation.

In this problem we have no fundamental identity connecting just the cosine and the cotangent; the relation connecting them, equation (13), Art. 22, involves an irrationality, which we wish to avoid if possible. But if we use the identity $\cot 2\theta = \cos 2\theta / \sin 2\theta$, we get

$$2 \cos 2\theta + \frac{\cos 2\theta}{\sin 2\theta} = 0,$$

whence

$$2 \cos 2\theta \sin 2\theta + \cos 2\theta = 0,$$

$$(\cos 2\theta)(2 \sin 2\theta + 1) = 0.$$

It should be noted that we have multiplied both members of our equation by $\sin 2\theta$, and it is therefore conceivable that the new equation may be redundant. Consequently it is essential that the solutions obtained be checked.

From the last equation we find (Art. 16):

$$\cos 2\theta = 0, \ 2\theta = \frac{\pi}{2}, \frac{3\pi}{2}, \frac{5\pi}{2}, \frac{7\pi}{2},$$

$$\theta = \frac{\pi}{4}, \frac{3\pi}{4}, \frac{5\pi}{4}, \frac{7\pi}{4};$$

$$\sin 2\theta = -\frac{1}{2}, \ 2\theta = \frac{7\pi}{6}, \frac{11\pi}{6}, \frac{19\pi}{6}, \frac{23\pi}{6},$$

$$\theta = \frac{7\pi}{12}, \frac{11\pi}{12}, \frac{19\pi}{12}, \frac{23\pi}{12}.$$

The student can readily show that all eight of these solutions satisfy the original equation.

*Example 3.*  Solve the equation

$$3 \tan \theta + \sec \theta + 1 = 0$$

for non-negative values of $\theta$ less than $2\pi$.

*Solution.*  Here the two functions involved are connected by the identity $\sec^2 \theta = 1 + \tan^2 \theta$. Since both functions appear to the first degree in the equation, the introduction of an irrationality is unavoidable.* Therefore a redundancy may arise, and all solutions obtained must be checked.

If we choose to eliminate $\sec \theta$, we get

$$3 \tan \theta + 1 = - \sec \theta = \pm \sqrt{1 + \tan^2 \theta},$$

$$9 \tan^2 \theta + 6 \tan \theta + 1 = 1 + \tan^2 \theta,$$

$$8 \tan^2 \theta + 6 \tan \theta = 0,$$

$$(2 \tan \theta)(4 \tan \theta + 3) = 0,$$

$$\tan \theta = 0, \qquad \tan \theta = -\tfrac{3}{4}.$$

Corresponding to $\tan \theta = 0$, we have $\theta = 0$ and $\theta = \pi$. Since $\sec 0 = 1$ and $\sec \pi = -1$, substitution in the original equation yields $3 \cdot 0 + 1 + 1 \neq 0$ and $3 \cdot 0 - 1 + 1 = 0$. Hence $\theta = \pi$ is correct, but $\theta = 0$ is an extraneous solution.

Since the tangent of an angle is negative when the angle lies in the second or fourth quadrant, there are two angles for which $\tan \theta = - \tfrac{3}{4}$. For the second quadrant angle, $\sec \theta = -\sqrt{1 + \tan^2 \theta} = -\tfrac{5}{4}$; and, for the fourth quadrant angle, $\sec \theta = \sqrt{1 + \tan^2 \theta} = \tfrac{5}{4}$. Since these angles are not among the special angles (Art. 16) but must be found by referring to trigonometric tables, we check these two angles before evaluating them; we then get: $3(-\tfrac{3}{4}) - \tfrac{5}{4} + 1 \neq 0$, $3(-\tfrac{3}{4}) + \tfrac{5}{4} + 1 = 0$. Therefore only the fourth quadrant angle is a valid solution. Using the relations of Art. 18 and the tables, we get $360° - \theta = 36° \, 52'$ approximately, whence $\theta = 323° \, 8' = 5.64$ radians approximately.

Thus the given equation has just two valid solutions,

$$\theta = \pi \qquad \text{and} \qquad \theta = 5.64.$$

To find all the angles in the range $0 \leqq \theta < 2\pi$, notice that there are in general, as in Example 3, two angles corresponding to a given function value. Exceptional cases may occur when the angle has its terminal side along a coordinate axis, between two quadrants; then there may be only one corresponding angle. A diagram on the coordinate axes will help in determining the angle sought.

---

* An alternative approach is to express $\tan \theta$ and $\sec \theta$ in terms of $\sin \theta$ and $\cos \theta$, but this leads to the same sort of situation. The student should compare the two methods.

## EXERCISES

Solve each of the following equations for non-negative values of $\theta$ less than $2\pi$.

**1.** $4 \sin^2 \theta - 4 \sin \theta + 1 = 0.$

**2.** $\cos^2 \theta - \cos \theta = 0.$

**3.** $\cos^2 \theta + 2 \cos \theta + 1 = 0.$

**4.** $2 \sin^2 \theta + 3 \sin \theta + 1 = 0.$

**5.** $2 \cos^2 \theta - 7 \cos \theta + 3 = 0.$

**6.** $\sin^2 \theta + \sin \theta = 0.$

**7.** $2 \sin^2 2\theta - \sin 2\theta = 0.$

**8.** $4 \cos^2 2\theta - 3 = 0.$

**9.** $2 \sin^2 \theta - \sqrt{3} \cos \theta - 2 = 0.$

**10.** $2 \cos^2 \theta - 3 \sin \theta - 3 = 0.$

**11.** $\cot \theta \csc \theta + \sqrt{2} = 0.$

**12.** $\sin \theta - \sqrt{3} \cos \theta = 0.$

**13.** $\sqrt{3} \sec^2 \theta = 4 \tan \theta.$

**14.** $\tan^2 \theta + \sec \theta = 1.$

**15.** $\sec^2 2\theta + \tan 2\theta = 1.$

**16.** $\cot^2 \theta + 2 \csc \theta + 1 = 0.$

**17.** $\cot \theta + \sqrt{3} \csc^2 \theta = \sqrt{3}.$

**18.** $\sqrt{3} \cos \theta + \sin \theta = 0.$

**19.** $3 \tan \dfrac{\theta}{2} = \cot \dfrac{\theta}{2}.$

**20.** $\sec \theta - \tan \theta = 1.$

**21.** $\sqrt{3} \tan \theta = 2 \sin \theta.$

**22.** $\sec \theta = 2 \cos \theta.$

**23.** $\cot \theta + 2 \cos \theta = 0.$

**24.** $2 \sec^2 \theta - \tan \theta = 2.$

**25.** $\cot \theta + \csc \theta = 1.$

**26.** $\cos \theta - 2 \sin \theta + 1 = 0.$

**27.** $16 \sin^4 \theta - 1 = 0.$

**28.** $4 \cos^4 \dfrac{\theta}{2} - 1 = 0.$

**29.** $3 \sin \theta + 4 \cos \theta = 5.$

**30.** $4 \sin \theta + 3 \cos \theta + 5 = 0.$

**31.** $\cos^2 \theta + \cos \theta \tan \theta = \sin \theta.$

**32.** $\sin \theta \cot \theta - 2 \sin^2 \theta = \cos \theta.$

**33.** $\sec \theta \tan \theta - \sin \theta = 2 \sin^3 \theta.$

**34.** $\csc \theta - \sec \theta + \cot \theta = \tan \theta.$

**35.** $\cos^4 \theta - \sin^4 \theta = 1.$

**36.** $\sin^6 \theta + \cos^6 \theta = 1.$

**37.** $2 \sec \theta \tan \theta - 2 \sin \theta = \sin \theta \tan \theta.$

**38.** $2(1 + \tan \theta)(\cos \theta - \sin \theta) - 2 \cos \theta = 3.$

**39.** $\sin^3 \theta + (1 - \sin \theta \cos \theta)\cos \theta + \cos^3 \theta = 0.$

**40.** $\sqrt{\dfrac{\sec \theta - 1}{\sec \theta + 1}} + \sqrt{\dfrac{\sec \theta + 1}{\sec \theta - 1}} = 1.$

## SUPPLEMENTARY EXERCISES

In Exercises 1–4, simplify and then classify each of the given functions according to the chart of Art. 21.

**1.** $2x^2 - x^{-2}.$

**2.** $x^2 \sin x + 4x \cos x.$

**3.** $\left(\dfrac{1}{\sqrt{x^2}}\right)^{-1} + \dfrac{1}{\sqrt{x^{-4}}}.$

**4.** $\dfrac{x^2 - \dfrac{x^3}{\sqrt{1 - x^2}}}{x - \sqrt{1 - x^2}} \sqrt{\dfrac{1}{x^2} - 1}.$

Establish the identity in each of Exercises 5–12 by transforming one member into the other.

**5.** $(\sec \theta - \csc \theta)(\sec \theta + \csc \theta) \sin^2 \theta \cos^2 \theta = 2 \sin^2 \theta - 1.$

**6.** $1 - (\tan \theta + \sec \theta)^2 (\sin \theta - 1)^2 = \sin^2 \theta.$

**7.** $(1 - \cos^3 \theta)(1 + \cos^3 \theta) = (3 - 3 \sin^2 \theta + \sin^4 \theta) \sin^2 \theta.$

**8.** $(\sin^4 \theta - \cos^4 \theta)(\sec^2 \theta + \csc^2 \theta) \sin^2 \theta = \tan^2 \theta - 1.$

**9.** $\dfrac{\sec\theta\tan\theta - \csc\theta\cot\theta}{\sin\theta - \cos\theta} = (\sec\theta\csc\theta + 1)\sec\theta\csc\theta.$

**10.** $\dfrac{(\tan\theta - \cot\theta)\sqrt{\sin\theta\cos\theta}}{\sqrt{\tan\theta} - \sqrt{\cot\theta}} = \sin\theta + \cos\theta.$

**11.** $(\sin\theta\sec\theta + \cos\theta\csc\theta)(\tan\theta - \cot\theta) = \sec^2\theta - \csc^2\theta.$

**12.** $\dfrac{(\sin\theta + \cos\theta + 1)^2(1 - \cos\theta)}{\sin\theta + 1} = 2\sin^2\theta.$

Solve each of the equations in Exercises 13–20 for the smallest positive value of $\theta$.

**13.** $\sin\theta = \tan\theta.$

**14.** $2\sqrt{3}\sin\theta\tan\theta = 1.$

**15.** $2\sin\theta + \cos\theta = \frac{3}{2}\sqrt{2}.$

**16.** $2\sin\theta + \cos\theta = \frac{1}{2}\sqrt{2}.$

**17.** $\sin\theta + 3\cos\theta = 3.$

**18.** $\sin(\frac{1}{4}\pi + \theta) = \cos(\frac{3}{4}\pi - \theta).$

**19.** $\tan\theta + 2\sec\theta + 2 = 0.$

**20.** $\cos^2\theta + \sin\theta\sqrt{3\sin^2\theta - 1} = 0.$

# V —————— Linear Equations and Determinants

**27. Type forms.** In Art. 21 we defined a rational integral function in one variable $x$ and of degree $n$ as a function of the form

$$a_0 x^n + a_1 x^{n-1} + \cdots + a_{n-1} x + a_n, \qquad a_0 \neq 0.$$

If the degree $n$ is equal to unity, we have as the type form

$$ax + b, \qquad a \neq 0, \tag{1}$$

where $a$ and $b$ are quantities independent of $x$. When the function of form (1) is plotted by setting $y = ax + b$, it is found that the plotted points appear to be ranged along a straight line. It is shown in plane analytic geometry that the graph of $y = ax + b$ is always a straight line, for all real values of $a$ and $b$. Accordingly, type form (1) is called a linear function of $x$.

In Art. 21 we further defined a rational integral function of two or more variables $x$, $y$, $\cdots$, as a sum of terms of the form $cx^m y^n \cdots$, where the $c$'s are constants and $m$, $n$, $\cdots$ are positive integers or zero. If the degree of such a function is unity, we say, by analogy with the case of a function of one variable, that the polynomial is a **linear function.** Thus, the type form of a linear function of two variables, $x$ and $y$, is

$$Ax + By + K, \tag{2}$$

where either $A$ or $B$ or both $A$ and $B$ are different from zero and where none of the quantities $A$, $B$, and $K$ involves $x$ or $y$; for three variables, $x$, $y$, and $z$, the type form is

$$Ax + By + Cz + K, \tag{3}$$

where at least one of the quantities $A$, $B$, and $C$ is different from zero, and where $A$, $B$, $C$, and $K$ are all independent of $x$, $y$, and $z$.

Sometimes we have occasion to deal with an expression that is linear in certain quantities that are themselves functions of the variables, although the expression is not linear in these variables. For example,

$$A \sin \theta + B \cos \theta + K$$

is linear in sin $\theta$ and cos $\theta$, although it is, of course, not linear in $\theta$—it is a transcendental function of $\theta$ (Art. 21). Here the identification as a linear expression in sin $\theta$ and cos $\theta$ is possible because we can make these two trigonometric functions correspond respectively to $x$ and $y$ in type form (2).

When a linear function in one or more quantities is set equal to zero, the resulting equation is likewise said to be linear. Thus, the equations

$$ax + b = 0, \quad Ax + By + K = 0, \quad Ax + By + Cz + K = 0,$$

corresponding to the linear functions (1)−(3), are all linear equations. The first equation is satisfied only by $x = -b/a$; the other two are respectively satisfied by indefinitely many pairs and indefinitely many triples of solution values.

**28. Systems of linear equations.** When we have two or more linear equations in two or more variables, the aggregate of equations is called a **system** of linear equations.

Consider first a system of two linear equations in two variables $x$ and $y$. These equations may be represented as:

$$a_1x + b_1y = k_1, \tag{1}$$

$$a_2x + b_2y = k_2. \tag{2}$$

It is to be understood that not both $a_1$ and $b_1$, nor both $a_2$ and $b_2$, are zero, and that the $a$'s, $b$'s and $k$'s are all independent of $x$ and $y$.

Now if these two equations were to be plotted on the same set of co-ordinate axes, any one of three things might happen. The two straight lines obtained as graphs might: (a) intersect in a single point; (b) be parallel; (c) be coincident. In the first case, the coordinates of the point of intersection give us one and only one value pair satisfying equations (1) and (2) *simultaneously.* In the second case, since the lines have no point in common, there would be no value pair simultaneously satisfying both (1) and (2); we say then that equations (1) and (2) are **inconsistent** or **incompatible.** Finally, in the third case, indefinitely many value pairs $(x, y)$ will satisfy (1) and (2) simultaneously, and equations (1) and (2) are then **dependent,** or they are equivalent (Art. 25).

Having discussed the system (1)–(2) from a geometric point of view, we now consider it from an algebraic standpoint. To solve (1) and (2) simultaneously, we may proceed as follows. If either $a_1$ or $b_1$ is zero (both cannot be zero, by supposition), equation (1) may be solved for one variable directly. Suppose, for definiteness, that $b_1 = 0$ but $a_1 \neq 0$; then (1) yields $x = k_1/a_1$. Now if $a_2 \neq 0$, the value $k_1/a_1$ may be substituted for $x$ in (2). When $b_2 \neq 0$, a corresponding value may then be found for $y$, namely, $y = (a_1k_2 - a_2k_1)/a_1b_2$, so that our system has a unique solution. If $b_2 = 0$, substitution of $k_1/a_1$ for $x$ in the left member of (2) yields $a_2k_1/a_1$, which may or may not equal the right member, $k_2$. Hence we have, when $a_2k_1/a_1 = k_2$, the case of dependent equations, for the system is satisfied by $x = k_1/a_1$ and *any* value of $y$; on the other hand, if $a_2k_1/a_1 \neq k_2$, the system is clearly incompatible. Next, when $b_1 = 0$, so that $x = k_1/a_1$ from (1), and if also $a_2 = 0$, (2) gives us $y = k_2/b_2$ (since $b_2 \neq 0$), and consequently the system has the unique solution $x = k_1/a_1$, $y = k_2/b_2$.

A similar analysis of special cases may be made when $a_1 = 0$, $b_1 \neq 0$. It is then evident that any one of the three cases—unique solution, incompatibility, or dependency—may arise, according to various circumstances. These different special situations are tabulated below:

| $a_1 \neq 0,$ | $b_2 \neq 0$ | Unique solution |
|---|---|---|
| $b_1 = 0$ | $b_2 = 0$ | Incompatible or dependent |
| $a_1 = 0,$ | $a_2 \neq 0$ | Unique solution |
| $b_1 \neq 0$ | $a_2 = 0$ | Incompatible or dependent |

We now consider the more general case in which both $x$ and $y$ appear in each equation. We multiply both members of (1) by $b_2$, and both members of (2) by $b_1$, so as to make the coefficients of $y$ alike in the new equivalent equations,

$$a_1b_2x + b_1b_2y = b_2k_1,$$
$$a_2b_1x + b_1b_2y = b_1k_2.$$

Subtraction of the corresponding members of these two equations then *eliminates* $y$, and we get

$$(a_1b_2 - a_2b_1)x = b_2k_1 - b_1k_2.$$

This leads to

$$x = \frac{b_2k_1 - b_1k_2}{a_1b_2 - a_2b_1} \tag{3}$$

provided that the denominator $\Delta_2$ is such that

$$\Delta_2 \equiv a_1b_2 - a_2b_1 \neq 0. \tag{4}$$

Similarly, elimination of $x$ between equations (1) and (2) gives us

$$y = \frac{a_1k_2 - a_2k_1}{a_1b_2 - a_2b_1} \tag{5}$$

under the same restriction (4) on the $a$'s and $b$'s.

If we compute the expression (4) for $\Delta_2$ in each of the special cases considered above, we find that, in these instances also, $\Delta_2 \neq 0$ when the system has a unique solution, and $\Delta_2 = 0$ when the equations are incompatible or dependent. Hence we may say, for all circumstances:

*The system (1)–(2) of two linear equations in two variables will have one and only one solution pair if and only if $\Delta_2 \equiv a_1b_2 - a_2b_1 \neq 0$.*

Consider next the system of three linear equations in three variables, $x$, $y$, and $z$:

$$a_1x + b_1y + c_1z = k_1, \tag{6}$$

$$a_2x + b_2y + c_2z = k_2, \tag{7}$$

$$a_3x + b_3y + c_3z = k_3. \tag{8}$$

By a similar, though lengthier, analysis, it is found that such a system will have a unique solution if and only if

$$\Delta_3 \equiv a_1b_2c_3 + a_3b_1c_2 + a_2b_3c_1 - a_3b_2c_1 - a_1b_3c_2 - a_2b_1c_3 \neq 0. \tag{9}$$

Then the values of $x$, $y$, and $z$ that satisfy the system (6)–(8) are given by

$$\Delta_3x = b_2c_3k_1 + b_1c_2k_3 + b_3c_1k_2 - b_2c_1k_3 - b_3c_2k_1 - b_1c_3k_2, \tag{10}$$

$$\Delta_3y = a_1c_3k_2 + a_3c_2k_1 + a_2c_1k_3 - a_3c_1k_2 - a_1c_2k_3 - a_2c_3k_1, \tag{11}$$

$$\Delta_3z = a_1b_2k_3 + a_3b_1k_2 + a_2b_3k_1 - a_3b_2k_1 - a_1b_3k_2 - a_2b_1k_3. \tag{12}$$

When the expression $\Delta_3$ given by (9) is equal to zero, the system (6)–(8) either has no solution or it has indefinitely many solutions. In the former case, we say as before that the system is incompatible, and in the latter case it is a dependent system.*

*Example 1.* Examine the system

$$2x - 3y = 5,$$

$$x + 2y = -1,$$

for solvability.

*Solution.* These equations are of the form (1)–(2), and we easily find, from (4), that $\Delta_2 = 2 \cdot 2 - 1 \cdot (-3) = 7 \neq 0$. Hence the system has a unique solution. By the usual elimination procedure, we find the solution to be $x = 1$, $y = -1$; this result may be checked by plotting the two equations.

---

* Dependency here cannot mean simple equivalence, as in the case of two equations. In this chapter, we shall mean, by dependency, *linear dependency*, as follows. A set of $n$ equations, written symbolically $E_1 = 0$, $E_2 = 0$, $\cdots$, $E_n = 0$, is said to be linearly dependent if there exist quantities $Q_1$, $Q_2$, $\cdots$, $Q_n$, not all zero, such that $Q_1E_1 + Q_2E_2 + \cdots + Q_nE_n \equiv 0$. Thus, the equations $x - 2y + z = 0$, $2x + 3y - z + 1 = 0$, and $3x + 8y - 3z + 2 \equiv 0$ are linearly dependent since $(x - 2y + z) - 2(2x + 3y - z + 1) + (3x + 8y - 3z + 2) \equiv 0$.

*Example 2.* Examine the system

$$x - 3y - z = -1,$$
$$2x + y + 2z = 5,$$
$$3x - 2y + z = 7,$$

for solvability.

*Solution.* From expression (9), we find $\Delta_3 = 0$ for this system. Hence there cannot be a unique solution for the system. To determine whether the system has no solution or indefinitely many solutions, we may proceed as follows. We regard the first two equations as a system of the form (1)–(2) in the unknowns $x$ and $y$, and write them accordingly:

$$x - 3y = -1 + z,$$
$$2x + y = 5 - 2z.$$

For this pair, $\Delta_2 = 7$ by (4), and hence we may solve for $x$ and $y$ in terms of $z$. This gives us

$$x = \frac{14 - 5z}{7}, \qquad y = \frac{7 - 4z}{7}.$$

Substitution of these expressions into the left member of the third of the given equations yields

$$\frac{42 - 15z}{7} - \frac{14 - 8z}{7} + z \equiv 4,$$

which differs from the right member, 7. Consequently the system is incompatible—it has no solutions.

*Example 3.* Examine the system

$$x - 3y - z = -1,$$
$$2x + y + 2z = 5,$$
$$3x - 2y + z = 4,$$

for solvability.

*Solution.* This system differs from that of Example 2 only in that the right member of the third equation is now 4, instead of 7. As a consequence of our discussion of Example 2, it is immediately evident that $\Delta_3 = 0$ again, so that the present system does not possess a unique solution. But the expressions for $x$ and $y$ in terms of $z$, as found in Example 2, now satisfy the third equation identically. Therefore we have here a system with indefinitely many solutions. To find a set of solutions, we may arbitrarily take any value of $z$ and compute the corresponding values of $x = (14 - 5z)/7$ and $y = (7 - 4z)/7$. Thus, when $z = 0$, we have $x = 2$ and $y = 1$; when $z = 7$, we get $x = -3$, $y = -3$; and so on.

There are two reasons for our having considered systems of linear equations in such detail. On the one hand, we have shown how a complete analysis enables us to establish a definite criterion for the solvability of such a system. In addition, we have prepared the way for the consideration, in the following articles, of a new concept of wide applicability in connection with linear systems.

### EXERCISES

Examine each of the linear systems in Exercises 1–10 for solvability. If the given system has a unique solution, determine it; if there are indefinitely many solutions, determine two sets.

1. $2x + y = 4$, $3x - y = 1$.
2. $3x - 2y = 12$, $4x + y = 5$.
3. $2x - 3y = 1$, $8x - 12y = 7$.
4. $x + 4y = 6$, $2x + 8y = 12$.

5. $x + y - z = 0$, $x - y + 2z = 5$, $x - 2y - 3z = 1$.
6. $x + 2y - z = 3$, $2x + 3y + z = 5$, $x + y + 2z = 2$.
7. $3x - y + z = 4$, $x + 2y - z = -1$, $2x - 3y + 2z = -5$.
8. $x + 4y - z = 7$, $2x - y + 3z = -16$, $3x + 5y - 2z = 15$.
9. $6x + y = 0$, $2x + 3y - z = -8$, $4x - y + 5z = 5$.
10. $3x - y - z = 7$, $2y - x + 2z = 1$, $z - 2x + 3y = 10$.

11. Show that the system $2x - y + z = 3$, $x + y - 2z = -1$, $3x - 3y + 4z = k$ fails to possess a unique solution whatever the value of $k$, and find the value of $k$ for which the system becomes dependent.

12. Determine the value of $c$ for which the system $4x - 2y + z = 3$, $x - 3y - 2z = 5$, $2x + 4y + cz = -7$ becomes dependent, and find the corresponding solution for which $x = 2$.

13. The system $x - 3y + 2z = 0$, $3x - 2y - z = 0$, $ax - 4y + 3z = 0$ has the solution $x = 0$, $y = 0$, $z = 0$ for every value of $a$. Determine the value of $a$ for which the system is dependent, and find the corresponding solution in which $z = 1$.

14. It is found by experiment that temperature measured on the centigrade scale is a linear function of that measured on the Fahrenheit scale. If the freezing point for water is $0°$ C and $32°$ F, and the boiling point is $100°$ C and $212°$ F, find the functional relation between the two scales.

15. The sum of the ages of a man and his son is 38. Seven years from now the man will be three times as old as his son. Find the man's age.

16. One angle of a triangle is twice a second angle, and their sum is half the third angle. Determine the angles in degrees.

17. The sum of three numbers is 83. The third exceeds the sum of the first two by 15, and the sum of the last two exceeds the first by 69. Find the numbers.

18. The sum of the three digits of a number is 14. If the hundreds' and tens' digits are interchanged, the resulting number exceeds the original number by 270, and if the units' and hundreds' digits are interchanged, the resulting number is 198 more than the original. Find the number.

19. The perimeter of an isosceles trapezoid is 38. The sum of the two bases exceeds the sum of the two non-parallel sides by 18, and the difference between the bases is 8. Find the altitude of the trapezoid.

**20.** If $x$ and $y$ are angles in a triangle such that $2 \sin (x - y) = 1$ and $2 \cos (x + y) = 1$, find $x$ and $y$.

**21.** If the sides of a rectangle are each increased by an amount $a$, the area is increased by an amount $b$; if the sides are each decreased by an amount $c$, the area is decreased by $d$. Show that this problem has no solution unless $bc - ad = ac(a + c)$, and that there are indefinitely many solutions when this relation holds.

**22.** Three numbers are such that, when each is subtracted from the average of the other two, the numbers 7, 29, and $-36$ are respectively obtained. Show that this problem has indefinitely many solutions represented by $x$, $x - \frac{44}{3}$, and $x + \frac{86}{3}$, where $x$ is any number.

**23.** Generalize Exercise 22 to the case where the numbers $a$, $b$, and $c$ are to be obtained. Show that this problem has no solution unless $a + b + c = 0$, and that there are indefinitely many solutions when this relation holds.

**24.** If the digits of a three-digit number are reversed in order, the new number obtained is 99 more than the original one. When the units' digit of the original number is removed and placed before the others, the new number is 594 more than that obtained from it by reversing its digits. The sum of the digits of the original number is 14. Find the number.

**25.** There are two brothers, A and B. When A was the age B is now, he was three times as old as B was at that time. When B becomes the age A is now, he will be $K$ times A's age then. Show that this problem has no solution unless $K = \frac{5}{7}$, but that there are indefinitely many solutions for this value of $K$.

## 29. Determinants of second and third order.

The criterion found in Art. 28 for the solvability of a system of two linear equations depends upon the coefficients $a_1$, $b_1$, $a_2$, and $b_2$ in the system (1)–(2). We may exhibit the four coefficients, which determine the character of the system, in a square array, giving them just the positions they have relative to one another in the system, and we enclose this array in vertical bars to denote symbolically their characterizing role for the system:

$$\begin{vmatrix} a_1 & b_1 \\ a_2 & b_2 \end{vmatrix} \tag{1}$$

Such a symbol is called a **determinant;** since it contains two rows and two columns, it is said to be of the **second order.** The four quantities constituting the array are the **elements** of the determinant. The **principal diagonal** is that running from upper left to lower right, containing the elements $a_1$ and $b_2$.

The **value** of determinant (1) is defined as the product of the elements in the principal diagonal, minus the product of the elements in the other diagonal. Hence the quantity $\Delta_2$ associated with the linear system (1)–(2) of Art. 28 is given by the value of determinant (1):

$$\Delta_2 \equiv \begin{vmatrix} a_1 & b_1 \\ a_2 & b_2 \end{vmatrix} \equiv a_1 b_2 - a_2 b_1. \tag{2}$$

For this reason, $\Delta_2$ is referred to as the **determinant of the system.**

We found in Art. 28 that, when $\Delta_2 \neq 0$, the solution of the linear system

$$a_1 x + b_1 y = k_1, \tag{3}$$

$$a_2 x + b_2 y = k_2, \tag{4}$$

is given by

$$\Delta_2 x = b_2 k_1 - b_1 k_2, \qquad \Delta_2 y = a_1 k_2 - a_2 k_1.$$

Now each of these right members is, like $\Delta_2$, the difference of two products. Consequently the solutions may be written in determinant form as

$$\Delta_2 x = \begin{vmatrix} k_1 & b_1 \\ k_2 & b_2 \end{vmatrix}, \qquad \Delta_2 y = \begin{vmatrix} a_1 & k_1 \\ a_2 & k_2 \end{vmatrix}. \tag{5}$$

We then see that each of the unknowns $x$ and $y$ is given by the quotient of two determinants, $\Delta_2$ being the common denominator, and that the numerator in each expression is the determinant obtained from $\Delta_2$ by respectively replacing the coefficients ($a_1$ and $a_2$ for $x$, $b_1$ and $b_2$ for $y$) by the constant right members of the system (3)–(4).

*Example 1.* Using determinants, solve the system

$$3x - y = 2,$$

$$2x + 7y = 5.$$

*Solution.* We first evaluate the determinant of the system. This is the proper first step for two reasons: (1) if $\Delta_2 = 0$, we know immediately that our system does not possess a unique solution, and there is no need to proceed further; (2) if $\Delta_2 \neq 0$, its value is required to complete the solution. Here we have

$$\Delta_2 = \begin{vmatrix} 3 & -1 \\ 2 & 7 \end{vmatrix} = 3 \cdot 7 - (-1) \cdot 2 = 23.$$

Since $\Delta_2 \neq 0$, we proceed as follows. The numerator in the expression for $x$ is obtained from $\Delta_2$ by replacing the coefficients of $x$, namely, 3 and 2, respectively by the right members, 2 and 5. Then

$$\Delta_2 x = 23x = \begin{vmatrix} 2 & -1 \\ 5 & 7 \end{vmatrix} = 14 + 5 = 19,$$

whence

$$x = \tfrac{19}{23}.$$

Similarly, replacing the coefficients of $y$, $-1$ and 7, by 2 and 5 respectively, we get for $y$

$$\Delta_2 y = 23y = \begin{vmatrix} 3 & 2 \\ 2 & 5 \end{vmatrix} = 15 - 4 = 11,$$

and therefore

$$y = \tfrac{11}{23}.$$

When solving a linear system in two variables by means of determinants, it is important that the equations be written in type form (3)–(4); that is, the order $x$, $y$ should be the same in both equations, and the constant terms should constitute the right members.

Consider now a linear system of three equations in three variables:

$$a_1x + b_1y + c_1z = k_1, \tag{6}$$

$$a_2x + b_2y + c_2z = k_2, \tag{7}$$

$$a_3x + b_3y + c_3z = k_3. \tag{8}$$

The square array made up of the coefficients

$$\begin{vmatrix} a_1 & b_1 & c_1 \\ a_2 & b_2 & c_2 \\ a_3 & b_3 & c_3 \end{vmatrix} \tag{9}$$

is called a **determinant of the third order**. The nine quantities in this symbol are the **elements**, and the diagonal from upper left to lower right, containing $a_1$, $b_2$, and $c_3$, is the **principal diagonal**.

The **value** of the determinant (9) is defined to be the expression $\Delta_3$ as given by (9), Art. 28. A convenient way of getting this value in a particular case is as follows. To the right of the determinant, rewrite the first two columns as they appear in the determinant:

$$\begin{vmatrix} a_1 & b_1 & c_1 \\ a_2 & b_2 & c_2 \\ a_3 & b_3 & c_3 \end{vmatrix} \begin{matrix} a_1 & b_1 \\ a_2 & b_2 \\ a_3 & b_3 \end{matrix}.$$

Now compute the product of the elements in the principal diagonal and the respective products of the elements in the next two diagonals running downward to the right, and take their algebraic sum: $a_1b_2c_3 + a_3b_1c_2 + a_2b_3c_1$. Then compute the respective products for the three diagonals running upward to the right, and find their algebraic sum: $a_3b_2c_1 + a_1b_3c_2 + a_2b_1c_3$. Finally, subtract the latter sum from the former one:

$$\Delta_3 \equiv a_1b_2c_3 + a_3b_1c_2 + a_2b_3c_1 - a_3b_2c_1 - a_1b_3c_2 - a_2b_1c_3. \tag{10}$$

Examination of the solution for $x$, $y$, and $z$ of the system (6)–(8), as given by equations (10)–(12) in Art. 28, shows that each unknown is expressible as the quotient of two determinants, the denominator being $\Delta_3$, the determinant of the system, for each unknown. Moreover, each of the respective numerators is obtainable from $\Delta_3$ by replacing the coefficients of the variable in question by the right members, as the student may readily verify:

$$\Delta_3 x = \begin{vmatrix} k_1 & b_1 & c_1 \\ k_2 & b_2 & c_2 \\ k_3 & b_3 & c_3 \end{vmatrix}, \quad \Delta_3 y = \begin{vmatrix} a_1 & k_1 & c_1 \\ a_2 & k_2 & c_2 \\ a_3 & k_3 & c_3 \end{vmatrix}, \quad \Delta_3 z = \begin{vmatrix} a_1 & b_1 & k_1 \\ a_2 & b_2 & k_2 \\ a_3 & b_3 & k_3 \end{vmatrix}. \quad (11)$$

Thus, the solution of a linear system of three equations in three variables may be found by means of determinants, and the rule for the formation of the determinants is exactly analogous to that given for a system of two linear equations in two variables.

*Example 2.*   Using determinants, solve the system

$$2x - y - 2z = 4,$$
$$x + 3y - z = -1,$$
$$x + 2y + 3z = 5.$$

*Solution.*   The determinant of the system is

$$\Delta_3 = \begin{vmatrix} 2 & -1 & -2 \\ 1 & 3 & -1 \\ 1 & 2 & 3 \end{vmatrix} = 18 + 1 - 4 + 6 + 4 + 3 = 28.$$

Since $\Delta_3 \neq 0$, the system possesses a unique solution.   Then we get, by application of the rule stated above,

$$\Delta_3 x = \begin{vmatrix} 4 & -1 & -2 \\ -1 & 3 & -1 \\ 5 & 2 & 3 \end{vmatrix} = 36 + 5 + 4 + 30 + 8 - 3 = 80,$$

$$\Delta_3 y = \begin{vmatrix} 2 & 4 & -2 \\ 1 & -1 & -1 \\ 1 & 5 & 3 \end{vmatrix} = -6 - 4 - 10 - 2 + 10 - 12 = -24,$$

$$\Delta_3 z = \begin{vmatrix} 2 & -1 & 4 \\ 1 & 3 & -1 \\ 1 & 2 & 5 \end{vmatrix} = 30 + 1 + 8 - 12 + 4 + 5 = 36,$$

whence

$$x = \tfrac{80}{28} = \tfrac{20}{7}, \quad y = -\tfrac{24}{28} = -\tfrac{6}{7}, \quad z = \tfrac{36}{28} = \tfrac{9}{7}.$$

That this solution satisfies the given system of equations is readily verified.

**EXERCISES**

Using determinants, solve each of the following systems of equations.

**1.** $5x + 2y = 7$,   $6x - 5y = 38$.

**2.** $4x - 3y = 12$,   $9x - 5y = 13$.

**3.** $x^2 + 2y^2 = 22$,   $3x^2 - y^2 = 3$.

**4.** $\dfrac{4}{x+2} + \dfrac{3}{y+1} = -1$,   $\dfrac{6}{x+2} - \dfrac{6}{y+1} = -5$.

**5.** $4x + 5y = 7xy$,   $2x - 7y = -6xy$.

**6.** $x - y + 2z = 4$,   $2x + 3y - z = 3$,   $3x + y + 4z = 6$.

**7.** $2x + y + z - 6 = 0$,   $4x - 3y + 2z + 3 = 0$,   $x + y + 2z = 0$.

**8.** $x - 2y = 8$,   $2y - 5z = -5$,   $z - 4x = 7$.

**9.** $3x + y - z = 2$,   $x + y = 3$,   $x^2 - y^2 = -3$.

**10.** $4xy - 3xz + yz = 0$,   $7xy - 3xz + 5yz = xyz$,   $3xy - xz - 2yz = -4xyz$.

**30. Determinants of order $n$.** Generalizing the definitions given in Art. 29 for determinants of the second and third orders, we say that the symbol

$$\begin{vmatrix} a_1 & b_1 & c_1 \cdots h_1 \\ a_2 & b_2 & c_2 \cdots h_2 \\ a_3 & b_3 & c_3 \cdots h_3 \\ \cdot & \cdot & \cdot \\ a_n & b_n & c_n \cdots h_n \end{vmatrix}, \qquad (1)$$

which consists of a square array of $n$ rows and $n$ columns, where $n$ is any positive integer, is a **determinant of order $n$.** The $n^2$ quantities constituting this array are called the **elements,** and the diagonal running from upper left to lower right, containing the elements $a_1$, $b_2$, $c_3$, $\cdots$, $h_n$, is called the **principal diagonal.**

The value of determinant (1) might be defined in various ways. It is manifestly desirable, however, that our definition be framed to yield the value as a function of $n$ which is such that, when $n = 2$ or $n = 3$, the values then obtained coincide respectively with the values of $\Delta_2$ and $\Delta_3$ already stipulated in Art. 29. Accordingly, let us examine the expressions for $\Delta_2$ and $\Delta_3$:

$$\Delta_2 \equiv a_1b_2 - a_2b_1,$$

$$\Delta_3 \equiv a_1b_2c_3 + a_3b_1c_2 + a_2b_3c_1 - a_3b_2c_1 - a_1b_3c_2 - a_2b_1c_3.$$

In both expressions, we see that every product contains one element from each row and each column: in $\Delta_2$, each term contains one $a$ and one $b$, and in $\Delta_3$, each term contains one $a$, one $b$, and one $c$. With regard to the numerical subscripts on these letters, we see further that every possible order of the numbers is represented when the letters are written, as here, in their normal alphabetical order. For example, in $\Delta_3$, the first subscript may be any one of the three numbers 1, 2, 3; the second may be either of the remaining two; and the third will be the one still unselected. Thus we have $3 \cdot 2 \cdot 1 = 6$ possible orders, and all are represented in $\Delta_3$.

Hence we shall require that: (a) the expression for the value $\Delta_n$ of determinant (1) involve terms each of which is the product of $n$ elements, one from each row and each column; (b) when the letters $a$, $b$, $c$, $\cdots$, $h$ are written in alphabetical order, there shall be a term corresponding to every possible order of the subscripts. Since the first subscript (for $a$) may be any one of $n$ numbers, the next (for $b$) any one of the remaining $n - 1$ numbers, and so on, there will then be $n! = n(n - 1) \cdots 2 \cdot 1$ terms * in the expansion of $\Delta_n$.

We have still to formulate a suitable rule for the determination of the algebraic sign to be attached to each term. Now when the subscripts appear in ascending order, the term ($a_1 b_2$ in $\Delta_2$, $a_1 b_2 c_3$ in $\Delta_3$) is prefixed by a positive sign. With regard to other terms, let us consider the number of **inversions** of the subscripts, that is, the number of times a greater integer precedes a smaller one. For example, in the sequence 32451, there are five inversions: 3 before 2, 3 before 1, 2 before 1, 4 before 1, and 5 before 1. In the second term of $\Delta_2$, there is but one inversion, and this term has a negative sign attached to it. In the second, third, $\cdots$, sixth terms of $\Delta_3$ there are respectively 2, 2, 3, 1, and 1 inversions. Thus, we see that positively signed terms have no or an even number of inversions of the subscripts, whereas negatively signed terms have an odd number of inversions of the subscripts.

We therefore use this concept of inversions as the criterion for the choice of sign attached to each term in the expansion of $\Delta_n$. Combining all the above ideas, we may then give the following general definition, which, for $n = 2$ and for $n = 3$, is consistent with the definitions of Art. 29:

The **value** $\Delta_n$ of determinant (1) is the algebraic sum of $n!$ distinct terms. Each term is the product of $n$ elements, one from each row and each column. The sign attached to each term is plus or minus according as the number of inversions of the subscripts is even (or zero) or odd.

This definition is evidently not a convenient rule for determining the value of a determinant. We shall consider a practical method for evaluating a given determinant later in this article, after we have established

* The symbol $n!$, read "factorial $n$," denotes, as indicated, the product of the positive integers from 1 to $n$. Thus, $1! = 1$, $2! = 1 \cdot 2 = 2$, $3! = 1 \cdot 2 \cdot 3 = 6$, etc. The symbol $\lfloor n$ is also used to denote factorial $n$. Evidently $n! = n \cdot (n - 1)!$.

some of the fundamental properties of determinants. At this point, however, it is important to note that, when $n > 3$, the value of a determinant can *not* be obtained by a "diagonal scheme" such as that employed in Art. 29 for determinants of the second and third orders. This is easily seen for $n = 4$, when the diagonal scheme yields only eight of the 4! = 24 terms actually in the expansion.

We consider now a few properties of determinant (1). Our notation has been such that the successive columns have been distinguished by letters alphabetically arranged, while the successive rows are indicated by numerical subscripts in ascending order. Every term in the expression for $\Delta_n$ involves, by definition, each letter once and each subscript once, and when the letters are in proper order the sign before a term is chosen in accordance with the number of inversions of the subscripts. Now suppose that we form a determinant $\Delta_n'$ whose rows and columns are respectively the corresponding columns and rows of $\Delta_n$. Again, every term in $\Delta_n'$ will contain each letter and each subscript once; and, if we arrange the subscripts in ascending order, the sign before a term will depend upon the number of inversions in the order of the letters in that term. Hence this interchange of rows and columns serves merely to change the notation—letters play the role of subscripts in inversion computations when numbers instead of letters are left in their normal order. Consequently the value $\Delta_n'$ will be identical with the value $\Delta_n$ of the original determinant (1), and we have, as one property of a determinant of order $n$:

I. *If the corresponding rows and columns of a determinant are interchanged, the value of the determinant remains unaltered.*

For example, we have

$$
\begin{vmatrix} a_1 & a_2 & a_3 \\ b_1 & b_2 & b_3 \\ c_1 & c_2 & c_3 \end{vmatrix} \equiv \begin{vmatrix} a_1 & b_1 & c_1 \\ a_2 & b_2 & c_2 \\ a_3 & b_3 & c_3 \end{vmatrix},
$$

as may readily be verified by evaluating each determinant by the method explained in Art. 29.

As a consequence of property I, any additional properties involving a statement regarding rows and columns will automatically become true when the words "row" and "column" are interchanged, so that a proof need be given only on the one basis.

Next suppose that two adjacent rows are interchanged. In the expansion of the new determinant so formed, the subscripts corresponding to the two rows in question will then be interchanged, and consequently the number of inversions in each term will be either increased or decreased by 1. Hence the sign of each term, and therefore of the determinant value, will be changed. Now suppose that, starting with determinant (1), any two rows are interchanged. If there were $r$ rows between the two involved, the interchange could be effected by first bringing the lower row just under the upper one by $r$ interchanges of adjacent rows, and then by bringing the upper row into the original position of the lower one by $r + 1$ additional interchanges of adjacent rows. Hence there would be $2r + 1$ interchanges all together, each entailing a change of sign, and since $2r + 1$ is an odd integer, the resulting sign would be changed. This result, together with property I, gives us

II. *If two rows, or two columns, of a determinant are interchanged, the value of the determinant is changed in sign.*

For example, we have, as is easily checked:

$$\begin{vmatrix} c_1 & b_1 & a_1 \\ c_2 & b_2 & a_2 \\ c_3 & b_3 & a_3 \end{vmatrix} \equiv - \begin{vmatrix} a_1 & b_1 & c_1 \\ a_2 & b_2 & c_2 \\ a_3 & b_3 & c_3 \end{vmatrix}.$$

III. *If two rows, or columns, of a determinant are identical, element for element, the value of the determinant is zero.*

For, when the two identical rows, say, are interchanged, the value changes from $\Delta_n$ to $-\Delta_n$, by II. But since such an interchange leaves the determinant actually unaltered, we must have $\Delta_n = -\Delta_n$, whence $\Delta_n = 0$. For example,

$$\begin{vmatrix} a_1 & b_1 & c_1 \\ a_2 & b_2 & c_2 \\ a_1 & b_1 & c_1 \end{vmatrix} \equiv 0.$$

IV. *If each element of a row (or column) in a determinant is multiplied by the same number $p$, the new determinant has a value $p$ times that of the original.*

For, since one and only one element from the row in question appears in each term of the expansion, every term, and therefore their algebraic sum, is multiplied by $p$ by the stated process. Thus, we have

$$\begin{vmatrix} a_1 & pb_1 & c_1 \\ a_2 & pb_2 & c_2 \\ a_3 & pb_3 & c_3 \end{vmatrix} \equiv p \begin{vmatrix} a_1 & b_1 & c_1 \\ a_2 & b_2 & c_2 \\ a_3 & b_3 & c_3 \end{vmatrix}.$$

As a corollary to theorem IV, we have:

*A quantity that is a factor of each element of a row or of a column is a factor of the expansion of the determinant.*

V. *If each element in a particular row (or column) is expressible as the sum of two terms, the determinant may be expressed as the sum of two determinants.*

For, every term in the expansion contains one and only one of these sums, and therefore the algebraic sum of the $n!$ terms is expressible as the sum of two such expansions, each of which represents the value of a determinant. For example,

$$
\begin{vmatrix} a_1 + a_1' & b_1 & c_1 \\ a_2 + a_2' & b_2 & c_2 \\ a_3 + a_3' & b_3 & c_3 \end{vmatrix} \equiv \begin{vmatrix} a_1 & b_1 & c_1 \\ a_2 & b_2 & c_2 \\ a_3 & b_3 & c_3 \end{vmatrix} + \begin{vmatrix} a_1' & b_1 & c_1 \\ a_2' & b_2 & c_2 \\ a_3' & b_3 & c_3 \end{vmatrix} .
$$

VI. *If each element of any row (or column) is multiplied by the same number $p$ and then added to the corresponding element of another row (or column), the value of the new determinant is the same as that of the original.*

This property follows directly from V, IV, and III. For example, we have

$$
\begin{vmatrix} a_1 + pc_1 & b_1 & c_1 \\ a_2 + pc_2 & b_2 & c_2 \\ a_3 + pc_3 & b_3 & c_3 \end{vmatrix} \equiv \begin{vmatrix} a_1 & b_1 & c_1 \\ a_2 & b_2 & c_2 \\ a_3 & b_3 & c_3 \end{vmatrix} + \begin{vmatrix} pc_1 & b_1 & c_1 \\ pc_2 & b_2 & c_2 \\ pc_3 & b_3 & c_3 \end{vmatrix}
$$

$$
\equiv \begin{vmatrix} a_1 & b_1 & c_1 \\ a_2 & b_2 & c_2 \\ a_3 & b_3 & c_3 \end{vmatrix} + p \begin{vmatrix} c_1 & b_1 & c_1 \\ c_2 & b_2 & c_2 \\ c_3 & b_3 & c_3 \end{vmatrix} \equiv \begin{vmatrix} a_1 & b_1 & c_1 \\ a_2 & b_2 & c_2 \\ a_3 & b_3 & c_3 \end{vmatrix} .
$$

It should be particularly noted that, when applying VI, the row (or column) whose elements are multiplied by $p$ is left intact, and it is the row (column) to which the products are added, element for element, that is replaced by the corresponding sums.

We consider now a method, called **development by minors,** for evaluating a determinant of order $n$. By the **minor** of any element is meant the determinant of order $n - 1$ obtained by deleting the row and column in which the element in question lies. For example, the minor of $b_3$ in the determinant of third order,

$$\begin{vmatrix} a_1 & b_1 & c_1 \\ a_2 & b_2 & c_2 \\ a_3 & b_3 & c_3 \end{vmatrix},$$

is the determinant

$$\begin{vmatrix} a_1 & c_1 \\ a_2 & c_2 \end{vmatrix}$$

of second order obtained by deleting the third row and second column, in which $b_3$ lies. We shall denote the minor of a given element by the corresponding capital letter; thus, the minor of $b_3$ is symbolized as $B_3$. The value of a determinant can be found by means of the following theorem.

VII. *Choose any row or column in terms of which to develop by minors. Form the n products of an element by its minor, and give to each product a plus or minus sign according as the sum of the number of row and number of column in which the corresponding element lies is even or odd. The algebraic sum of the n terms thereby obtained is the value* $\Delta_n$ *of the determinant.*

As an illustration, we have, if we arbitrarily choose the second column for our development,

$$\begin{vmatrix} a_1 & b_1 & c_1 \\ a_2 & b_2 & c_2 \\ a_3 & b_3 & c_3 \end{vmatrix} \equiv -b_1 \begin{vmatrix} a_2 & c_2 \\ a_3 & c_3 \end{vmatrix} + b_2 \begin{vmatrix} a_1 & c_1 \\ a_3 & c_3 \end{vmatrix} - b_3 \begin{vmatrix} a_1 & c_1 \\ a_2 & c_2 \end{vmatrix}.$$

We may prove this theorem by the following argument. In the first place, we note that the total coefficient of the element $a_1$ in the expansion of determinant (1) is the minor $A_1$ of $a_1$. For, $A_1$ is a determinant of order $n - 1$ in the $b$'s, $c$'s, $\cdots$, $h$'s with the subscripts 2, 3, $\cdots$, $n$, the expansion of which involves the $(n - 1)!$ terms obtained from all possible arrangements of the subscripts, and the signs of these terms are all correct since the number of inversions is not changed by prefixing $a_1$. Now an element in row $j$ and column $k$ can be brought into the leading positions, normally occupied by $a_1$, by $j - 1$ interchanges of adjacent rows followed by $k - 1$ interchanges of adjacent columns. The new determinant so obtained then has the value $\Delta'_n = (-1)^{j+k-2}\Delta_n = (-1)^{j+k}\Delta_n$, by property II. Combining this result with the foregoing, we see that the coefficient of any particular element in the expansion of $\Delta_n$ is $(-1)^{j+k}$

times the product of that element and its minor, whence VII follows, for, if $j + k$ is even, $(-1)^{j+k} = 1$, and if $j + k$ is odd, $(-1)^{j+k} = -1$.

Property VII therefore provides a means of evaluating a determinant by successive stages. The development by minors of a determinant of order $n$ gives $n$ terms, each of which contains a determinant of order $n - 1$; each of these may in turn be evaluated by development by minors, yielding determinants of order $n - 2$; and so on. The judicious use of property VI will be of considerable practical aid in reducing the amount of labor necessary, as illustrated in the following example.

*Example.* Evaluate the determinant

$$\begin{vmatrix} 2 & 1 & 3 & 0 \\ 1 & 2 & 1 & 2 \\ -1 & 0 & 4 & -1 \\ 3 & -1 & -2 & 3 \end{vmatrix}.$$

*Solution.* We first note the presence of two zero elements. Evidently it is desirable to have as many zeros as possible in the row or column taken for development by minors, since it will then not be necessary to evaluate the minors of such elements—the product of the zero element and its minor must be zero. Accordingly, we apply VI to introduce additional zero elements.

We may advantageously decide to develop by minors with respect to the third row, since this contains not only a zero element but also two elements equal to $-1$. In order to introduce the additional desired zeros, we multiply the elements of the first column by 4 and add to the corresponding elements of the third column; at the same time, we subtract the elements of our basic column 1 from the corresponding elements of column 4. Then the new equivalent determinant is

$$\begin{vmatrix} 2 & 1 & 11 & -2 \\ 1 & 2 & 5 & 1 \\ -1 & 0 & 0 & 0 \\ 3 & -1 & 10 & 0 \end{vmatrix}.$$

We now develop with respect to the third row. Since $-1$ is in the third row and first column, so that $j + k = 3 + 1 = 4$ is even, VII yields the expansion

$$-1 \cdot \begin{vmatrix} 1 & 11 & -2 \\ 2 & 5 & 1 \\ -1 & 10 & 0 \end{vmatrix} - 0 \cdot \begin{vmatrix} 2 & 11 & -2 \\ 1 & 5 & 1 \\ 3 & 10 & 0 \end{vmatrix} + 0 \cdot \begin{vmatrix} 2 & 1 & -2 \\ 1 & 2 & 1 \\ 3 & -1 & 0 \end{vmatrix} - 0 \cdot \begin{vmatrix} 2 & 1 & 11 \\ 1 & 2 & 5 \\ 3 & -1 & 10 \end{vmatrix}.$$

Consequently only one third order determinant need be evaluated. This can be done as shown in Art. 29, but, to illustrate the present methods more fully, we continue as follows. We multiply the elements of the second row by 2 and add to the corresponding elements of the first row; the new determinant, multiplied by $-1$ as required, is then

$$-\begin{vmatrix} 5 & 21 & 0 \\ 2 & 5 & 1 \\ -1 & 10 & 0 \end{vmatrix}.$$

Developing by minors with respect to the third column, we get, since two minors have zero coefficients, merely

$$-(-1)\begin{vmatrix} 5 & 21 \\ -1 & 10 \end{vmatrix}.$$

This second-order determinant is easily evaluated by the method of Art. 29; we get finally, as the value of the original fourth-order determinant,

$$5\cdot 10 - (-1)\cdot 21 = 71.$$

Before proceeding with the applications of determinants to the solution of linear systems, we establish one more property that will be of use later.

VIII. *In the development by minors with respect to a certain row (or column), if the elements of that row (or column) are replaced by the corresponding elements of another row (or column), the resulting expression is equal to zero.*

This is an immediate consequence of III, for the expression obtained as stipulated is just that resulting from the replacement of the original row (or column) by the elements of some other row, giving us a determinant with two like rows (or columns), and hence one of value zero. For example, if we take

$$\begin{vmatrix} a_1 & b_1 & c_1 \\ a_2 & b_2 & c_2 \\ a_3 & b_3 & c_3 \end{vmatrix} \equiv -b_1\begin{vmatrix} a_2 & c_2 \\ a_3 & c_3 \end{vmatrix} + b_2\begin{vmatrix} a_1 & c_1 \\ a_3 & c_3 \end{vmatrix} - b_3\begin{vmatrix} a_1 & c_1 \\ a_2 & c_2 \end{vmatrix},$$

and replace the $b$'s by, say, the $c$'s, we have

$$-c_1\begin{vmatrix} a_2 & c_2 \\ a_3 & c_3 \end{vmatrix} + c_2\begin{vmatrix} a_1 & c_1 \\ a_3 & c_3 \end{vmatrix} - c_3\begin{vmatrix} a_1 & c_1 \\ a_2 & c_2 \end{vmatrix} \equiv \begin{vmatrix} a_1 & c_1 & c_1 \\ a_2 & c_2 & c_2 \\ a_3 & c_3 & c_3 \end{vmatrix} \equiv 0.$$

## EXERCISES

Evaluate each of the determinants in Exercises 1–6.

**1.** $\begin{vmatrix} 1 & -1 & 2 & 1 \\ 2 & 1 & -1 & 2 \\ 1 & 1 & 2 & 2 \\ 0 & 2 & 1 & -1 \end{vmatrix}$.

**2.** $\begin{vmatrix} 3 & 1 & -1 & 2 \\ 0 & 2 & -2 & -1 \\ 2 & 4 & 1 & 2 \\ -1 & 3 & 2 & 1 \end{vmatrix}$.

**3.** $\begin{vmatrix} -2 & 3 & 5 & 1 \\ 3 & 4 & -2 & -2 \\ 4 & 1 & 1 & 3 \\ 2 & -2 & 3 & 1 \end{vmatrix}$.

**4.** $\begin{vmatrix} 3 & -1 & -2 & -4 \\ 5 & 2 & 3 & -1 \\ 2 & 1 & -6 & 3 \\ -3 & 3 & 1 & -2 \end{vmatrix}$.

**5.** $\begin{vmatrix} 0 & 1 & -1 & 1 & 0 \\ 1 & 0 & 0 & 0 & 1 \\ 0 & -1 & 0 & 1 & 0 \\ 1 & 0 & -1 & 0 & 1 \\ 0 & 1 & 0 & -1 & 0 \end{vmatrix}$.

**6.** $\begin{vmatrix} 1 & 0 & 2 & 0 & 1 \\ 1 & -1 & 0 & -1 & 1 \\ 0 & 1 & 2 & 1 & 0 \\ 1 & 2 & 0 & -2 & -1 \\ -2 & -1 & 0 & 1 & 2 \end{vmatrix}$.

**7.** Use property VI to introduce zeros into the first column of the determinant

$$\begin{vmatrix} 1 & a & a^2 \\ 1 & b & b^2 \\ 1 & c & c^2 \end{vmatrix}.$$

Then apply the corollary to theorem IV, and show that the value of this determinant can be written in factored form as $(c - b)(c - a)(b - a)$.

Using the method of Exercise **7**, obtain the expansion, in factored form, of the determinants in Exercises 8 and 9.

**8.** $\begin{vmatrix} 1 & 1 & 1 \\ a & a^2 & a^3 \\ b & b^2 & b^3 \end{vmatrix}$

**9.** $\begin{vmatrix} a & b & c \\ a^3 & b^3 & c^3 \\ a^5 & b^5 & c^5 \end{vmatrix}$.

**10.** If $a^3 + b^3 + c^3 \neq 3abc$, show that $x = 0$ is the only solution of the equation

$$\begin{vmatrix} x & a & b & c \\ x & b & c & a \\ x & c & a & b \\ 0 & a & b & c \end{vmatrix} = 0.$$

**31. Non-homogeneous systems.** It was found in Art. 29 that determinants of the second and third orders can be used to solve linear systems of equations. Now that we have a general definition and some fundamental properties of determinants of any order $n$, it is natural to ask the question: Can determinants be used to solve a system of $n$ linear equations in $n$ variables when $n$ is an integer greater than 3?

This question can be answered in the affirmative, subject only to the restriction that the determinant of the system, composed of the coefficients of the variables as in the special cases of $n = 2$ and $n = 3$, be different from zero. To show this, and to indicate the method of solution, we shall for simplicity and brevity consider the case where $n = 4$, but the argument used here will clearly apply to the cases where $n > 4$ also.

Consider, then, the linear system

$$a_1x + b_1y + c_1z + d_1w = k_1, \tag{1}$$

$$a_2x + b_2y + c_2z + d_2w = k_2, \tag{2}$$

$$a_3x + b_3y + c_3z + d_3w = k_3, \tag{3}$$

$$a_4x + b_4y + c_4z + d_4w = k_4. \tag{4}$$

We suppose that the determinant of the system (1)–(4) is not zero:

$$\Delta_4 \equiv \begin{vmatrix} a_1 & b_1 & c_1 & d_1 \\ a_2 & b_2 & c_2 & d_2 \\ a_3 & b_3 & c_3 & d_3 \\ a_4 & b_4 & c_4 & d_4 \end{vmatrix} \neq 0. \tag{5}$$

We denote the minor of an element of $\Delta_4$ by the corresponding capital letter, as in Art. 30. If we multiply the two members of each of equations (1)–(4) respectively by $A_1$, $-A_2$, $A_3$, and $-A_4$, we get

$$a_1A_1x + b_1A_1y + c_1A_1z + d_1A_1w = k_1A_1, \tag{6}$$

$$-a_2A_2x - b_2A_2y - c_2A_2z - d_2A_2w = -k_2A_2, \tag{7}$$

$$a_3A_3x + b_3A_3y + c_3A_3z + d_3A_3w = k_3A_3, \tag{8}$$

$$-a_4A_4x - b_4A_4y - c_4A_4z - d_4A_4w = -k_4A_4. \tag{9}$$

Now, if we add the corresponding members of these four equations, we find that the coefficient of $x$ is $\Delta_4$ (property VII, Art. 30), while all the coefficients of $y$, $z$, and $w$ are zero (property VIII, Art. 30). Moreover, the sum of the right members of (6)–(9) is the expansion of the determinant derived from (5) when the coefficients of $x$ are replaced by the corresponding $k$'s.  Hence we have

$$\Delta_4 x = \begin{vmatrix} k_1 & b_1 & c_1 & d_1 \\ k_2 & b_2 & c_2 & d_2 \\ k_3 & b_3 & c_3 & d_3 \\ k_4 & b_4 & c_4 & d_4 \end{vmatrix}. \tag{10}$$

Similarly, if we operate on equations (1)–(4) with the $B$'s, $C$'s, and $D$'s in turn, instead of the $A$'s, we find

$$\Delta_4 y = \begin{vmatrix} a_1 & k_1 & c_1 & d_1 \\ a_2 & k_2 & c_2 & d_2 \\ a_3 & k_3 & c_3 & d_3 \\ a_4 & k_4 & c_4 & d_4 \end{vmatrix}, \tag{11}$$

$$\Delta_4 z = \begin{vmatrix} a_1 & b_1 & k_1 & d_1 \\ a_2 & b_2 & k_2 & d_2 \\ a_3 & b_3 & k_3 & d_3 \\ a_4 & b_4 & k_4 & d_4 \end{vmatrix}, \tag{12}$$

$$\Delta_4 w = \begin{vmatrix} a_1 & b_1 & c_1 & k_1 \\ a_2 & b_2 & c_2 & k_2 \\ a_3 & b_3 & c_3 & k_3 \\ a_4 & b_4 & c_4 & k_4 \end{vmatrix}. \tag{13}$$

Since, by hypothesis, $\Delta_4 \neq 0$, equations (10)–(13) yield a solution of system (1)–(4).

As stated above, the same type of reasoning will apply to a system of $n$ linear equations in $n$ variables, and we therefore have the following general rule for solving such a system, provided only that the determinant $\Delta_n$ of the system is not zero:

*The value of each variable, in the solution of a linear system, is given by the quotient of two determinants. For each unknown, the denominator of the quotient is the determinant $\Delta_n$ of the system, by hypothesis different from zero, and the numerator is the determinant obtained from $\Delta_n$ by replacing the coefficients of the variable in question respectively by the constant terms in the right members of the system.*

It can be shown that, when $\Delta_n \neq 0$, the solution obtained by the process described is unique.  When $\Delta_n = 0$, the system may have either no solution or indefinitely many solutions, according as the equations of the system are incompatible or dependent (Art. 28).

When every equation of the system is homogeneous (Art. 21), we have a **homogeneous system,** but if at least one of the $k$'s is different from zero, the system is said to be non-homogeneous. Under the supposition that $\Delta_n \neq 0$, a homogeneous system will have as its solution a set of zeros, for, if all the $k$'s are zero, each numerator determinant will have a column of zeros, and development by minors with respect to that column will produce the value zero for the numerator, whence each variable has the value $0/\Delta_n = 0$.* Since every such homogeneous system, regardless of the values of the individual coefficients but provided only that $\Delta_n \neq 0$, has the solution $0, 0, \cdots, 0$, we say that this is a **trivial solution.**

On the other hand, not all the solution values for a non-homogeneous system can be zero, and the non-homogeneous system with $\Delta_n \neq 0$ therefore presents a definite problem for solution.

**32. Homogeneous systems.** We have already, in the preceding article, disposed of the case of a homogeneous system for which $\Delta_n \neq 0$ and which possesses only the trivial solution set of zeros. We now consider briefly the more interesting case of a homogeneous system for which $\Delta_n = 0$.

For definiteness and simplicity, consider a homogeneous system of three linear equations in three variables,

$$a_1x + b_1y + c_1z = 0, \tag{1}$$

$$a_2x + b_2y + c_2z = 0, \tag{2}$$

$$a_3x + b_3y + c_3z = 0, \tag{3}$$

for which the determinant of the system vanishes:

$$\Delta_3 \equiv \begin{vmatrix} a_1 & b_1 & c_1 \\ a_2 & b_2 & c_2 \\ a_3 & b_3 & c_3 \end{vmatrix} = 0. \tag{4}$$

We suppose further that not every minor of $\Delta_3$ is equal to zero. If $C_3 \equiv a_1b_2 - a_2b_1 \neq 0$, say, we may solve equations (1) and (2) simultaneously for $x$ and $y$ in terms of $z$; we get

$$C_3x = \begin{vmatrix} -c_1z & b_1 \\ -c_2z & b_2 \end{vmatrix} = -z \begin{vmatrix} c_1 & b_1 \\ c_2 & b_2 \end{vmatrix} = A_3z, \tag{5}$$

$$C_3y = \begin{vmatrix} a_1 & -c_1z \\ a_2 & -c_2z \end{vmatrix} = -z \begin{vmatrix} a_1 & c_1 \\ a_2 & c_2 \end{vmatrix} = -B_3z. \tag{6}$$

---

* It is also apparent that each homogeneous equation in the homogeneous system will be satisfied identically when all the variables are set equal to zero.

When we substitute the expressions for $x$ and $y$ so obtained, in the left member of (3), we find

$$\frac{a_3 A_3 z}{C_3} - \frac{b_3 B_3 z}{C_3} + c_3 z = \frac{z}{C_3}(a_3 A_3 - b_3 \dot{B}_3 + c_3 C_3). \tag{7}$$

But the quantity in parentheses is the development of $\Delta_3$ by minors with respect to the third row, and, by (4), this expression must be zero. Hence the values of $x$ and $y$ obtained from equations (1) and (2) identically satisfy (3), whatever value may be assigned to $z$.

Similar reasoning may be applied to other homogeneous systems whose determinants are equal to zero. The general conclusion then reached may be stated as follows:

Let there be given a homogeneous system of $n$ linear equations in $n$ variables, for which $\Delta_n = 0$. If at least one minor of $\Delta_n$ is different from zero, it is possible to solve certain $n - 1$ equations of the system for $n - 1$ of the variables in terms of the remaining variable, and the expressions so obtained will satisfy the remaining equation identically. The single variable may be assigned a value at pleasure, and the corresponding values of the other $n - 1$ variables may then be determined. Thus the homogeneous system will have indefinitely many solutions, and the equations of the system are dependent.

*Example.* Examine for solvability the homogeneous system

$$x - 2y + z - w = 0,$$
$$x + y - 3z \qquad = 0,$$
$$2x + y \qquad + w = 0,$$
$$y + z + w = 0.$$

*Solution.* We readily find, for the determinant of the system,

$$\Delta_4 \equiv \begin{vmatrix} 1 & -2 & 1 & -1 \\ 1 & 1 & -3 & 0 \\ 2 & 1 & 0 & 1 \\ 0 & 1 & 1 & 1 \end{vmatrix} = 0.$$

By test, it is found that the minor of the element $d_4 = 1$ in the lower right corner of $\Delta_4$ is different from zero:

$$D_4 = \begin{vmatrix} 1 & -2 & 1 \\ 1 & 1 & -3 \\ 2 & 1 & 0 \end{vmatrix} = 14.$$

Hence it is possible to solve the first three equations for $x$, $y$, and $z$ in terms of $w$. There is found:

$$14x = \begin{vmatrix} w & -2 & 1 \\ 0 & 1 & -3 \\ -w & 1 & 0 \end{vmatrix} = -2w, \qquad x = -\frac{w}{7};$$

$$14y = \begin{vmatrix} 1 & w & 1 \\ 1 & 0 & -3 \\ 2 & -w & 0 \end{vmatrix} = -10w, \qquad y = -\frac{5w}{7};$$

$$14z = \begin{vmatrix} 1 & -2 & w \\ 1 & 1 & 0 \\ 2 & 1 & -w \end{vmatrix} = -4w, \qquad z = -\frac{2w}{7}.$$

The values of $x$, $y$, and $z$ so obtained are readily seen to satisfy the fourth equation. Hence the relations $x = -w/7$, $y = -5w/7$, $z = -2w/7$ furnish indefinitely many solutions of the given system. For example, if we wish an integral set, we may take $w = 7$, whence $x = -1$, $y = -5$, $z = -2$.

**33. Defective systems.** Up to this point we have been discussing linear systems for which the number of equations is equal to the number of variables. We now consider a system containing fewer equations than variables; since such a system lacks equations sufficient to yield the general case discussed in Art. 31, we shall call it a **defective system**.

Let there be given $n$ linear equations involving $m$ variables, and suppose that $n < m$. Let the coefficients of the $m$ variables in the $n$ equations be written down in a rectangular array of $n$ rows and $m$ columns. If there exists a non-zero determinant of order $n$ formed by taking $n$ of the $m$ columns from the array, it is possible to solve for the corresponding $n$ variables in terms of the remaining $m - n$ variables. The latter $m - n$ variables may be individually assigned values at pleasure, and the matching values of the former $n$ variables may then be computed.

*Example.*   Examine for solvability the system

$$x - 2y + z - w = 1,$$

$$2x + y + 2z - 2w = 3.$$

*Solution.*   The rectangular array for this system is

$$\begin{matrix} 1 & -2 & 1 & -1 \\ 2 & 1 & 2 & -2 \end{matrix}$$

Here all the determinants formed from the first and third columns, the first and fourth columns, and the third and fourth columns have the value zero, but the three other possible determinants have non-zero values. We choose the first two columns, and solve for $x$ and $y$; we get

$$\begin{vmatrix} 1 & -2 \\ 2 & 1 \end{vmatrix} x = 5x = \begin{vmatrix} 1 - z + w & -2 \\ 3 - 2z + 2w & 1 \end{vmatrix} = 7 - 5z + 5w,$$

$$5y = \begin{vmatrix} 1 & 1 - z + w \\ 2 & 3 - 2z + 2w \end{vmatrix} = 1.$$

Hence

$$x = \tfrac{7}{5} - z + w, \qquad y = \tfrac{1}{5}.$$

In this particular case, the expression for $y$ is a constant, so that $y = \tfrac{1}{5}$ for each choice of $z$ and $w$. However, values must be independently assigned to $z$ and $w$ in order that the corresponding $x$ may be evaluated.

**34. Redundant systems.** As opposed to the situation discussed in Art. 33, there is the case in which the number $n$ of equations exceeds the number $m$ of variables. Because there are more equations than are normally needed to solve the system, we call such a system **redundant.**

We have already considered one kind of redundant system in Art. 32. As we saw there, it is often possible to solve a homogeneous system for which $\Delta_n = 0$ for $n - 1$ variables in terms of the remaining variable by using $n - 1$ of the given equations. Then, the $n$th equation is linearly dependent upon the other $n - 1$, and hence is superfluous in the solving process, so that we have a redundancy.

Now suppose that we have a non-homogeneous system of $n$ equations in $m$ variables, where $n > m$. We form a rectangular array of $n$ rows and $m$ columns from the coefficients, as in Art. 33. Then if there exists a non-zero determinant of order $m$ formed by taking $m$ of the $n$ rows from the array, the corresponding $m$ equations may be solved for all the variables. If the solution so found satisfies each of the remaining $n - m$ equations, the redundant system is a consistent one; but if at least one of the $n - m$ equations fails to be satisfied by the values obtained as described, the given system is incompatible.

*Example.* Examine for solvability the system

$$x + 2y = 3,$$
$$2x + 5y = 8,$$
$$3x - y = -5,$$
$$x - 3y = 4.$$

*Solution.* It is easy to see that the first two equations may be solved for $x$ and $y;$ there is found

$$x = -1, \qquad y = 2.$$

Now the third of the given equations is satisfied by this value pair, but the fourth is not. Hence the redundant system has no solution; it is incompatible.

With regard to a consistent redundant system of $n$ equations containing one more equation than there are variables, something further may be said. Suppose the constant terms in the right members to be transposed to the left members and all to be multiplied by a new letter that will serve as an $n$th variable. The given system is thereby transformed into a homogeneous system of $n$ equations in $n$ variables. Now since the original system is, by hypothesis, consistent, it will possess a solution involving a non-zero value for at least one variable (Art. 31). Hence the new homogeneous system will have a non-trivial solution. But as this can occur only if the determinant of the system has the value zero, we have the following result:

*Let there be given a non-homogeneous redundant system of n equations in n − 1 variables. If this system is consistent, then the determinant of order n, whose first n − 1 columns are made up of the coefficients and whose nth column consists of the constant terms in the right members of the system, must have the value zero.*

As an illustration, consider the first three equations of the above example, involving two variables. These three equations were found to be consistent; the common solution is $x = -1$, $y = 2$. The determinant formed as described is here

$$\begin{vmatrix} 1 & 2 & 3 \\ 2 & 5 & 8 \\ 3 & -1 & -5 \end{vmatrix}.$$

That the value of this determinant is zero is readily verified.

The student should note that the converse of the preceding theorem is not necessarily true. That is, if the determinant of the coefficients and constant terms is zero, the redundant system may not be consistent. For instance, with regard to the system

$$2x - y = 3,$$
$$4x - 2y = 5,$$
$$8x - 4y = 7,$$

the determinant in question is easily seen to vanish, but no two of the three equations are consistent.

## EXERCISES

Using determinants, solve each of the linear systems in Exercises 1–8.

**1.**
$$\begin{aligned}
x + y \qquad\quad &= 1, \\
x \quad\; - z \quad\; &= 0, \\
y \qquad - w &= 1, \\
z + w &= 0.
\end{aligned}$$

**2.**
$$\begin{aligned}
x - y - z \qquad\quad &= 0, \\
y + z - w &= 3, \\
x \qquad - z - w &= 4, \\
x + y \qquad\; + w &= 1.
\end{aligned}$$

**3.**
$$\begin{aligned}
2x \qquad\quad - z \qquad\quad &= 1, \\
x - y - z \qquad\quad &= -1, \\
2y + z - w &= 0, \\
x - 3y - 2z + 2w &= 2.
\end{aligned}$$

**4.**
$$\begin{aligned}
5x - 3y + 2z - w &= 0, \\
x + 4y + 3z - 2w &= -5, \\
2x + y - 4z - 5w &= 12, \\
-x - y + 5z + 3w &= -15.
\end{aligned}$$

**5.**
$$\begin{aligned}
2x - 2y - 4z + w &= 1, \\
x + y - 3z + 2w &= 0, \\
3x - 2y + 5z - 3w &= -2, \\
4x - 2y + 6z - 4w &= -6.
\end{aligned}$$

**6.**
$$\begin{aligned}
4x - y + 2z + w &= 4, \\
3x - y + 6z + 2w &= 8, \\
5x + 2y - 2z - w &= 9, \\
2x - 2y + 4z - 3w &= -13.
\end{aligned}$$

**7.**
$$\begin{aligned}
x - y \qquad + u \qquad\quad &= 0, \\
x + 2y - z \qquad\quad &= 1, \\
y + 2z + u + 2v &= 1, \\
3y \qquad - u - 2v &= -1, \\
x \qquad + 2z \qquad - v &= 0.
\end{aligned}$$

**8.**
$$\begin{aligned}
3x - y + 2z \qquad\quad - v &= 3, \\
x + 2y \qquad + 2u \qquad\quad &= 2, \\
3y - z + 3u - 2v &= 2, \\
2x - 3y \qquad - 2u + v &= -1, \\
x \qquad + 2z - u \qquad\quad &= 0.
\end{aligned}$$

**9.** Show that the homogeneous system

$$\begin{aligned}
3x - y + 2z + u + 2v &= 0, \\
x + y - z + 3u - v &= 0, \\
4x - 2y + 3z - 2u + 2v &= 0, \\
x + 3y + 4z - u &= 0, \\
x - 4y - 3z + u + v &= 0
\end{aligned}$$

is a dependent system, and find the solution in which $x = -4$.

In Exercises 10 and 11, find the values of $k$ making the given homogeneous systems dependent.

**10.**
$$\begin{aligned}
2x + y - 2z - w &= 0, \\
x - y - z + 2w &= 0, \\
3x - 2y + 4z - w &= 0, \\
2x - 4y + 5z + kw &= 0.
\end{aligned}$$

**11.**
$$\begin{aligned}
3x + 3y - 2z - 2w &= 0, \\
x + 3y + z + kw &= 0, \\
x + 2y - 3z - 4w &= 0, \\
7x - ky - 7z + kw &= 0.
\end{aligned}$$

**12.** Show that the defective system

$$\begin{aligned}
4x + 3y - 2z - w &= 0, \\
x - 2y + 5z - 2w &= 3, \\
x + 6y - 4z + 3w &= 1
\end{aligned}$$

may be solved for $x$, $y$, and $z$ in terms of $w$, and find such a solution.

**13.** Show that the defective system

$$\begin{aligned}
2x + y - 3z - w &= -3, \\
x - 3y - 5z + 10w &= 16, \\
x + 4y + 2z - 11w &= -19
\end{aligned}$$

cannot be solved for any three of the variables in terms of the fourth. Obtain a solution for $x$ and $y$ in terms of $z$ and $w$.

**14.** Show that the redundant system

$$\begin{aligned}
5x + 4y - 2z &= \phantom{-}0, \\
3x - 2y - 4z &= -4, \\
x + 6y + \phantom{2}z &= -1, \\
2x + 9y + 2z &= \phantom{-}1
\end{aligned}$$

is consistent, and find its solution.

**15.** Determine the value of $K$ for which the redundant system

$$\begin{aligned}
x + \phantom{3}y - \phantom{5}z &= \phantom{-}5, \\
2x + 3y + 2z &= -4, \\
3x - \phantom{3}y + 5z &= \phantom{-}K, \\
4x + 3y + 3z &= -K
\end{aligned}$$

is consistent, and find the solution of the system.

## SUPPLEMENTARY EXERCISES

**1.** Generalize Exercise 25, Art. 28, by supposing that, when A was the age B is now, he was $n$ times (instead of three times) as old as B was at that time, and keeping the second condition, involving the ratio $K$, the same as before. Find $K$ as a function of $n$ in order that the problem have solutions, and check the result by getting $K = \frac{5}{7}$ when $n = 3$.

**2.** It is shown in analytic geometry that, when the X- and Y-axes are rotated about the origin $O$ through an angle $\theta$ into the positions of new perpendicular X'- and Y'-axes, respectively, the original coordinates $(x, y)$ of any point $P$ are given in terms of the new coordinates $(x', y')$ by the equations

$$\begin{aligned}
x &= x' \cos \theta - y' \sin \theta, \\
y &= x' \sin \theta + y' \cos \theta.
\end{aligned}$$

Using determinants, solve these equations for $x'$ and $y'$, in terms of $x$, $y$, and $\theta$, to get

$$\begin{aligned}
x' &= x \cos \theta + y \sin \theta, \\
y' &= -x \sin \theta + y \cos \theta.
\end{aligned}$$

Note that the determinant of either system has the value 1 for all values of $\theta$, and that the new system has the same form as the original with $\theta$ replaced by $-\theta$.

**3.** Using the method of Exercise 7, Art. 30, show that

$$\begin{vmatrix}
1 & a & a^2 & a^3 \\
1 & b & b^2 & b^3 \\
1 & c & c^2 & c^3 \\
1 & d & d^2 & d^3
\end{vmatrix} = (d-c)(d-b)(d-a)(c-b)(c-a)(b-a).$$

**4.** Solve the equation

$$\begin{vmatrix}
x & p & 1 \\
a & x & 1 \\
a & b & 1
\end{vmatrix} = 0.$$

Note that the solutions are independent of the quantity $p$. (Cf. Exercises 9 and 15, below.)

**5.** Evaluate the determinant

$$\begin{vmatrix} 1^2 & 2^2 & 3^2 & 4^2 \\ 2^2 & 3^2 & 4^2 & 5^2 \\ 3^2 & 4^2 & 5^2 & 6^2 \\ 4^2 & 5^2 & 6^2 & 7^2 \end{vmatrix}.$$

**6.** Show that

$$\begin{vmatrix} 0 & 1 & a & a^2 \\ 1 & a & a^2 & 0 \\ a & a^2 & 0 & 1 \\ a^2 & 0 & 1 & a \end{vmatrix} = 1 + a^4 + a^8.$$

**7.** Show that

$$\begin{vmatrix} a & b & b & b \\ a & a & b & a \\ a & b & a & a \\ b & b & b & a \end{vmatrix} = (a - b)^4.$$

**8.** Show that

$$\begin{vmatrix} x & 0 & 0 & -x \\ 0 & x & 0 & -x \\ 0 & 0 & x & -x \\ -a & -b & -c & x - d \end{vmatrix} = x^3(x - a - b - c - d).$$

**9.** Form an equivalent determinant from

$$\begin{vmatrix} x & p & q & 1 \\ a & x & r & 1 \\ a & b & x & 1 \\ a & b & c & 1 \end{vmatrix}$$

by subtracting $a$, $b$, and $c$ times the fourth column from the first, second, and third columns, respectively. Hence show that the value of the original determinant is $(x - a)(x - b)(x - c)$, an expression independent of the quantities $p$, $q$, and $r$.

**10.** Show that

$$\begin{vmatrix} 1 + a & 1 & 1 \\ 1 & 1 + b & 1 \\ 1 & 1 & 1 + c \end{vmatrix} = abc\left(1 + \frac{1}{a} + \frac{1}{b} + \frac{1}{c}\right).$$

**11.** Show that

$$\begin{vmatrix} 1 + a & 1 & 1 & 1 \\ 1 & 1 + b & 1 & 1 \\ 1 & 1 & 1 + c & 1 \\ 1 & 1 & 1 & 1 + d \end{vmatrix} = abcd\left(1 + \frac{1}{a} + \frac{1}{b} + \frac{1}{c} + \frac{1}{d}\right).$$

**12** Show that

$$\begin{vmatrix} x & 1 & 1 \\ 1 & x & 1 \\ 1 & 1 & x \end{vmatrix} = (x-1)^2(x+2).$$

**13.** Show that

$$\begin{vmatrix} x & 1 & 1 & 1 \\ 1 & x & 1 & 1 \\ 1 & 1 & x & 1 \\ 1 & 1 & 1 & x \end{vmatrix} = (x-1)^3(x+3).$$

**14.** Show that

$$\begin{vmatrix} x & 1 & 1 & 1 & 1 \\ 1 & x & 1 & 1 & 1 \\ 1 & 1 & x & 1 & 1 \\ 1 & 1 & 1 & x & 1 \\ 1 & 1 & 1 & 1 & x \end{vmatrix} = (x-1)^4(x+4).$$

**15.** Using the method of Exercise 9, show that the value of the determinant

$$\begin{vmatrix} x & p & q & s & 1 \\ a & x & r & t & 1 \\ a & b & x & u & 1 \\ a & b & c & x & 1 \\ a & b & c & d & 1 \end{vmatrix}$$

is $(x-a)(x-b)(x-c)(x-d)$, an expression independent of the quantities $p$, $q$, $r$, $s$, $t$, and $u$.

# VI ———————————— Functions of Several Angles

**35. Sine and cosine of the sum or difference of two angles.** In Chapter III we were concerned principally with fundamental relations among trigonometric functions of a single angle. We now continue our study of trigonometry with a consideration of relations involving two or more angles.

To begin with, suppose that two angles, $\alpha$ and $\beta$, are given, and that the trigonometric functions of these angles are known. We wish to derive a relation from which the sine of the sum of the angles may then be determined. As far as computation is concerned, such a relation will be of little practical value, for $\sin(\alpha + \beta)$ may be determined by referring to tables of trigonometric functions; however, the relation sought will have considerable utility in connection with further developments of analytic trigonometry.

For definiteness, let $\alpha$ and $\beta$ both be positive acute angles: $0 < \alpha < \pi/2$, $0 < \beta < \pi/2$. Then $\alpha + \beta$ will be an angle whose terminal side lies in either the first or second quadrant.* These two cases are shown in Fig. $19(a)$ and $(b)$, respectively. In each case the $X$-axis is the initial side of both $\alpha$ and $\alpha + \beta$, and the initial side $OB$ of $\beta$ is the terminal side of $\alpha$. From a point $P$ on the terminal side $OP$ of $\alpha + \beta$, perpendiculars $PA$ and $PB$ are drawn to the initial sides of $\alpha$ and $\beta$, respectively, and from $B$ perpendiculars $BC$ and $BD$ are drawn to $OX$ and $PA$ respectively.

In both diagrams we then have, from the definition of a sine function (Art. 15) and the geometric relations,

$$\sin(\alpha + \beta) = \frac{AP}{OP} = \frac{AD + DP}{OP} = \frac{CB}{OP} + \frac{DP}{OP}.$$

Now $CB = OB \sin \alpha$, and, since angle $DPB$ is also equal to $\alpha$ from geometry, we have $DP = PB \cos \alpha$. Hence

$$\sin(\alpha + \beta) = \frac{OB}{OP} \sin \alpha + \frac{PB}{OP} \cos \alpha.$$

---

* The intermediate case, $\alpha + \beta = \pi/2$, will be considered later.

But $OB/OP = \cos \beta$, and $PB/OP = \sin \beta$ (Art. 17). Therefore

$$\sin (\alpha + \beta) = \sin \alpha \cos \beta + \cos \alpha \sin \beta. \tag{1}$$

This is the desired relation.

In the intermediate case, where $\alpha + \beta = \pi/2$, we have, since $\alpha$ and $\beta$ are then complementary angles, $\cos \beta = \sin \alpha$ and $\sin \beta = \cos \alpha$ (Art. 17). Hence the right member of (1) gives us $\sin^2 \alpha + \cos^2 \alpha = 1$ (Art. 22). But $\sin (\alpha + \beta) = \sin (\pi/2) = 1$ (Art. 16), and therefore relation (1) holds in this case also.

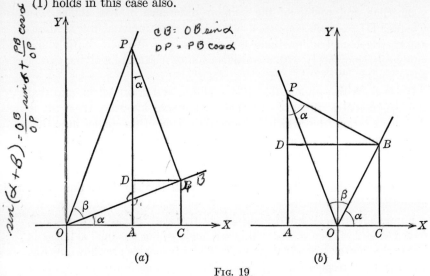

*handwritten:* $CB: OB \sin \alpha$

$DP = PB \cos \alpha$

*handwritten left margin:* $\sin (\alpha + \beta) = \dfrac{OB}{OP} \sin \alpha + \dfrac{PB}{OP} \cos \alpha$

(a)             (b)

FIG. 19

From the same figure, we may deduce a formula for $\cos (\alpha + \beta)$. Here, however, particular care must be exercised with regard to algebraic signs, since $\cos (\alpha + \beta)$ is positive when $0 < \alpha + \beta < \pi/2$ but negative when $\pi/2 < \alpha + \beta < \pi$. Now, in each diagram, $\cos (\alpha + \beta) = OA/OP$. In (a) we have $OA = OC - AC$; in (b), the length of $OA$ is $|OA| = |AC| - |OC|$, and, to take into account the fact that $OA$ is negative while $OC$ is positive, we again must write $OA = |OC| - |AC| = OC - AC$. Consequently, in either case,

$$\cos (\alpha + \beta) = \frac{OA}{OP} = \frac{OC - AC}{OP} = \frac{OC}{OP} - \frac{DB}{OP}.$$

Since $OC = OB \cos \alpha$, and $DB = PB \sin \alpha$,

$$\cos (\alpha + \beta) = \frac{OB}{OP} \cos \alpha - \frac{PB}{OP} \sin \alpha;$$

and, as $OB/OP = \cos \beta$, $PB/OP = \sin \beta$, we get

$$\cos (\alpha + \beta) = \cos \alpha \cos \beta - \sin \alpha \sin \beta. \qquad (2)$$

Again, when $\alpha + \beta = \pi/2$, $\cos \beta = \sin \alpha$ and $\sin \beta = \cos \alpha$, so that the right member of (2) becomes $\sin \alpha \cos \alpha - \sin \alpha \cos \alpha = 0$. But $\cos (\alpha + \beta) = \cos (\pi/2) = 0$ (Art. 16), and therefore (2) holds in the intermediate case also.

We have thus shown that relations (1) and (2) hold identically in $\alpha$ and $\beta$ when these angles both lie anywhere in quadrant I. It is natural to expect that these relations will be true when $\alpha$ and $\beta$ each lie in any quadrant. To show that this is true, we employ the following argument. The type of reasoning involved is a particular example of a general and powerful logical method which we shall examine more thoroughly in the next chapter.

Before entering into the details of the argument, we outline the procedure so that the motivation and aims are clearly seen. We suppose that relations (1) and (2) hold whenever $\alpha$ and $\beta$ are angles, respectively, in certain quadrants, $r$ and $s$, say. This supposition is evidently tenable, for we have already shown the truth of (1) and (2) when $r = 1$ and $s = 1$. We then proceed to show that these relations hold when $\alpha$ is in quadrant $r$ and $\beta$ in quadrant $s + 1$, that is, when $\beta$ is in a quadrant one beyond its original one. Then, this having been proved, the argument allowing for a passage of $\beta$ from quadrant $s$ to quadrant $s + 1$ equally allows for a passage of $\beta$ from quadrant $s + 1$ to quadrant $s + 2$, and from $s + 2$ to $s + 3$, so that ultimately the relations under discussion hold for $\alpha$ in quadrant $r$ and $\beta$ in any quadrant. Finally, since $\alpha$ and $\beta$ may be interchanged in (1) and (2) without actually altering these relations, we can conclude that they hold for $\beta$ in a fixed but unspecified quadrant and $\alpha$ successively in quadrants $r + 1$, $r + 2$, $r + 3$. The verification for $r = 1$, $s = 1$ gives to relations (1) and (2) the necessary initial validity, and therefore the passage to all other quadrants, for both $\alpha$ and $\beta$, will likewise be validated.

Once the nature of this reasoning is understood, the analysis is quickly and easily executed. When (1) and (2) are true for $\alpha$ in quadrant $r$ and $\beta$ in quadrant $s$, let $\phi = \beta + \pi/2$, so that $\phi$ is in quadrant $s + 1$. Replacing $\beta$ in the right member of (1) by $\phi$, we get (Art. 18)

$$\sin \alpha \cos \phi + \cos \alpha \sin \phi = \sin \alpha \cos \left( \beta + \frac{\pi}{2} \right) + \cos \alpha \sin \left( \beta + \frac{\pi}{2} \right)$$

$$= - \sin \alpha \sin \beta + \cos \alpha \cos \beta.$$

But this is the expression for cos $(\alpha + \beta)$ given by (2), and, since cos $(\alpha + \beta)$ = sin $(\alpha + \beta + \pi/2)$ = sin $(\alpha + \phi)$, the result is the left member of (1) with $\phi$ replacing $\beta$. Hence (1) is correct for angles respectively in quadrants $r$ and $s + 1$.

Similarly, the right member of (2), with $\phi$ replacing $\beta$, yields

$$\cos \alpha \cos \phi - \sin \alpha \sin \phi = \cos \alpha \cos \left(\beta + \frac{\pi}{2}\right) - \sin \alpha \sin \left(\beta + \frac{\pi}{2}\right)$$

$$= - \cos \alpha \sin \beta - \sin \alpha \cos \beta$$

$$= - \sin (\alpha + \beta)$$

$$= \cos \left(\alpha + \beta + \frac{\pi}{2}\right)$$

$$= \cos (\alpha + \phi),$$

the left member of (2) with $\phi$ in place of $\beta$. Therefore (2) holds for angles respectively in quadrants $r$ and $s + 1$.

This is all the analysis necessary. The reasoning outlined above then completes the argument, and we find that (1) and (2) hold for all $\alpha$ and all $\beta$; that is, (1) and (2) are identities.

Consider now the sine and cosine of the difference of two angles. It is possible to repeat the entire sequence of steps above, basing the initial derivations on suitable figures, but it is simpler to get the desired results as follows. Since identities (1) and (2) are true for all angles, they are true when $\beta$ is a negative angle, for such an angle will have the same trigonometric functions as the angle $2n\pi$ greater, where $n$ is a positive integer sufficiently large to produce a positive angle. Hence we need merely replace $\beta$ by $-\beta$ in (1) and (2); there is found (Art. 18)

$$\sin (\alpha - \beta) = \sin \alpha \cos (-\beta) + \cos \alpha \sin (-\beta),$$

$$\underline{\sin (\alpha - \beta) = \sin \alpha \cos \beta - \cos \alpha \sin \beta;} \tag{3}$$

$$\cos (\alpha - \beta) = \cos \alpha \cos (-\beta) - \sin \alpha \sin (-\beta),$$

$$\underline{\cos (\alpha - \beta) = \cos \alpha \cos \beta + \sin \alpha \sin \beta.} \tag{4}$$

Identities (3) and (4) are thus formulas for the sine and cosine of the difference of two angles.

Because the difference between (1) and (3), and between (2) and (4), consists of merely a change of algebraic sign in each member, the four identities may be written compactly in two lines, using double signs:

$$\sin (\alpha \pm \beta) = \sin \alpha \cos \beta \pm \cos \alpha \sin \beta, \tag{1), (3}$$

$$\cos (\alpha \pm \beta) = \cos \alpha \cos \beta \mp \sin \alpha \sin \beta. \tag{2), (4}$$

It is understood here that, in each line, the upper signs correspond and the lower signs correspond.

The identities derived here are of considerable importance, as has been stated, and the student should become thoroughly familiar with them. They should be learned as verbal statements, involving no symbols; thus:

*The sine of the sum (difference) of two angles is equal to the sine of the first times the cosine of the second plus (minus) the cosine of the first times the sine of the second.*

*The cosine of the sum (difference) of two angles is equal to the cosine of the first times the cosine of the second minus (plus) the sine of the first times the sine of the second.*

When the theorems are learned in this way, the symbolism employed for each angle in a particular instance cannot cause uncertainty due to confusion with symbolism memorized; and, what is of even more importance, the form of each right member will be more readily recognized when it appears in a specific discussion.

*Example 1.* Find the sine and cosine of 75°.

*Solution.* The angle 75° may be expressed as the sum or difference of two special angles, whose functions are known (Art. 16), in various ways: $75° = 45° + 30°$, $75° = 120° - 45°$, etc. If we choose the first of these, we get from identities (1) and (2),

$$\sin 75° = \sin (45° + 30°) = \sin 45° \cos 30° + \cos 45° \sin 30°$$

$$= \frac{\sqrt{2}}{2} \cdot \frac{\sqrt{3}}{2} + \frac{\sqrt{2}}{2} \cdot \frac{1}{2} = \tfrac{1}{4}(\sqrt{6} + \sqrt{2}),$$

$$\cos 75° = \cos (45° + 30°) = \cos 45° \cos 30° - \sin 45° \sin 30°$$

$$= \frac{\sqrt{2}}{2} \cdot \frac{\sqrt{3}}{2} - \frac{\sqrt{2}}{2} \cdot \frac{1}{2} = \tfrac{1}{4}(\sqrt{6} - \sqrt{2}).$$

If we use the approximate values, $\sqrt{6} = 2.4494$, $\sqrt{2} = 1.4142$, we find

$$\sin 75° = 0.9659, \qquad \cos 75° = 0.2588,$$

which check with the values given in the tables.

*Example 2.* Simplify the expression

$$\cos^2 \left(\theta - \frac{\pi}{6}\right) - \cos \left(\theta - \frac{\pi}{6}\right) \cos \left(\theta + \frac{\pi}{6}\right) + \sin^2 \left(\frac{\pi}{3} - \theta\right).$$

*Solution.* This expression may be transformed by means of identities (2), (3), and (4). We then get, as an equivalent expression,

$$\left( \cos\theta \cos\frac{\pi}{6} + \sin\theta \sin\frac{\pi}{6} \right)^2 - \left( \cos\theta \cos\frac{\pi}{6} + \sin\theta \sin\frac{\pi}{6} \right)\left( \cos\theta \cos\frac{\pi}{6} \right.$$

$$\left. - \sin\theta \sin\frac{\pi}{6} \right) + \left( \sin\frac{\pi}{3} \cos\theta - \cos\frac{\pi}{3} \sin\theta \right)^2$$

$$= \left( \frac{\sqrt{3}}{2} \cos\theta + \frac{1}{2} \sin\theta \right)^2 - \left( \frac{\sqrt{3}}{2} \cos\theta + \frac{1}{2} \sin\theta \right)\left( \frac{\sqrt{3}}{2} \cos\theta \right.$$

$$\left. - \frac{1}{2} \sin\theta \right) + \left( \frac{\sqrt{3}}{2} \cos\theta - \frac{1}{2} \sin\theta \right)^2$$

$$= \frac{3}{4} \cos^2\theta + \frac{\sqrt{3}}{2} \sin\theta \cos\theta + \frac{1}{4} \sin^2\theta - \frac{3}{4} \cos^2\theta + \frac{1}{4} \sin^2\theta$$

$$+ \frac{3}{4} \cos^2\theta - \frac{\sqrt{3}}{2} \sin\theta \cos\theta + \frac{1}{4} \sin^2\theta$$

$$= \tfrac{3}{4} \sin^2\theta + \tfrac{3}{4} \cos^2\theta = \tfrac{3}{4}(\sin^2\theta + \cos^2\theta) = \tfrac{3}{4}.$$

Thus, the given expression reduces to a constant, $\tfrac{3}{4}$.

## EXERCISES

**1.** Verify identities (1)–(4) by using the fact that $60° = 150° - 90°$.

**2.** Verify identities (1)–(4) by using the fact that $225° = 180° + 45°$.

**3.** Verify identities (1)–(4) by using the fact that $240° = 300° - 60°$.

**4.** Find $\sin 75°$ and $\cos 75°$, using the fact that $75° = 210° - 135°$.

**5.** Find $\sin 15°$ and $\cos 15°$ by use of the identities (1)–(4), and check by means of the results of Example 1.

**6.** If $\sin\alpha = \frac{4}{5}$, $\sin\beta = \frac{5}{13}$, and $\alpha$ and $\beta$ are acute angles, find $\sin(\alpha+\beta)$ and $\cos(\alpha+\beta)$.

**7.** If $\cos\alpha = \frac{3}{5}$, $\tan\beta = \frac{12}{5}$, and $\alpha$ and $\beta$ are acute angles, find $\sin(\alpha-\beta)$ and $\cos(\alpha-\beta)$.

**8.** If $\sin\alpha = \frac{1}{4}$, $\sec\beta = \sqrt{5}$, and $\alpha$ and $\beta$ are acute angles, find $\sin(\alpha+\beta)$ and $\cos(\alpha-\beta)$.

**9.** If $\tan\alpha = -\frac{1}{2}$, $\cot\beta = -\frac{1}{3}$, and $\alpha$ and $\beta$ are in the second quadrant, find $\sin(\alpha-\beta)$ and $\cos(\alpha+\beta)$.

**10.** If $\cos\alpha = \frac{1}{4}$, $\cos\beta = \frac{1}{5}$, and $\alpha$ and $\beta$ are in the fourth quadrant, find $\sin(\alpha+\beta)$ and $\cos(\alpha+\beta)$.

**11.** Show that $2\cos^2(\theta + 3\pi/4) = 1 + 2\sin\theta \cos\theta$.

**12.** Show that

$$\frac{\cot\alpha \cot\beta + 1}{\cot\alpha \cot\beta - 1} = \frac{\cos(\alpha-\beta)}{\cos(\alpha+\beta)}.$$

**13.** Show that $\sin(\theta - \pi/4) - \cos(\theta + \pi/4) = \sqrt{2}(\sin\theta - \cos\theta)$.

**14.** Show that $\cos (\theta - \pi/6) - \cos (\theta + \pi/6) = \sin \theta$.

**15.** If $\sin \alpha - \sin \beta = a$ and $\cos \alpha - \cos \beta = b$, show that $2 \cos(\alpha - \beta) = 2 - a^2 - b^2$.

**16.** Show that $\sin \theta \cos (\theta - \pi/6) - \cos \theta \sin (\theta - \pi/6) = \frac{1}{2}$.

**17.** Show that $\cos (\theta + \pi/4) \cos (\theta - \pi/4) + \sin (\theta + \pi/4) \sin (\theta - \pi/4) = 0$.

**18.** If $\theta$ is an acute angle, and if $\sin 2\theta \cos 3\theta + \cos 2\theta \sin 3\theta = \frac{1}{2}$, find $\theta$.

**19.** If $\theta$ is an acute angle, and if $\cos 4\theta = \cos 27° \cos 7° + \sin 27° \sin 7°$, find $\theta$.

**20.** If $\theta$ is an acute angle, and if $\sin 2\theta = \sin (\alpha + 49°) \cos (\alpha - 7°) - \cos (\alpha + 49°) \sin (\alpha - 7°)$, find $\theta$.

**21.** If $\theta$ is a positive angle in the second quadrant, and if $\cos 3\theta = \cos (\alpha + 11°) \cos (5° - \alpha) - \sin (\alpha + 11°) \sin (5° - \alpha)$, find $\theta$.

**22.** Derive the formulas

$$\csc (\alpha \pm \beta) = \frac{\sec \alpha \sec \beta \csc \alpha \csc \beta}{\sec \alpha \csc \beta \pm \csc \alpha \sec \beta}.$$

**23.** Derive the formulas

$$\sec (\alpha \pm \beta) = \frac{\sec \alpha \sec \beta \csc \alpha \csc \beta}{\csc \alpha \csc \beta \mp \sec \alpha \sec \beta}.$$

**24.** Derive the formula

$\sin (\alpha + \beta + \gamma) =$

$\qquad \sin \alpha \cos \beta \cos \gamma + \cos \alpha \sin \beta \sin \gamma + \cos \alpha \cos \beta \sin \gamma - \sin \alpha \sin \beta \sin \gamma.$

**25.** Derive the formula $\quad cos(A+B)\, cos\, x \, - \, sin\,(A+B)\, sin\, x$

$\cos (\alpha + \beta + \gamma) = \quad (cos \alpha\, cos\, B - sin \alpha\, sin\, B)\, cos\, y\, \big[(sin \alpha\, cos\, B + cos \alpha\, sin\, B)\, sin\, y$

$\qquad = \cos \alpha \cos \beta \cos \gamma - \sin \alpha \sin \beta \cos \gamma - \sin \alpha \cos \beta \sin \gamma - \cos \alpha \sin \beta \sin \gamma.$

## 36. Tangent of the sum or difference of two angles.

Using the identities obtained in Art. 35, it is easy to find a formula for the tangent of the sum or difference of two angles, $\alpha$ and $\beta$. Since $\tan \theta = \sin \theta/\cos \theta$ (Art. 22), we have

$$\tan (\alpha + \beta) = \frac{\sin (\alpha + \beta)}{\cos (\alpha + \beta)} = \frac{\sin \alpha \cos \beta + \cos \alpha \sin \beta}{\cos \alpha \cos \beta - \sin \alpha \sin \beta},$$

from (1) and (2) of Art. 35. This result may be transformed into a somewhat simpler and more useful form. Dividing numerator and denominator of the last fraction by the product $\cos \alpha \cos \beta$, and again using the fundamental identity $\tan \theta = \sin \theta/\cos \theta$, we get

$$\tan (\alpha + \beta) = \frac{\dfrac{\sin \alpha}{\cos \alpha} + \dfrac{\sin \beta}{\cos \beta}}{1 - \dfrac{\sin \alpha}{\cos \alpha} \cdot \dfrac{\sin \beta}{\cos \beta}},$$

$$\boxed{\tan (\alpha + \beta) = \frac{\tan \alpha + \tan \beta}{1 - \tan \alpha \tan \beta}.} \qquad (1)$$

In the same way, we obtain from identities (3) and (4) of Art. 35,

$$\tan (\alpha - \beta) = \frac{\sin (\alpha - \beta)}{\cos (\alpha - \beta)} = \frac{\sin \alpha \cos \beta - \cos \alpha \sin \beta}{\cos \alpha \cos \beta + \sin \alpha \sin \beta},$$

$$\tan (\alpha - \beta) = \frac{\tan \alpha - \tan \beta}{1 + \tan \alpha \tan \beta}. \qquad (2)$$

This identity may be derived alternatively from (1) by replacing $\beta$ by $-\beta$ in both members, for $\tan (-\beta) = -\tan \beta$ (Art. 18).

With regard to identity (1), it is understood that $\tan \alpha \tan \beta \neq 1$, for, when $\tan \alpha \tan \beta = 1$, relation (1) has no meaning. Similarly, it is tacitly assumed in connection with (2) that $\tan \alpha \tan \beta \neq -1$.

It is evident that relations (1) and (2) may be exhibited together in a single line, using double signs; thus, we have

$$\tan (\alpha \pm \beta) = \frac{\tan \alpha \pm \tan \beta}{1 \mp \tan \alpha \tan \beta}, \qquad (1), (2)$$

where, as before, the upper signs correspond and the lower signs correspond.

Identities (1) and (2) may be stated verbally as follows:

*The tangent of the sum (difference) of two angles is equal to the tangent of the first angle plus (minus) the tangent of the second, all divided by one minus (plus) the product of the two tangents.*

*Example.* Evaluate tan 15°.
*Solution.* Since $15° = 45° - 30°$, we may use formula (2) and the known values of the tangents of the special angles (Art. 16). Then we have

$$\tan 15° = \tan (45° - 30°) = \frac{\tan 45° - \tan 30°}{1 + \tan 45° \tan 30°}$$

$$= \frac{1 - \dfrac{1}{\sqrt{3}}}{1 + \dfrac{1}{\sqrt{3}}} = \frac{\sqrt{3} - 1}{\sqrt{3} + 1} \cdot \frac{\sqrt{3} - 1}{\sqrt{3} - 1}$$

$$= \frac{3 - 2\sqrt{3} + 1}{3 - 1} = 2 - \sqrt{3}.$$

Taking $\sqrt{3} = 1.73205+$, we then find

$$\tan 15° = 0.26795-,$$

which agrees with the value given in the tables.

*monday Nov 4*

**EXERCISES**

**1.** Find $\tan 15°$ by using $15° = 150° - 135°$.

**2.** Find $\tan 15°$ by using $15° = 240° - 225°$.

**3.** Find $\tan 165°$ by using $165° = 120° + 45°$.

**4.** If $\alpha$ and $\beta$ are acute angles, where $\tan \alpha = \frac{3}{4}$ and $\tan \beta = \frac{12}{5}$, find $\tan (\alpha + \beta)$ and $\tan (\alpha - \beta)$.

**5.** If $\alpha$ and $\beta$ are acute angles, where $\tan \alpha = 3$ and $\tan \beta = 4$, find $\tan (\alpha + \beta)$ and $\tan (\alpha - \beta)$.

**6.** If $\alpha$ and $\beta$ are acute angles, where $\cos \alpha = \sqrt{6}/3$ and $\cos \beta = 3\sqrt{11}/11$, find $\tan (\alpha + \beta)$ and $\tan (\alpha - \beta)$.

**7.** If $\alpha$ and $\beta$ are positive angles in the second quadrant, where $\tan \alpha = -2\sqrt{2}$ and $\sin \beta = \frac{3}{5}$, find $\tan (\alpha + \beta)$ and $\tan (\alpha - \beta)$.

**8.** If $\alpha$ and $\beta$ are acute angles, where $\tan \alpha = \frac{1}{7}$ and $\tan \beta = \frac{3}{4}$, show that $\alpha + \beta = \pi/4$.

**9.** If $\alpha$ and $\beta$ are positive angles in the first and second quadrants, respectively, where $\tan \alpha = \frac{3}{2}$ and $\tan \beta = -\frac{1}{5}$, show that $\alpha + \beta = 5\pi/4$.

**10.** If $\tan \alpha = m/(m + 2)$ and $\tan \beta = 1/(m + 1)$, show that $\alpha + \beta = (4n + 1)\pi/4$, where $n$ is some integer or zero.

**11.** If $\alpha$ and $\beta$ are acute angles, where $\tan \alpha = 3$ and $\tan \beta = \frac{1}{2}$, show that $\alpha - \beta = \pi/4$.

**12.** If $\alpha$ and $\beta$ are positive angles in the third and second quadrants, respectively, where $\tan \alpha = \frac{1}{3}$ and $\tan \beta = -\frac{1}{2}$, show that $\alpha - \beta = \pi/4$.

**13.** If $\tan \alpha = 2m + 1$ and $\tan \beta = m/(m + 1)$, show that $\alpha - \beta = (4n + 1)\pi/4$, where $n$ is some integer or zero.

**14.** If $a$, $b$, and $c$ are, respectively, the two legs and hypotenuse of a right triangle, and if $A$, $B$, $C$ are the vertices opposite $a$, $b$, and $c$, respectively, show that $\tan (A - B) = (a^2 - b^2)/2ab$.

**15.** Derive the formulas
$$\cot (\alpha \pm \beta) = \frac{\cot \alpha \cot \beta \mp 1}{\cot \beta \pm \cot \alpha}.$$

**16.** Prove the identity
$$\frac{\csc \alpha \sin \beta \tan \alpha}{\cos (\alpha + \beta)} + \tan \alpha = \tan (\alpha + \beta).$$

**17.** Prove the identity
$$\tan \alpha - \frac{\sec \alpha \sin \beta}{\cos (\alpha - \beta)} = \tan (\alpha - \beta).$$

**18.** If $\alpha$, $\beta$, $\gamma$, and $\delta$ are acute angles whose tangents are $\frac{1}{3}$, $\frac{1}{4}$, $\frac{1}{7}$, $\frac{1}{13}$, respectively, show that $\alpha + \beta + \gamma + \delta = \pi/4$.

**19.** Show that
$$\tan (\alpha + \beta + \gamma) = \frac{\tan \alpha + \tan \beta + \tan \gamma - \tan \alpha \tan \beta \tan \gamma}{1 - \tan \alpha \tan \beta - \tan \beta \tan \gamma - \tan \alpha \tan \gamma}.$$

**20.** If $A$, $B$, and $C$ are the angles of an oblique triangle, show that
$$\tan A + \tan B + \tan C = \tan A \tan B \tan C$$

(a) by using $\tan C = \tan [180° - (A + B)] = - \tan (A + B)$; (b) by using the identity of Exercise 19.

**37. Functions of double angles.** It is frequently desirable to have expressions for functions of twice a given angle in terms of functions of the angle itself. Such expressions are easily obtained from the identities established in Arts. 35–36.

If, in equations (1) and (2), Art. 35, and in (1), Art. 36, we set $\beta = \alpha$, we get

$$\sin (\alpha + \alpha) = \sin \alpha \cos \alpha + \cos \alpha \sin \alpha,$$

$$\cos (\alpha + \alpha) = \cos \alpha \cos \alpha - \sin \alpha \sin \alpha,$$

$$\tan (\alpha + \alpha) = \frac{\tan \alpha + \tan \alpha}{1 - \tan \alpha \tan \alpha}.$$

Hence we have

$$\sin 2\alpha = 2 \sin \alpha \cos \alpha, \tag{1}$$

$$\cos 2\alpha = \cos^2 \alpha - \sin^2 \alpha, \tag{2}$$

$$\tan 2\alpha = \frac{2 \tan \alpha}{1 - \tan^2 \alpha}. \tag{3}$$

If we make use of the identity $\sin^2 \alpha + \cos^2 \alpha = 1$, we may express $\cos 2\alpha$ in two alternative forms, one involving $\sin \alpha$ alone, the other containing only $\cos \alpha$:

$$\cos 2\alpha = 1 - 2 \sin^2 \alpha = 2 \cos^2 \alpha - 1. \tag{2'}$$

According to the point of view adopted above, identities (1)–(3) are interpreted as relations giving functions of double angles. We may, however, equally well regard these relations as formulas yielding functions of an angle in terms of functions of half that angle. This interpretation is more emphatically exhibited by setting $2\alpha = \theta$, so that (1)–(3) become

$$\sin \theta = 2 \sin \frac{\theta}{2} \cos \frac{\theta}{2},$$

$$\cos \theta = \cos^2 \frac{\theta}{2} - \sin^2 \frac{\theta}{2},$$

$$\tan \theta = \frac{2 \tan \dfrac{\theta}{2}}{1 - \tan^2 \dfrac{\theta}{2}}.$$

Again, however, it is the *form* of each relation that is important; the symbols used for angles are entirely immaterial as long as the notation is consistent.

*Example 1.* Derive a formula for sin $3\alpha$ in terms of sin $\alpha$.

*Solution.* We may regard $3\alpha$ as $\alpha + 2\alpha$, and use identity (1), Art. 35, to get

$$\sin 3\alpha = \sin (\alpha + 2\alpha) = \sin \alpha \cos 2\alpha + \cos \alpha \sin 2\alpha.$$

Now replace sin $2\alpha$ and cos $2\alpha$ by the expressions given in (1) and (2); we find

$$\sin 3\alpha = (\sin \alpha) (\cos^2 \alpha - \sin^2 \alpha) + (\cos \alpha)(2 \sin \alpha \cos \alpha)$$

$$= 3 \sin \alpha \cos^2 \alpha - \sin^3 \alpha.$$

Finally, since we wish a result involving only sin $\alpha$, replace $\cos^2 \alpha$ by $1 - \sin^2 \alpha$; then

$$\sin 3\alpha = 3(\sin \alpha)(1 - \sin^2 \alpha) - \sin^3 \alpha$$

$$= 3 \sin \alpha - 4 \sin^3 \alpha.$$

This is the desired identity.

*Example 2.* Solve the equation

$$2 \sin 2\theta + \cos 2\theta + 2 \sin \theta = 1$$

for non-negative values of $\theta$ less than $2\pi$.

*Solution.* Here we have functions of both $\theta$ itself and $2\theta$. Hence we first transform so as to get an equivalent equation involving functions of $\theta$ only. We set sin $2\theta = 2 \sin \theta \cos \theta$ and cos $2\theta = 1 - 2 \sin^2 \theta$, the latter form being chosen so that the constant terms in the equation will cancel.

This leads to

$$4 \sin \theta \cos \theta + 1 - 2 \sin^2 \theta + 2 \sin \theta = 1,$$

$$2(\sin \theta)(2 \cos \theta - \sin \theta + 1) = 0.$$

When the factor sin $\theta$ is set equal to zero, the last equation is satisfied, whence we get

$$\theta = 0, \qquad \theta = \pi.$$

It is easy to verify these solutions in the original equation.

To find possible solutions of the equation $2 \cos \theta - \sin \theta + 1 = 0$, we transpose to get $2 \cos \theta + 1 = \sin \theta$, replace sin $\theta$ by $\pm\sqrt{1 - \cos^2 \theta}$, and rationalize, as we did in a similar example in Art. 26. This process may, as we have seen, lead to extraneous roots, and all ostensible solutions must therefore be checked. We find

$$4 \cos^2 \theta + 4 \cos \theta + 1 = 1 - \cos^2 \theta,$$

$$(\cos \theta)(5 \cos \theta + 4) = 0,$$

$$\cos \theta = 0, \qquad \cos \theta = -\tfrac{4}{5}.$$

Corresponding to cos $\theta = 0$, we get $\theta = \pi/2$ and $\theta = 3\pi/2$. Of these, only $\theta = \pi/2$ satisfies the given equation. If cos $\theta = -\tfrac{4}{5}$, $\theta$ may be in either the second or third quadrant; from tables we then get $\theta = 143° 8'$ and $\theta = 216° 52'$

(approx.). Only the latter of these is found to satisfy the original equation. Hence there are two more valid solutions:

$$\theta = \frac{\pi}{2}, \qquad \theta = 216° \, 52' = 3.785 \text{ approx.}$$

*MONDAY Nov 4*

### EXERCISES

**1.** If $\theta$ is an acute angle, where $\sin \theta = \frac{12}{13}$, find $\sin 2\theta$, $\cos 2\theta$, and $\tan 2\theta$.

**2.** If $\theta$ is an angle in the second quadrant, where $\sin \theta = \frac{3}{5}$, find $\sin 2\theta$, $\cos 2\theta$, and $\tan 2\theta$.

**3.** If $\theta$ is an angle in the third quadrant, where $\cos \theta = -\frac{5}{13}$, find $\sin 2\theta$, $\cos 2\theta$, and $\tan 2\theta$.

**4.** If $\theta$ is an angle in the fourth quadrant, where $\tan \theta = -\frac{4}{3}$, find $\sin 2\theta$, $\cos 2\theta$, and $\tan 2\theta$.

**5.** If $\theta$ is an acute angle, where $\tan \theta = 3$, find $\sin 2\theta$, $\cos 2\theta$, and $\tan 2\theta$.

Prove the identities in Exercises 6–25.

**6.** $\cot \theta - \tan \theta = 2 \cot 2\theta$.

**7.** $\cot \theta + \tan \theta = 2 \csc 2\theta$.

**8.** $\cos 3\theta = 4 \cos^3 \theta - 3 \cos \theta$.

**9.** $\tan 3\theta = \dfrac{3 \tan \theta - \tan^3 \theta}{1 - 3 \tan^2 \theta}$.

**10.** $\sin 4\theta = 4(2 \cos^2 \theta - 1) \sin \theta \cos \theta$.

**11.** $\cos 4\theta = \sin^4 \theta - 6 \sin^2 \theta \cos^2 \theta + \cos^4 \theta$.

**12.** $\tan 4\theta = \dfrac{4(1 - \tan^2 \theta) \tan \theta}{1 - 6 \tan^2 \theta + \tan^4 \theta}$.

**13.** $\dfrac{\cot^2 \theta - 1}{\cot^2 \theta + 1} = \cos 2\theta$.

**14.** $\dfrac{1 - \sin 2\theta}{\sin \theta - \cos \theta} = \sin \theta - \cos \theta$.

**15.** $\tan (\theta + 3\pi/4) + \tan (\theta - 3\pi/4) = 2 \tan 2\theta$.

**16.** $\cot 2\theta = \dfrac{\cot^2 \theta - 1}{2 \cot \theta}$.

**17.** $\dfrac{\cos 3\theta}{\sin \theta} - \dfrac{\sin 3\theta}{\cos \theta} = 2 \csc 2\theta - 4 \sin 2\theta$.

**18.** $\tan 2\theta - \sec 2\theta = \dfrac{\tan \theta - 1}{\tan \theta + 1}$.

**19.** $\dfrac{(\sin \theta - \cos \theta)(\sin^3 \theta - \cos^3 \theta)}{1 - \sin 2\theta} = 1 + \dfrac{1}{2} \sin 2\theta$.

**20.** $\dfrac{2 \sin^3 2\theta}{(1 - \cos 2\theta)(1 - \cos 4\theta)} = \cot \theta$.

**21.** $\cos 4\theta = 1 - 8 \cos^2 \theta + 8 \cos^4 \theta$.

**22.** $\sin 5\theta = (5 - 20 \sin^2 \theta + 16 \sin^4 \theta) \sin \theta$.

**23.** $\cos 5\theta = (5 - 20 \cos^2 \theta + 16 \cos^4 \theta) \cos \theta$.

**24.** $\sin 6\theta = 2(3 - 16 \cos^2 \theta + 16 \cos^4 \theta) \sin \theta \cos \theta$.

**25.** $\cos 6\theta = 32 \cos^6 \theta - 48 \cos^4 \theta + 18 \cos^2 \theta - 1$.

In Exercises 26–35, solve each equation for non-negative values of $\theta$ less than $2\pi$.

**26.** $\sin\theta - \sin 2\theta = 0.$                    **27.** $\cos\theta - \cos 2\theta = 0.$
**28.** $\cos\theta - \sin 2\theta = 0.$                    **29.** $\sin\theta - \cos 2\theta = 0.$
**30.** $\sin 2\theta + \sin 4\theta = 0.$                    **31.** $\tan\theta - \tan 2\theta = 0.$
**32.** $\tan\theta + \sin 2\theta = 0.$                    **33.** $\cos 2\theta + \tan\theta = 1.$

**34.** $\sin\theta - \sin 2\theta + \sin^2\theta = 0.$
**35.** $\sin\theta + \cos\theta - \sin 2\theta - \cos 2\theta = 1.$

Establish the relations of Exercises 36–40, where $A$ and $B$ are respectively the two acute angles of a right triangle.

**36.** $\sin 2A = \sin 2B.$                    **37.** $\sin(A - B) + \cos 2A = 0.$
**38.** $\cos(A - B) - \sin 2A = 0.$                    **39.** $\tan(A - B) + \cot 2A = 0.$
**40.** $\sin^2(A - B) + \cos^2 2A = 1 + \cos 4A.$

**38. Functions of half angles.** Using the identities established in Art. 37, it is easy to derive formulas for functions of half an angle in terms of functions of the angle.

Since $\cos 2\alpha = 1 - 2\sin^2\alpha$, we may solve for $\sin\alpha$ to get

$$\sin\alpha = \pm\sqrt{\frac{1 - \cos 2\alpha}{2}}.$$

This is an expression for the sine of half an angle, but, for emphasis, we may replace $2\alpha$ by $\theta$, and write

$$\sin\frac{\theta}{2} = \pm\sqrt{\frac{1 - \cos\theta}{2}}. \tag{1}$$

The sign before the radical must, of course, be chosen according to the quadrant in which the half angle, $\theta/2$, lies.

Similarly, from $\cos 2\alpha = 2\cos^2\alpha - 1$, we get

$$\cos\alpha = \pm\sqrt{\frac{1 + \cos 2\alpha}{2}},$$

or, in other notation,

$$\cos\frac{\theta}{2} = \pm\sqrt{\frac{1 + \cos\theta}{2}}. \tag{2}$$

Again the algebraic sign must be properly chosen.

If we divide corresponding members of (1) and (2), we find

$$\tan\frac{\theta}{2} = \pm\sqrt{\frac{1 - \cos\theta}{1 + \cos\theta}}. \tag{3}$$

It is possible to get two other expressions for tan $(\theta/2)$. If we multiply numerator and denominator of the radicand in (3) by $1 - \cos\theta$, there is found

$$\tan\frac{\theta}{2} = \pm\sqrt{\frac{(1-\cos\theta)^2}{1-\cos^2\theta}} = \pm\sqrt{\frac{(1-\cos\theta)^2}{\sin^2\theta}} = \pm\frac{1-\cos\theta}{\sin\theta}.$$

If we multiply numerator and denominator by $1 + \cos\theta$, we also have

$$\tan\frac{\theta}{2} = \pm\sqrt{\frac{1-\cos^2\theta}{(1+\cos\theta)^2}} = \pm\frac{\sin\theta}{1+\cos\theta}.$$

Moreover, it is possible to dispense with the ambiguous double signs in the two last expressions; this may be shown as follows. The cosine of an angle cannot exceed 1 nor can it be less than $-1$; consequently, $1 - \cos\theta$ and $1 + \cos\theta$ can never be negative. Hence the sign of $(1 - \cos\theta)/\sin\theta$ and the sign of $(\sin\theta)/(1 + \cos\theta)$ will depend only upon the algebraic sign of $\sin\theta$. Now $\sin\theta$ is positive when $\theta$ lies in the first or second quadrant, and $\sin\theta$ is negative when $\theta$ is in either the third or fourth quadrant; that is, $\sin\theta$ is positive for $0 < \theta < \pi$ and negative for $\pi < \theta < 2\pi$. But in these respective cases $0 < \theta/2 < \pi/2$, for which range tan $(\theta/2)$ is positive, and $\pi/2 < \theta/2 < \pi$, for which range tan $(\theta/2)$ is negative. Therefore, the relations

$$\tan\frac{\theta}{2} = \frac{1-\cos\theta}{\sin\theta} = \frac{\sin\theta}{1+\cos\theta} \qquad (4)$$

give not only the proper magnitude of tan $(\theta/2)$ but also the correct algebraic sign, regardless of the quadrants concerned.

In the majority of instances, the facts that expressions (4) are rational functions of $\sin\theta$ and $\cos\theta$, and that no ambiguity of sign is involved, make these formulas more convenient and more useful than relation (3) from which they stem.

*Example.* Prove the identity

$$\tan\left(\frac{\pi}{4} + \frac{\theta}{2}\right) = \sec\theta + \tan\theta.$$

*Solution.* The left member may be regarded as the tangent of a half angle, and hence transformed, as follows.

$$\tan\left(\frac{\pi}{4} + \frac{\theta}{2}\right) = \tan\frac{1}{2}\left(\frac{\pi}{2} + \theta\right) = \frac{1-\cos\left(\frac{\pi}{2}+\theta\right)}{\sin\left(\frac{\pi}{2}+\theta\right)}.$$

Since the desired result is rational in form, we have naturally used one of the two rational expressions (4). Moreover, since the final result is to consist of the sum of two terms, we choose the expression containing one term in the denominator, so that the indicated division may be performed. Now (Art. 18), $\cos (\pi/2 + \theta) = -\sin \theta$ and $\sin (\pi/2 + \theta) = \cos \theta$. Hence

$$\tan \left(\frac{\pi}{4} + \frac{\theta}{2}\right) = \frac{1 + \sin \theta}{\cos \theta} = \frac{1}{\cos \theta} + \frac{\sin \theta}{\cos \theta} = \sec \theta + \tan \theta.$$

## EXERCISES

*Tuesday Nov 5*

**1.** Find $\sin 75°$, $\cos 75°$, $\tan 75°$, using the fact that $75° = 150°/2$.

**2.** Find the sine, cosine, and tangent of $67° 30'$.

**3.** Find the sine, cosine, and tangent of $112° 30'$.

**4.** Find the sine, cosine, and tangent of $157° 30'$.

**5.** If $\theta$ is an acute angle, where $\cos \theta = \frac{1}{4}$, find the sine, cosine, and tangent of $\theta/2$.

**6.** If $\theta$ is an angle in the second quadrant, where $\cos \theta = -\frac{1}{3}$, find the sine, cosine, and tangent of $\theta/2$.

**7.** If $\theta$ is an angle in the third quadrant, where $\sin \theta = -\frac{3}{5}$, find the sine, cosine, and tangent of $\theta/2$.

**8.** If $\theta$ is an angle in the fourth quadrant, where $\tan \theta = -\frac{5}{12}$, find the sine, cosine, and tangent of $\theta/2$.

**9.** If $\theta$ is an acute angle such that $\tan \theta = \frac{3}{4}$, find $\sin (\pi/4 - \theta/2)$.

**10.** If $\theta$ is an acute angle such that $\sin \theta = \frac{24}{25}$, find $\cos (3\pi/4 + \theta/2)$.

**11.** If $\theta$ is an acute angle such that $\cos \theta = \frac{5}{13}$, find $\tan (5\pi/4 - \theta/2)$.

**12.** If $\theta$ is an acute angle such that $\sin \theta = \frac{1}{4}$, find $\sin (3\pi/4 - \theta/2)$.

**13.** If $\theta$ is an acute angle such that $\tan \theta = 3$, find $\tan (3\pi/4 + \theta/2)$.

**14.** If $a$, $b$, and $c$ are, respectively, the two legs and the hypotenuse of a right triangle, and if $A$ is the angle opposite side $a$, show that $\tan \dfrac{A}{2} = \dfrac{a}{b + c}$.

**15.** With the notation of Exercise 14, show that $\sin \dfrac{A}{2} = \sqrt{\dfrac{c - b}{2c}}$.

Prove the identities in Exercises 16–24.

**16.** $\tan \left(\dfrac{3\pi}{4} + \dfrac{\theta}{2}\right) = \tan \theta - \sec \theta.$

**17.** $\cot \left(\dfrac{5\pi}{4} + \dfrac{\theta}{2}\right) = \sec \theta - \tan \theta.$

**18.** $\cot \left(\dfrac{\theta}{2} - \dfrac{3\pi}{4}\right) = \sec \theta - \tan \theta.$

**19.** $\dfrac{1 - \tan (\theta/2)}{1 + \tan (\theta/2)} = \sec \theta - \tan \theta.$

**20.** $\dfrac{\sin 2\theta - 2 \sin \theta}{\sin 2\theta + 2 \sin \theta} + \tan^2 \dfrac{\theta}{2} = 0.$

**21.** $\dfrac{1 + \tan^2\left(\dfrac{3\pi}{4} + \theta\right)}{1 - \tan^2\left(\dfrac{3\pi}{4} + \theta\right)} = \csc 2\theta.$

**22.** $\sin^4\dfrac{\theta}{2} - 6\sin^2\dfrac{\theta}{2}\cos^2\dfrac{\theta}{2} + \cos^4\dfrac{\theta}{2} = \cos 2\theta.$

**23.** $16\cos^4\dfrac{\theta}{2} - 16\cos^2\dfrac{\theta}{2} + 3 = \dfrac{\sin 3\theta}{\sin \theta}.$

**24.** $32\cos^6\dfrac{\theta}{2} - 48\cos^4\dfrac{\theta}{2} + 18\cos^2\dfrac{\theta}{2} - 1 = \cos 3\theta.$

Solve the equations of Exercises 25–30 for non-negative values of $\theta$ less than $2\pi$.

**25.** $4\sin^2\dfrac{\theta}{2} - \cos^2\theta = 3.$          **26.** $2\cos^2\dfrac{\theta}{2} - 3\cos\theta = \sin^2\theta.$

**27.** $\tan\dfrac{\theta}{2} - 2\sin\theta = 0.$          **28.** $\tan\left(\dfrac{3\pi}{4} - \dfrac{\theta}{2}\right) + \cos\theta = 0.$

**29.** $\cos\left(\dfrac{\pi}{4} + \dfrac{\theta}{2}\right) = \tfrac{1}{4}.$          **30.** $\sin\left(\dfrac{\pi}{4} + \theta\right) = -\tfrac{1}{3}.$

**39. Relations between sums and products of functions.** In addition to the identities derived in Arts. 37–38, the formulas originally established in Art. 35 give rise to further useful relations. We consider here two sets of relations connecting sums and products of trigonometric functions.

If we add corresponding members of the identities

$$\sin(\alpha + \beta) = \sin\alpha\cos\beta + \cos\alpha\sin\beta, \tag{1}$$

$$\sin(\alpha - \beta) = \sin\alpha\cos\beta - \cos\alpha\sin\beta, \tag{2}$$

we get

$$\sin(\alpha + \beta) + \sin(\alpha - \beta) = 2\sin\alpha\cos\beta,$$

or

$$\sin\alpha\cos\beta = \tfrac{1}{2}\sin(\alpha + \beta) + \tfrac{1}{2}\sin(\alpha - \beta). \tag{3}$$

Similarly, if we subtract the two members of identity (2) from the corresponding members of (1), we are led to the relation

$$\cos\alpha\sin\beta = \tfrac{1}{2}\sin(\alpha + \beta) - \tfrac{1}{2}\sin(\alpha - \beta). \tag{4}$$

We may treat the identities

$$\cos(\alpha + \beta) = \cos\alpha\cos\beta - \sin\alpha\sin\beta,$$

$$\cos(\alpha - \beta) = \cos\alpha\cos\beta + \sin\alpha\sin\beta,$$

in like fashion. Adding and subtracting in turn, we find

$$\cos \alpha \cos \beta = \tfrac{1}{2} \cos (\alpha + \beta) + \tfrac{1}{2} \cos (\alpha - \beta), \tag{5}$$

$$\sin \alpha \sin \beta = -\tfrac{1}{2} \cos (\alpha + \beta) + \tfrac{1}{2} \cos (\alpha - \beta). \tag{6}$$

The identities (3)–(6) thus obtained enable us to express the product of a sine and a cosine, or of two sines or two cosines, as linear expressions in functions of the sum and difference of the two angles involved. These relations have application to integration techniques in calculus as well as to problems in analytic trigonometry.

*Example 1.* Transform the product $\sin \theta \sin 2\theta \sin 3\theta$ into a linear expression in trigonometric functions.

*Solution.* In this triple product we may segregate one factor, say $\sin \theta$, and transform the remaining product, $\sin 2\theta \sin 3\theta$, by means of identity (6). This yields

$$(\sin \theta)(\sin 2\theta \sin 3\theta) = (\sin \theta)[-\tfrac{1}{2} \cos (2\theta + 3\theta) + \tfrac{1}{2} \cos (2\theta - 3\theta)].$$

Since $\cos (2\theta - 3\theta) = \cos (-\theta) = \cos \theta$ (Art. 18), we have

$$\sin \theta \sin 2\theta \sin 3\theta = -\tfrac{1}{2} \sin \theta \cos 5\theta + \tfrac{1}{2} \sin \theta \cos \theta.$$

Using identity (3), or (4) may be used, this expression transforms into

$$-\tfrac{1}{2}[\tfrac{1}{2} \sin (\theta + 5\theta) + \tfrac{1}{2} \sin (\theta - 5\theta)] + \tfrac{1}{2}[\tfrac{1}{2} \sin (\theta + \theta) + \tfrac{1}{2} \sin (\theta - \theta)]$$

$$= -\tfrac{1}{4} \sin 6\theta - \tfrac{1}{4} \sin (-4\theta) + \tfrac{1}{4} \sin 2\theta + \tfrac{1}{4} \sin 0.$$

But $\sin (-4\theta) = -\sin 4\theta$ (Art. 18), and $\sin 0 = 0$ (Art. 16). Hence we get, as the desired expression,

$$\sin \theta \sin 2\theta \sin 3\theta = \tfrac{1}{4}(\sin 2\theta + \sin 4\theta - \sin 6\theta).$$

Instead of transforming products into sums, we sometimes have occasion to transform sums of functions into products. The identities (3)–(6), viewed from the opposite direction, so to speak, serve this purpose also. Now in these relations, the angles $\alpha$ and $\beta$ are respectively equal to half the sum and half the difference of the angles $\alpha + \beta$ and $\alpha - \beta$. Consequently, if we set $x = \alpha + \beta$ and $y = \alpha - \beta$, so that $\alpha = \tfrac{1}{2}(x + y)$ and $\beta = \tfrac{1}{2}(x - y)$, identities (3)–(6) assume the following forms:

$$\sin x + \sin y = 2 \sin \tfrac{1}{2}(x + y) \cos \tfrac{1}{2}(x - y), \tag{7}$$

$$\sin x - \sin y = 2 \cos \tfrac{1}{2}(x + y) \sin \tfrac{1}{2}(x - y), \tag{8}$$

$$\cos x + \cos y = 2 \cos \tfrac{1}{2}(x + y) \cos \tfrac{1}{2}(x - y), \tag{9}$$

$$\cos x - \cos y = -2 \sin \tfrac{1}{2}(x + y) \sin \tfrac{1}{2}(x - y). \tag{10}$$

Relations (7)–(10) are thus merely restatements of the preceding four identities, written in such a way as to emphasize their character as expressions equivalent to the sum or difference of two sines or two cosines.

*Example 2.* Prove the identity

$$\frac{\sin \theta + \sin 2\theta + \sin 3\theta}{\cos \theta + \cos 2\theta + \cos 3\theta} = \tan 2\theta.$$

*Solution.* We naturally attempt to transform the more complicated left member into the simpler right member. Now since a function of $2\theta$ is ultimately desired, we leave the functions of $2\theta$ in the left member intact, and only transform the remaining sums in numerator and denominator, $\sin \theta + \sin 3\theta$ and $\cos \theta + \cos 3\theta$, respectively, by means of identities (7) and (9). This gives us

$$\frac{\sin \theta + \sin 2\theta + \sin 3\theta}{\cos \theta + \cos 2\theta + \cos 3\theta} = \frac{\sin 2\theta + 2 \sin \frac{1}{2}(\theta + 3\theta) \cos \frac{1}{2}(\theta - 3\theta)}{\cos 2\theta + 2 \cos \frac{1}{2}(\theta + 3\theta) \cos \frac{1}{2}(\theta - 3\theta)}.$$

Since $\cos \frac{1}{2}(\theta - 3\theta) = \cos (-\theta) = \cos \theta$ (Art. 18), the last expression reduces to

$$\frac{\sin 2\theta + 2 \sin 2\theta \cos \theta}{\cos 2\theta + 2 \cos 2\theta \cos \theta} = \frac{\sin 2\theta (1 + 2 \cos \theta)}{\cos 2\theta (1 + 2 \cos \theta)} = \frac{\sin 2\theta}{\cos 2\theta} = \tan 2\theta,$$

the desired result.

*Tuesday*

### EXERCISES

In Exercises 1–10, evaluate the given expressions without using tables.

1. $\sin 15° \cos 45°$.
2. $\sin 22° \ 30' \sin 67° \ 30'$.
3. $\cos 15° \cos 165°$.
4. $\cos 127° \ 30' \sin 7° \ 30'$.
5. $\sin 52° \ 30' \sin 262° \ 30'$.
6. $\sin 105° + \sin 15°$.
7. $\sin 75° - \sin 15°$.
8. $\cos 255° + \cos 165°$.
9. $\cos 165° - \cos 75°$.
10. $\dfrac{\sin 7° + \cos 7°}{\sin 52°}$.

Prove the identities in Exercises 11–30.

11. $\dfrac{\sin \alpha - \sin \beta}{\cos \alpha - \cos \beta} = - \cot \frac{1}{2}(\alpha + \beta)$.

12. $\dfrac{\sin 4\theta - \sin 2\theta}{\cos 4\theta + \cos 2\theta} = \tan \theta$.

13. $\sin \left(\dfrac{\pi}{6} + \theta\right) + \sin \left(\dfrac{\pi}{6} - \theta\right) = \cos \theta$.

14. $\cos \left(\theta - \dfrac{\pi}{3}\right) + \cos \left(\theta + \dfrac{\pi}{3}\right) = \cos \theta$.

15. $\sin \left(\theta + \dfrac{\pi}{4}\right) - \cos \left(\theta + \dfrac{\pi}{4}\right) = \sqrt{2} \sin \theta$.

**16.** $4 \sin^3 \theta = 3 \sin \theta - \sin 3\theta.$      **17.** $4 \cos^3 \theta = 3 \cos \theta + \cos 3\theta.$
**18.** $4 \sin \theta \cos^2 \theta = \sin \theta + \sin 3\theta.$      **19.** $4 \sin^2 \theta \cos \theta = \cos \theta - \cos 3\theta.$

**20.** $16 \sin^3 \theta \cos^2 \theta = 2 \sin \theta + \sin 3\theta - \sin 5\theta.$
**21.** $16 \sin^2 \theta \cos^3 \theta = 2 \cos \theta - \cos 3\theta - \cos 5\theta.$
**22.** $16 \sin^4 \theta \cos \theta = 2 \cos \theta - 3 \cos 3\theta + \cos 5\theta.$
**23.** $16 \sin \theta \cos^4 \theta = 2 \sin \theta + 3 \sin 3\theta + \sin 5\theta.$
**24.** $16 \sin^5 \theta = 10 \sin \theta - 5 \sin 3\theta + \sin 5\theta.$
**25.** $16 \cos^5 \theta = 10 \cos \theta + 5 \cos 3\theta + \cos 5\theta.$
**26.** $\sin \theta + \sin 3\theta + \sin 5\theta + \sin 7\theta = 4 \cos \theta \cos 2\theta \sin 4\theta.$
**27.** $\cos \theta + \cos 3\theta + \cos 5\theta + \cos 7\theta = 4 \cos \theta \cos 2\theta \cos 4\theta.$
**28.** $\cos \theta \cos 2\theta \cos 3\theta = \frac{1}{4}(1 + \cos 2\theta + \cos 4\theta + \cos 6\theta).$
**29.** $\sin \theta + 2 \sin 3\theta - \sin 5\theta = 2(\sin \theta)(1 + \cos 2\theta - \cos 4\theta).$
**30.** $\sin \theta - 3 \sin 3\theta - 2 \sin 5\theta = -2(\sin \theta \cos 2\theta)(5 + 4 \cos 2\theta).$

If $A$, $B$, and $C$ are the angles of any triangle, show that the relations of Exercises 31–35 are true.

**31.** $\sin A + \sin B + \sin C = 4 \cos \dfrac{A}{2} \cos \dfrac{B}{2} \cos \dfrac{C}{2}.$

**32.** $\cos A + \cos B + \cos C = 1 + 4 \sin \dfrac{A}{2} \sin \dfrac{B}{2} \sin \dfrac{C}{2}.$

**33.** $\sin 2A + \sin 2B + \sin 2C = 4 \sin A \sin B \sin C.$
**34.** $\cos 2A + \cos 2B + \cos 2C = -1 - 4 \cos A \cos B \cos C.$
**35.** $\sin 4A + \sin 4B + \sin 4C = -4 \sin 2A \sin 2B \sin 2C.$

Solve the equations in Exercises 36–45 for non-negative values of $\theta$ less than $2\pi$.

**36.** $\sin \theta - \sin 3\theta = 0.$      **37.** $\sin \theta + \sin 3\theta = 0.$
**38.** $\cos \theta - \cos 3\theta = 0.$      **39.** $\cos \theta + \cos 3\theta = 0.$
**40.** $\cos 3\theta - \cos 5\theta = 0.$      **41.** $\cos 3\theta + \cos 5\theta = 0.$
**42.** $\sin \theta - \sin 2\theta + \sin 3\theta = 0.$      **43.** $\cos \theta - \cos 2\theta + \cos 3\theta = \theta.$
**44.** $\sin \theta + \sin 3\theta + \sin 5\theta = 0.$      **45.** $\cos \theta + \cos 3\theta + \cos 5\theta = 0.$

## 40. Sine, cosine, and tangent laws.

In this article we shall consider three relations among the sides and angles of a triangle. These relations can be used to obtain further dependencies among the parts of a triangle and to solve various types of problems involving planar and spatial configurations.

Two of the relations under consideration can be obtained directly from the geometry of the triangle. Let $A$, $B$, and $C$ be the vertex angles of the triangle, and let $a$, $b$, $c$ denote the sides opposite these angles, respectively. Draw an altitude from one vertex, say $A$, and denote the length of this altitude by $h$. According as angles $B$ and $C$ are acute, one is a right angle, or one is obtuse, we then have the corresponding diagram in Fig. 20. In all three cases, $h = c \sin B$; in (i), (ii), and (iii), we also have, respectively: $h = b \sin C$, $h = b$, and $h = b \sin (\pi - C)$. But in (ii), $C = \pi/2$, and $\sin C = 1$; and in (iii),

$\sin{(\pi - C)} = \sin{C}$ (Art. 18). Hence in all cases it is correct to say that $h = b \sin{C}$. Equating the two expressions for $h$, we have

$$h = c \sin{B} = b \sin{C}, \tag{1}$$

whence

$$\frac{c}{\sin{C}} = \frac{b}{\sin{B}}. \tag{2}$$

By drawing another altitude and equating two expressions for its length, we can find a second relation between two sides and the sines of the angles opposite, of the same form as (2). However, since the

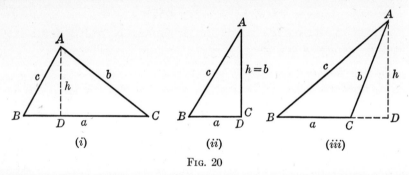

Fig. 20

labeling of the vertices $A$, $B$, and $C$ is arbitrary, it is clear that another relation can be obtained from (2) merely by a cyclic change of letters; that is, we change $A$ into $B$, $B$ into $C$, $C$ into $A$, $a$ into $b$, $b$ into $c$, and $c$ into $a$. Then (2) is replaced by

$$\frac{a}{\sin{A}} = \frac{c}{\sin{C}}. \tag{3}$$

Combining (2) and (3), we get the continued equality

$$\frac{a}{\sin{A}} = \frac{b}{\sin{B}} = \frac{c}{\sin{C}}. \tag{4}$$

Thus, we have the so-called **law of sines:**

*In any triangle, the ratio of a side to the sine of the opposite angle is the same for all three choices of corresponding parts.*

Now let $d$ denote the length of the segment $BD$, so that the length of $DC$ is $a - d$, 0, or $d - a$ according as we have case (i), (ii), or (iii) of Fig. 20. From the right triangle $ABD$, we get $h^2 = c^2 - d^2$; from the right triangle $ACD$, $h^2 = b^2 - (DC)^2 = b^2 - (a - d)^2$. Equating the two expressions for $h^2$ and simplifying, we find

$$c^2 - d^2 = b^2 - (a - d)^2 = b^2 - a^2 + 2ad - d^2,$$
$$c^2 = b^2 - a^2 + 2ad.$$

But, in right triangle $ABD$, $d = c \cos B$. Inserting this value for $d$, and rearranging terms, there is obtained

$$b^2 = a^2 + c^2 - 2ac \cos B. \tag{5}$$

Cyclic change of the letters involved in (5) gives us, in turn,

$$c^2 = b^2 + a^2 - 2ba \cos C, \tag{6}$$
$$a^2 = c^2 + b^2 - 2cb \cos A. \tag{7}$$

Any of the three relations (5), (6), or (7) may be regarded as representing the **law of cosines**, which may be stated as follows:

*In any triangle, the square of one side is equal to the sum of the squares of the other two sides, minus twice the product of the latter two sides and the cosine of their included angle.*

Our third relation may be obtained from the law of sines by the application of identities established in Art. 39. If we denote the common value of the ratios in (4) by $r$, we have, in particular, $a = r \sin A$ and $b = r \sin B$. Hence

$$\frac{a - b}{a + b} = \frac{r \sin A - r \sin B}{r \sin A + r \sin B} = \frac{\sin A - \sin B}{\sin A + \sin B}.$$

The last fraction may be transformed by means of identities (7) and (8) of Art. 39; this yields

$$\frac{a - b}{a + b} = \frac{2 \cos \frac{1}{2}(A + B) \sin \frac{1}{2}(A - B)}{2 \sin \frac{1}{2}(A + B) \cos \frac{1}{2}(A - B)}$$
$$= \cot \tfrac{1}{2}(A + B) \tan \tfrac{1}{2}(A - B),$$

or

$$\frac{a - b}{a + b} = \frac{\tan \frac{1}{2}(A - B)}{\tan \frac{1}{2}(A + B)}. \tag{8}$$

Similar relations among other pairs of sides and the corresponding angles may be written down by cyclic changes of letters. This relation, known as the **law of tangents,** may be expressed verbally as follows:

*In any triangle, the difference of two sides is to their sum as the tangent of half the difference of the corresponding opposite angles is to the tangent of half the sum of these angles.*

Since $A + B = \pi - C$ in any triangle, $\tan \frac{1}{2}(A + B) = \tan \frac{1}{2}(\pi - C)$ $= \cot (C/2)$ (Art. 18). Therefore another form of the tangent law may be written as

$$\tan \tfrac{1}{2}(A - B) = \frac{a - b}{a + b} \cot \frac{C}{2}. \tag{8'}$$

*Example.* Prove that, in any triangle,

$$(a + b) \cos C + (b + c) \cos A + (c + a) \cos B = a + b + c.$$

*Solution.* The sine law (4) may be used to solve this problem. Letting $r$ denote the common value of the ratios in (4), we have $a = r \sin A$, $b = r \sin B$, and $c = r \sin C$. Substituting these expressions in the left member, we get

$$r(\sin A \cos C + \sin B \cos C + \cos A \sin B + \cos A \sin C$$
$$+ \cos B \sin C + \sin A \cos B).$$

Now these six terms inside the parentheses may be grouped in three pairs, each pair involving the same two angles. Thus, the first and fourth terms yield $\sin A \cos C + \cos A \sin C = \sin (A + C)$, by identity (1), Art. 35. Similarly, the second and fifth terms yield $\sin (B + C)$, and the third and sixth give us $\sin (A + B)$. Hence the original left member becomes

$$r[\sin (A + C) + \sin (B + C) + \sin (A + B)].$$

Using $A + B + C = \pi$, we have $\sin (A + C) = \sin (\pi - B) = \sin B$, $\sin (B + C) = \sin (\pi - A) = \sin A$, and $\sin (A + B) = \sin (\pi - C) = \sin C$. Consequently the above expression is transformed into

$$r(\sin B + \sin A + \sin C).$$

Finally, $r \sin B = b$, $r \sin A = a$, and $r \sin C = c$ by the definition of $r$. Therefore the last expression reduces to

$$a + b + c,$$

the desired result.

This problem may also be solved by replacing $\cos A$, $\cos B$, and $\cos C$ by their values in terms of $a$, $b$, and $c$, as given by the cosine law. The resulting expression, however, requires considerable algebraic manipulation to reduce it to the final result.

**41. Oblique triangles.** We have already dealt with problems involving right triangles and with certain oblique triangles (Art. 17). As regards oblique triangles in general, it is evident that a triangle is determined, that is, may be geometrically constructed, in each of four cases: (*a*) one side and two angles given; (*b*) two sides and the included angle given; (*c*) two sides and the angle opposite one of them given; (*d*) the three sides given. In all four cases (except for certain special circum-

stances to be considered later), the given triangle will be completely
solvable by application of one or more of the three laws derived above;
that is, all the remaining parts may be calculated. We consider briefly
the four cases in turn.

(a) When two angles are known, the third may be easily found since
the sum of all three must be 180°. The sine law then enables us to
determine the remaining two sides. Thus, if $a$, $A$, and $B$ are given, we
get $C = 180° - (A + B)$, and then compute $b = a(\sin B)/\sin A$ and
$c = a(\sin C)/\sin A$. Evidently the only unsolvable problem is the ob-

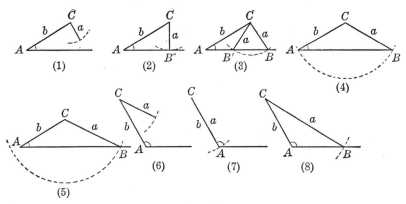

FIG. 21

viously impossible one in which the sum of the two given angles exceeds or is equal to 180°.

(b) When two sides and the included angle are known, one method
of solving the triangle is first to find the third side by means of the
cosine law, and then to find a second angle from the sine law; finally,
the third angle may be determined from the relation $A + B + C =$
180°. Thus, if $a$, $b$, and $C$ are known, we find $c$ from $c^2 = a^2 + b^2 -$
$2ab \cos C$, then $A$, say, from $\sin A = a(\sin C)/c$, and finally $B = 180°$
$- (A + C)$. Alternatively, $A - B$ may be found from the tangent
law (8'), and since $A + B = 180° - C$, $A$ and $B$ may be obtained by
solving two linear equations. No unsolvable problems may arise in
this case.

(c) When two sides, say $a$ and $b$, and the angle $A$ opposite one of
them are known, eight distinct situations may arise (apart from the
case in which $A$ is a right angle), as illustrated in Fig. 21: (1) if $A < 90°$
and $b \sin A > a$, no triangle can be constructed; (2) if $A < 90°$ and
$b \sin A = a$, there is just one triangle, a right triangle; (3) if $A < 90°$

and $b \sin A < a < b$, there exist two different triangles with the given parts; (4) if $A < 90°$ and $a = b$, there exists just one (isosceles) triangle; (5) if $A < 90°$ and $a > b$, there is just one triangle; (6) if $A > 90°$ and $a < b$, no triangle can be constructed; (7) if $A > 90°$ and $a = b$, no actual triangle exists; (8) if $A > 90°$ and $a > b$, there is just one triangle.

The last five subcases are easily identified by mere inspection of the magnitudes of the given parts. If subcase (6) or (7) is encountered, it may be discarded immediately, since no solution is possible. The unique solution arising in subcase (4), (5), or (8) is readily obtained; we may determine the acute angle $B$ from the sine law, $\sin B = b(\sin A)/a$, then find $C = 180° - (A + B)$, and finally determine $c = a(\sin C)/\sin A$. Subcases (1), (2), and (3) may be distinguished by means of the sine law, $\sin B = b(\sin A)/a$. For, if $b \sin A > a$, we get $\sin B > 1$, which is impossible; if $b \sin A = a$, then $\sin B = 1$ and $B = 90°$, whence $C$ and $c$ may be calculated; if $b \sin A < a$ (and $A < 90°$), then $\sin B = b(\sin A)/a$ yields an acute angle $B$ and its supplement $B'$, for each of which the corresponding parts $C$ and $c$, and $C'$ and $c'$, may be computed.

(*d*) When the three sides are known, two applications of the cosine law (5)–(7) enable us to determine two angles, say $A$ and $B$. Then $C = 180° - (A + B)$. The only unsolvable problem is that in which the sum of two of the given sides fails to exceed the third side. Other relations, derivable from the cosine law, may be used as an alternative method, which we shall consider in Chapter XIV in connection with logarithmic computation.

*Example.* The distance from a point $A$ on a straight river bank to a point $P$ on the other side and upstream is to be determined. Since an obstruction prevents sighting $P$ from $A$, a distance $a$ is measured from $A$ to a point $B$ on the same bank part way upstream, from which $P$ may be seen, and the acute angle $\alpha$ between $BP$ and the bank is measured. Continuing upstream a distance $BC = b$, a point $C$ is fixed from which $P$ is again visible, and the acute angle $\beta = BCP$ is measured. It is required to find an equation determining the distance $AP$.

*Solution.* Figure 22 indicates the known distances and angles and the unknown distance $x = AP$. Now $x$ may be regarded as one side of the triangle $ABP$, in which another side $a$ and one angle, $ABP = \pi - \alpha$, are known. Hence $x$ may be determined by the cosine law if $BP$ can be found. But $BP$ is one side of the triangle $BCP$, in which another side $b$ and two angles, $\alpha$ and $\beta$, are known. Hence we may find $BP$ by means of the sine law. We have

$$\frac{BP}{\sin \beta} = \frac{b}{\sin BPC},$$

and since $BPC = \pi - (\alpha + \beta)$, $\sin BPC = \sin (\alpha + \beta)$ (Art. 18), whence

$$BP = \frac{b \sin \beta}{\sin (\alpha + \beta)}.$$

Applying the cosine law to triangle $ABP$, we get, since angle $ABP = \pi - \alpha$, $\cos ABP = -\cos \alpha$ (Art. 18), and

$$x^2 = a^2 + (BP)^2 - 2a(BP)(-\cos \alpha),$$

$$x^2 = a^2 + \frac{b^2 \sin^2 \beta}{\sin^2 (\alpha + \beta)} + \frac{2ab \sin \beta \cos \alpha}{\sin (\alpha + \beta)}.$$

This is the desired result.

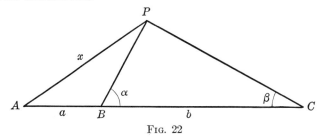

FIG. 22

## EXERCISES

If $a$, $b$, and $c$ are the sides and $A$, $B$, $C$ are the respective opposite angles in any triangle, prove the relations in Exercises 1–5.

**1.** $a^2 + b^2 + c^2 = 2(ab \cos C + bc \cos A + ca \cos B)$.

**2.** $a^2 - b^2 = c(a \cos B - b \cos A)$.

**3.** $a(\sin B + \cos B) - b(\sin A - \cos A) = c$.

**4.** $(a + b) \sin (A + B) = c(\sin A + \sin B)$.

**5.** $\sin^2 A + \sin^2 B - \sin^2 C = 2 \sin A \sin B \cos C$.

**6.** If two sides, $a$ and $b$, and the included angle $C$ of a triangle are known, show that the area of the triangle is given by $\frac{1}{2}ab \sin C$.

**7.** If one side, $a$, and the two adjacent angles, $B$ and $C$, are known, show that the area of the triangle is given by $a^2(\sin B \sin C)/2 \sin (B + C)$.

**8.** Show that each ratio of a side of a triangle to the sine of the opposite angle is equal to the diameter of the circumscribed circle.

**9.** Show that the area of any quadrilateral is equal to half the product of the two diagonals and the sine of either angle between the diagonals.

**10.** The two parallel sides of a trapezoid are $a$ and $b$ ($a > b$), and the two non-parallel sides form acute angles $\alpha$ and $\beta$ with the side $a$. Show that the lengths of the non-parallel sides are respectively given by $(a - b)(\sin \alpha)/\sin (\alpha + \beta)$ and $(a - b)(\sin \beta)/\sin (\alpha + \beta)$.

**11.** A right circular cone has an altitude $h$ and semivertical angle $\alpha$ (angle between axis and each element). From the base of the cone, a line segment forming a prolongation of the axis subtends an angle $\beta$. Show that the length of the segment is $h(\sin \beta)/\cos \alpha \sin (\alpha - \beta)$.

**12.** From two points, a distance $a$ apart and in line with the foot of a tree, the angles of elevation of the top of the tree are respectively $\alpha$ and $\beta$. Show that the height of the tree is $a(\sin \alpha \sin \beta)/\sin (\alpha - \beta)$. (Cf. Example 2, Art. 17.)

**13.** From two points, a distance $a$ apart and in the plane of the foot of a tree, the angles of elevation of the top of the tree are respectively $\alpha$ and $\beta$. The line joining the given points forms angles $\theta$ and $\phi$, respectively, with the lines joining each point to the foot of the tree. Show that the height of the tree is given by either $a(\tan \alpha \sin \phi)/\sin (\theta + \phi)$ or $a(\tan \beta \sin \theta)/\sin (\theta + \phi)$.

**14.** If, in Exercise 13, angle $\phi$ is not known but $\theta = \pi/2$, show that the height of the tree can be obtained in terms of $a$, $\alpha$, and $\beta$ as

$$\frac{a \sin \alpha \sin \beta}{\sqrt{\sin (\alpha + \beta) \sin (\alpha - \beta)}}.$$

**15.** Given a right triangle $ABC$, with $C$ as right angle, and a point $P$ inside the triangle and at a perpendicular distance $PD = a$ from side $BC$. If the angles $BAP = \alpha$, $PAC = \beta$, and $BPD = \theta$ are known, show that the distance $AP$ is given by $a \sin (\theta - \alpha - \beta)/(\sin \alpha \cos \theta)$.

**16.** In order to find the distance between two points $P$ and $Q$, a distance $AB = a$ is measured in the horizontal plane through $P$ and $Q$, and the angles $PAB = \alpha$, $QBA = \beta$, $QAB = \theta$, and $PBA = \phi$ are also measured. Show that the distance $x = PQ$ is given by

$$x^2 = \frac{a^2 \sin^2 \phi}{\sin^2 (\alpha + \phi)} + \frac{a^2 \sin^2 \beta}{\sin^2 (\beta + \theta)} - \frac{2a^2 \sin \beta \sin \phi \cos (\alpha - \theta)}{\sin (\alpha + \phi) \sin (\beta + \theta)}.$$

**17.** In a quadrilateral $ABCD$, $AB = a$, $AD = b$, angle $DAB = \theta$, and angles $ABC$ and $ADC$ are right angles. Show that the area of the quadrilateral is equal to $ab \csc \theta - \frac{1}{2}(a^2 + b^2) \cot \theta$.

**18.** A triangle $ABC$ is revolved about the side $AC$ through an angle $\alpha$. Show that the angle $\theta$ between the original and final positions of $AB$ is given by

$$\sin \frac{\theta}{2} = \sin A \sin \frac{\alpha}{2}.$$

**19.** From a point $P$ on the hypotenuse $AB$ of a right triangle $ABC$, a line $PQ$ is drawn meeting the side $CA$, produced, in the point $Q$. Let $AC = a$, $BP = d$, angle $BAC = \alpha$, and angle $PQA = \beta$. Show that the length $CQ$ is given by $a \tan \alpha \cot \beta - d \csc \beta \sin (\alpha - \beta)$.

**20.** The side $c$ and the two adjacent angles $A$ and $B$ of a triangle $ABC$ are given. Show that the length of the median drawn from the vertex $C$ is equal to

$$\frac{c\sqrt{\sin^2 (A - B) + 4 \sin^2 A \sin^2 B}}{2 \sin (A + B)}.$$

## SUPPLEMENTARY EXERCISES

Solve the equations of Exercises 1–8 for non-negative values of $x$ less than $2\pi$.

**1.** $\tan x + \cot 3x = 0$.   **2.** $\tan x + \tan 3x = 0$.

**3.** $\sin x + \sin 3x + \cos x = 0$.   **4.** $\sin x - \sin 3x + \cos 2x = 0$.

**5.** $\cos x - \cos 3x + \sin x = 0$.   **6.** $\cos x - \cos 3x - \sin 2x = 0$.

**7.** $\sin x + \sin 3x = \cos x + \cos 3x$.

**8.** $\sin x - \sin 3x = \cos x - \cos 3x$.

Prove the identities in Exercises 9–11.

**9.** $\dfrac{1}{2}\left(1 + \tan \dfrac{\theta}{2}\right)^2 = \dfrac{1 + \sin \theta}{1 + \cos \theta}$.

**10.** $\cos^4 \theta = \tfrac{1}{8}(3 + 4\cos 2\theta + \cos 4\theta)$.

**11.** $\sin^4 \theta + \cos^4 \theta = \tfrac{1}{4}(3 + \cos 4\theta)$.

**12.** If $A + B + C = 90°$, show that

$$\tan A \tan B + \tan A \tan C + \tan B \tan C = 1.$$

If $A$, $B$, and $C$ are the angles of any triangle, show that the relations of Exercises 13–16 are true.

**13.** $\cos 4A + \cos 4B + \cos 4C = 4\cos 2A \cos 2B \cos 2C - 1$.

**14.** $\cot A \cot B + \cot A \cot C + \cot B \cot C = 1$.

**15.** $\sin A \cos B \cos C + \cos A \sin B \cos C + \cos A \cos B \sin C - \sin A \sin B \sin C = 0$.

**16.** $\cos A \cos B \cos C - \sin A \sin B \cos C - \sin A \cos B \sin C - \cos A \sin B \sin C = -1$.

**17.** Using the fact that $\cos \tfrac{1}{2}\theta = \cos (\theta - \tfrac{1}{2}\theta)$, and expanding the latter expression, derive the first of formulas (4), Art. 38.

**18.** Using the fact that $\sin \tfrac{1}{2}\theta = \sin (\theta - \tfrac{1}{2}\theta)$, and expanding the latter expression, derive the second of formulas (4), Art. 38.

Let $A$, $B$, and $C$ be the vertex angles of any triangle, and let $a$, $b$, $c$ denote the sides opposite these angles, respectively. Using the law of sines, derive the relations of Exercises 19–20, known as *Mollweide's equations*, which, since each contains all six parts of a triangle, are useful for checking purposes in computational work with oblique triangles.

**19.** $\dfrac{a - b}{c} = \dfrac{\sin \tfrac{1}{2}(A - B)}{\cos \tfrac{1}{2}C}$.

**20.** $\dfrac{a + b}{c} = \dfrac{\cos \tfrac{1}{2}(A - B)}{\sin \tfrac{1}{2}C}$.

# VII—— Mathematical Induction and the Binomial Theorem

**42. Mathematical induction.** When a certain theorem or principle has been established in a specific instance, it is natural to speculate concerning its generality. Thus, having derived formulas in Art. 35 for the sine and cosine of the sum of two acute angles, we asked the question: Are these formulas true for the sum of any two angles, whatever their magnitudes? It will be remembered that we were able to answer this question in the affirmative when we attacked the problem in a logically proper manner.

The reasoning employed in Art. 35 to prove a general result was one example of the logical process known as **mathematical induction.** It is our purpose in this article to examine the nature and further uses of mathematical induction, which is one of the most powerful modes of reasoning in mathematics.

We first consider the essential nature of the logic applied, as exemplified by the argument given in Art. 35. We have, to begin with, a particular case in which the result in question is known to be true. We next assume that it is true in some particular but *unspecified* case; thus, in Art. 35, we assumed that the identities hold for $\alpha$ and $\beta$ respectively in the particular but unspecified quadrants $r$ and $s$. Using this assumption as a working basis, we then attempt to deduce the truth of the result in the *next succeeding* case; thus, we proved that *if* the formulas are correct for $\alpha$ in quadrant $r$ and $\beta$ in quadrant $s$, *then, as a logical consequence of just this assumption,* they must be true when $\alpha$ is in quadrant $r$ and $\beta$ in quadrant $s + 1$, next following $s$.

If we are successful, we have deduced that the result is true in some particular instance *provided that* it is true in the one immediately before, *whatever* that may be. We now reason as follows. Since it is true in the case first verified, it follows that it must likewise be true in the one following. Since it is true in the second case, the general nature of the reasoning insures truth in the third. By proceeding in this way, we can pass from each case to the next, one by one, until every possible one has ultimately been reached, and consequently our result is generally true.

The method of mathematical induction therefore entails three steps, as follows:

1. The result in question must be verified for one specific instance. For simplicity and completeness, this should be chosen as the first of the chain, since it is this on which the reasoning builds, case after case.

2. The result must be assumed true for an unspecified case, $s$, and the truth for case $s + 1$ deduced from this assumption.

3. Using the case $s = 1$, known to be true by the first step, the truth for case $s + 1 = 2$ follows from the second step. Verbal logic then completes the task, by using the second step successively to pass from case $s + 1$ to case $s + 2$, $s + 3$, and so on indefinitely.

*Example 1.* We know from experience that $a - b$ is a factor of itself, of $a^2 - b^2$, and of $a^3 - b^3$ (Art. 6):

$$a - b = (a - b) \cdot 1,$$

$$a^2 - b^2 = (a - b)(a + b),$$

$$a^3 - b^3 = (a - b)(a^2 + ab + b^2).$$

Hence we pose the question whether or not $a - b$ is a factor of $a^n - b^n$ when $n$ is an integer greater than 3; that is, we attempt to prove that $a^n - b^n$ is divisible by $a - b$ for every positive integer $n$.

*Solution.* We follow the three steps stated above.

1. The simplest case is that in which $n = 1$, since this is the least positive integer. As already mentioned, it is clear that $a - b$ is divisible by itself.

2. Assume that $a^s - b^s$ is divisible by $a - b$ for some unspecified positive integer $s$, and consider the expression $a^{s+1} - b^{s+1}$. Now, in order to make use of our assumption, we must express $a^{s+1} - b^{s+1}$ so as to bring $a^s - b^s$ into play. Since the first term of $a^{s+1} - b^{s+1}$ is obtained from the first term of $a^s - b^s$ by multiplying by $a$, we take $a(a^s - b^s) = a^{s+1} - ab^s$ as a basic identity. Then $a^{s+1} = a(a^s - b^s) + ab^s$, and

$$a^{s+1} - b^{s+1} = a(a^s - b^s) + ab^s - b^{s+1}$$

$$= a(a^s - b^s) + b^s(a - b).$$

But $b^s(a - b)$ is evidently divisible by $a - b$. Hence, if $a^s - b^s$ is divisible by $a - b$, the sum of the two terms in the above right member is divisible by $a - b$. Consequently the expression $a^{s+1} - b^{s+1}$, identically equal to that sum, is divisible by $a - b$ if $a^s - b^s$ is so divisible.

3. Since $a^1 - b^1$ is divisible by $a - b$ ($s = 1$), $a^2 - b^2$ is likewise divisible. Since $a^2 - b^2$ has $a - b$ as a factor ($s = 2$), $a^3 - b^3$ has $a - b$ as a factor; and so on for $s = 3, 4, \cdots, n$. Therefore it is true that $a^n - b^n$ is divisible by $a - b$ for every positive integer $n$.

*Example 2.* Prove that the sum of the first, second, $\cdots$, $n$th powers of 3 is $\frac{3}{2}(3^n - 1)$.

*Solution.* We are to show that the sum of the $n$ terms, $3 + 3^2 + \cdots + 3^n$, has the stated value. Now when $n = 1$, so that there is just one term, 3, in the sum, we have $\frac{3}{2}(3 - 1) = 3$, whence the theorem is verified for $n = 1$. We then assume that, for some positive integer $s$, the sum of $s$ terms has the value $\frac{3}{2}(3^s - 1)$:

$$3 + 3^2 + \cdots + 3^s = \tfrac{3}{2}(3^s - 1).$$

To get the sum of $s + 1$ terms, we must add the $(s + 1)$th term, $3^{s+1}$, to the left member. Hence we add $3^{s+1}$ to both members of the assumed equality, to obtain an equivalent relation:

$$3 + 3^2 + \cdots + 3^s + 3^{s+1} = \tfrac{3}{2}(3^s - 1) + 3^{s+1}.$$

We now have to show that the latter right member is identical with the expression obtained when $n$ is replaced by $s + 1$ in $\frac{3}{2}(3^n - 1)$. We find, in fact, that

$$\tfrac{3}{2}(3^s - 1) + 3^{s+1} = \tfrac{1}{2} \cdot 3^{s+1} - \tfrac{3}{2} + 3^{s+1} = \tfrac{3}{2}(3^{s+1} - 1).$$

Hence, if the sum of $s$ terms is given by the formula with $n = s$, it follows that the sum of $s + 1$ terms is obtained when $n$ is replaced by $s + 1$.

Since the formula is correct for $n = 1$, it must therefore be correct for $n = 2$; hence, for $n = 3$; and so on. Therefore it is true for every positive integer $n$.

### EXERCISES

Prove each of the following by means of mathematical induction. In each exercise, $n$ denotes a positive integer.

**1.** $1 + 2 + 3 + \cdots + n = \frac{1}{2}n(n + 1)$.

**2.** $1 + 3 + 5 + \cdots + (2n - 1) = n^2$.

**3.** $a^{2n} - b^{2n}$ is divisible by $a + b$.

**4.** $2 + 2^2 + 2^3 + \cdots + 2^n = 2(2^n - 1)$.

**5.** $1^2 + 2^2 + 3^2 + \cdots + n^2 = \frac{1}{6}n(n + 1)(2n + 1)$.

**6.** $a^{2n-1} + b^{2n-1}$ is divisible by $a + b$.

**7.** $\frac{1}{2}n(n - 1)$ straight lines are determined by $n$ points no three of which are collinear.

**8.** $\dfrac{1}{1 \cdot 2} + \dfrac{1}{2 \cdot 3} + \cdots + \dfrac{1}{n(n + 1)} = \dfrac{n}{n + 1}$.

**9.** $1 + 5 + 9 + \cdots + (4n - 3) = n(2n - 1)$.

**10.** $1 + \dfrac{1}{2} + \dfrac{1}{2^2} + \cdots + \dfrac{1}{2^{n-1}} = \dfrac{2^n - 1}{2^{n-1}}$.

**11.** $a + (a + d) + \cdots + [a + (n - 1)d] = \frac{1}{2}n[2a + (n - 1)d]$.

**12.** $a + ar + ar^2 + \cdots + ar^{n-1} = \dfrac{a(1 - r^n)}{1 - r}$.

**13.** $1^2 + 3^2 + 5^2 + \cdots + (2n - 1)^2 = \frac{1}{3}n(2n + 1)(2n - 1)$.

**14.** $1 \cdot 3 + 3 \cdot 3^2 + 5 \cdot 3^3 + \cdots + (2n - 1)3^n = 3^{n+1}(n - 1) + 3$.

**15.** $1^3 + 2^3 + 3^3 + \cdots + n^3 = \frac{1}{4}n^2(n+1)^2$.

**16.** $1^3 + 3^3 + 5^3 + \cdots + (2n-1)^3 = n^2(2n^2 - 1)$.

**17.** $2 + 5 + 8 + \cdots + (3n-1) = \frac{1}{2}n(3n+1)$.

**18.** $1 \cdot 3 + 2 \cdot 5 + \cdots + n(2n+1) = \frac{1}{6}n(n+1)(4n+5)$.

**19.** $\frac{1}{3}(n^3 + 2n)$ is an integer.

**20.** $1 \cdot 2 + 2 \cdot 3 + \cdots + n(n+1) = \frac{1}{3}n(n+1)(n+2)$.

**21.** $1 \cdot 3 + 2 \cdot 4 + \cdots + n(n+2) = \frac{1}{6}n(n+1)(2n+7)$.

**22.** $2 \cdot 5 + 3 \cdot 6 + \cdots + (n+1)(n+4) = \frac{1}{3}n(n+4)(n+5)$.

**23.** $2 + 5 + 10 + \cdots + (n^2 + 1) = \frac{1}{6}n(2n^2 + 3n + 7)$.

**24.** $2^{2n+1} + 1$ is divisible by 3.

**25.** $1 \cdot 3 + 3 \cdot 5 + \cdots + (2n-1)(2n+1) = \frac{1}{3}n(4n^2 + 6n - 1)$.

**26.** $\dfrac{1}{1 \cdot 3} + \dfrac{1}{3 \cdot 5} + \cdots + \dfrac{1}{(2n-1)(2n+1)} = \dfrac{n}{2n+1}$.

**27.** $1 \cdot 2 + 2 \cdot 2^2 + 3 \cdot 2^3 + \cdots + n \cdot 2^n = 2 + (n-1)2^{n+1}$.

**28.** $1 \cdot 2 \cdot 3 + 2 \cdot 3 \cdot 4 + \cdots + n(n+1)(n+2) = \frac{1}{4}n(n+1)(n+2)(n+3)$.

**29.** In the sequence 1, 2, 3, 5, 8, $\cdots$, each member, starting with the third, is formed by adding the two preceding members; that is, if $a_n$ is the $n$th member, $a_{n+1} = a_{n-1} + a_n$. Prove that $a_{n+1}^2 - a_n a_{n+2} = (-1)^{n+1}$.

**30.** $\sin \theta + \sin 2\theta + \cdots + \sin n\theta = \dfrac{\sin \frac{1}{2}(n+1)\theta \sin \frac{1}{2}n\theta}{\sin \frac{1}{2}\theta}$.

**31.** $\cos \theta + \cos 2\theta + \cdots + \cos n\theta = \dfrac{\cos \frac{1}{2}(n+1)\theta \sin \frac{1}{2}n\theta}{\sin \frac{1}{2}\theta}$.

**32.** $\sin \theta + \sin 3\theta + \cdots + \sin (2n-1)\theta = \dfrac{\sin^2 n\theta}{\sin \theta}$.

**33.** $\cos \theta + \cos 3\theta + \cdots + \cos (2n-1)\theta = \dfrac{\sin 2n\theta}{2 \sin \theta}$.

**34.** $\sin \alpha + \sin (\alpha + \beta) + \cdots + \sin [\alpha + (n-1)\beta]$
$$= \dfrac{\sin [\alpha + \frac{1}{2}(n-1)\beta] \sin \frac{1}{2}n\beta}{\sin \frac{1}{2}\beta}.$$

**35.** $\cos \alpha + \cos (\alpha + \beta) + \cdots + \cos [\alpha + (n-1)\beta]$
$$= \dfrac{\cos [\alpha + \frac{1}{2}(n-1)\beta] \sin \frac{1}{2}n\beta}{\sin \frac{1}{2}\beta}.$$

**43. The binomial theorem.** We frequently have occasion to deal with positive integral powers of a binomial expression, that is, with expressions of the form $(a + b)^n$, where $n$ is a positive integer. By repeated multiplication of $a + b$ by itself, we get, corresponding to $n = 1, 2, 3,$ and 4,

$$a + b = a + b,$$

$$(a + b)^2 = a^2 + 2ab + b^2,$$

$$(a + b)^3 = a^3 + 3a^2b + 3ab^2 + b^3,$$

$$(a + b)^4 = a^4 + 4a^3b + 6a^2b^2 + 4ab^3 + b^4.$$

When we examine the right members of these identities, we find that certain characteristics are common to all, and that the following statements hold for $n = 1, 2, 3,$ or 4:

1. The expansion contains $n + 1$ terms.

2. The total degree in each term is $n$; the successive degrees in $a$, the first term of the binomial, are $n, n - 1, \cdots, 1, 0$; and the successive degrees in $b$, the second term of the binomial, are $0, 1, \cdots, n - 1, n$.

3. The coefficient in the leading term, $a^n$, is unity; for any following term, the product of the coefficient and exponent of $a$, divided by the number of the term, yields the coefficient of the term next following. Thus, for the expansion of $(a + b)^4$, we have

$$1 \cdot a^4 + \frac{1 \cdot 4}{1} a^3 b + \frac{4 \cdot 3}{2} a^2 b^2 + \frac{6 \cdot 2}{3} ab^3 + \frac{4 \cdot 1}{4} b^4.$$

As a consequence of these observations, it is seen that, when $n = 1, 2, 3,$ or 4, the expansion of $(a + b)^n$ is given by

$$a^n + \frac{n}{1} a^{n-1}b + \frac{n(n - 1)}{1 \cdot 2} a^{n-2}b^2$$
$$+ \frac{n(n - 1)(n - 2)}{1 \cdot 2 \cdot 3} a^{n-3}b^3 + \cdots + b^n. \quad (1)$$

The question obviously raised by these findings is: Does this method of expansion hold for positive integral values of $n$ greater than 4? Our first impulse is to try the method when $n = 5$; this gives us

$$a^5 + 5a^4b + 10a^3b^2 + 10a^2b^3 + 5ab^4 + b^5,$$

and, by multiplying the expansion of $(a + b)^4$ by $a + b$, we find that the result is, in fact, the above expression. However, no matter how many specific cases we try, we are still in doubt concerning the next, as yet untested, case.

The natural way to settle the question is to apply mathematical induction. In order to make a proof by mathematical induction complete, we shall need an expression for a typical term of the expansion— the $r$th term, where $r$ may have any of the values $1, 2, \cdots, n + 1$. Now it is seen that, in expression (1), the $r$th term contains $a^{n-r+1}$ and $b^{r-1}$; thus, the exponent of $a$ in the fourth term is $n - 4 + 1 = n - 3$, and that of $b$ is $4 - 1 = 3$. Also, the coefficient in the $r$th term is expressed as a fraction; the numerator contains $r - 1$ factors, starting with $n$ and decreasing by unity until the $(r - 1)$th factor is $n - r + 2$; the denominator contains $r - 1$ factors, starting with 1 and increasing by unity until the $(r-1)$th factor is $r-1$, that is, the denominator is factorial $(r-1)$, $(r-1)! = 1 \cdot 2 \cdots (r-1)$.

We are now ready to attempt a proof by mathematical induction. The first step, verification of the truth of the theorem for $n = 1$ (and also for $n = 2, 3, 4,$ and $5$), has already been made. We therefore assume that the expansion holds for $n = s$:

$$(a+b)^s = a^s + sa^{s-1}b + \cdots$$
$$+ \frac{s(s-1)\cdots(s-r+2)}{(r-1)!} a^{s-r+1}b^{r-1} + \cdots + b^s. \quad (2)$$

Now multiply both members of (2) by $a + b$. We get $(a+b)^{s+1}$ on the left, as desired, and on the right we have the following expression:

$$a^{s+1} + sa^s b + \cdots + \frac{s(s-1)\cdots(s-r+2)}{(r-1)!} a^{s-r+2}b^{r-1} + \cdots + ab^s$$
$$+ a^s b + \cdots + \frac{s(s-1)\cdots(s-r+3)}{(r-2)!} a^{s-r+2}b^{r-1} + \cdots + sab^s$$
$$+ b^{s+1}.$$

Here the first line represents the product of $a$ and the first, second, $\cdots$, $r$th, $\cdots$, $(s+1)$th terms of the right member of (2), and the second line is the product of $b$ and the first, $\cdots$, $(r-1)$th, $\cdots$, $s$th, $(s+1)$th terms. It should be noticed that the $(r-1)$th term, not the $r$th, is used as typical term in the second line, so that the $r$th term of the sum, containing $a^{s-r+2}b^{r-1}$, can be determined; for this term the coefficient will then be

$$\frac{s(s-1)\cdots(s-r+2)}{(r-1)!} + \frac{s(s-1)\cdots(s-r+3)}{(r-2)!}$$
$$= \frac{s(s-1)\cdots(s-r+3)}{(r-1)!}(s-r+2) + \frac{s(s-1)\cdots(s-r+3)}{(r-1)(r-2)!}(r-1)$$
$$= \frac{s(s-1)\cdots(s-r+3)}{(r-1)!}(s-r+2+r-1)$$
$$= \frac{(s+1)s(s-1)\cdots(s-r+3)}{(r-1)!}.$$

Consequently the $r$th term of $(a+b)^{s+1}$ is found to be

$$\frac{(s+1)s\cdots(s-r+3)}{(r-1)!} a^{s-r+2}b^{r-1}.$$

But this is exactly what is obtained when $s$ is replaced by $s + 1$ in the $r$th term of the right member of (2). Therefore, if the expansion is correct for $n = s$, it must be correct for $n = s + 1$.

The third step of the mathematical induction is carried out in the usual way, and we have then proved that the method of expansion holds for every positive integral value of $n$.

The statement of this result, known as the **binomial theorem,** is therefore given by

$$\left( (a + b)^n = a^n + na^{n-1}b + \cdots \right.$$

$$\left. + \frac{n(n-1) \cdots (n-r+2)}{(r-1)!} a^{n-r+1}b^{r-1} + \cdots + b^n, \right)(3)$$

where the typical, or $r$th, term is as shown.

Although $n$ is restricted to positive integral values, no restrictions have been placed on the quantities $a$ and $b$. Hence the binomial theorem may be used to find the $n$th power of any expression that may be written as the sum of two quantities.

*Example 1.* Expand $(3p^2 - 2q^{\frac{1}{2}})^4$ by means of the binomial theorem.

*Solution.* We identify $3p^2$ with $a$, $-2q^{\frac{1}{2}}$ with $b$, and $n$ with 4. The binomial theorem then gives us

$$(3p^2 - 2q^{\frac{1}{2}})^4$$

$$= (3p^2)^4 + 4(3p^2)^3(-2q^{\frac{1}{2}}) + 6(3p^2)^2(-2q^{\frac{1}{2}})^2 + 4(3p^2)(-2q^{\frac{1}{2}})^3 + (-2q^{\frac{1}{2}})^4$$

$$= 81p^8 - 216p^6q^{\frac{1}{2}} + 216p^4q - 96p^2q^{\frac{3}{2}} + 16q^2.$$

*Example 2.* Find the term free of $x$ in the expansion of $\left( 2x^2 + \frac{1}{x} \right)^9$.

*Solution.* The $r$th term in the expansion will contain the factors $(2x^2)^{9-r+1}$ and $(1/x)^{r-1}$. Hence, as far as powers of $x$ are concerned, the $r$th term will involve

$$\frac{(x^2)^{10-r}}{x^{r-1}} = x^{21-3r}.$$

If the desired term is to be free of $x$, we must have $21 - 3r = 0$, whence $r = 7$. Using the above method for finding the seventh term, we get

$$\frac{9 \cdot 8 \cdot 7 \cdot 6 \cdot 5 \cdot 4}{1 \cdot 2 \cdot 3 \cdot 4 \cdot 5 \cdot 6} (2x^2)^3 \left( \frac{1}{x} \right)^6 = 672.$$

The coefficients in a binomial expansion are called **binomial coefficients.** In the expansion of $(a + b)^n$, the $(r + 1)$th term has as coefficient a number depending upon $n$ and $r$; that is, this coefficient is a function of $n$ and $r$, which we accordingly denote by a functional symbol: *

$$C(n, r) \equiv \frac{n(n-1) \cdots (n-r+1)}{r!}. \qquad (4)$$

Now the numerator of (4) contains some of the factors of $n!$. If we multiply numerator and denominator of (4) by $(n-r)!$, we get

$$C(n, r) \equiv \frac{n!}{r!(n-r)!}. \qquad (5)$$

It follows that, when $r$ is replaced by $n-r$,

$$C(n, n-r) \equiv \frac{n!}{(n-r)!r!} \equiv C(n, r). \qquad (6)$$

Consequently the binomial coefficients of a given expansion will be symmetrically distributed: those of the first and last terms will be alike, unity; those of the second and next to last alike, $n$; and so on toward the middle position of the expansion from each end. This fact is illustrated by the expansions for $n = 1, 2, 3, 4$, and 5, already obtained.

Let us now write the binomial coefficients in a triangular array, as shown below:

$$
\begin{array}{ccccccccccc}
& & & & & 1 & & & & & \\
& & & & 1 & & 1 & & & & \\
& & & 1 & & 2 & & 1 & & & \\
& & 1 & & 3 & & 3 & & 1 & & \\
& 1 & & 4 & & 6 & & 4 & & 1 & \\
1 & & 5 & & 10 & & 10 & & 5 & & 1 \\
\end{array}
$$

*interior — sum of 2 above.*

$$\cdot \quad \cdot \quad \cdot \quad \cdot \quad \cdot \quad \cdot$$

For completeness, we have topped the array with the single entry 1, corresponding to $n = 0$, and followed this with lines corresponding respectively to $n = 1, 2, 3, 4, 5, \cdots$. Inspection of this array, known as Pascal's triangle, shows that each interior element is the sum of the two

---

* The student who is familiar with the theory of permutations and combinations will recognize $C(n, r)$ as the number of combinations of $n$ things taken $r$ at a time; this is also denoted by $_nC_r$ or $^nC_r$. (See Chapter XVI.)

immediately above and respectively to left and right of it. It is easy to show that this is true generally; we have

$$C(n, r-1) + C(n, r) \equiv \frac{n(n-1)\cdots(n-r+2)}{(r-1)!}$$
$$+ \frac{n(n-1)\cdots(n-r+1)}{r!}$$
$$\equiv \frac{n(n-1)\cdots(n-r+2)}{r!}(r+n-r+1)$$
$$\equiv \frac{(n+1)n(n-1)\cdots(n-r+2)}{r!},$$

whence

$$C(n, r-1) + C(n, r) \equiv C(n+1, r). \tag{7}$$

This relation thus enables us to continue the construction of Pascal's triangle as far as desired.

### EXERCISES

In Exercises 1–20, obtain the expansions indicated.

1. $(a - b)^6$.
2. $(a + 2b)^5$.
3. $(x + 2)^7$.
4. $(a + a^{-1})^6$.
5. $(x^2 - y)^5$.
6. $(a^3 - 2b^2)^6$.
7. $(a^{\frac{1}{2}} - x^{\frac{1}{2}})^6$.
8. $(a^{\frac{2}{3}} - x^{\frac{2}{3}})^4$.
9. $\left(\dfrac{3}{x} - \dfrac{x}{3}\right)^6$.
10. $\left(\dfrac{x}{y^2} - \dfrac{y}{x^2}\right)^5$.
11. $(a^{-1} - b^{-2})^5$.
12. $(2a^2 + \frac{1}{2}a^{-\frac{1}{2}})^6$.
13. $\begin{vmatrix} a & b \\ c & d \end{vmatrix}^5$.
14. $\begin{vmatrix} a & a^{-1} \\ a^2 & a^{-2} \end{vmatrix}^5$.
15. $\left(\sqrt{\dfrac{x}{y^3}} + \sqrt{\dfrac{y^3}{x}}\right)$.
16. $\left(\dfrac{a}{\sqrt{b}} - \dfrac{b}{\sqrt{a}}\right)^4$.
17. $(1 + a)^6 - (1 - a)^6$.
18. $(x + y)^7 + (x - y)^7$.
19. $(a - b + c)^3$.
20. $(a - 1 + a^{-1})^4$.

In Exercises 21–30, find the indicated terms in the expansions.

21. $(2x - y)^7$; fifth term.
22. $(1 + ab)^9$; sixth term.
23. $(a^2 - b)^{10}$; middle term.
24. $(2x^2 - 3y)^8$; fourth term.
25. $(a + a^{-1})^{12}$; eighth term.
26. $(ab^{\frac{1}{2}} - a^{\frac{1}{2}}b)^{10}$; ninth term.
27. $\left(\dfrac{x}{y} - \dfrac{y}{x}\right)^{10}$; term free of $x$ and $y$.
28. $\left(\dfrac{2a}{b} + \dfrac{b}{2a}\right)^8$; term free of $a$ and $b$.
29. $(a^2 - 2a^{-1})^8$; term involving $a^4$.
30. $(a^{\frac{3}{2}} + 2a^{\frac{1}{2}})^{10}$; term involving $a^{12}$.

In Exercises 31–36, use the binomial theorem to evaluate the numbers indicated.

**31.** $(101)^3$.    **32.** $(99)^4$.    **33.** $(1.02)^5$.

**34.** $(9.7)^5$.    **35.** $(0.8)^6$.    **36.** $(1.1)^7$.

**37.** If $2C(n, 2) = 3C(n - 1, 3)$, find $n$.

**38.** Using the fact that

$$(1 + a)^n = 1 + C(n, 1)a + C(n, 2)a^2 + \cdots + C(n, n - 1)a^{n-1} + C(n, n)a^n,$$

evaluate $C(8, 1) + C(8, 2) + \cdots + C(8, 7) + C(8, 8)$.

**39.** If $C(27, r) = 3C(27, r - 1)$, find $r$.

**40.** If $C(p, 2) = kC(n + 1, 4)$, where $p = C(n, 2)$, find $k$.

## SUPPLEMENTARY EXERCISES

**1.** Show that $C(n, r)C(n - r, s - r) = C(n, s)C(s, r)$.

**2.** Show that $C(n - 2, r) + 2C(n - 2, r - 1) + C(n - 2, r - 2) = C(n, r)$.

**3.** Obtain the expansion of $(1 + x + x^2 + x^3)^4$ by considering $1 + x + x^2 + x^3$ as (a) the binomial expression $(1 + x) + (x^2 + x^3)$; (b) the product of the binomials $1 + x$ and $1 + x^2$.

Prove the relations of Exercises 4–7 by means of mathematical induction. In each exercise, $n$ denotes a positive integer.

**4.** $1^4 + 2^4 + \cdots + n^4 = \frac{1}{30}n(n + 1)(2n + 1)(3n^2 + 3n - 1)$.

**5.** $1^5 + 2^5 + \cdots + n^5 = \frac{1}{12}n^2(n + 1)^2(2n^2 + 2n - 1)$.

**6.** $1^6 + 2^6 + \cdots + n^6 = \frac{1}{42}n(n + 1)(2n + 1)(3n^4 + 6n^3 - 3n + 1)$.

**7.** $1^7 + 2^7 + \cdots + n^7 = \frac{1}{24}n^2(n + 1)^2(3n^4 + 6n^3 - n^2 - 4n + 2)$.

In Exercise 29, Art. 42, reference was made to the sequence 1, 2, 3, 5, 8, $\cdots$, for which $a_{n+1} = a_{n-1} + a_n$, with $a_1 = 1$, $a_2 = 2$. Using mathematical induction, prove that the relations of Exercises 8–10 hold for these *Fibonacci numbers* when $n$ is any positive integer.

**8.** $a_1 + a_3 + \cdots + a_{2n-1} = a_{2n} - 1$.

**9.** $a_2 + a_4 + \cdots + a_{2n} = a_{2n+1} - 1$.

**10.** $a_1 + a_2 + \cdots + a_{2n-1} = a_{2n+1} - 2$.

# VIII————————— Complex Numbers

**44. Definitions and representations.** In all the foregoing work, we have restricted ourselves to the real number system. So far as the four rational operations of arithmetic are concerned, and even when dealing with linear algebraic equations with rational coefficients, as we did in Chapter V, we saw that the rational number system (Art. 1) suffices. In other connections, such as the determination of trigonometric functions of special angles (Art. 16) and the treatment of some non-linear algebraic functions (Art. 21), we had occasion to use irrational numbers.

However, it will be recalled that certain operations were not taken into consideration. Thus, in Art. 4, we said that, when $a$ is negative and $p$ is an even positive integer, $a^{\frac{1}{p}}$ is to be undefined in our real number system. Accordingly, although an equation such as $x^2 - 2 = 0$ could be solved to get $\pm 2^{\frac{1}{2}}$ as solutions, an equation like $x^2 + 2 = 0$ was avoided, since its solutions do not exist in the real number system— we should merely have the symbol $x = \pm(-2)^{\frac{1}{2}}$, of the form stated above, with $a = -2$ and $p = 2$.

We wish now to remove such restrictions by extending our number system. To do this we may take as our starting point the symbol $a^{\frac{1}{p}}$, where $a$ is a negative real number and $p$ an even positive integer. In the simplest instance, $a = -1$ and $p = 2$. Let us therefore *define* $(-1)^{\frac{1}{2}}$ as a new number, which may be denoted by the letter $i$: *

$$i = (-1)^{\frac{1}{2}} = \sqrt{-1}. \tag{1}$$

Otherwise expressed, $i$ is a new number such that its square is $-1$:

$$i^2 = -1. \tag{2}$$

Applying the fundamental properties of algebraic quantities to the number $i$, we have, by definition,

$$i^3 = i^2 \cdot i = -i, \tag{3}$$

$$i^4 = i^3 \cdot i = -i \cdot i = -i^2 = -(-1) = 1, \tag{4}$$

* In some texts, notably in electrical work where $i$ signifies current, the letter $j$ is used to denote the number $\sqrt{-1}$. In this book, however, the symbol for $\sqrt{-1}$ will invariably be $i$.

160

and, in general, if $n$ is any positive integer,

$$i^n = i^{n-1} \cdot i. \tag{5}$$

Since, by (4), $i^4 = 1$, then, expressing $n$ as $4m + k$, where $m$ is a positive integer or zero and $k = 1$, 2, or 3, we have

$$i^n = i^{4m+k} = (i^4)^m i^k = 1^m \cdot i^k = i^k. \tag{6}$$

Thus,

$$i^7 = i^3 = -i, \qquad i^{13} = i, \qquad i^{20} = 1.$$

Any number of the form $(-q)^{\frac{1}{2}}$, where $q$ is a positive real number, may then be expressed as the product of a positive real number and $i$; by definition,

$$(-q)^{\frac{1}{2}} = (-1)^{\frac{1}{2}} q^{\frac{1}{2}} = q^{\frac{1}{2}} i.$$

Thus, the solutions of $x^2 + 2 = 0$ may be written as $x = \pm(-2)^{\frac{1}{2}} = \pm\sqrt{2}i$.

We therefore have a class of numbers of the form $bi$, where $b$ is real and $i$ is given by (1). Such numbers are called **pure imaginary numbers.** The designation imaginary is, of course, merely a label for the new numbers created; numbers of the form $bi$ are "imaginary" with respect to "real" numbers in the same way that "irrational" numbers are imaginary with respect to "rational" numbers.

We now combine a real number $a$ and an imaginary number $bi$, where $b$ is real, by addition. Such a number, $a + bi$, is called a **complex number.** For example, consider the equation

$$x^2 + 6x + 14 = 0.$$

Now $x^2 + 6x$ may be regarded as the first two terms of the expansion of the square of a binomial: $(x + 3)^2 = x^2 + 6x + 9$. Hence, if we add $-5$ to both sides of the given equation, we have

$$(x + 3)^2 = -5,$$

whence

$$x + 3 = \pm\sqrt{-5} = \pm\sqrt{5}i,$$

and

$$x = -3 \pm \sqrt{5}i$$

are solutions of the equation; they are complex numbers of the form $a + bi$, where $a = -3$ and $b = \sqrt{5}$ or $b = -\sqrt{5}$.

In Art. 1 it was mentioned that all real numbers could be represented geometrically by points on a line (Fig. 1). Since the complex number $a + bi$ involves two real numbers, $a$ and $b$, as well as the **imaginary unit**

$i$, we may represent such numbers geometrically by points in a plane. To do this, we refer to a rectangular coordinate system (Art. 11). Let the real component $a$ be measured along the $X$-axis (now called the axis of reals), and let the imaginary component $bi$ be measured off as $b$ units in the direction of the $Y$-axis (axis of imaginaries). The point $P$ whose rectangular coordinates are $(a, b)$ then represents the complex number $a + bi$ geometrically.

Let $r$ denote the distance (always *non-negative*) from the origin $O$ to the point $P(a, b)$, and let $\theta$ be the non-negative angle measured from the positive direction of the $X$-axis to the line $OP$. Then $(r, \theta)$ are the polar coordinates of $P$ when $r \geqq 0$ and $\theta \geqq 0$ (Art. 19). Since $a = r \cos \theta$ and $b = r \sin \theta$ (see Fig. 18), we have

$$a + bi = r(\cos \theta + i \sin \theta). \tag{7}$$

The representation $a + bi$ of a complex number is called the **rectangular form,** and the representation $r(\cos \theta + i \sin \theta)$ is called the **polar form** of the number. The length $r$ is called the **modulus or absolute value,** and the angle $\theta$ is called the **amplitude** or **argument,** of the complex number.

The modulus and amplitude of a complex number are given respectively (see Fig. 18) by

$$r = \sqrt{a^2 + b^2}, \tag{8}$$

$$\tan \theta = \frac{b}{a}, \qquad a \neq 0; \tag{9}$$

$\theta = \pi/2$ if $a = 0$ and $b > 0$, $\theta = 3\pi/2$ if $a = 0$ and $b < 0$. The modulus $r$ may be computed directly from (8), but since there are, in general, two non-negative angles less than $2\pi$, whose tangents are equal to $b/a$, the amplitude $\theta$ should be determined from the plot of $a + bi$, which shows the quadrant in which $\theta$ lies.

Thus, for the complex number $-\sqrt{3} + i$, we have $r = \sqrt{3 + 1} = 2$ and $\tan \theta = 1/(-\sqrt{3}) = -\sqrt{3}/3$. Since $-\sqrt{3} + i$ is represented by a point in the second quadrant, we must have $\theta = 5\pi/6$, whence

$$-\sqrt{3} + i = 2\left(\cos \frac{5\pi}{6} + i \sin \frac{5\pi}{6}\right).$$

Evidently all real numbers are included in the complex number system, for, if $b = 0$ in the typical complex number $a + bi$, we have the real number $a$. The modulus of a real number $a \neq 0$ is $r = |a|$, and its amplitude is $\theta = 0$ if $a > 0$ or $\pi$ if $a < 0$; if $a = 0$, then $r = 0$ and $\theta$ is indeterminate.

*Homework for tues*

**EXERCISES**

In Exercises 1–12, plot each of the given complex numbers, and determine its modulus and amplitude.

*1–12*

1. $1 - i$.
2. $3 + 3i$.
3. $-2 + 2i$.
4. $-2 - 2i$.
5. $\sqrt{3} - i$.
6. $-2 - 2\sqrt{3}\, i$.
7. $5i$.
8. $-4$.
9. $4 + 3i$.
10. $-3 - 4i$.
11. $1 + 2i$.
12. $-12 + 5i$.

In Exercises 13–20, plot each of the given complex numbers and write it in rectangular form.

13. $\cos \dfrac{\pi}{3} + i \sin \dfrac{\pi}{3}$.

14. $4\left( \cos \dfrac{3\pi}{4} + i \sin \dfrac{3\pi}{4} \right)$.

15. $2\left( \cos \dfrac{\pi}{2} + i \sin \dfrac{\pi}{2} \right)$.

16. $3(\cos 0 + i \sin 0)$.

17. $5(\cos \pi + i \sin \pi)$.

18. $\cos \dfrac{2\pi}{3} + i \sin \dfrac{2\pi}{3}$.

19. $3\left( \cos \dfrac{3\pi}{2} + i \sin \dfrac{3\pi}{2} \right)$.

20. $\cos 1 + i \sin 1$.

**45. Operations with complex numbers.** Two complex numbers $a + bi$ and $c + di$, where, as usual, $a$, $b$, $c$, and $d$ are real, are said to be equal if and only if $a = c$ and $b = d$. Consequently, if $a + bi = 0 = 0 + 0i$, then $a = 0$ and $b = 0$.

We now consider the four arithmetic operations as applied to complex numbers. The sum of two complex numbers, $a + bi$ and $c + di$, is defined to be the complex number $(a + c) + (b + d)i$:

$$(a + bi) + (c + di) \equiv (a + c) + (b + d)i. \tag{1}$$

That is, the real component of the sum is the sum of the two real components, and the coefficient of $i$ in the sum is the sum of the two coefficients of $i$. For example, $(5 + 3i) + (-2 - 7i) = 3 - 4i$, $4i + (\sqrt{2} - 3i) = \sqrt{2} + i$.

The *negative* of a complex number $a + bi$ is defined as $-a - bi$. Accordingly, we define *subtraction* of one complex number from a second as the sum of the second and the negative of the first:

$$(a + bi) - (c + di) \equiv (a + bi) + (-c - di)$$

$$\equiv (a - c) + (b - d)i. \tag{2}$$

Thus, $(3 - 5i) - (5 - 9i) = -2 + 4i$.

The *product* of two complex numbers $a + bi$ and $c + di$ is defined as the complex number obtained by formally multiplying $a + bi$ by $c + di$

as if $i$ were an unspecified algebraic quantity and then interpreting $i^2$ as $-1$; that is, since formal multiplication gives us

$$(a + bi)(c + di) = ac + adi + bci + bdi^2,$$

we say that

$$(a + bi)(c + di) \equiv (ac - bd) + (ad + bc)i. \qquad (3)$$

For example, $(2 - 3i)(5 + 4i) = 10 + 8i - 15i - 12i^2 = 22 - 7i$.

To get a convenient and useful definition of the quotient of two complex numbers, we try the effect of formal algebraic manipulation. If $i$ were an unspecified algebraic quantity, we would have

$$\frac{a + bi}{c + di} = \frac{(a + bi)(c - di)}{(c + di)(c - di)} = \frac{ac - adi + bci - bdi^2}{c^2 - d^2 i^2}.$$

If, now, $i^2$ is interpreted as $-1$, the last fraction becomes

$$\frac{(ac + bd) + (bc - ad)i}{c^2 + d^2}.$$

Accordingly, we define *division* as follows:

$$\frac{a + bi}{c + di} \equiv \frac{ac + bd}{c^2 + d^2} + \frac{bc - ad}{c^2 + d^2}i, \qquad c + di \neq 0. \qquad (4)$$

For example,

$$\frac{6 - 5i}{2 + 3i} = \frac{(6 - 5i)(2 - 3i)}{(2 + 3i)(2 - 3i)} = \frac{12 - 18i - 10i + 15i^2}{4 - 9i^2}$$

$$= \frac{-3 - 28i}{13} = -\frac{3}{13} - \frac{28}{13}i.$$

It should be particularly noticed that the above definitions require us to express each of the complex numbers in the typical form $a + bi$, where $a$ and $b$ are real, before performing operations upon them. Thus, it is *not* correct to write

$$(2 + \sqrt{-3})(3 + \sqrt{-2}) = 6 + 2\sqrt{-2} + 3\sqrt{-3} + \sqrt{(-3)(-2)}$$

$$= 6 + \sqrt{6} + 2\sqrt{-2} + 3\sqrt{-3}.$$

Instead, we actually have

$$(2 + \sqrt{-3})(3 + \sqrt{-2}) = (2 + \sqrt{3}i)(3 + \sqrt{2}i)$$

$$= 6 + 2\sqrt{2}i + 3\sqrt{3}i + \sqrt{6}i^2$$

$$= 6 - \sqrt{6} + (2\sqrt{2} + 3\sqrt{3})i,$$

which differs from the false result above in that the real component of the product is $6 - \sqrt{6}$ and not $6 + \sqrt{6}$. It therefore appears that, although $\sqrt{a}\cdot\sqrt{b} = \sqrt{ab}$ when $a$ and $b$ are positive real numbers, we have, by our definitions, when $a$ and $b$ are negative, so that $-a$ and $-b$ are positive, $\sqrt{a}\cdot\sqrt{b} = \sqrt{-a}i\cdot\sqrt{-b}i = \sqrt{(-a)(-b)}i^2 = -\sqrt{ab}$. All difficulty may be easily avoided if the complex numbers treated are written in typical form, $a + bi$, operations carried out formally with the symbol $i$ regarded as an unspecified algebraic quantity, and then powers of $i$ interpreted in accordance with the definitions stated in Art. 44.

The operations of multiplication and division may be simply treated when the complex numbers are written in polar form. For, let there be given two complex numbers, $a + bi \equiv r(\cos\theta + i\sin\theta)$ and $c + di \equiv r'(\cos\theta' + i\sin\theta')$. Then

$$(a + bi)(c + di) = [r(\cos\theta + i\sin\theta)][r'(\cos\theta' + i\sin\theta')]$$

$$= rr'(\cos\theta\cos\theta' + i\cos\theta\sin\theta' + i\sin\theta\cos\theta' + i^2\sin\theta\sin\theta')$$

$$= rr'[(\cos\theta\cos\theta' - \sin\theta\sin\theta') + i(\sin\theta\cos\theta' + \cos\theta\sin\theta')].$$

But $\cos\theta\cos\theta' - \sin\theta\sin\theta' = \cos(\theta + \theta')$, and $\sin\theta\cos\theta' + \cos\theta\sin\theta' = \sin(\theta + \theta')$ (Art. 35). Hence we have

$$r(\cos\theta + i\sin\theta)\cdot r'(\cos\theta' + i\sin\theta')$$
$$= rr'[\cos(\theta + \theta') + i\sin(\theta + \theta')]. \quad (5)$$

That is, *the modulus of the product of two complex numbers is equal to the product of their two moduli, and the amplitude of the product is equal to the sum of the individual amplitudes.* For example,

$$(\sqrt{2} + \sqrt{2}i)(3i) = \left[2\left(\cos\frac{\pi}{4} + i\sin\frac{\pi}{4}\right)\right]\left[3\left(\cos\frac{\pi}{2} + i\sin\frac{\pi}{2}\right)\right]$$

$$= 6\left(\cos\frac{3\pi}{4} + i\sin\frac{3\pi}{4}\right) = -3\sqrt{2} + 3\sqrt{2}i.$$

In like fashion, we have, when $r' \neq 0$,

$$\frac{a + bi}{c + di} = \frac{r(\cos\theta + i\sin\theta)}{r'(\cos\theta' + i\sin\theta')} = \frac{r(\cos\theta + i\sin\theta)(\cos\theta' - i\sin\theta')}{r'(\cos\theta' + i\sin\theta')(\cos\theta' - i\sin\theta')}$$

$$= \frac{r(\cos\theta\cos\theta' - i\cos\theta\sin\theta' + i\sin\theta\cos\theta' - i^2\sin\theta\sin\theta')}{r'(\cos^2\theta' - i^2\sin^2\theta')}$$

$$= \frac{r[(\cos\theta\cos\theta' + \sin\theta\sin\theta') + i(\sin\theta\cos\theta' - \cos\theta\sin\theta')]}{r'(\cos^2\theta' + \sin^2\theta')}$$

$$= \frac{r}{r'}[\cos(\theta - \theta') + i\sin(\theta - \theta')]. \quad (6)$$

That is, *the modulus of the quotient of two complex numbers is the quotient of their moduli, and the amplitude of the quotient is the difference (that of numerator minus that of denominator) of the two amplitudes.*

For example,

$$\frac{\sqrt{2} + \sqrt{2}i}{3i} = \frac{2\left(\cos\dfrac{\pi}{4} + i\sin\dfrac{\pi}{4}\right)}{3\left(\cos\dfrac{\pi}{2} + i\sin\dfrac{\pi}{2}\right)} = \frac{2}{3}\left[\cos\left(-\frac{\pi}{4}\right) + i\sin\left(-\frac{\pi}{4}\right)\right]$$

$$= \frac{2}{3}\left(\frac{\sqrt{2}}{2} - \frac{\sqrt{2}}{2}i\right) = \frac{\sqrt{2}}{3} - \frac{\sqrt{2}}{3}i.$$

Two particular cases are worth noting. With regard to multiplication of a complex number $a + bi$ by the imaginary unit $i$, (5) yields

$$(a + bi)i = r(\cos\theta + i\sin\theta) \cdot \left(\cos\frac{\pi}{2} + i\sin\frac{\pi}{2}\right)$$

$$= r\left[\cos\left(\theta + \frac{\pi}{2}\right) + i\sin\left(\theta + \frac{\pi}{2}\right)\right]. \tag{7}$$

Hence the new complex number has the same modulus as $a + bi$, and the amplitude has been increased by $\pi/2$. Thus, the operation of multiplication by $i$ has the geometric effect of rotating the point $P(a, b)$ about the origin $O$ in the positive direction through one-quarter of a revolution. This interpretation of $i$ as an operator producing rotation through $90°$ is of considerable utility in physical applications.

With regard to the reciprocal of a complex number, (6) gives us, when $r \neq 0$,

$$\frac{1}{a + bi} = \frac{\cos 0 + i\sin 0}{r(\cos\theta + i\sin\theta)} = \frac{1}{r}\left[\cos(-\theta) + i\sin(-\theta)\right]. \tag{8}$$

Hence the modulus of the reciprocal of a number is the reciprocal of the number's modulus, and the amplitude of the reciprocal is the negative of the number's amplitude.

Two complex numbers, $a + bi$ and $a - bi$, that differ only in the sign of the imaginary components, are called **conjugate complex numbers,** and each is said to be the conjugate of the other. Thus, $3 + 2i$ and $3 - 2i$ are conjugate numbers. Since

$$(a + bi) + (a - bi) = 2a,$$

$$(a + bi) - (a - bi) = 2bi,$$

$$(a + bi)(a - bi) = a^2 + b^2,$$

it is evident that the sum of two conjugate numbers is a real number, the difference is a pure imaginary number, and their product is a real number.

## EXERCISES

Perform the indicated operations in Exercises 1–24.   Express the results in rectangular form.

**1.** $(1 + 2i) + (4 + 3i)$.

**2.** $(5 - 2i) + (6 + 3i)$.

**3.** $(8 - 3i) - (2 + 6i)$.

**4.** $(10 - 5i) - (12 - 8i)$.

**5.** $4 + (3 - 2i) + 5i$.

**6.** $4i - (2 - 5i) - (3 + 7i)$.

**7.** $(3 + i)(4 + 2i)$.

**8.** $(6 - 4i)(5 + 2i)$.

**9.** $(5 - i)(4 - 5i)$.

**10.** $2(3 + 4i)(6 - 2i)$.

**11.** $(4 - 2i)(6 - 4i)i$.

**12.** $(\sqrt{3} + 2i)(\sqrt{3} - 2i)$.

**13.** $(\sqrt{5} + \sqrt{3}\,i)(\sqrt{3} - \sqrt{5}\,i)$.

**14.** $(4 + \sqrt{-3}\,)(3 - \sqrt{-12}\,)$.

**15.** $(1 - i)^3$.

**16.** $(1 + i)^4$.

**17.** $\dfrac{2 + 3i}{i}$.

**18.** $\dfrac{1 - i}{1 + i}$.

**19.** $\dfrac{1}{1 - i}$.

**20.** $\dfrac{\sqrt{3} + i}{1 + \sqrt{3}\,i}$.

**21.** $\dfrac{8}{(1 - \sqrt{3}\,i)^3}$.

**22.** $\dfrac{2}{i^2 - i^3}$.

**23.** $\dfrac{3}{(1 - i)^4}$.

**24.** $\dfrac{(a + bi)(a - bi)}{(2i - 2)^4}$.

Determine real values of $x$ and $y$ satisfying the complex equations of Exercises 25–30.

**25.** $4x - 3y + (x - 2y)i = 1 - i$.

**26.** $x + 2y + (5x - 4y)i = 14i$.

**27.** $(3 + 2i)x - (4 + i)y = 1 + 4i$.

**28.** $(2 + i)x^2 + (3 - 2i)y^2 = 8 - 3i$.

**29.** $(1 - 2i)x - (2 + i)y^2 = -9 - 2i$.

**30.** $(i - 2)x - (2i + 3)y = (2 - 8i)xy$.

**31.** Show that $i - 1$ is a solution of the equation $3x^3 + 4x^2 + 2x - 4 = 0$.

**32.** If $f(x) = (x^2 - 4x)^2 + 5(x^2 - 4x) - 24$, find $f(2 - 2i)$.

**33.** If $x = 1 + \sqrt{3}\,i$, evaluate

$$\frac{x^3 + 7}{x^2 - 2x + 3}.$$

**34.** Given $f(x) = Ax^2 + Bx + C$, where $A$, $B$, and $C$ are real numbers.   If $f(a + bi) = 0$, where $a$ and $b$ are real, show that $f(a - bi) = 0$.

**35.** Given two complex numbers, $a + bi$ and $c + di$, where $b \neq 0$ and $d \neq 0$.   If the sum and product of these two numbers are both real, show that the numbers are conjugate.

## 46. De Moivre's theorem.   If the rectangular form of a complex number, $a + bi$, is used, the $n$th power of the number can be obtained by

means of the binomial theorem when $n$ is a positive integer (Art. 43). However, the polar form, $r(\cos \theta + i \sin \theta)$, is more convenient in this connection. We have, using relation (5) of Art. 45, with $r' = r$ and $\theta' = \theta$,

$$[r(\cos \theta + i \sin \theta)]^2 = r^2(\cos 2\theta + i \sin 2\theta),$$

$$[r(\cos \theta + i \sin \theta)]^3 = r^2(\cos 2\theta + i \sin 2\theta) \cdot r(\cos \theta + i \sin \theta)$$

$$= r^3(\cos 3\theta + i \sin 3\theta).$$

It is an easy application of mathematical induction to show that

$$[r(\cos \theta + i \sin \theta)]^n = r^n(\cos n\theta + i \sin n\theta), \tag{1}$$

where $n$ is any positive integer. This relation is known as **De Moivre's theorem:**

*The modulus of the nth power of a complex number is the nth power of the number's modulus, and the amplitude of the nth power is n times the number's amplitude, for every positive integral value of n.*

For example, we have

$$(3\sqrt{2} - 3\sqrt{2}i)^4 = \left[ 6\left( \cos \frac{7\pi}{4} + i \sin \frac{7\pi}{4} \right) \right]^4$$

$$= 1296(\cos 7\pi + i \sin 7\pi) = -1296.$$

If $n$ is a negative integer, say $n = -m$, where $m$ is a positive integer, we have, from relation (8), Art. 45,

$$[r(\cos \theta + i \sin \theta)]^n = \frac{1}{[r(\cos \theta + i \sin \theta)]^m} = \frac{\cos 0 + i \sin 0}{r^m(\cos m\theta + i \sin m\theta)}$$

$$= r^{-m}[\cos (-m\theta) + i \sin (-m\theta)]$$

$$= r^n(\cos n\theta + i \sin n\theta).$$

Therefore De Moivre's theorem holds also for negative integral powers.

If $n = 1/p$, where $p$ is an integer, let $\phi = n\theta$, so that $\theta = p\phi$. Then

$$[r(\cos \theta + i \sin \theta)]^n = [r(\cos p\phi + i \sin p\phi)]^{\frac{1}{p}}$$

$$= r^{\frac{1}{p}}[(\cos \phi + i \sin \phi)^p]^{\frac{1}{p}}$$

$$= r^{\frac{1}{p}}(\cos \phi + i \sin \phi)$$

$$= r^n(\cos n\theta + i \sin n\theta).$$

Consequently De Moivre's theorem (1) is true for $n = 1/p$ also. It is understood that, in keeping with the meaning given a fractional power of a positive number (Art. 4), the value of $r^{\frac{1}{p}}$ is real and positive. Combining all these results, it is therefore found that *relation* (1) *holds for all rational values of n—positive or negative, integral or fractional.*

**47. Trigonometric formulas.** An interesting combined application of the binomial theorem and De Moivre's theorem may be made in trigonometry. Since

$$\cos n\theta + i \sin n\theta = (\cos \theta + i \sin \theta)^n,$$

where $n$ is any positive integer, we get, by expansion of the right member,

$$\cos n\theta + i \sin n\theta = \cos^n \theta + in \cos^{n-1} \theta \sin \theta$$

$$+ i^2 \frac{n(n-1)}{2!} \cos^{n-2} \theta \sin^2 \theta + \cdots + i^n \sin^n \theta. \quad (1)$$

Now each power of $i$ may be expressed as $\pm 1$ or $\pm i$, so that the right member of (1) assumes the form $a + bi$, where $a$ and $b$ are real expressions involving $\sin \theta$ and $\cos \theta$. Since two complex numbers are equal only if their real components are equal and their imaginary components are equal, identity (1) yields two identities: one expresses $\cos n\theta$ in terms of $\sin \theta$ and $\cos \theta$ and the other gives $\sin n\theta$ in terms of functions of $\theta$. Numerous identities previously encountered may thus be obtained.

*Example.* Derive formulas for $\cos 3\theta$ and $\sin 3\theta$.

*Solution.* Proceeding as above, we have

$$\cos 3\theta + i \sin 3\theta = (\cos \theta + i \sin \theta)^3$$

$$= \cos^3 \theta + 3i \cos^2 \theta \sin \theta + 3i^2 \cos \theta \sin^2 \theta + i^3 \sin^3 \theta,$$

whence

$$\cos 3\theta + i \sin 3\theta = \cos^3 \theta - 3 \cos \theta \sin^2 \theta + i(3 \cos^2 \theta \sin \theta - \sin^3 \theta),$$

and

$$\cos 3\theta = \cos^3 \theta - 3 \cos \theta \sin^2 \theta,$$

$$\sin 3\theta = 3 \cos^2 \theta \sin \theta - \sin^3 \theta.$$

If desired, $\cos 3\theta$ may be expressed in terms of $\cos \theta$ alone, and $\sin 3\theta$ in terms of $\sin \theta$ alone, by means of the identity $\sin^2 \theta + \cos^2 \theta = 1$. Thus we find

$$\cos 3\theta = \cos^3 \theta - 3(\cos \theta)(1 - \cos^2 \theta)$$

$$= 4 \cos^3 \theta - 3 \cos \theta,$$

$$\sin 3\theta = 3(1 - \sin^2 \theta) \sin \theta - \sin^3 \theta$$

$$= 3 \sin \theta - 4 \sin^3 \theta.$$

These agree with the results of Example 1 and Exercise 8, Art. 37.

## EXERCISES

Using De Moivre's theorem, evaluate each of the expressions in Exercises 1–14. Express the results in rectangular form.

1. $(\cos 15° + i \sin 15°)^3$.
2. $(\cos 105° + i \sin 105°)^3$.
3. $(1 - i)^2$.
4. $(1 + i)^4$.
5. $(1 + \sqrt{3}\, i)^3$.
6. $(\sqrt{3} - i)^3$.
7. $(\cos 20° + i \sin 20°)^6$.
8. $[2(\cos 40° + i \sin 40°)]^9$.
9. $(\cos 50° + i \sin 50°)^9$.
10. $(\cos 7° 30' + i \sin 7° 30')^8$.
11. $(\cos 5° + i \sin 5°)^{12}$.
12. $(-\sqrt{2} + \sqrt{2}\, i)^{10}$.
13. $(\sqrt{3} + \sqrt{3}\, i)^{10}$.
14. $(\sqrt{3} - i)^8$.

Using De Moivre's theorem, obtain formulas for the functions stated in Exercises 15–18. Check the results thus found with those established in Art. 37.

15. $\sin 2\theta$ and $\cos 2\theta$.
16. $\sin 4\theta$ and $\cos 4\theta$.
17. $\sin 5\theta$ and $\cos 5\theta$.
18. $\sin 6\theta$ and $\cos 6\theta$.

19. Using the results of the example of Art. 47, obtain a formula for $\tan 3\theta$. (See Exercise 9, Art. 37.)

20. Using the results of Exercise 16, obtain a formula for $\tan 4\theta$. (See Exercise 12, Art. 37.)

**48. Roots of numbers.** Since De Moivre's theorem holds for fractional values of $n$, it may be conveniently used to extract roots of complex numbers. Thus, if $p$ is any positive integer greater than unity, we have

$$(a + bi)^{\frac{1}{p}} \equiv [r(\cos \theta + i \sin \theta)]^{\frac{1}{p}} \equiv r^{\frac{1}{p}}\left(\cos \frac{\theta}{p} + i \sin \frac{\theta}{p}\right).$$

Now if the amplitude $\theta$ of the given number were increased by any integral multiple of $2\pi$, we should have an equally correct polar representation of the number; that is, since $\cos (\theta + 2k\pi) \equiv \cos \theta$ and $\sin (\theta + 2k\pi) \equiv \sin \theta$, when $k$ is an integer or zero, $a + bi \equiv r[\cos (\theta + 2k\pi) + i \sin (\theta + 2k\pi)]$, and therefore

$$(a + bi)^{\frac{1}{p}} \equiv r^{\frac{1}{p}}\left(\cos \frac{\theta + 2k\pi}{p} + i \sin \frac{\theta + 2k\pi}{p}\right). \tag{1}$$

We may take $\theta$ in the range $0 \leqq \theta < 2\pi$. We then call $\theta$ the *fundamental* amplitude.

Corresponding to $k = 0$, we get one $p$th root, with modulus $r^{\frac{1}{p}}$ and amplitude $\theta/p$; with $k = 1$, a second root, with the same modulus but with amplitude $(\theta + 2\pi)/p$, is found; and so on for $k = 2, 3, \cdots, p - 1$. If we set $k = p$, the amplitude is $(\theta + 2p\pi)/p = \theta/p + 2\pi$, which yields the same root as $k = 0$, and still larger integral values of $k$ yield duplicates of other of the $p$ roots originally obtained.

Consequently there exist $p$ and only $p$ distinct $p$th roots of every complex number. Since all $p$ roots have the same modulus, and successive amplitudes differ by $2\pi/p$, the plots of these roots all lie equally spaced on a circle with center at the origin $O$ and radius $r^{\frac{1}{p}}$.

*Example 1.*  Find the four fourth roots of 16.

*Solution.*  We first express the number 16 in general polar form. Since the modulus is 16 and the fundamental amplitude is 0, we have

$$16 = 16[\cos (0 + 2k\pi) + i \sin (0 + 2k\pi)].$$

Hence the fourth roots of 16 will all have the common modulus $16^{\frac{1}{4}} = 2$, and the amplitudes will be given by

$$\theta_1 = \frac{0}{4} = 0, \qquad k = 0;$$

$$\theta_2 = \frac{2\pi}{4} = \frac{\pi}{2}, \qquad k = 1;$$

$$\theta_3 = \frac{4\pi}{4} = \pi, \qquad k = 2;$$

$$\theta_4 = \frac{6\pi}{4} = \frac{3\pi}{2}, \qquad k = 3.$$

Therefore the four fourth roots of 16 are

$$2(\cos 0 + i \sin 0) = 2,$$

$$2\left(\cos \frac{\pi}{2} + i \sin \frac{\pi}{2}\right) = 2i,$$

$$2(\cos \pi + i \sin \pi) = -2,$$

$$2\left(\cos \frac{3\pi}{2} + i \sin \frac{3\pi}{2}\right) = -2i.$$

It is easily verified that $(\pm 2)^4 = 16$ and $(\pm 2i)^4 = 16$.

*Example 2.*  Find the solutions of the equation $x^2 + 12 - 5i = 0$.

*Solution.*  An equivalent statement of the problem is: Find the two square roots of $-12 + 5i$. Now the modulus of $-12 + 5i$ is $\sqrt{12^2 + 5^2} = 13$, and its fundamental amplitude is an angle $\theta$ in the second quadrant (Fig. 23). Since $\theta$ is not one of the special angles (Art. 16), we may find an approximate value from the table and hence find approximate answers to our problem, but a better way is the following. In polar form, we have

$$-12 + 5i = 13[\cos (\theta + 2k\pi) + i \sin (\theta + 2k\pi)],$$

and the two square roots of $-12 + 5i$ will be given by

$$\sqrt{13}\left(\cos\frac{\theta}{2} + i\sin\frac{\theta}{2}\right) \quad (k = 0),$$

$$\sqrt{13}\left[\cos\left(\frac{\theta}{2} + \pi\right) + i\sin\left(\frac{\theta}{2} + \pi\right)\right] = -\sqrt{13}\left(\cos\frac{\theta}{2} + i\sin\frac{\theta}{2}\right) \quad (k = 1).$$

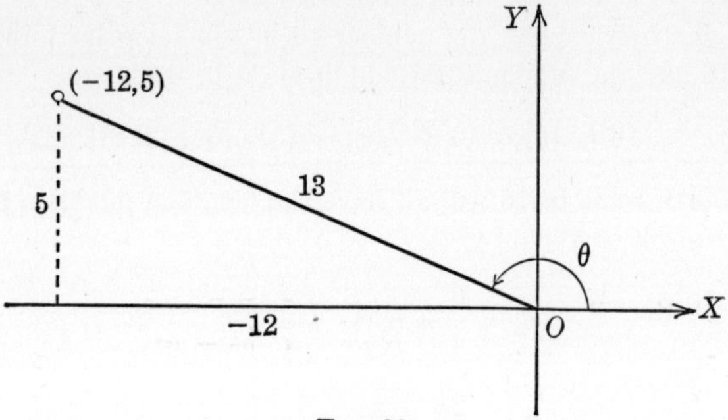

FIG. 23

It is therefore necessary to find only $\cos(\theta/2)$ and $\sin(\theta/2)$, using the formulas of Art. 38. Since $\theta$ is in the second quadrant, $\theta/2$ is in the first, and consequently

$$\cos\frac{\theta}{2} = \sqrt{\frac{1 + \cos\theta}{2}} = \sqrt{\frac{1 - \frac{12}{13}}{2}} = \frac{1}{\sqrt{26}},$$

$$\sin\frac{\theta}{2} = \sqrt{\frac{1 - \cos\theta}{2}} = \sqrt{\frac{1 + \frac{12}{13}}{2}} = \frac{5}{\sqrt{26}}.$$

Hence the desired roots are

$$\pm\sqrt{13}\left(\frac{1}{\sqrt{26}} + \frac{5i}{\sqrt{26}}\right) = \pm\left(\frac{1}{\sqrt{2}} + \frac{5i}{\sqrt{2}}\right) = \pm\left(\frac{\sqrt{2}}{2} + \frac{5\sqrt{2}}{2}i\right).$$

That the square of each of these complex numbers is, in fact, $-12 + 5i$ is easily checked.

### EXERCISES

Find all solutions of each of the following equations. Express each result in rectangular form.

1. $x^3 = 8$.
2. $x^4 = 16$.
3. $x^3 + 27 = 0$.
4. $x^5 = 32$.
5. $x^5 + 1 = 0$.
6. $x^6 = 1$.
7. $x^4 + 16 = 0$.
8. $x^6 + 64 = 0$.
9. $2x^4 + 1 - \sqrt{3}\,i = 0$.
10. $x^4 + 8 + 8\sqrt{3}\,i = 0$.
11. $x^3 = 32\sqrt{2}\,(1 - i)$.
12. $2x^4 = \sqrt{2}\,(i - 1)$.
13. $x^3 + 4\sqrt{2}\,(1 + i) = 0$.
14. $\sqrt{2}\,x^3 + 1 - i = 0$.
15. $x^5 = i$.
16. $x^5 + i = 0$.
17. $x^6 = i$.
18. $x^6 + i = 0$.
19. $x^2 = 4 + 3i$.
20. $x^3 = 2 + i$.

## SUPPLEMENTARY EXERCISES

**1.** If $a + bi = r(\cos\theta + i\sin\theta)$, where $a$ and $b$ are positive, obtain the two square roots of $a + bi$ as

$$\pm\tfrac{1}{2}\sqrt{2}(\sqrt{r+a} + i\sqrt{r-a}).$$

**2.** Given that $\sin 18° = \tfrac{1}{4}(\sqrt{5} - 1)$, show that the sum of the five fifth roots of 1 is zero.

**3.** Using mathematical induction, prove that

$$1 + 2i + 3i^2 + \cdots + (4k+1)i^{4k} = 2k + 1 - 2ki,$$

where $k$ is any positive integer.

Derive the relations of Exercises 4–8, where 1, $R_1$, and $R_2$ are the three cube roots of 1.

**4.** $1 + R_1 + R_2 = 0.$          **5.** $R_1R_2 = 1.$
**6.** $R_1 = R_2^2.$          **7.** $R_2 = R_1^2.$
**8.** $R_1 + R_2 + R_1R_2 = 0.$

In Exercises 9–15, $z = x + iy$ and $w = u + iv$, where $x$, $y$, $u$, and $v$ are real. Find $u$ and $v$ as functions of $x$ and $y$.

**9.** $w = z + a + bi.$          **10.** $w = (a + bi)z.$
**11.** $w = z^2.$          **12.** $w = z^3.$
**13.** $w = z^4.$          **14.** $w = 1/z.$
**15.** $w = (a + bi)/z.$

# Equations in Quadratic Form

**49. Methods of solving quadratic equations.** In Art. 21 we designated a function of the form

$$a_0 x^n + a_1 x^{n-1} + \cdots + a_{n-1} x + a_n$$

as a rational integral function of $x$ when $n$ is a positive integer and the $a$'s are quantities independent of $x$. When such a function is set equal to zero, we get a rational integral equation, which may conceivably be solved for $x$. Thus, the equations given in the list of exercises following Art. 48 are rational integral equations with complex numbers as coefficients, and it is possible to solve these by means of De Moivre's theorem.

The equations just cited as illustrations are, however, of a somewhat special type in that all the $a$'s except $a_0$ and $a_n$ are zero, and hence only root extractions are required to solve them. When there are no restrictions on the coefficients, the problem of solving a rational integral equation may be expected to be less direct and more complicated. The linear equation, in which $n = 1$, presents no difficulty, and we shall consider now the rational integral equation of second degree, or **quadratic equation**. This may be represented by the type form

$$ax^2 + bx + c = 0, \qquad a \neq 0. \tag{1}$$

It will be understood that the letters $a$, $b$, $c$ represent any numbers or algebraic quantities independent of $x$, except that, as indicated, $a \neq 0$, so that we actually have an equation of the second degree.

Two special cases may be quickly disposed of. If $b = 0$, the equation becomes

$$ax^2 + c = 0, \tag{2}$$

which is of the form treated in Art. 48. We evidently have, as solutions of (2), the two values

$$x = \pm \sqrt{-\frac{c}{a}}. \tag{3}$$

In general, when $a$ and $c$ are complex numbers, the two solutions given by (3) are also complex numbers. When $a$ and $c$ are real and like in sign, the roots (3) will be pure imaginary numbers; and when $a$ and $c$ are real but opposite in sign, the solutions will be real.

As a second special case, suppose that $c = 0$. Then (1) becomes

$$ax^2 + bx = 0, \tag{4}$$

which factors into

$$x(ax + b) = 0.$$

Hence there will again be two solutions,

$$x = 0 \quad \text{and} \quad x = -\frac{b}{a}. \tag{5}$$

When $a$ and $b$ are complex numbers, the second of solutions (5) will, in general, be complex; but if both $a$ and $b$ are real, both roots of (4) will likewise be real. If $b = 0$ as well as $c = 0$, both the solutions of the quadratic equation will be equal to zero.

We consider now the general equation (1). To solve this equation, we use the method of *completing the square*, as we did in the illustrative example of Art. 44. First divide both members of (1) by $a$, to make the coefficient of $x^2$ equal to unity, and add $-c/a$ to both members of the resulting relation to get the equivalent equation

$$x^2 + \frac{b}{a}x = -\frac{c}{a}.$$

Now $(x + k)^2 \equiv x^2 + 2kx + k^2$, whence it is seen that the term free of $x$ in the expansion of the squared binomial is equal to the square of half the coefficient of $x$. We therefore add $b^2/4a^2$ to both members of the above equation, and get

$$x^2 + \frac{b}{a}x + \frac{b^2}{4a^2} = \frac{b^2}{4a^2} - \frac{c}{a}.$$

or

$$\left(x + \frac{b}{2a}\right)^2 = \frac{b^2 - 4ac}{4a^2}.$$

Therefore

$$x + \frac{b}{2a} = \pm \frac{\sqrt{b^2 - 4ac}}{2a},$$

and

$$x = \frac{-b \pm \sqrt{b^2 - 4ac}}{2a}. \tag{6}$$

These are the two solutions of the typical quadratic equation (1), which may be verified by the usual criterion (Art. 24). Relation (6) is often referred to as the quadratic formula, since it enables one to find the solutions of a given quadratic equation by substituting the coefficients $a$, $b$, and $c$.

*Example.* Solve the quadratic equation

$$6x^2 - x - 35 = 0.$$

*Solution.* Here we have $a = 6$, $b = -1$, $c = -35$. Substituting in (6), we find

$$x = \frac{-(-1) \pm \sqrt{(-1)^2 - 4 \cdot 6(-35)}}{2 \cdot 6} = \frac{1 \pm \sqrt{1 + 840}}{12} = \frac{1 \pm 29}{12}.$$

Hence the roots are

$$x = \frac{1 + 29}{12} = \frac{30}{12} = \frac{5}{2}, \quad x = \frac{1 - 29}{12} = -\frac{28}{12} = -\frac{7}{3}.$$

The quadratic equation of this example could also be solved by factoring. We find that

$$6x^2 - x - 35 \equiv (2x - 5)(3x + 7),$$

and since the equation will be satisfied if either of the two linear factors is set equal to zero, we get the two solutions found above.

When the coefficients $a$, $b$, and $c$ of (1) are simple numbers, it is often easiest to solve by the latter method of factoring. However, if linear factors are not readily determined, the quadratic formula (6) provides a certain method for solving the equation in hand.

Since the need for solving a quadratic equation arises frequently, the student should memorize formula (6) and be able to use it whenever necessary.

### EXERCISES

Solve each of the following quadratic equations.

1. $x^2 - 5x + 6 = 0$.
2. $x^2 - 7x + 12 = 0$.
3. $x^2 + x - 2 = 0$.
4. $2x^2 - 7x + 3 = 0$.
5. $4x^2 + 13x + 3 = 0$.
6. $x^2 - 2x + 5 = 0$.
7. $x^2 + 4x + 2 = 0$.
8. $3x^2 - 6x + 2 = 0$.
9. $5x^2 + 2x - 1 = 0$.
10. $\sqrt{3}\,x^2 - 4x + \sqrt{3} = 0$.
11. $2y^2 + 4y - 5 = 0$.
12. $8t^2 - 3t - 2 = 0$.
13. $x^2 - 4ax - 45a^2 = 0$.
14. $x^2 - (2a + 3)x + 6a = 0$.
15. $x^2 - 2\sqrt{a}\,x + a = 0$.
16. $x^2 + cx + k = 0$.
17. $2ax^2 - 4bx + 3c = 0$.
18. $bx^2 + cx + a = 0$.
19. $cx^2 + ax + b = 0$.
20. $ax^2 - bx - c = 0$.
21. $rx^2 - sx + t^2 = 0$.
22. $mx^2 + n^2x + p^3 = 0$.
23. $x^2 - 5ix - 6 = 0$.
24. $2ix^2 - 3x + 2i = 0$.
25. $D^2 + 2aD + b^2 = 0$.
26. $mD^2 + KgD + k^2g = 0$.
27. $x^4 - 5x^2 + 4 = 0$.
28. $x^4 + 2x^2 - 8 = 0$.
29. $z^2 + z - 1 + 3i = 0$.
30. $z^2 + 7(i - 1)z - 25i = 0$.

**50. Relations between coefficients and roots.** The quadratic formula derived in the preceding article shows that the character of the roots depends upon the nature and values of the coefficients of the quadratic equation. In this article we shall investigate the dependencies between coefficients and solutions more thoroughly.

We first establish two simple but basic theorems concerning quadratic equations. Let $x = r$ be a solution of the quadratic equation

$$ax^2 + bx + c = 0, \qquad a \neq 0, \tag{1}$$

so that we have

$$ar^2 + br + c \equiv 0.$$

Then

$$\begin{aligned}
ax^2 + bx + c &= ax^2 + bx + c - (ar^2 + br + c)\\
&= a(x^2 - r^2) + b(x - r)\\
&= (x - r)(ax + ar + b).
\end{aligned} \tag{2}$$

That is, $x - r$ is a linear factor of the quadratic function if $r$ is a zero of that function. Conversely, if $x - r$ is a factor of $ax^2 + bx + c$, then the latter will reduce to zero for $x = r$. Thus we have the following theorem:

*The quantity $r$ is a root of the quadratic equation* (1) *if and only if $x - r$ is a factor of the quadratic expression $ax^2 + bx + c$.*

Now let $r_1$ and $r_2$ denote the two solutions of equation (1) found by the quadratic formula:

$$r_1 = \frac{-b + \sqrt{b^2 - 4ac}}{2a}, \quad r_2 = \frac{-b - \sqrt{b^2 - 4ac}}{2a}. \tag{3}$$

By the above theorem, there will be a linear factor corresponding to each of these roots, namely, $x - r_1$ and $x - r_2$. If we form the product of these two linear factors, we get, on the one hand,

$$(x - r_1)(x - r_2) = x^2 - (r_1 + r_2)x + r_1 r_2. \tag{4}$$

Using the values of $r_1$ and $r_2$ given by (3), we also find

$$\begin{aligned}
(x - r_1)(x - r_2) &= \left(x + \frac{b}{2a} - \frac{\sqrt{b^2 - 4ac}}{2a}\right)\left(x + \frac{b}{2a} + \frac{\sqrt{b^2 - 4ac}}{2a}\right)\\
&= \left(x + \frac{b}{2a}\right)^2 - \frac{b^2 - 4ac}{4a^2}\\
&= x^2 + \frac{b}{a}x + \frac{b^2}{4a^2} - \frac{b^2}{4a^2} + \frac{c}{a},
\end{aligned}$$

whence

$$(x - r_1)(x - r_2) = x^2 + \frac{b}{a}x + \frac{c}{a}, \qquad (5)$$

or, equivalently,

$$a(x - r_1)(x - r_2) = ax^2 + bx + c. \qquad (6)$$

Combining (4) and (5), we therefore have

$$x^2 - (r_1 + r_2)x + r_1r_2 = x^2 + \frac{b}{a}x + \frac{c}{a}. \qquad (7)$$

If, now, $R$ is any quantity different from $r_1$ and $r_2$, it follows from (6) that

$$aR^2 + bR + c \equiv a(R - r_1)(R - r_2) \neq 0.$$

Therefore we have the following theorem:

*A quadratic equation (1) has only two roots; they are given by expressions (3).*

The relations obtained in the development of the above results have further important consequences. Examination of relation (7) shows immediately that

$$r_1 + r_2 = -\frac{b}{a}, \qquad r_1r_2 = \frac{c}{a}. \qquad (8)$$

That is, the sum of the roots of the quadratic equation (1) is equal to the negative of the quotient of the coefficient of the first-degree term by that of the second-degree term, and the product of the roots is equal to the quotient of the term independent of $x$ by the coefficient of the second-degree term. Relations (8) may also be established directly from expressions (3) for $r_1$ and $r_2$.

If $b = 0$, the first of relations (8) shows that $r_1 + r_2 = 0$, or $r_1 = -r_2$; that is, one solution is the negative of the other. This was found to be true in Art. 49 also. Conversely, if one solution is the negative of the other, $r_1 + r_2 = 0$, and therefore $b = 0$.

If $c = 0$, the second of relations (8) shows that at least one root must be equal to zero, as was found in Art. 49. Conversely, if one or both roots are zero, we must have $c = 0$.

If $b = 0$ and $c = 0$, evidently both solutions must be zero. Conversely, if both roots are zero, relations (8) show that $b = 0$ and $c = 0$.

Suppose now that the two solutions are equal: $r_1 = r_2$. Equating the two expressions (3) for $r_1$ and $r_2$, we then find that we must have

$$b^2 - 4ac = 0.$$

Conversely, if $b^2 - 4ac = 0$, it follows immediately that $r_1 = r_2$. Thus we have the theorem:

*The two solutions of a quadratic equation are equal if and only if $b^2 - 4ac = 0$.*

All the above discussion has been made without any restrictions as to whether the coefficients $a$, $b$, and $c$ were real or complex numbers, or algebraic quantities independent of $x$. If, now, we stipulate that $a$, $b$, and $c$ are real numbers, we can deduce additional relations between these coefficients and the solutions $r_1$ and $r_2$. Examination of expressions (3) for $r_1$ and $r_2$ shows that: (*a*) if $b^2 - 4ac > 0$, the roots are real and different; (*b*) if $b^2 - 4ac = 0$, the roots are real and equal; (*c*) if $b^2 - 4ac < 0$, the roots are conjugate complex numbers.

Since the nature of the roots thus depends upon the quantity $b^2 - 4ac$, when $a$, $b$, and $c$ are real numbers, the expression $b^2 - 4ac$ is called the **discriminant** of the quadratic equation (1).

When $a$, $b$, and $c$ are real, the nature of the quadratic function and its zeros can be exhibited geometrically by plotting the curve $y = ax^2 + bx + c$. One such example has already been considered (Art. 11, Fig. 3). When $a > 0$, as in the function $2x^2 - 5x + 1$, the curve will open upward as indicated in Fig. 3; when $a < 0$, the curve extends indefinitely downward. In either case, the curve $y = ax^2 + bx + c$ is a *parabola*. When $b^2 - 4ac > 0$, the parabola will cut the $X$-axis in two distinct points, the abscissas of which are the real zeros of the function; if $b^2 - 4ac = 0$, the curve touches the $X$-axis at just one point whose abscissa is the common value of the two real and equal zeros of the function; and when $b^2 - 4ac < 0$, the parabola will lie entirely on one side of the $X$-axis, since the function then possesses no real zeros. The parabola is an important curve studied extensively in analytic geometry.

## EXERCISES

In each of Exercises 1–10, form a quadratic equation having the two given quantities as roots.

**1.** 3, 7.  
**2.** $-4$, 6.  
**3.** $2i$, $-2i$.  
**4.** $1 + \sqrt{2}$, $1 - \sqrt{2}$.  
**5.** $2 + 3i$, $2 - 3i$.  
**6.** $4 + 2i$, $3 - i$.  
**7.** $3a$, $-4a$.  
**8.** $a + b$, $a - b$.  
**9.** $\sqrt{a} + b$, $\sqrt{a} - b$.  
**10.** $a + bi$, $a - bi$.

**11.** If the equation $2x^2 + 4x + k^2 + 2k - 8 = 0$ is to have a zero root, what values of $k$ are permissible?

**12.** If the equation $x^2 + (2a - b)x + a - 3b - 15 = 0$ is to have two zero roots, what values must $a$ and $b$ have?

**13.** If the sum of the roots of the equation $kx^2 + (5k - 4)x + 2 = 0$ is to be equal to $-1$, what value must $k$ have?

**14.** If the product of the roots of the equation $kx^2 + 4x + 2 - 3k = 0$ is to be equal to $-5$, what value must $k$ have?

**15.** If one root of the equation $2kx^2 - (k - 3)x + k^2 + 3k - 2 = 0$ is to be equal to the reciprocal of the other root, what are the permissible values of $k$?

**16.** Determine the values of $k$ making the roots of the equation $kx^2 - 6x + 5 + 4k = 0$ equal.

**17.** Determine the values of $k$ if the equation $3x^2 - kx + k^2 - k - 18 = 0$ is to have the solution $x = 1$.

**18.** If the difference between the roots of the equation $2x^2 + kx + 10 - k^2 = 0$ is to be 4, determine $k$.

**19.** If one root of the equation $kx^2 + (8 + k)x + 18 = 0$ is to be twice the other root, determine $k$.

**20.** If one root of the equation $2k^2x^2 + 3kx + 1 = 0$ is to equal the square of the other root, determine $k$.

**21.** A rectangle is to be 3 in. longer than wide and is to have an area of 40 sq. in. Find its dimensions.

**22.** Two-inch squares are cut from each corner of a piece of cardboard that is twice as long as it is wide, and the ends are turned up to form an open box. If the volume of the box is 320 cu. in., what are the dimensions of the original piece of cardboard?

**23.** If a projectile is thrown upward with an initial speed of $v_0$ ft./sec., the speed $v$ (ft./sec.) at the end of $t$ seconds is approximately given by $v = v_0 - 32.2t$, and the distance $s$ (ft.) from the starting point is approximately given by $s = v_0 t - 16.1t^2$. If $v_0 = 150$ ft./sec., what time is required to return to the starting point?

**24.** Using the data of Exercise 23, determine the distance traveled during the fourth second.

**25.** Using the data of Exercise 23, determine the time required to reach a point 200 ft. from the starting point.

**26.** For the projectile of Exercise 23, show that the distance $s$ cannot be greater than $v_0^2/64.4$ ft., and that this distance is attained when $t = v_0/32.2$ sec.

**27.** On the same coordinate axes, plot the curves $y = x^2 - 6x + k$, when $k$ is given the values 8, 9, and 10 in turn. Deduce the nature of the zeros of these three quadratic functions from their graphs, and verify your results by means of the discriminant.

**28.** On the same coordinate axes, plot the curves $y = kx^2 - 2x - 1$, when $k$ is given the values 1, $\frac{1}{2}$, and $\frac{1}{10}$ in turn. As $k$ successively assumes smaller and smaller positive values, what is the apparent effect on the zeros of the quadratic function $kx^2 - 2x - 1$? Verify your deductions by determining the effect of allowing $k$ to become numerically smaller in the expressions for the zeros:

$$\frac{1 + \sqrt{1 + k}}{k} \quad \text{and} \quad \frac{1 - \sqrt{1 + k}}{k} \equiv -\frac{1}{1 + \sqrt{1 + k}}.$$

**29.** Show that the equation $x^2 + ax - b = 0$, where $a$ and $b$ are positive real numbers, has real solutions, one of which is positive and the other negative.

**30.** The edges of a cube are all decreased 2 in. in length, thereby decreasing the volume of the cube by 728 cu. in. Find the original volume.

**31.** Lines are drawn through each pair of a group of points, no three of which are collinear. If the number of such points is doubled, 210 additional lines may be so drawn. Find the original number of points.

**32.** A right circular cylinder has altitude $h$ and base radius $r$. If $h$ and $r$ are in turn changed by the same quantity $x$, the volume will be changed by the same amount $y$. Show that $x$ must be positive or negative according as $r > 2h$ or $r < 2h$.

**33.** Using the relations $r_1 + r_2 = -b/a$, $r_1 r_2 = c/a$, show that $b^2 - 4ac = 0$ if and only if $r_1 = r_2$.

**34.** The perimeter of a circular sector is $P$ and its area is $A$. Show that $P^2 \geq 16A$.

**35.** Show that the sum of the reciprocals of the roots of the quadratic equation $ax^2 + bx + c = 0$ is equal to $-b/c$.

**51. Algebraic equations in quadratic form.** The equations discussed thus far have been quadratics in the variable or unknown itself. If, now, $f(x)$ is any function of $x$, we say that the equation

$$a[f(x)]^2 + bf(x) + c = 0, \qquad a \neq 0, \tag{1}$$

is of **quadratic form,** even though (1) may not be a quadratic in the variable $x$.

By the methods of Art. 49, it is possible to solve equation (1) for $f(x)$. If $r_1$ and $r_2$ are the solutions, in terms of $a$, $b$, and $c$, we then have the problem of solving the two equations,

$$f(x) = r_1 \qquad \text{and} \qquad f(x) = r_2, \tag{2}$$

for $x$. Frequently this procedure is easier or otherwise more desirable than the process of solving (1) for $x$ directly. Consequently it is important that the student be able to recognize quadratic form and the possibility of transforming or reducing a given equation to the quadratic form. By means of examples we shall illustrate various types of situations that arise.

*Example 1.* Solve the equation

$$2x^4 + 7x^2 - 4 = 0.$$

*Solution.* This equation is clearly of the form (1), with $f(x) = x^2$, $a = 2$, $b = 7$, and $c = -4$. We easily find

$$x^2 = \tfrac{1}{2}, \qquad x^2 = -4,$$

whence

$$x = \pm \frac{\sqrt{2}}{2}, \qquad x = \pm 2i.$$

Thus the given equation of fourth degree has four solutions.

*Example 2.*   Solve the equation

$$4\sqrt{\frac{3-x}{3+x}} - \sqrt{\frac{3+x}{3-x}} = \sqrt{2}.$$

*Solution.*  Although this equation is not in quadratic form, the fact that the two radicals in the left member are reciprocal to each other suggests that the equation may be reduced to a tractable form.   For brevity, let

$$y = \sqrt{\frac{3-x}{3+x}}.$$

Then the equation becomes

$$4y - \frac{1}{y} = \sqrt{2},$$

whence we get

$$4y^2 - \sqrt{2}\,y - 1 = 0,$$

a quadratic in $y$.   The solutions of this equation are found to be

$$y = \frac{\sqrt{2}}{2}, \qquad y = -\frac{\sqrt{2}}{4}.$$

Now $y$ denotes a square root with a prefixed positive sign understood.   Hence $y$ may be either real and positive or complex, but not real and negative.   Consequently the value $y = -\sqrt{2}/4$ can lead only to extraneous solutions and may therefore be discarded.   We do have

$$y = \sqrt{\frac{3-x}{3+x}} = \frac{\sqrt{2}}{2},$$

whence

$$\frac{3-x}{3+x} = \frac{1}{2},$$

$$6 - 2x = 3 + x,$$

$$3x = 3,$$

$$x = 1.$$

This is the only solution of the given equation; its correctness may readily be checked.

*Example 3.*   Solve the equation

$$x^2 - x + 2\sqrt{x^2 - x - 5} = 8.$$

*Solution.*   One method of solving this equation is to rationalize it.   This yields, as the student may show, an equation of the fourth degree,

$$x^4 - 2x^3 - 19x^2 + 20x + 84 = 0.$$

By certain processes to be considered in Chapter XV, the four solutions possessed by this equation may be determined. Even then, all four must be tested, since it is quite possible that the rationalizing process has introduced extraneous solutions.

A better method is as follows. We notice that the first two terms of the left member, $x^2 - x$, appear under the radical also. Hence we add $-5$ to both members, to get

$$x^2 - x - 5 + 2\sqrt{x^2 - x - 5} = 3.$$

Then, setting

$$y = \sqrt{x^2 - x - 5}$$

for brevity, we have

$$y^2 + 2y - 3 = 0,$$

whence there is found

$$y = -3, \qquad y = 1.$$

As in Example 2, the positively signed radical denoted by $y$ cannot have the negative real value, $-3$. But $y = 1$ is permissible; we get

$$\sqrt{x^2 - x - 5} = 1,$$
$$x^2 - x - 6 = 0,$$
$$x = 3, \qquad x = -2.$$

Thus there are two solutions of the given equation.

## EXERCISES

*any 5 part 3*

Solve each of the following equations.

1. $x^4 - 7x^2 + 12 = 0.$

2. $2x^4 + 17x^2 - 9 = 0.$

3. $y + \sqrt{y} - 6 = 0.$

4. $t^{\frac{2}{3}} - 2t^{\frac{1}{3}} - 8 = 0.$

5. $10x^{-2} + 3x^{-1} - 1 = 0.$

6. $x - 3\sqrt{x - 2} - 6 = 0.$

7. $y^6 - 7y^3 - 8 = 0.$

8. $(x - 1)^{\frac{1}{2}} - 2(x - 1)^{\frac{1}{4}} - 15 = 0.$

9. $x^2 - 5\sqrt{x^2 - 5} + 1 = 0.$

10. $17 - 4(x + x^{-1}) = 0.$

11. $3x^{-\frac{1}{2}} + 2x^{\frac{1}{2}} - 2x^{-\frac{3}{2}} = 0.$

12. $6 - 5(y + 1)^{-\frac{1}{3}} - (y + 1)^{-\frac{2}{3}} = 0.$

13. $3x^2 + 15x - 4x\sqrt{x + 5} = 15x.$

14. $24\sqrt{x} - 2x^{\frac{3}{2}} - x^{\frac{5}{2}} = 0.$

15. $8\left(\dfrac{t}{t + 1}\right)^2 + \dfrac{6t}{t + 1} - 5 = 0.$

16. $3\left(\dfrac{y - 2}{y}\right)^2 + \dfrac{10(y - 2)}{y} - 8 = 0.$

17. $5(\sqrt{x} - 1)^2 + 7\sqrt{x}\,(\sqrt{x} - 1) - 6x = 0.$

18. $4(2 - \sqrt{x})^2 - 3\sqrt{x}\,(2 - \sqrt{x}) - 7x = 0.$

19. $\dfrac{x^2 + 1}{2x} - \dfrac{4x}{x^2 + 1} + 1 = 0.$

20. $\dfrac{x^2 + x}{x - 1} = \dfrac{9}{2} - \dfrac{9 - 9x}{x^2 + x}.$

**21.** $3\sqrt{\dfrac{x+16}{x}} - 5\sqrt{\dfrac{x}{x+16}} = 2.$      **22.** $\dfrac{3\sqrt{x+1}}{x} + \dfrac{2x}{\sqrt{x+1}} = 5.$

**23.** $10x^2 - 12x - 5\sqrt{5x^2 - 6x - 4} = 6.$

**24.** $x^4 + 2x^3 - 7x^2 - 8x + 12 = 0.$

**25.** $x^4 + 8x^3 + 20x^2 + 16x - 5 = 0.$

**52. Trigonometric equations reducible to quadratic form.** A trigonometric equation may often be reduced or transformed into the quadratic form

$$a[f(x)]^2 + bf(x) + c = 0, \tag{1}$$

where, as in the preceding article, $a$, $b$, and $c$ are quantities independent
of $x$, and in which $f(x)$ now represents a trigonometric expression involving the variable $x$. If $f(x) = r_1$ and $f(x) = r_2$ are solutions of this
equation, the processes previously discussed (Chapters IV and VI) may
serve to determine permissible values of $x$.

*Example.* Solve the equation

$$\sin^2 2x - 2\cos^2 x + 1 = 0$$

for non-negative values of $x$ less than 360°.

*Solution.* Since trigonometric functions of both $x$ and $2x$ are involved, we
first transform to an equivalent equation containing functions of $x$ only. Using
the identity $\sin 2x = 2 \sin x \cos x$, we get

$$4 \sin^2 x \cos^2 x - 2 \cos^2 x + 1 = 0.$$

Now, since two functions of $x$ appear in this equation, we replace $\sin^2 x$ by its
equal, $1 - \cos^2 x$; this gives us

$$4 \cos^2 x - 4 \cos^4 x - 2 \cos^2 x + 1 = 0,$$

or

$$4 \cos^4 x - 2 \cos^2 x - 1 = 0.$$

Here we have an equation of form (1), with $f(x) = \cos^2 x$. The quadratic formula then yields

$$\cos^2 x = \frac{1 + \sqrt{5}}{4}, \qquad \cos^2 x = \frac{1 - \sqrt{5}}{4}.$$

It is clear that $\cos^2 x$ cannot be negative, for then $\cos x$ would be a complex
number, and no angle value would exist; the second of the above equations
may therefore be discarded. From the first relation, however, we find

$$\cos^2 x = 0.8090, \qquad \cos x = \pm 0.8995,$$

whence reference to tables, together with the relations of Art. 18, gives us four
values of $x$:

$$25° \, 55', \qquad 154° \, 5', \qquad 205° \, 55', \qquad 334° \, 5',$$

approximately, all of which fall in the range $0 \le x < 360°$. The student may
show that all these four angle values satisfy the given equation.

The negative value for $\cos^2 x$ was discarded since no angle $x$ could satisfy such a relation. Likewise, if $\cos^2 x$ had been greater than unity, no angle values would be obtainable. Thus, a trigonometric equation may fail, in various ways, to possess a solution.

*[handwritten annotations: $\sin x = $ any $3$      $-\dfrac{\pm\sqrt{4ac}}{2a}$]*

**EXERCISES**

Determine which of the following equations possess solutions. If a solution exists, find the smallest non-negative value of $x$ satisfying the equation, and express the result in sexagesimal measure.

**1.** $\sin^2 x + 2 \sin x + 3 = 0.$
**2.** $\cos^2 x - 4 \cos x + 5 = 0.$
**3.** $\cos^2 x + 2 \cos x - 8 = 0.$
**4.** $\sin^2 x - \sin x - 5 = 0.$
**5.** $\cos^2 x - 3 \sin x + 9 = 0.$
**6.** $\sin^2 x + 2 \cos x + 14 = 0.$
**7.** $2 \cos^2 x + \sin x - 1 = 0.$
**8.** $2 \sin^2 x - 3\sqrt{3} \cos x - 5 = 0.$
**9.** $3 \sin^2 x - 2 \cos x - 2 = 0.$
**10.** $20 \cos^2 x - 13 \sin x - 22 = 0.$
**11.** $\sec^2 x + 2 \tan x + 2 = 0.$
**12.** $\cot^2 x - \csc x + 3 = 0.$
**13.** $\csc^2 x + 3 \cot x + 1 = 0.$
**14.** $\tan^2 x - \sec x - 2 = 0.$

**15.** $3 \cos x - 2 \cos \dfrac{x}{2} - 5 = 0.$
**16.** $\sin^2 2x + 2 \cos^2 x + 2 = 0.$

**17.** $2 \cos^4 x + 9 \sin^2 x - 5 = 0.$
**18.** $2 \tan^4 x + 3 \sec^2 x - 5 = 0.$
**19.** $\sin x - (\sqrt{\tan x} + 2)\cos x = 0.$
**20.** $\sin 2x + \sin x - \cos x = 1.$

**53. Systems of quadratic equations.** Up to this point we have considered quadratic functions of only one variable. The general expression of second degree in two variable, $x$ and $y$, has the form

$$Ax^2 + Bxy + Cy^2 + Dx + Ey + F, \qquad (1)$$

where $A$, $B$, $C$, $D$, $E$, and $F$ are quantities independent of both $x$ and $y$; this is called the general **quadratic function of two variables.** If we set equal to zero an expression of the form (1) in which at least one of the coefficients $A$, $B$, $C$ is different from zero, we get a **quadratic equation in two variables:**

$$Ax^2 + Bxy + Cy^2 + Dx + Ey + F = 0. \qquad (2)$$

When $A \neq 0$, so that (2) is a quadratic equation in $x$, with coefficients containing $y$, the quadratic formula may be used to solve for $x$ in terms of $y$, for we have merely to substitute $a = A$, $b = By + D$, and $c = Cy^2 + Ey + F$. Similarly, when $C \neq 0$, (2) may be solved for $y$ in terms of $x$ by means of the quadratic formula; here $a = C$, $b = Bx + E$, and $c = Ax^2 + Dx + F$.

Corresponding to each value assigned to, say, $x$, equation (2) thus yields, in general, two values of $y$. When the coefficients $A$, $\cdots$, $F$ are specific numbers, we then generally find two numerical values of $y$ for each $x$; these may, of course, be real or complex. If we restrict ourselves to real coefficients and to those real values of $x$ yielding real $y$-values, the points $(x, y)$ so found may be plotted. It is shown in analytic geometry that the curve so obtained will be one of several types collectively called conic sections, since they are curves of intersection of a plane and a conical surface. For example, the parabola $y = ax^2 + bx + c$, discussed in Art. 50, is obtainable from our equation (2) by setting $A = a$, $B = 0$, $C = 0$, $D = b$, $E = -1$, and $F = c$.

Consider now a **quadratic system** consisting of two equations of type (2):

$$A_1x^2 + B_1xy + C_1y^2 + D_1x + E_1y + F_1 = 0, \tag{3}$$

$$A_2x^2 + B_2xy + C_2y^2 + D_2x + E_2y + F_2 = 0. \tag{4}$$

These equations may be equivalent, incompatible, or consistent, depending upon the values of the coefficients. For example, the system

$$3x^2 - y^2 + 7x + 2y - 1 = 0,$$

$$6x^2 - 2y^2 + 14x + 4y - 2 = 0,$$

is obviously an equivalent system, since the second equation is obtainable from the first by multiplying both members by 2; the system

$$x^2 + y^2 = 1,$$

$$x^2 + y^2 = 4,$$

is incompatible, since $x^2 + y^2$ cannot simultaneously be 1 and 4; and the system

$$x^2 - y = 0,$$

$$y^2 - 8x = 0,$$

is consistent, for it has the following solutions:

$$x = 0, \quad y = 0; \quad x = -1 + \sqrt{3}i, \quad y = -2 - 2\sqrt{3}i;$$

$$x = 2, \quad y = 4; \quad x = -1 - \sqrt{3}i, \quad y = -2 + 2\sqrt{3}i,$$

and no others, as may easily be shown.

In general, if we solve one equation of the system (3)–(4) for one variable in terms of the other, substitute into the second equation, and then rationalize the result, we shall be led to an equation of the fourth degree. For example, elimination of $y$ from the equations of the last illustrative pair above leads to the relation $x^4 - 8x = 0$, whence the four values of $x$ are found. Application of this elimination process to the general equations (3)–(4) shows that the degree of the resulting rational integral equation in one variable cannot be more than four

Moreover, just as it was shown in Art. 50 that an equation of the second degree cannot have more than two solutions, so it may be proved (see Chapter XV) that the fourth-degree equation cannot have more than four solutions. Hence, apart from equivalent equations, a system of the type (3)–(4) may be expected to have no more than four corresponding pairs $(x, y)$ as its solutions.

Since we have not yet considered methods for solving fourth-degree equations, we cannot properly discuss here the solution of all systems of the form (3)–(4). However, a few special types and processes that arise from time to time in later mathematical work may be treated now.

Suppose first that the two quadratic equations are of the form

$$A_1x^2 + C_1y^2 + F_1 = 0, \tag{5}$$

$$A_2x^2 + C_2y^2 + F_2 = 0. \tag{6}$$

These constitute a special case of the general system (3)–(4), with all the $B$'s, $D$'s, and $E$'s taken equal to zero. Now the system (5)–(6), although quadratic in $x$ and $y$ themselves, may be regarded as a linear system in the quantities $x^2$ and $y^2$. Hence, if these equations are consistent, which they will be if the determinant of the system, $A_1C_2 - A_2C_1$, is different from zero, we may determine one solution pair, $x^2 = a$ and $y^2 = b$, say, by the methods of Chapter V. Consequently there will be four solutions of the quadratic system (5)–(6): $(\sqrt{a}, \sqrt{b})$, $(\sqrt{a}, -\sqrt{b})$, $(-\sqrt{a}, \sqrt{b})$, and $(-\sqrt{a}, -\sqrt{b})$.

*Example 1.* Solve the quadratic system

$$3x^2 + y^2 = 1,$$

$$2x^2 - 3y^2 = -14.$$

*Solution.* This system is certainly consistent, for its determinant is $-9 - 2 = -11 \neq 0$. We easily find $x^2 = -1$, $y^2 = 4$, whence the four solutions of the system are

$$(i, 2), \qquad (i, -2), \qquad (-i, 2), \qquad (-i, -2).$$

Another easily solved system is that in which one equation is any quadratic and the other is linear:

$$A_1x^2 + B_1xy + C_1y^2 + D_1x + E_1y + F_1 = 0, \tag{7}$$

$$D_2x + E_2y + F_2 = 0; \tag{8}$$

this is obtainable from (3)–(4) by setting $A_2 = B_2 = C_2 = 0$. For, if (8) is solved for either variable in terms of the other, and the result substituted into (7), we get a quadratic equation in the second variable.

Thus we get no more than two solutions of such a system, as in the following example.

*Example 2.*   Solve the system

$$2x^2 - 3xy - 4y^2 + x + y - 1 = 0,$$

$$2x - y = 3.$$

*Solution.*   From the second equation, $y = 2x - 3$. Replacing $y$ by this linear function of $x$ in the first equation, we find

$$2x^2 - 3x(2x - 3) - 4(2x - 3)^2 + x + 2x - 3 - 1 = 0.$$

This reduces to

$$x^2 - 3x + 2 = 0,$$

which is satisfied by $x = 1$ and $x = 2$. The linear relation then yields the respective values $y = -1$ and $y = 1$. Therefore the two solutions of the system are

$$(1, -1), \qquad (2, 1).$$

We sometimes have to deal with a quadratic system in which one quadratic function is factorable into two linear expressions. Such a quadratic equation is therefore equivalent to two linear equations, since the vanishing of either linear expression entails the vanishing of their product. Each linear equation thus obtained may then be solved simultaneously with the other quadratic equation of the system, and consequently we obtain, in general, four solutions of the system. If, in particular, one quadratic equation of the given system is homogeneous, then two linear factors may always be determined, as in the following example.

*Example 3.*   Solve the system

$$3x^2 - xy - y^2 - 5x + 2 = 0,$$

$$3x^2 - 5xy - 2y^2 = 0.$$

*Solution.*   The second of these quadratic equations is homogeneous and may therefore be factored. The factors of this function are obtainable by inspection; we have

$$3x^2 - 5xy - 2y^2 \equiv (3x + y)(x - 2y).$$

Alternatively, we can use the general method of dividing by, say, $y^2$ to produce a quadratic equation in the quantity $x/y$; this may be solved by means of the quadratic formula, and the corresponding factors thus determined.

Combining the relation $y = -3x$, obtained by setting one linear factor equal to zero, with the first of the given equations, we are led to the quadratic equation

$$3x^2 + 5x - 2 = 0,$$

which has the solutions $x = \frac{1}{3}$ and $x = -2$. Hence two solutions of the system are found to be

$$(\tfrac{1}{3}, -1), \qquad (-2, 6).$$

Similarly, using the other factor, we get $x = 2y$. When substituted into the first equation of the system, this yields

$$9y^2 - 10y + 2 = 0,$$

whence we find

$$y = \frac{5 \pm \sqrt{7}}{9}.$$

Therefore two additional solutions of the system are

$$\left(\frac{10 + 2\sqrt{7}}{9}, \frac{5 + \sqrt{7}}{9}\right), \quad \left(\frac{10 - 2\sqrt{7}}{9}, \frac{5 - \sqrt{7}}{9}\right).$$

As variants of the two last cases, we sometimes have two quadratic equations that may be combined to yield either a single linear relation or a factorable quadratic function. Thus, if we have given the system

$$2x^2 - 3xy - 4y^2 + x + y - 1 = 0,$$

$$2x^2 - 3xy - 4y^2 + 3x - 4 = 0$$

it is evident that subtraction yields a linear relation, $2x - y - 3 = 0$, which may be combined with either quadratic equation; this system is therefore equivalent to that of Example 2. Similarly, if we have the system

$$3x^2 - xy - y^2 - 5x + 2 = 0,$$

$$4xy + y^2 - 5x + 2 = 0,$$

subtraction yields the homogeneous relation $3x^2 - 5xy - 2y^2 = 0$, so that this system is equivalent to that of Example 3.

A system of the form

$$A_1 x^2 + B_1 xy + C_1 y^2 + F_1 = 0, \tag{9}$$

$$A_2 x^2 + B_2 xy + C_2 y^2 + F_2 = 0, \tag{10}$$

in which the linear terms are lacking, is frequently dealt with. Such a system is best treated by the method suggested in the preceding paragraph. By elimination of the constants, we get a homogeneous equation that can be combined with one of the given equations, as was done in Example 3.

*Example 4.* Solve the system

$$2x^2 - 3xy + 4y^2 = 3,$$

$$x^2 + xy - 8y^2 = -6.$$

*Solution.* If we multiply both members of the first equation by 2, and add the result to the second equation, we get

$$5x^2 - 5xy = 0.$$

This is immediately factorable, yielding

$$x = 0, \qquad x = y,$$

as the two linear relations. When $x = 0$, either of the given equations gives $y = \pm\frac{1}{2}\sqrt{3}$; when $x = y$, we get $y = \pm 1$. Hence the four solutions of the system are

$$(0, \tfrac{1}{2}\sqrt{3}), \quad (0, -\tfrac{1}{2}\sqrt{3}), \quad (1, 1), \quad (-1, -1).$$

No attempt has been made here to treat all systems of the form (3)–(4), and the student will find in the following exercises various systems best solved by other methods that can be devised to suit the circumstances. The list also includes equations whose degrees exceed two, and systems involving more than two variables, but it will be found that the methods we have considered suggest techniques for solving many such systems as well.

### EXERCISES

Solve each of the systems in Exercises 1–25.

**1.** $2x^2 - y^2 = 14, \; x^2 + 2y^2 = 17.$
**2.** $x^2 + 3y^2 = 1, \; 2x^2 - y^2 = 9.$
**3.** $x^2 - 4y^2 = 5, \; x - 2y = 1.$
**4.** $x^2 + y^2 = 13, \; 3x - y = 3.$
**5.** $3x^2 - y^2 = 11, \; 4x + 5y = 3.$
**6.** $2xy - 3x = 1, \; x^2y^2 - x^2 = 3.$
**7.** $x^2 - 2xy - y^2 + 3y - 4 = 0, \; x - 3y = 5.$
**8.** $xy + 2y^2 + 4x + 5y + 6 = 0, \; 3x - 4y = 2.$
**9.** $3x^2 + 2xy + 2x + y = 0, \; 2x^2 + 3xy + y^2 = 0.$
**10.** $x^2 - 2xy + y^2 + 4x - 5y + 2 = 0, \; x^2 - y^2 = 0.$
**11.** $x^2 + xy - y^2 + 3x - 2y - 1 = 0, \; x^2 + 2xy + y^2 + 2x + 2y + 1 = 0.$
**12.** $x^2 - xy - 3y^2 = 3, \; x^2 - 5y^2 = 5.$
**13.** $4x^2 + 2xy + y^2 = 7, \; 2xy + 3 = 0.$
**14.** $2x^2 - 3xy = 8, \; 2xy - 3y^2 = 4.$

**15.** $3x^2 - 2xy = 4,\ x^2 - 2xy + y^2 - x + y = 0.$

**16.** $5x^2 + 3xy + y^2 = 3,\ 2x^2 + y^2 = 6.$

**17.** $x^2 - xy + x - y = 0,\ 4x^2 + xy + y^2 = 10.$

**18.** $2x^2 - 3xy + y^2 = 2,\ x^2 + xy - 2x - y + 1 = 0.$

**19.** $2x^2 - y^2 = x^2y^2,\ x + 2y - xy = 0.$

**20.** $x^3 - y^3 = 9,\ x^2 + xy + y^2 = 3.$

**21.** $8x^3 + y^3 = 16,\ 2x + y = 4.$

**22.** $\sqrt{x} + \sqrt{y} = 2,\ x + y = 4.$

**23.** $x + y + \sqrt{x + y} - 6 = 0,\ x^2 - y^2 = 8.$

**24.** $x^2 + y^2 - 3z^2 = 2,\ x + y + 2z = 1,\ x - y - z = 2.$

**25.** $xy + xz = 3,\ xy + yz = -5,\ xz + yz = 4.$

**26.** The circle $x^2 + y^2 = r^2$ and the straight line $y = mx + k$ will intersect in two points, be tangent, or will not intersect according as the solutions of the simultaneous equations are real and distinct, real and equal, or complex. Find the values of $k$ in terms of $r$ and $m$ that will produce tangency, and plot the circle and line using a suitable set of values for $r$, $m$, and $k$.

**27.** Find the relation that must be satisfied by $a$, $b$, $m$, and $k$ if the hyperbola $b^2x^2 - a^2y^2 = a^2b^2$ and the line $y = mx + k$ are to be tangent, and plot a typical graph.

**28.** Find the relation that must be satisfied by $a$, $b$, and $c$ if the system $x^2 + y^2 = a^2$, $xy = b^2$, $x + y = c$ is to be consistent.

**29.** A method sometimes used to solve a system of the form (9)–(10) is as follows. Substitute $y = mx$, where $m$ is a new auxiliary variable, in both equations, and obtain two expressions, involving $m$, for $x^2$. Equate these, and solve the resulting relation for $m$. Corresponding to each value of $m$, two values of $x$, and hence two values of $y = mx$, may then be determined. Apply this method to the system

$$2x^2 + xy + 2y^2 = 6, \qquad x^2 - 3xy - 3y^2 = 2,$$

and hence find all its solutions.

**30.** Apply the method of Exercise 29 to the system of Example 4. It will be found that only two solutions are thereby obtained. Try to find a reason for failing to get all four solutions. Show that a similar procedure, using the substitution $x = m'y$, will yield all the solutions of this system.

**31.** Apply the method of Exercise 29 to the general system (9)–(10), and show that the relation determining $m$ is $(C_1F_2 - C_2F_1)m^2 + (B_1F_2 - B_2F_1)m + A_1F_2 - A_2F_1 = 0$. Under what condition on the coefficients of the system will this relation yield only one value of $m$, and therefore only two solutions of the system? Verify the statement that this condition is satisfied by the system of Example 4.

**32.** A quadratic function of two variables, $x$ and $y$, is said to be *symmetrical* if $x$ and $y$ can be interchanged without altering the function. Hence the quadratic function (1) is symmetrical if and only if $A = C$ and $D = E$. A method for solving a system of two symmetrical equations is as follows. Substitute $x = u + v$ and $y = u - v$ and eliminate $v^2$ from the resulting equations to obtain a quadratic in $u$. Solve this for $u$, then get corresponding values of $v$ from the transformed system, and hence determine $x$ and $y$. Apply this method to solve the system

$$x^2 - 2xy + y^2 + 2x + 2y - 7 = 0, \qquad 2x^2 + xy + 2y^2 - x - y - 9 = 0.$$

**33.** Prove that the method of Exercise 32 is applicable to any system of two symmetrical equations.

**34.** Show that, when $A_1B_2 \neq A_2B_1$, the method of Exercise 32 yields two values of $u$, so that there may be four solutions of the symmetrical system, but that, when $A_1B_2 = A_2B_1$, only one value of $u$, and therefore only two solutions of the system, exist.

**35.** Verify the second part of the statement of Exercise 34 for the system

$$x^2 - 2xy + y^2 + x + y - 8 = 0, \qquad 2x^2 - 4xy + 2y^2 - x - y - 4 = 0.$$

Solve this system also by combining the two equations to get a linear relation.

**36.** The sum of the areas of two externally tangent circles is $34\pi$ sq. in., and the distance between their centers is 8 in. Find the radii of the two circles.

**37.** A circular cylinder is inscribed in a sphere of radius 6 in. If the total surface area of the cylinder is half that of the sphere, find the radius and altitude of the cylinder.

**38.** The total number of sides and the total number of diagonals of two polygons taken together are 12 and 19, respectively. Find the number of sides of each polygon.

**39.** The sum of the units' and tens' digits of a three-digit number is 7, the sum of the squares of the three digits is 29, and the units' digit is equal to the square of the hundreds' digit. Find the number.

**40.** The sum of the edge lengths of a rectangular parallelepiped is 38 and its diagonal is 26 in. The product of two of the edge lengths is equal to twice the third. Find the dimensions.

## SUPPLEMENTARY EXERCISES

**1.** The difference between the perimeters of two squares is 24 in. and the sum of their areas is 146 sq. in. Find the sum of the perimeters.

**2.** A mosaic of 60 sq. ft. is to be laid in a rectangular area 8 ft. by 10 ft. Find the width in inches of the surrounding border, assumed to be the same on all four sides of the rectangle.

**3.** By averaging 9 miles per hour more, one train completes a 540-mile run in 2 hours less than a second train. Find the average speed of the faster train.

**4.** The perimeter of a rectangle is 30 in. and its diagonal is 12 in. long. Find its area.

**5.** Generalize Exercise 4 by taking $P$ in. as the perimeter and $D$ in. as the length of the diagonal of the rectangle, and find the area as a function of $P$ and $D$.

**6.** For the rectangle of Exercise 5, show that $P$ cannot exceed $2\sqrt{2}\,D$, and that when $P = 2\sqrt{2}\,D$ the figure is a square.

Solve each of the equations in Exercises 7–12.

**7.** $8x^6 + 63x^3 - 8 = 0.$

**8.** $2x - \sqrt{x+5} - 5 = 0.$

**9.** $\sqrt{4-x} - \sqrt{2x+3} = 2.$

**10.** $\sqrt{x^2+11} - \sqrt{2x^2-1} = 1.$

**11.** $\sqrt{x^2 - 8x + 24} + \sqrt{x^2 + 8x + 24} = 10.$

**12.** $\sqrt{x^2 - 10x + 34} - \sqrt{x^2 + 10x + 34} = 6.$

In each of Exercises 13–16, find the smallest positive value of $x$ satisfying the equation, and express the result in sexagesimal measure.

**13.** $5 \cos^2 x - 2 \sin x = 2.$                    **14.** $\sec^2 x - 3 \tan x = 5.$

**15.** $\sqrt{3 + 4 \sin x} = 8 \sin x.$

**16.** $\sqrt{8 - 5 \cos x} - \sqrt{2 + 5 \cos x} = 2.$

Solve each of the systems in Exercises 17–20.

**17.** $x^2 + y^2 = 13, \quad \sqrt{x - y} = 2 - x + y.$

**18.** $x^2 - 2y^2 = 7, x^2 - 4xy + 4y^2 + 2x - 4y + 1 = 0.$

**19.** $x + y + z = 1, x^2 + y^2 + z^2 = 1, xyz = 0.$

**20.** $x^2 + y^2 + z^2 = 9, xy + yz + xz = 8, x + y - z = 1.$

Test dec 13

Chapter 6 A 40 P 141

7 8, 9,

*[handwritten: $a_N$ or $L$ last term    $S_N$ sum.
$a_1$ or $a$ first term
$d$, common difference]*

## 54. Arithmetic progressions.

In Art. 1 we spoke briefly of sequences of numbers, the successive members of which progress according to a definite pattern or law of formation. In this chapter we shall discuss certain sequences that arise in a variety of problems.

Consider first the type of sequence whose first member is a given quantity $a_1$ and in which each member after the first is obtained by adding a quantity $d$ to the preceding one. Such a sequence, called an **arithmetic progression,** is then represented by the notation

$$a_1, a_1 + d, a_1 + 2d, \cdots. \tag{1}$$

If, for brevity, we denote the successive members of an arithmetic progression by $a_1, a_2, a_3, \cdots$, we have

$$a_1 = a_1, a_2 = a_1 + d, a_3 = a_1 + 2d, \cdots.$$

Evidently the coefficient of $d$ in each case will be one less than the number of the member, so that, for any positive integer $n$,

$$a_n = a_1 + (n - 1)d. \tag{2}$$

Usually we are concerned only with a finite number $n$ of members or terms. Then, with $a_1$ as **first term,** and $d$ as **common difference,** the $n$th term $a_n$ given by (2) is called the **last term.**

The **sum** $s_n$ of $n$ terms of an arithmetic progression will be

$$s_n = a_1 + (a_1 + d) + (a_1 + 2d) + \cdots + [a_1 + (n - 1)d], \tag{3}$$

or, expressed in terms of $a_n$,

$$s_n = a_1 + (a_1 + d) + (a_1 + 2d) + \cdots + (a_n - d) + a_n. \tag{4}$$

If we write the $n$ terms of the right member of (4) in reverse order, we also have

$$s_n = a_n + (a_n - d) + (a_n - 2d) + \cdots + (a_1 + d) + a_1. \tag{5}$$

Adding corresponding members of (4) and (5), we therefore get

$$2s_n = (a_1 + a_n) + (a_1 + a_n) + (a_1 + a_n) + \cdots + (a_1 + a_n) + (a_1 + a_n)$$
$$= n(a_1 + a_n),$$

whence

$$s_n = \frac{n}{2}(a_1 + a_n). \tag{6}$$

Thus, the last term $a_n$ is obtainable from (2), and the sum $s_n$ may be found by means of (6).

An alternative expression for the sum $s_n$ may be obtained by inserting expression (2) for $a_n$ in (6); this yields        *combined 2 and 6.*

$$s_n = \frac{n}{2}[2a_1 + (n - 1)d]. \tag{7}$$

This relation may also be proved by means of mathematical induction. (Cf. Art. 42, Exercise 11.)

Since we have two relations, (2) and (6), involving five quantities, any two of the five elements of an arithmetic progression may be determined when the other three are known.

*Example 1.* If the first term of an arithmetic progression is 7, and the common difference is $-2$, find the fifteenth term and the sum of the first fifteen terms.

*Solution.* From (2) we get immediately, with $a_1 = 7$, $d = -2$, and $n = 15$,

$$a_{15} = 7 + (15 - 1)(-2)$$
$$= 7 - 28 = -21.$$

Then formula (6) yields

$$s_{15} = \tfrac{15}{2}(7 - 21) = -105.$$

The first and last terms of an arithmetic progression, $a_1$ and $a_n$, are sometimes called the **extremes,** and the intermediate terms $a_2, \cdots, a_{n-1}$ are called **arithmetic means.** If we are given $n$ and the extremes, relation (2) serves to determine the common difference, whence the $n - 2$ arithmetic means are easily constructed.

*Example 2.* Insert five arithmetic means between 13 and 31.

*Solution.* Here we evidently have $n = 7$, and $a_1 = 13$ and $a_7 = 31$. Hence, from (2),

$$31 = 13 + (7 - 1)d,$$
$$6d = 18, \qquad d = 3.$$

Consequently the five arithmetic means are

$$a_2 = 13 + 3 = 16, \quad a_3 = 19, \quad a_4 = 22, \quad a_5 = 25, \quad a_6 = 28.$$

It is easy to show that the single arithmetic mean between two numbers is equal to half their sum, for, from the definition of an arithmetic progression, we have

$$d = a_2 - a_1 = a_3 - a_2,$$

whence

$$2a_2 = a_1 + a_3.$$

Therefore the arithmetic mean between $a_1$ and $a_3$ is

$$a_2 = \frac{a_1 + a_3}{2}. \tag{8}$$

This result agrees with the everyday idea of an arithmetic mean or average.

### EXERCISES

*[handwritten: $a_N = a_1 + (N-1)d$]*

*[handwritten: $S_N = \frac{N}{2}(a_1 + a_2)$]*

**1.** Given $a_1 = 2$, $d = 6$; find $a_{10}$ and $s_{10}$.
**2.** Given $a_1 = -30$, $d = -3$; find $a_{15}$ and $s_{15}$.
**3.** Given $a_1 = 4$, $a_{12} = -18$; find $d$ and $s_{12}$.
**4.** Given $a_1 = 2\sqrt{3}$, $s_{20} = 420\sqrt{3}$; find $d$ and $a_{20}$.
**5.** Given $a_7 = 29$, $d = -3$; find $a_1$ and $s_7$.
**6.** Given $a_{16} = -11$, $s_{16} = 64$; find $a_1$ and $d$.
**7.** Given $d = 5$, $s_{25} = -1000$; find $a_1$ and $a_{25}$.
**8.** Given $a_5 = 400$, $a_{10} = 800$; find $a_1$ and $d$.
**9.** Given $a_{12} = -12$, $a_{20} = -60$; find $s_{12}$ and $s_{20}$.
**10.** Given $s_4 = 36$, $s_8 = 136$; find $a_4 + a_8$.
**11.** Insert six arithmetic means between $-2$ and $19$.
**12.** Insert ten arithmetic means between $59$ and $-7$.
**13.** Find the sum of the five arithmetic means between $5$ and $14$.
**14.** If $a_1 = -6$, $a_n = 22$, and $s_n = 64$, find $n$ and $d$.
**15.** If $s_6 = 75$ and $a_1 = 4a_6$, find $a_1$ and $d$.
**16.** Solve equation (7) for $n$ in terms of $a_1$, $d$, and $s_n$.
**17.** Show that
$$s_n = \frac{(a_n + a_1)(a_n - a_1 + d)}{2d}.$$

**18.** Show that
$$s_n = na_n - \tfrac{1}{2}n(n - 1)d.$$

**19.** Solve the equation of Exercise 17 for $a_n$ in terms of $a_1$, $d$, and $s_n$.
**20.** Solve the equation of Exercise 18 for $n$ in terms of $a_n$, $d$, and $s_n$.
**21.** Show that, if every term of an arithmetic progression is multiplied by the same quantity, the resulting sequence is also an arithmetic progression.
**22.** Show that, if $a_{2n} = 2a_n$, then $d = a_1$.
**23.** Show that the sum of the first $n$ odd positive integers is equal to $n^2$. (Cf. Art. 42, Exercise 2.)
**24.** Show that there cannot exist an arithmetic progression for which $s_{2n} = 2s_n$, except in the trivial case $d = 0$.

**25.** A freely falling body travels $g/2$ ft. in the first second, $3g/2$ ft. during the next second, $5g/2$ ft. the next, and so on ($g = 32.2$ approximately). Find the distance fallen during the $n$th second.

**26.** Using the result of Exercise 25, deduce the law of freely falling bodies: The total distance fallen in $t$ seconds is equal to $\frac{1}{2}gt^2$ ft.

**27.** The digits of a three-digit number are in arithmetic progression. The sum of the digits is 18, and if the digits are reversed the new number is 396 less than the original. Find the number. *Hint:* Denote the three digits by $a - d$, $a$, and $a + d$.

**28.** The digits of a three-digit number are in arithmetic progression. The sum of the digits is 18, and the sum of their squares is 126. If the units' digit exceeds each of the other two, find the number.

**29.** Show that the sum of an arithmetic progression with an odd number of terms is equal to the product of the number of terms and the middle term.

**30.** In an arithmetic progression, show that

$$(n - 2)a_n - (n - 1)a_{n-1} + a_1 = 0.$$

**55. Geometric progressions.** Another type of sequence that has considerable importance is constructed as follows. Let $a_1$ denote the first member, and let each member thereafter be formed by multiplying its antecedent by a quantity $r$:

$$a_1, \qquad a_2 = a_1 r, \qquad a_3 = a_1 r^2, \qquad \cdots. \tag{1}$$

Since the index of $r$ in each term is one less than the number of the term, we have, for any positive integer $n$,

$$a_n = a_1 r^{n-1}. \tag{2}$$

The sequence whose terms are thus formed is called a **geometric progression.** The quantity $r$ is called the **common ratio,** since it is the ratio of any term (after the first) to the one preceding it in the progression. When only a finite number $n$ of terms are under consideration, the $n$th term, given by (2), is called the **last term.**

The **sum** $s_n$ of $n$ terms of a geometric progression will be

$$s_n = a_1 + a_1 r + a_1 r^2 + \cdots + a_1 r^{n-2} + a_1 r^{n-1}. \tag{3}$$

Now if we multiply both members of (3) by $r$, we get

$$r s_n = \qquad a_1 r + a_1 r^2 + a_1 r^3 + \cdots + a_1 r^{n-1} + a_1 r^n.$$

Hence, if we subtract corresponding members of these two relations, we find

$$(1 - r)s_n = a_1 - a_1 r^n = a_1(1 - r^n),$$

whence

$$s_n = \frac{a_1(1 - r^n)}{1 - r}. \tag{4}$$

Since $a_1 r^n = r \cdot a_1 r^{n-1} = r a_n$, another expression for the sum $s_n$ is

$$s_n = \frac{a_1 - r a_n}{1 - r}. \tag{5}$$

The correctness of formula (4) may also be established by mathematical induction. (Cf. Art. 42, Exercise 12.) When any three of the five elements of a geometric progression, namely, $n$, $a_1$, $a_n$, $r$, and $s_n$, are known, formulas (2) and (4) serve to determine the other two.

Given any two non-adjacent terms of a geometric progression, the terms between these two are **geometric means.** If merely the first and $n$th terms are stated, and we have to insert $n - 2$ geometric means between them, there will be $n - 1$ values of $r$ obtainable from (2), for a number has $n - 1$ $(n - 1)$th roots (Art. 48). Unless otherwise stated, we shall agree that, when $a_1$ and $a_n$ are real, as they usually are, the convention of Art. 4 shall be followed; then $r$ will be real and positive if $a_n/a_1$ is positive, real and negative if $n$ is even and $a_n/a_1$ is negative. Also, using the concept of complex numbers, which we were not in a position to do in Art. 4, when $n$ is odd and $a_n/a_1$ is negative, and whenever $a_n/a_1$ is complex, we shall take for $r$ that root which corresponds to the fundamental amplitude (Art. 48). This convention is illustrated in the following example.

*Example.* Insert eight geometric means between 3 and $-48\sqrt{2}$, and find the sum of these ten terms.

*Solution.* Here $a_1 = 3$ and $a_{10} = -48\sqrt{2}$, whence formula (2) yields

$$-48\sqrt{2} = 3r^9,$$

$$r^9 = -16\sqrt{2} = -2^{\frac{9}{2}}.$$

Since $n = 10$ is even and $a_n/a_1$ is negative, we take for $r$ the real negative value namely,

$$r = -2^{\frac{1}{2}} = -\sqrt{2}.$$

The eight geometric means are consequently

$$3, \quad -3\sqrt{2}, \quad 6, \quad -6\sqrt{2}, \quad 12, \quad -12\sqrt{2}, \quad 24, \quad -24\sqrt{2}, \quad 48. \qquad 48\sqrt{2}$$

Formula (4) now gives us

$$s_{10} = \frac{3[1 - (-\sqrt{2})^{10}]}{1 - \sqrt{2}} = \frac{3(-31)}{1 - \sqrt{2}}$$

$$= \frac{93}{\sqrt{2} - 1} \cdot \frac{\sqrt{2} + 1}{\sqrt{2} + 1} = 93(\sqrt{2} + 1).$$

To find the geometric mean of two numbers we have merely to note that

$$r = \frac{a_2}{a_1} = \frac{a_3}{a_2},$$

whence

$$a_2^2 = a_1 a_3. \tag{6}$$

Thus, the square of the geometric mean of two numbers is equal to the product of the numbers. The geometric mean itself is that one of the two square roots of the product obtained as described above.

### EXERCISES

**1.** Given $a_1 = 3$, $r = 4$; find $a_5$ and $s_5$.

**2.** Given $a_1 = -2$, $r = -3$; find $a_8$ and $s_8$

**3.** Given $a_1 = 128$, $a_8 = 1$; find $r$ and $s_8$.

**4.** Given $r = -\frac{1}{2}$, $s_5 = \frac{11}{2}$; find $a_1$ and $a_5$.

**5.** Given $a_7 = 64$, $r = \frac{2}{3}$; find $a_1$ and $s_7$.

**6.** Given $a_1 = 18$, $s_3 = 74$; find $a_3$. (Two solutions.)

**7.** Given $a_1 = 1$, $r = 1 - i$; find $a_4$ and $s_4$.

**8.** Given $r = 1 + \sqrt{2}$, $a_3 = 9 + 6\sqrt{2}$; find $a_1$ and $s_3$.

**9.** Insert seven geometric means between 3 and 48.

**10.** Insert two geometric means between $1 - i$ and $32i$.

**11.** Obtain a formula for $s_n$ in terms of $n$, $r$, and $a_n$.

**12.** Show that, if each term of a geometric progression is multiplied by the same quantity, the resulting sequence constitutes a geometric progression.

**13.** Show that, if each term of a geometric progression is raised to the same power, the resulting sequence is a geometric progression.

**14.** Each swing of a certain pendulum is $\frac{1}{4}$ less than the preceding one, owing to the effect of friction. If the first swing is through a distance of 8 in., find the entire distance traveled in six swings.

**15.** A ball is dropped from a height of 16 ft. If it rebounds half the height from which it falls, how far will it have traveled by the time it hits for the eighth time?

**16.** If 1, $a$, and $b$ are in arithmetic progression, and $a$, 1, $b$ form a geometric progression, where $a \neq b$, find $a$ and $b$.

**17.** Show that there exists a number $x$ which, added to each of three given distinct numbers $a$, $b$, and $c$, produces a geometric progression if and only if $a$, $b$, and $c$ are not in arithmetic progression.

**18.** The first of three numbers in arithmetic progression is 2. If 1, 6, and 38 are respectively added to these three numbers, the resulting sums are in geometric progression. Find the original numbers. (Two solutions.)

**19.** The first of three numbers in arithmetic progression is 1. If they are multiplied respectively by 5, 3, and 5, the resulting products are in geometric progression. Find the original numbers. (Two solutions.)

**20.** The side of one square is $k$ times that of a smaller square. If the difference of the areas of the squares is $\frac{3}{2}$ of the geometric mean of their areas, find $k$.

**21.** If an amount of money $P$ is invested at an interest rate $r$ (expressed decimally), compounded annually, show that the compound amount at the end of $n$ years is $P(1 + r)^n$.

**22.** An annuity consists of a series of payments of $P$ dollars annually. Show that the value of the annuity at the end of $n$ years, with an interest rate $r$ compounded annually, is $P[(1 + r)^n - 1]/r$ dollars.

**23.** Show that the present value of the annuity of Exercise 22 is $P[1 - (1 + r)^{-n}]/r$ dollars.

**24.** Find four numbers in geometric progression such that the sum of the first and third is 20 and the sum of the other two is $-60$.

**25.** Four numbers are in arithmetic progression. The first, second, and fourth form a geometric progression, and the fourth is equal to the square of the first. Find the numbers.

**26.** Find four numbers in geometric progression such that the sum of the first and last is 140 and the sum of the other two is 60.

**27.** The three digits of a certain number are in geometric progression, and the sum of the digits is 14. If the digits are reversed, the new number is 594 more than the original. Find the original number.

**28.** Show that the three cube roots of unity form a geometric progression.

**29.** If the numbers $a$, $b$, $c$, and $d$ are in geometric progression, show that

$$(a - d)^2 - (b - d)^2 = (a - c)^2 + (b - c)^2.$$

**30.** The sum of three numbers in geometric progression is 39, and the sum of their squares is 819. Find the numbers.

**56. Infinite sequences; limits.** All the instances of sequences or progressions that we have so far discussed in this chapter have had a definite number $n$ of terms. We turn now to a consideration of infinite sequences, involving indefinitely many terms:

$$a_1, a_2, a_3, \cdots, a_n, \cdots. \tag{1}$$

Consider first an infinite arithmetic progression, the general or $n$th term of which has been found to have the expression

$$\left( a_n = a_1 + (n - 1)d. \right) \tag{2}$$

If $n$ is permitted to increase without bound, we say that $n$ becomes infinite, and we denote this process by the symbolism $n \to \infty$. Now examination of (2) shows that, as $n \to \infty$, $a_n$ will become numerically large; if $d > 0$, then, no matter what the value of $a_1$, $a_n$ will become positively infinite, and if $d < 0$, $a_n$ will become negatively infinite. It follows from this, and also from an examination of the formula for the sum $s_n$ of $n$ terms of an arithmetic progression, that $s_n$ becomes positively infinite ($s_n \to \infty$) if $d > 0$, and $s_n$ becomes negatively infinite ($s_n \to -\infty$) if $d < 0$.

For example, if $a_1 = -10$ and $d = 2$, we have

$$a_n = -10 + 2(n - 1) = 2n - 12,$$

$$s_n = \frac{n}{2}(-10 + 2n - 12) = n(n - 11),$$

so that, for $n > 6$, $a_n$ is positive and increasing, and for $n > 11$, $s_n$ is positive and increasing. If $a_1 = 6$ and $d = -4$,

$$a_n = 6 - 4(n - 1) = 10 - 4n,$$

$$s_n = \frac{n}{2}(6 + 10 - 4n) = n(8 - 2n),$$

whence, for $n > 2$, $a_n$ is negative and decreasing algebraically, and for $n > 4$, $s_n$ is negative and decreasing algebraically.

In a geometric progression, we have

$$a_n = a_1 r^{n-1}. \tag{3}$$

If $r$ is numerically greater than unity, that is, if $|r| > 1$, we have $|r|^2 > |r|$, $|r|^3 > |r|^2$, and, in general, $|r|^{n+1} > |r|^n$ since $|r|^{n+1} - |r|^n = |r|^n(|r| - 1) > 0$. Hence $|a_n| \to \infty$ as $n \to \infty$ when $|r| > 1$. If $r > 1$, $a_n$ will become positively or negatively infinite according as $a_1$ is positive or negative; if $r < -1$, $a_n$ will be alternately positive and negative as $n$ assumes successive positive integral values, but the absolute value of $a_n$ will become positively infinite for such values of $r$ also. Consequently the sum $s_n$ of $n$ terms of a geometric progression will be such that $|s_n| \to \infty$ as $n \to \infty$.

For example, if $a_1 = 1$ and $r = 2$,

$$a_n = 1 \cdot 2^{n-1},$$

$$s_n = \frac{1 \cdot (1 - 2^n)}{1 - 2} = 2^n - 1,$$

so that both $a_n$ and $s_n$ are positive and increase with $n$. If $a_1 = -1$ and $r = -2$,

$$a_n = -1 \cdot (-2)^{n-1} = (-1)^n 2^{n-1},$$

$$s_n = \frac{-1 \cdot [1 - (-2)^n]}{1 + 2} = \frac{(-2)^n - 1}{3},$$

whence both $a_n$ and $s_n$ alternate between positive and negative values which become larger in absolute value as $n$ increases.

On the other hand, suppose that we have a geometric progression in which $|r| < 1$. This is the case of most interest and importance, and we shall therefore first consider a simple example that will suggest the possibility of a conclusion that may be drawn in more general circumstances. If $a_1 = 1$ and $r = \frac{1}{2}$, we get

$$a_n = 1 \cdot (\tfrac{1}{2})^{n-1} = \frac{1}{2^{n-1}},$$

$$s_n = \frac{1 \cdot [1 - (\tfrac{1}{2})^n]}{1 - \tfrac{1}{2}} = 2\left(1 - \frac{1}{2^n}\right) = 2 - \frac{1}{2^{n-1}}.$$

It is evident here that, as $n$ successively increases, $a_n$ remains positive but becomes smaller and smaller, and $s_n$ remains less than 2 but can be made to get as close to 2 as we please by taking a sufficiently large value of $n$. We may say then that $a_n$ and $s_n$ respectively *approach* 0 and 2 as $n$ becomes infinite.

If $x$ is a variable that thus successively assumes values approaching a fixed number $A$, then $A$ is called the **limit** of $x$; this idea, which is fundamental to differential and integral calculus and to many other branches of mathematics, is denoted symbolically by writing either $x \to A$ (read "$x$ approaches $A$") or

$$\lim x = A, \qquad (4)$$

read "the limit of $x$ is $A$." More precisely, if the absolute value of the difference between the variable $x$ and the fixed number $A$ becomes and remains less than any preassigned positive quantity, however small, then $A$ is said to be the limit of $x$.

Accordingly, in the above example, we have $\lim a_n = 0$ and $\lim s_n = 2$. To exhibit the fact that $n$ is increasing beyond all bound, we write, as a more explicit notation,

$$\lim_{n \to \infty} a_n = 0, \qquad \lim_{n \to \infty} s_n = 2.$$

To illustrate the variation of $a_n$ and $s_n$ graphically, the student should plot successive values of these two quantities on the line representation of real numbers (Fig. 1) and observe how the respective groups of points cluster toward 0 and 2.

We now examine the geometric progression in which the ratio $r$ is any real number numerically less than unity. Since $|r|^{n+1} - |r|^n = |r|^n(|r| - 1) < 0$ when $|r| < 1$, we have $|r|^{n+1} < |r|^n$, and

$$|a_n| = |a_1 r^{n-1}| = |a_1| \cdot |r^{n-1}|$$

therefore is positive and decreases as $n$ increases. Hence, whether $a_n$ remains positive (when $a_1 > 0$ and $0 < r < 1$), or remains negative (when $a_1 < 0$ and $0 < r < 1$), or is alternately positive and negative (when $-1 < r < 0$), we infer that

$$\lim_{n \to \infty} a_n = 0, \qquad |r| < 1. \tag{5}$$

Moreover, we have

$$s_n = \frac{a_1(1 - r^n)}{1 - r} = \frac{a_1}{1 - r} - \frac{a_1}{1 - r} r^n,$$

and since $a_1/(1 - r)$ remains fixed as $n$ increases, but $r^n \to 0$, it appears that

$$\lim_{n \to \infty} s_n = \frac{a_1}{1 - r}, \qquad |r| < 1. \tag{6}$$

Let us now examine matters somewhat more closely. It was said that "we infer" and that "it appears" that certain conclusions may be drawn. However, it is conceivable that, although $|r|^n$ decreases as $n$ increases, the limit may be some small positive number instead of zero. To settle this point, suppose, for definiteness, that $r$ is positive and less than 1; then we may write

$$r = \frac{1}{1 + k},$$

where $k$ is some positive number. Consequently we get, with the aid of the binomial theorem (Art. 43),

$$r^n = \frac{1}{(1 + k)^n} = \frac{1}{1 + nk + c},$$

where $c$ is a symbol used for simplicity to denote the positive number representing the remaining $n - 1$ terms of the expansion. Now since $1 + nk + c > nk$, it follows that $1/(1 + nk + c) < 1/nk$, whence

$$r^n < \frac{1}{nk}$$

for every positive integer $n$. Therefore the limit of the positive quantity $r^n$ cannot be more than the limit of $1/nk$. But the latter limit is clearly equal to zero, and hence

$$\lim_{n \to \infty} r^n = 0, \qquad 0 < r < 1. \tag{7}$$

If $r$ is negative, the same result holds, for $(-r)^n = (-1)^n r^n$, and (7) is therefore true whenever $|r| < 1$. This insures that the limits (5) and (6) are correct as stated.

The limit of $s_n$, given by (6), is called the **sum** of the infinite geometric progression or **series** and is denoted by $s$:

$$s = \lim_{n \to \infty} s_n = a_1(1 + r + r^2 + \cdots + r^{n-1} + \cdots) = \frac{a_1}{1 - r}, \quad |r| < 1.$$

Of course, $s$ is not an actual sum, in the usual sense; the designation sum is used merely as a convenient label for the limit of the sum of $n$ terms as $n$ becomes infinite. From the above relation, it is seen that the expression $1/(1 - r)$ is represented by an infinite series when $|r| < 1$:

$$\frac{1}{1 - r} \equiv 1 + r + r^2 + \cdots r^{n-1} + \cdots, \quad |r| < 1. \tag{8}$$

Formal division of 1 by $1 - r$ does, in fact, yield just this infinite series. From what has been said, meaning can be given to the resulting series provided that $|r| < 1$, but not when $|r| \geqq 1$.

The creation of infinite series representing other expressions or functions, and the investigation of the domain of validity of such series, are important problems that are treated by means of calculus methods.

To illustrate the manner in which infinite geometric series arise, consider the following example.

*Example.* Each swing of a certain pendulum is $\frac{1}{5}$ less than the preceding one, owing to the effect of friction. If the first swing is through a distance of 10 in., find the entire distance traveled by the pendulum before coming to rest. (Cf. Exercise 14, Art. 55.)

*Solution.* Theoretically, if the time of each swing is the same, and if the stated law of decrease applies exactly, then the pendulum will never come completely to rest. However, what we wish to find is the limit of the sum of the distances traversed, which is very nearly attained after a sufficiently large number of swings. We have here a geometric progression in which $a_1 = 10$ and $r = \frac{4}{5}$; then the limit is

$$s = \frac{a_1}{1 - r} = \frac{10}{1 - \frac{4}{5}} = 50 \text{ in.}$$

**57. Repeating decimals.** An interesting application of the concept of infinite geometric progressions is found in repeating decimals. If we divide one integer by a second, we find that either the decimal terminates in the sense that only zeros are obtained beyond a certain point, or the decimal contains a repeated group of digits beyond some position. Thus, we have

$$\tfrac{1}{8} = 0.125, \qquad \tfrac{6}{55} = 0.1090909 \cdots.$$

It may be shown by advanced mathematics that the decimal equivalent of every rational number belongs to one of these two types, whereas the decimal equivalent of an irrational number, such as $\sqrt{2}$ or $\pi$, is a non-repeating decimal.

Conversely, if we have given a repeating decimal, it is possible to find the rational fraction to which it is equivalent. One way of doing this is to consider the repeating part of the decimal as an infinite geometric progression, as in the following example.

*Example.* Find the rational fraction whose decimal value is $0.31212\cdots$.

*Solution.* We may write this number as an infinite series:

$$0.3 + 0.012 + 0.00012 + 0.0000012 + \cdots.$$

After the first term 0.3, the remaining repeating part is seen to constitute an infinite geometric progression with $a_1 = 0.012$ and $r = 0.01$. Hence the limit of the entire sum is

$$\tfrac{3}{10} + \left(\tfrac{12}{1000} \div \tfrac{99}{100}\right) = \tfrac{3}{10} + \tfrac{2}{165} = \tfrac{103}{330}.$$

This is easily checked by dividing 103 by 330 to get the given repeating decimal.

**58. Harmonic progressions.** We shall consider, briefly, only one more type of progression. A sequence $a_1, a_2, \cdots, a_n$ is said to be a **harmonic progression** with $n$ terms if the $n$ respective reciprocals $1/a_1, 1/a_2, \cdots, 1/a_n$ form an arithmetic progression. Thus, the sequence

$$1, \frac{1}{2}, \frac{1}{3}, \cdots, \frac{1}{n}$$

is a harmonic progression since the reciprocals $1, 2, \cdots, n$ form an arithmetic progression with common difference 1.

No general formulas can be developed for the $n$th term and for the sum of $n$ terms of a harmonic progression, but we can treat the corresponding arithmetic progression by the methods of Art. 54 in each individual sequence.

The terms of a harmonic progression that lie between two of the members are called the **harmonic means** of those two members.

*Example.* Insert three harmonic means between 2 and 10.

*Solution.* Corresponding to the harmonic progression of five terms, there is an arithmetic progression of five terms, of which the first and last are the re-

$a_{10} \quad 2 \ (4) \ (d)$

$10 = 2 (4)(d) \cdot \quad 4 =$

spective reciprocals of 2 and 10. Hence, in the arithmetic progression, $a_1 = \frac{1}{2}$ and $a_5 = \frac{1}{10}$. Consequently

$$a_5 = a_1 + (n - 1)d,$$

$$\tfrac{1}{10} = \tfrac{1}{2} + 4d,$$

$$4d = \tfrac{1}{10} - \tfrac{1}{2} = -\tfrac{2}{5},$$

$$d = -\tfrac{1}{10}.$$

Therefore the three arithmetic means of $\frac{1}{2}$ and $\frac{1}{10}$ are $\frac{2}{5}$, $\frac{3}{10}$, and $\frac{1}{5}$, and we have, as the three desired harmonic means, the reciprocals of these numbers:

$$\tfrac{5}{2}, \tfrac{10}{3}, 5.$$

## EXERCISES

In Exercises 1–5, find the limit of the sum of the terms of each of the given infinite sequences.

**1.** $1, \frac{2}{3}, \frac{4}{9}, \frac{8}{27}, \cdots$.

**2.** $0.6, 0.06, 0.006, 0.0006, \cdots$.

**3.** $3\sqrt{3}, 3, \sqrt{3}, 1, \cdots$.

**4.** $-1 - \sqrt{2}, 1, 1 - \sqrt{2}, 3 - 2\sqrt{2}, \cdots$.

**5.** $1, \sqrt{10} - 3, 19 - 6\sqrt{10}, 37\sqrt{10} - 117, \cdots$.

In Exercises 6–10, find the rational fractions whose decimal equivalents are given.

**6.** $0.7777\cdots$.           **7.** $0.292929\cdots$.

**8.** $0.3555\cdots$.           **9.** $13.115115\cdots$.

**10.** $49.727727\cdots$.

**11.** Find the twelfth term of the harmonic progression $\frac{1}{2}, \frac{1}{4}, \frac{1}{6}, \frac{1}{8}, \cdots$.

**12.** Find the ninth term of the harmonic progression $\frac{1}{5}, \frac{1}{2}, -1, -\frac{1}{4}, \cdots$.

**13.** Insert two harmonic means between 4 and $-4$.

**14.** Find the harmonic mean of $a/(1 - ab)$ and $a/(1 + ab)$.

**15.** Obtain a formula for the harmonic mean of two numbers $x$ and $y$. Hence show that the harmonic mean exists for any two numbers except when one number is the negative of the other.

**16.** If $A$, $G$, and $H$ respectively denote the arithmetic, geometric, and harmonic means of two numbers, show that $G^2 = AH$.

**17.** The arithmetic mean of two numbers is 8 and their harmonic mean is 6. Find the numbers.

**18.** Show that the arithmetic mean and the harmonic mean of two different numbers can never be equal.

**19.** The harmonic mean of two numbers is 1 more than their arithmetic mean, and one number is twice the other. Find the numbers.

**20.** If $a$, $b$, and $c$ are in harmonic progression, show that $a - \frac{1}{2}b$, $\frac{1}{2}b$, and $c - \frac{1}{2}b$ are in geometric progression.

**21.** If $a + b$, $b + c$, and $c + a$ are in harmonic progression, show that $c^2$, $a^2$, $b^2$ are in arithmetic progression.

**22.** Show that the harmonic mean of the roots of the quadratic equation $ax^2 + bx + c = 0$ is equal to $-2c/b$, provided that $b \neq 0$.

**23.** The numbers 1, $a$, and $b$ are in arithmetic progression, and $a$, 1, $b$ are in harmonic progression, where $a \neq b$. Find $a$ and $b$.

**24.** On one side of an acute angle $\theta$ and at a distance $a$ from the vertex, a point $P$ is located. From $P$ a perpendicular $PQ$ is drawn to the other side of the angle, from $Q$ a perpendicular $QR$ is drawn to the first side, and so on, this process being continued indefinitely. Show that the limit of the sum of the lengths of these perpendiculars is $a \cot (\theta/2)$.

**25.** Determine the roots of the quadratic equation

$$2(a + b)x^2 - (a^2 + 6ab + b^2)x + 2ab(a + b) = 0,$$

and show that these roots are the arithmetic mean and the harmonic mean of $a$ and $b$.

## SUPPLEMENTARY EXERCISES

**1.** Given a square of side 1 in. A second square has its vertices at the midpoints of the sides of the original square, a third has its vertices at the midpoints of the sides of the second, and so on indefinitely. Find the limit of the sum of the areas of this sequence of nested squares.

**2.** Find the limit of the sum of the perimeters of the sequence of squares in Exercise 1.

**3.** A square is inscribed in a circle of radius 1 in., a circle is inscribed in the square, another square is inscribed in the second circle, and so on indefinitely. Find the limit of the sum of the areas of the sequence of circles.

**4.** Find the limit of the sum of the perimeters of the sequence of circles in Exercise 3.

**5.** Given an equilateral triangle of side 1. A second triangle has its vertices at the midpoints of the sides of the first, a third has its vertices at the midpoints of the sides of the second, and so on indefinitely. Find the limit of the sum of the areas of this sequence of triangles.

**6.** Show that the perimeter of a regular polygon of $n$ sides inscribed in a circle of radius $r$ is

$$P_i = 2nr \sin \frac{\pi}{n} = 2\pi r \frac{\sin (\pi/n)}{\pi/n}.$$

Since $P_i$ has the limit $2\pi r$ as $n$ becomes infinite, deduce the fact that

$$\lim_{\theta \to 0} \frac{\sin \theta}{\theta} = 1.$$

This result has considerable importance in calculus, in connection with the differentiation of the trigonometric functions.

**7.** Show that the perimeter of a regular polygon of $n$ sides circumscribed about a circle of radius $r$ is

$$P_c = 2nr \tan \frac{\pi}{n} = 2\pi r \frac{\tan (\pi/n)}{\pi/n}.$$

Since $P_c$ has the limit $2\pi r$ as $n$ becomes infinite, deduce the fact that

$$\lim_{\theta \to 0} \frac{\tan \theta}{\theta} = 1.$$

Hence, using the fact that $\cos \theta$ approaches 1 as $\theta$ approaches zero, obtain also the limit deduced in Exercise 6.

**8.** If $a$, $b$, and $c$ are in arithmetic progression, and $a$, $k$, and $c$ are in harmonic progression, show that $k = ac/b$.

**9.** If $a$, $b$, and $c$ are in harmonic progression, show that $a$, $a - c$, and $a - b$ are also in harmonic progression.

**10.** If $a$, $b$, and $c$ are in geometric progression, show that $b - c$, $2b$, and $b - a$ are in harmonic progression.

**11.** If $a$, $b$, and $c$ are in harmonic progression, show that

$$\frac{a - b}{b - c} = \frac{a}{c}.$$

**12.** If the $m$th term of a geometric progression is $x$ and the $n$th term is $y$, show that the first term $a_1$ and the common ratio $r$ are given by

$$a_1 = (x^{1-n}y^{m-1})^{\frac{1}{m-n}}, \qquad r = (x/y)^{\frac{1}{m-n}}.$$

**13.** If $a$, $b$, and $c$ are in geometric progression, show that

$$\frac{1}{a^3} + \frac{1}{b^3} + \frac{1}{c^3} = \frac{a^3 + b^3 + c^3}{a^2 b^2 c^2}.$$

**14.** If $x$, $y$, and $z$ are the $m$th, $n$th, and $p$th terms of a geometric progression, respectively, show that

$$x^{p-n}y^{m-p} = z^{m-n}.$$

**15.** Let $a$, $b$, $c$ form an arithmetic progression, $b$, $c$, $d$ a geometric progression, and $c$, $d$, $e$ a harmonic progression. Show that $a$, $c$, $e$ are in geometric progression.

# XI——————————————— Inequalities

**59. Definitions and principles.** Although most of our work in preceding chapters has pertained to equalities, we have occasionally made statements concerning unequal algebraic quantities. We now wish to systematize and extend our knowledge of inequalities; the information we shall thereby gain regarding the nature of inequalities and the techniques to which they may be subjected will be of considerable utility in later work.

It will be recalled that the notation $a < b$ means that $a$ is less than $b$, or, in other words, that $a - b$ is negative. Similarly, $c > d$ means that $c$ is greater than $d$, or that $c - d$ is positive. It is understood that $a$, $b$, $c$, and $d$ are *real numbers*, for it would be meaningless to say that one complex number is greater or less than another. If we wish to express the fact that $a$ is not greater than $b$, that is, that $a$ is less than or equal to $b$, we write $a \leq b$; in like manner, $c \geq d$ means that $c$ is not less than $d$, or $c$ is greater than or equal to $d$.

In Art. 20 a distinction was made between identities, true for all permissible values of the variables, and conditional equations, satisfied only by certain values of the variables. In the same way, we distinguish between two types of inequalities. Inequalities involving only specific real numbers, and those that are true for all real values of the variables involved, are called **absolute inequalities**. Inequalities that are true for only certain real values of the variables are called **conditional inequalities**. For example,
$$-2 < -1 \qquad \text{and} \qquad a^2 + b^4 + 2 > 0$$
are absolute inequalities, whereas
$$x^2 - 3x > 0$$
is a conditional inequality. For $-2 < -1$ is a fact following from the definition: $-2 - (-1) = -1$ is negative; whether the quantities $a$ and $b$ are individually positive, negative, or zero, $a^2$ and $b^4$ are both nonnegative, so that their sum increased by 2 must always be positive; and the last inequality is satisfied, for instance, by $x = 4$ but not by $x = 1$

209

We often have occasion to write a double inequality. Thus, if we wish to express the fact that a quantity $r$ is to be numerically less than unity, as we did in our discussion of infinite geometric progressions possessing limits (Art. 56), we may write $-1 < r < 1$, or, equivalently, $1 > r > -1$. It should be noticed that, in such a case, the two signs of inequality point the same way; we say then that they have the same *sense*. If, on the other hand, we wish to express the fact that the absolute value of $r$ exceeds unity (without using the bar notation for absolute values), we must write two separate inequalities connected by "or," thus: $r < -1$ or $r > 1$.

We next establish a few fundamental principles of operations with inequalities.

I. *If $a > b$ and $b > c$, then $a > c$. Likewise, if $a < b$ and $b < c$, then $a < c$.*

For, when $a > b$ and $b > c$, we have $a - b = p$ and $b - c = q$, where $p$ and $q$ are positive. By the addition of the corresponding members of these two equations, we get $a - c = p + q$, whence $a > c$. The second part of the principle may be similarly established. However, when we have two inequalities that differ in sense, $a > b$ and $b < c$, no conclusion can be drawn concerning the relative values of $a$ and $c$.

II. *The sense of an inequality is not changed if the same quantity (positive or negative) is added to both members.*

Thus, if $a > b$, then $a + c > b + c$. For $a > b$ means that $a - b = p$, a positive quantity. Hence $a + c - b - c = (a + c) - (b + c) = p$, whence $a + c > b + c$.

III. *If both members of an inequality are multiplied by the same quantity, the sense of the inequality is or is not changed according as the multiplier is negative or positive.*

For example, take the inequality $-2 < -1$. If we multiply both members by $-3$, we get $6 > 3$; but, if we multiply by 3, we have $-6 < -3$. To prove this principle, suppose that $a > b$, so that $a - b = p$, a positive number. Then $aq - bq = pq$. If $q$ is negative, $pq$ is negative, whence $aq < bq$; if $q$ is positive, $pq$ is positive, and $aq > bq$.

All three of these principles will be found very useful in our subsequent discussion of inequalities. Principle II allows us to transpose a term from one side of an inequality to the other provided that its sign is changed in the process, just as in working with equalities. Since principle III embodies two alternatives, depending upon the sign of the multiplier, care must be taken when clearing of fractions and in other reduction processes involving multiplication or division.

**60. Absolute inequalities.**  Some absolute inequalities, like $a^2 + b^4 + 2 > 0$, are readily established by means of a brief verbal argument. If, however, we have to verify a less evident absolute inequality, it is possible to proceed as follows. Tentatively assume the inequality to be correct and, if possible, use the principles of Art. 59 to transform it into another that may be easily shown to be true; this process may be regarded as a preliminary analysis. Then, with the simple inequality as a starting point, try to retrace the steps of the analysis by application of the fundamental principles; if this synthesis is successful, the desired inequality will thereby be established.

*Example.*  Show that the sum of any positive number and its reciprocal cannot be less than 2.

*Solution.*  If $a$ represents the positive number, we are to show that

$$a + \frac{1}{a} \geqq 2, \qquad a > 0.$$

If this relation be true, the following inequalities will also hold. (The Roman numerals at the right refer to the principles of Art. 59.)

$$a^2 + 1 \geqq 2a, \tag{III}$$

$$a^2 - 2a + 1 \geqq 0, \tag{II}$$

or

$$(a - 1)^2 \geqq 0.$$

Now this simple relation is easily shown to be true, for, whether $a - 1$ is positive, negative, or zero, its square must be non-negative. This is therefore a suitable starting point, and our synthesis, constituting the actual proof, is as follows. Since

$$(a - 1)^2 \geqq 0,$$

for the reason just stated, expansion of the left member gives us the equivalent relation

$$a^2 - 2a + 1 \geqq 0.$$

Now, using principle II, we get

$$a^2 + 1 \geqq 2a,$$

and then principle III, with $a > 0$, gives us

$$a + \frac{1}{a} \geqq 2,$$

as desired. We see, incidentally, that the equality holds only if $a = 1$; if $0 < a < 1$, or if $a > 1$, the inequality holds.

## EXERCISES

**1.** If $a > b$ and $c > d$, show that $a + c > b + d$.

**2.** If $a > b > 0$ and $c > d > 0$, show that $ac > bd$. Give an example in which not all the quantities $a$, $b$, $c$, and $d$ are positive, for which $a > b$ and $c > d$ but $ac < bd$.

**3.** If $a > b > 0$, show that $a^2 > b^2$.

**4.** If $a > b > 0$, show, by mathematical induction or otherwise, that $a^n > b^n$ for every positive integer $n$.

**5.** If $a > b > 0$, show that $\sqrt{a} > \sqrt{b}$.

**6.** If $a > b > 0$, show that $1/a < 1/b$.

**7.** If $a > b > 0$, show that $1/a^n < 1/b^n$ for every positive integer $n$.

**8.** If $a \neq b$, show that $a^2 + b^2 > 2ab$.

**9.** Show that the arithmetic mean of two different positive numbers exceeds their geometric mean.

**10.** Show that the arithmetic mean of two different positive numbers exceeds their harmonic mean.

**11.** Show that the geometric mean of two different positive numbers exceeds their harmonic mean.

**12.** If $a > b > 0$, show that $a^3 + b^3 > ab(a + b)$.

**13.** If $a > b > 0$, show that $a^3 - b^3 > 3ab(a - b)$.

**14.** If $a$, $b$, $c$, and $d$ are all positive, and if $a^2 + b^2 = 1$ and $c^2 + d^2 = 1$, show that $ab + cd \leq 1$.

**15.** If $a$, $b$, $c$, and $d$ are all positive and different, and if $a/b < c/d$, show that $a/b < (a + c)/(b + d) < c/d$.

**16.** Show that $|a + b| \leq |a| + |b|$.

**17.** Show that $|a - b| \geq |a| - |b|$.

**18.** If $a$, $b$, and $c$ are all positive and different, show that $a^2 + b^2 + c^2 > ab + bc + ca$.

**19.** If $a$, $b$, and $c$ are all positive and different, show that $(a + b)(b + c)(c + a) > 8abc$.

**20.** Show that $a^4 + b^4 > 4ab(a - b)^2$.

**21.** If $a \neq b$, show that $a^4 + b^4 > ab(a^2 + b^2)$.

**22.** If $a$, $b$, and $c$ are all positive and different, show that $3(a^2 + b^2 + c^2) > (a + b + c)^2$.

**23.** If $a$ and $b$ are positive and different, show that $a^2 + b^2 + 1 > ab + a + b$.

**24.** If $a$ and $b$ are positive and different, show that $a/\sqrt{b} + b/\sqrt{a} > \sqrt{a} + \sqrt{b}$.

**25.** A faulty beam scale has unequal arms. In one transaction, the commodity to be sold is put into one scale pan and the weight into the second. In another, like transaction, the procedure is reversed. Show that the seller loses on the two transactions together.

## 61. Conditional inequalities.

To solve a conditional inequality containing one variable means to find all the real values of the variable that satisfy the inequality. As opposed to a conditional equation in one variable, which is satisfied only by discrete values of the variable, an inequality will usually be satisfied by all the values of the variable falling within one or more ranges. Thus, the inequality $x^2 > 4$ is satisfied by every $x > 2$ and every $x < -2$.

When attempting to solve an inequality, it is generally advisable to use principle II (Art. 59) wherever necessary to reduce an inequality to the form $f(x) > 0$, or $f(x) < 0$, for it is usually easier to determine the values of $x$ that make $f(x)$ positive and those that make $f(x)$ negative than to compare two functions or to compare one function with a non-zero constant. Also, with regard to the warning given at the end of Art. 59, concerning the two alternatives of principle III, it is best to avoid multiplication or division by a variable expression whose sign is itself doubtful. These precepts and others are illustrated in the following examples.

*Example 1.*   Solve the inequality $x^2 > 4$.

*Solution.*   This inequality may be solved almost by inspection, but to illustrate general procedures we reason as follows. By principle II, the given relation may be replaced by the equivalent one,

$$x^2 - 4 > 0. \tag{1}$$

Now $x^2 - 4$ may easily be factored into two linear expressions, whence we have

$$(x + 2)(x - 2) > 0. \tag{2}$$

Here we have the product of two factors, one of which vanishes for $x = -2$ and the other for $x = 2$. These are therefore the *critical values*: as $x$ increases from values less than $-2$ to values greater than $-2$, the expression $x + 2$ changes sign, from negative to positive; likewise, $x - 2$ changes from negative to positive as $x$ passes through the critical value 2.

We now make use of the fact that the product of two quantities of like sign (both positive or both negative) is positive, whereas the product of two quantities of unlike sign is negative (Art. 3). Hence $x$ must be such that either both factors in (2) are positive or both are negative. This yields the desired ranges

$$x > 2 \qquad \text{or} \qquad x < -2. \tag{3}$$

It will often be found helpful to plot the critical values on a line representation of the real numbers (Fig. 1), and then to consider in turn those values of $x$ less than the leftmost critical point, those between each adjacent pair of critical points, and finally those greater than the rightmost critical point. It is possible also to plot the function $y = f(x)$ and thus determine the values of $x$ for which $f(x) > 0$. Thus, if we plot $y = x^2 - 4$, we find that the graph lies above the $X$-axis when either of the inequalities (3) is obeyed.

*Example 2.* Determine the real values of $x$ for which $\sqrt{x^3 - 3x^2 + 2x}$ is real.

*Solution.* The given expression will be real for those real values of $x$ yielding a non-negative radicand, and thus we have to solve the inequality

$$x^3 - 3x^2 + 2x \geqq 0.$$

The left member is easily factored, whence we get the equivalent relation

$$x(x - 1)(x - 2) \geqq 0.$$

Therefore the critical values are $x = 0$, $x = 1$, and $x = 2$. Only if all three factors are positive or two are negative and one positive will the product be positive. Testing, in turn, $x < 0$, $0 < x < 1$, $1 < x < 2$, and $x > 2$, we find that the permissible ranges are

$$0 \leqq x \leqq 1, \qquad x \geqq 2.$$

The end points $x = 0$, $1$, and $2$ are included to satisfy the equality.

This type of problem is of importance in analytic geometry. Thus, to determine the extent of the curve $y^2 = x^3 - 3x^2 + 2x$, that is, to determine the regions of the coordinate plane occupied by the curve, we would make the above analysis. (See Example 1, Art. 68.)

*Example 3.* Solve the inequality

$$x - 6 > \frac{18 - 15x}{x^2 + 2x - 3}.$$

*Solution.* We first transpose the fraction in accordance with principle II, and then simplify the resulting left member into a single fraction. We have

$$x - 6 - \frac{18 - 15x}{x^2 + 2x - 3} > 0,$$

$$\frac{x^3 - 4x^2}{x^2 + 2x - 3} > 0,$$

or, in factored form,

$$\frac{x^2(x - 4)}{(x - 1)(x + 3)} > 0.$$

Now the linear factor $x$ appears to the second power, and thus $x^2$ does not change sign as $x$ passes from negative to positive values. However, $x = 0$ must be taken into account with the critical values $x = -3$, $x = 1$, and $x = 4$, since $x = 0$ itself obviously fails to satisfy the inequality. Proceeding as usual, we then find that the permissible ranges for which the inequality holds are

$$-3 < x < 0, \qquad 0 < x < 1, \qquad x > 4.$$

**EXERCISES**

Solve the following inequalities.

**1.** $3x - 2 > 2x + 3$.

**2.** $x + 4 > 4x - 5$.

**3.** $x^2 - 2 > 2x^2 - 6$.

**4.** $x^2 - 2x > 3$.

**5.** $3x^2 + 11x > 4$.

**6.** $x^2 + 6x + 9 > 0$.

**7.** $x + 3 > 2x^2$.

**8.** $x^2 - 4x + 5 > 0$.

**9.** $\dfrac{1}{x} > \dfrac{1}{4}$.

**10.** $\dfrac{3}{x+1} > \dfrac{1}{2}$.

**11.** $x^3 - 4x^2 + 4x > 0$.

**12.** $x^3 - 2\sqrt{2}\,x^2 + 2x > 0$.

**13.** $x^4 + 2x^2 > 0$.

**14.** $x^4 - 8x^2 + 16 > 0$.

**15.** $\sqrt{x+2} > 3$.

**16.** $\sqrt{1-x} > 2$.

**17.** $\sqrt{4x-1} + 2 > 0$.

**18.** $\sqrt{8-2x} + 1 > 0$.

**19.** $\dfrac{x-2}{x-3} > 0$.

**20.** $\dfrac{2x-1}{x+2} > 0$.

**21.** $\dfrac{x^2 - x}{2x + 4} > 0$.

**22.** $\dfrac{x+3}{x^3 - x^2} < 0$.

**23.** $\dfrac{x^2 - 3}{2 - x^2} > 0$.

**24.** $\dfrac{3}{x-1} > \dfrac{6}{x+1}$.

**25.** $x - 1 < \dfrac{2}{x}$.

**26.** $\dfrac{1}{\sqrt{x-2}} > 2$.

**27.** $\sqrt{x-2} + \sqrt{x+3} > 5$.

**28.** $\sqrt{4-x} + \sqrt{x+1} > 3$.

**29.** $\sqrt{x+5} - \sqrt{x} > 1$.

**30.** $\sqrt{x-1} - \dfrac{3}{\sqrt{x-1}} > 2$.

## 62. Trigonometric inequalities.

All the inequalities so far considered have involved only algebraic functions of the variables. Sometimes we are concerned with inequalities containing trigonometric functions. They may be either absolute or conditional inequalities, and they are, of course, subject to the same principles and operations as algebraic inequalities.

An example of an absolute trigonometric inequality is $\sin x < 2$, for the sine of any angle cannot exceed unity. On the other hand, $\cos x > 0$ is a conditional inequality satisfied only by angles in the first and fourth quadrants. Further illustrations of trigonometric inequalities and their treatment are given in the following examples.

*Example 1.* Show that

$$\sin \theta + \cos \theta \leqq \sqrt{2} \qquad (1)$$

for every angle $\theta$.

*Solution.* If we attempt to prove this absolute inequality by a preliminary analysis, as was done in Art. 60, we encounter a difficulty, for the rationalizing process thereby entailed must itself be justified, and, in the synthesis constituting the actual proof, the reverse operation of root extraction must likewise be shown to be valid. Although this process can be validated by a proper logical argument, it is easier to solve our problem by the following device.

Since both $\sin \theta$ and $\cos \theta$ have unity as their respective maximum values, we deal with the equivalent inequality,

$$\frac{\sqrt{2}}{2} \sin \theta + \frac{\sqrt{2}}{2} \cos \theta \leqq 1, \tag{2}$$

obtained from the given one by multiplying both members by $\sqrt{2}/2$, thus getting an expression to be compared with unity. Now the presence of two terms, one containing $\sin \theta$ and the other $\cos \theta$, together with the fact that $\sqrt{2}/2$ is the value of both $\sin (\pi/4)$ and $\cos (\pi/4)$, suggest the possible application of the trigonometric formula $\sin (\alpha + \beta) = \sin \alpha \cos \beta + \cos \alpha \sin \beta$ (Art. 35). For, if we identify $\alpha$ with $\theta$ and $\beta$ with $\pi/4$, the left member of (2) is seen to be identical with

$$\sin \theta \cos \frac{\pi}{4} + \cos \theta \sin \frac{\pi}{4} = \sin \left( \theta + \frac{\pi}{4} \right).$$

Therefore another equivalent inequality is

$$\sin \left( \theta + \frac{\pi}{4} \right) \leqq 1, \tag{3}$$

and since this is known to be true for every $\theta$, the desired inequality (1) may be established: Starting with the known relation (3), expansion of the left member and evaluation of functions of $\pi/4$ lead to (2), whence multiplication by $\sqrt{2}$ gives us (by principle III, Art. 59), the result (1).

*Example 2.* Determine the non-negative values of $x$ less than $2\pi$ for which

$$2 \cos^2 x + \sin x - 2 > 0. \tag{4}$$

*Solution.* We first transform the left member by means of the identity $\sin^2 x + \cos^2 x = 1$, to get

$$2 - 2 \sin^2 x + \sin x - 2 > 0,$$

a relation involving only one trigonometric function. Multiplying by $-1$ (or transposing), we have

$$2 \sin^2 x - \sin x < 0,$$

or

$$(\sin x)(2 \sin x - 1) < 0. \tag{5}$$

Now the product of two quantities will be negative only if the quantities are of unlike sign. If $\sin x > 0$, $x$ must be in the first or second quadrant; combining this fact with the restriction $2 \sin x - 1 < 0$, or $\sin x < \frac{1}{2}$, we get as permissible ranges:

$$0 < x < \frac{\pi}{6} \quad \text{or} \quad \frac{5\pi}{6} < x < \pi. \tag{6}$$

If $\sin x < 0$, so that $x$ is in the third or fourth quadrant, we must also have $\sin x > \frac{1}{2}$ in order that (5) be satisfied. But these two conditions are incompatible; hence the ranges (6) constitute the entire answer to our problem.

## EXERCISES

Establish the absolute inequalities in Exercises 1–10.

**1.** $4 \sin \theta - 3 \cos \theta \leqq 5$.
**2.** $12 \sin \theta + 5 \cos \theta \leqq 13$.
**3.** $A \sin \theta + B \cos \theta \leqq \sqrt{A^2 + B^2}$.
**4.** $\sin^2 \theta + \csc^2 \theta \geqq 2$.
**5.** $\cos^2 \theta + \sec^2 \theta \geqq 2$.
**6.** $\cos^2 \theta + \tan^2 \theta \geqq 2 \sin \theta$.
**7.** $\sin^2 \theta + \tan^2 \theta \geqq 2(\sec \theta - \cos \theta)$.
**8.** $\tan^2 \theta \leqq 4 \csc^2 2\theta$.
**9.** $\sin^2 (\alpha + \beta) \cos^2 (\alpha - \beta) \leqq 1$.
**10.** $\sin^6 \theta + \cos^6 \theta \geqq \frac{1}{4}$.

Solve the inequalities in Exercises 11–30 for non-negative values of $x$ less than $2\pi$.

**11.** $2 \sin^2 x < 1$.
**12.** $4 \cos^2 x > 3$.
**13.** $\sin^2 x > \sin x$.
**14.** $\cos^2 x < \cos x$.
**15.** $2 \cos^2 x - \sin x < 2$.
**16.** $2 \sin^2 x + \cos x < 2$.
**17.** $\sin 2x - \sin x < 0$.
**18.** $\sin 2x - \cos x > 0$.
**19.** $2 \sin^2 x - 3 \cos x > 3$.
**20.** $\sec^2 x + \tan x > 1$.
**21.** $\csc^2 x - \cot x < 1$.
**22.** $\tan^2 x - 2 \sec x + 1 < 0$.
**23.** $\sin^2 x < 3(1 - \cos x)$.
**24.** $2 \cos^2 x > 5(1 + \sin x)$.
**25.** $\sqrt{3} \csc^2 x < 4 \cot x$.
**26.** $1 + \tan x + \sin x + \cos x \geqq 0$.
**27.** $\sec^2 x - 3 \tan x + 3 > 0$.
**28.** $2 \csc^2 x - 4 \cot x + 1 > 0$.
**29.** $\sin 2x + 6 > 4 \sin x + 3 \cos x$.
**30.** $\sin 2x - 3 \sin x + 2 \cos x < 3$.

## SUPPLEMENTARY EXERCISES

Solve the inequalities in Exercises 1–2.

**1.** $\dfrac{x^2 - 2x}{x^2 + x - 2} > 0$.
**2.** $\dfrac{\sqrt{x}(x - 1)}{\sqrt{2 - x}} < 0$.

Solve the inequalities in Exercises 3–6 for non-negative values of $x$ less than $2\pi$.

**3.** $\sin x > \tan x$.
**4.** $\cos x < \sec x$.
**5.** $\cos x + \cot x > 0$.
**6.** $\sqrt{\sin x} < \sqrt{\cos x}$.

**7.** Show that, for all positive values of $x$,

$$x^2 + x + \frac{1}{x} + \frac{1}{x^2} \geqq 4.$$

**8.** If $a$, $b$, and $x$ are all positive, show that $(a + x)/(b + x)$ is greater or less than $a/b$ according as $b$ is greater or less than $a$.

**9.** If $a^2 + b^2 + c^2 = 1$ and $x^2 + y^2 + z^2 = 1$, show that $ax + by + cz \leqq 1$. (Cf. Exercise 14, Art. 60.)

**10.** If $a$, $b$, and $c$ are all positive and different, show that

$$(a - b - c)^2 + (b - c - a)^2 + (c - a - b)^2 > ab + bc + ca.$$

**11.** Show that, for all values of $\theta$, $\sin^6 \theta + \cos^6 \theta \leq 1$. (Cf. Exercise 10, Art. 62.)

**12.** Show that, for all values of $\theta$,

$$\tfrac{1}{2} \leq \sin^4 \theta + \cos^4 \theta \leq 1.$$

**13.** If $a$, $b$, and $c$ are all positive and different, show that

$$\frac{a^2 + b^2}{a + b} + \frac{b^2 + c^2}{b + c} + \frac{c^2 + a^2}{c + a} > a + b + c.$$

**14.** If $a$, $b$, $c$, and $d$ are positive numbers in harmonic progression, show that $a + d > b + c$.

**15.** If $a_1$, $a_2$, $\cdots$, $a_n$ are positive numbers less than 1, and $s_n = a_1 + a_2 \cdots + a_n$, show that

$$(1 - a_1)(1 - a_2) \cdots (1 - a_n) \geq 1 - s_n.$$

# XII — Inverse Functions

**63. Inverses of algebraic functions.** In Art. 21 a rational integral function of the variables $x, y, \cdots$ was defined as a sum of terms of the form $cx^m y^n \cdots$, where the $c$'s are constants and $m, n, \cdots$ are positive integers or zero. A rational integral equation is obtained by setting such a function equal to zero. Particular cases are the linear equations (Chapter V) and the quadratic equations in two variables $x$ and $y$ (Chapter IX).

Suppose that we have a rational integral equation involving two variables $x$ and $y$, expressed symbolically by the functional notation

$$R(x, y) = 0. \tag{1}$$

If $y = f(x)$ is a relation connecting the variables such that replacement of $y$ by $f(x)$ in (1) yields an identity, $R[x, f(x)] \equiv 0$, then (Art. 21) $y$ is an algebraic function of $x$. We may say that $y = f(x)$ is a solution of (1) for $y$ in terms of $x$. Similarly, if $x = g(y)$ is such that $R[g(y), y] \equiv 0$, then $x$ is an algebraic function of $y$, and $x = g(y)$ is a solution of (1) for $x$ in terms of $y$.

For example, consider the rational integral equation

$$x^2 - 2xy + y^2 + 2x - 3 = 0. \tag{2}$$

By means of the quadratic formula we may readily solve for $y$ in terms of $x$ to get

$$y = x \pm \sqrt{3 - 2x}. \tag{3}$$

Likewise, using the quadratic formula to find $x$ in terms of $y$, we have

$$x = y - 1 \pm \sqrt{4 - 2y}. \tag{4}$$

That the algebraic functions given by (3) and (4) satisfy (2) identically is also easy to verify.

Now suppose that we originally have, not the rational integral equation (1), but an equation $y = f(x)$ giving us $y$ as an algebraic function of $x$. If we can solve this equation for $x$ in terms of $y$, to get the algebraic functional relation $x = g(y)$, we say that $g(y)$ is the function **inverse** to $f(x)$. Likewise, if we start with $x = g(y)$ and from it derive $y = f(x)$, then the latter is the inverse of the former. Combining these two state-

219

ments, we may say that $f(x)$ and $g(y)$ are inverse algebraic functions, each of which is obtainable from the other, and both stem from some rational integral equation.

Evidently (3) and (4) are examples of inverse algebraic functions, either of which is derivable from the other, and both originate from the rational equation (2).

When an equation such as (1) can be solved explicitly for $x$ or for $y$, and particularly when both these inverse functions are obtainable, considerable information concerning the behavior of the functional relation can be gained. Moreover, the explicit functions $y = f(x)$ and $x = g(y)$ have practical advantages in connection with computations and plotting. These matters are illustrated in the following example.

*Example.* Discuss the rational integral equation

$$x^2 - 2xy + y^2 + 2x - 3 = 0, \tag{2}$$

and plot its graph.

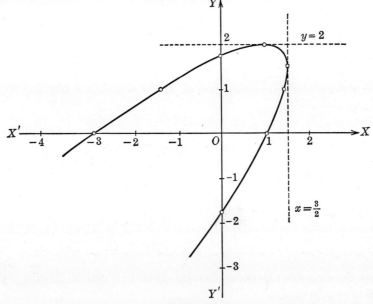

Fig. 24

*Solution.* We have already solved this equation for $y$ in terms of $x$ to get

$$y = x \pm \sqrt{3 - 2x}. \tag{3}$$

This explicit relation shows immediately that: (a) for every real value of $x$ less than $\frac{3}{2}$, there are two distinct real values of $y$; (b) for $x = \frac{3}{2}$, the two $y$-values coalesce into the single value $y = \frac{3}{2}$; (c) for $x > \frac{3}{2}$, $y$ is complex. Hence we know that the graph of equation (2) will not extend to the right of the line $x = \frac{3}{2}$, and we also infer that the graph is tangent to that line. In addition, relation (3) enables us to compute the two values of $y$ corresponding to each permissible value of $x$; thus, when $x = 0$, $y = \pm\sqrt{3}$, and when $x = 1$, we get $y = 2$ and $y = 0$.

In the same way, the inverse functional relation previously found,

$$x = y - 1 \pm \sqrt{4 - 2y}, \qquad (4)$$

shows that: (a) for every real value of $y$ less than 2, there are two distinct real values of $x$; (b) when $y = 2$, the two $x$-values coalesce into the single value $x = 1$; (c) for $y > 2$, $x$ is complex. Therefore the graph will not extend above the line $y = 2$, to which the curve is apparently tangent. When $y = 0$, $x = 1$ or $-3$; when $y = 1$, (4) yields $x = \pm\sqrt{2}$, and so on.

The graph obtained with the help of the above discussion is shown in Fig. 24. By the methods of analytic geometry, it may be shown that this curve is a parabola, and additional characteristics of the curve may be determined.

## EXERCISES

Find the inverses of each of the functions in Exercises 1–10.

**1.** $y = 3x + 2$.

**2.** $y = x^2 - 1$.

**3.** $y = x^2 - 4x$.

**4.** $y = \pm\sqrt{x - 3}$.

**5.** $y = \dfrac{x - 2}{x}$.

**6.** $y = \dfrac{x}{x + 3}$.

**7.** $y = \dfrac{x - 4}{2x - 1}$.

**8.** $y = \dfrac{x^2 + 1}{x^2 - 1}$.

**9.** $y = \dfrac{\sqrt{x} + 2}{\sqrt{x}}$.

**10.** $y = \pm\dfrac{2x}{\sqrt{x^2 - 4}}$.

**11–20.** If $x$ and $y$ are restricted to real values, determine the permissible values of $x$ for each of the functions of Exercises 1–10 and the corresponding permissible values of $y$ for each inverse function. Plot the graph in each case.

Discuss and plot the graph of each equation in Exercises 21–32.

**21.** $x^2 + y^2 = 4$.

**22.** $x^2 - y^2 = 9$.

**23.** $x^2 + 4y^2 = 4$.

**24.** $x^2 - 4y^2 = 4$.

**25.** $xy + x + y = 0$.

**26.** $x^2 - xy - 2y^2 = 0$.

**27.** $x^2 + 2xy + 2y^2 = 4$.

**28.** $x^2 - 4xy - y^2 = 5$.

**29.** $x^2 + 2xy + 5y^2 - 4x - 4y = 0$.

**30.** $x^2 - 2xy + 3y^2 - 2x + 4y = 3$.

**31.** $x^2y - x + 4y = 0$.

**32.** $x^2y^2 - x + 1 = 0$.

**33.** Show that the curve of Fig. 24 extends indefinitely far downward and to the left in the third quadrant.

**34.** Find the inverse of the general quadratic function $y = ax^2 + bx + c$, where the discriminant $b^2 - 4ac > 0$. (a) If $a > 0$, show that $x$ is real for $y \geqq (4ac - b^2)/4a$, and that the graph crosses the $X$-axis in two distinct points and extends indefinitely upward. (b) If $a < 0$, show that $x$ is real for $y \leqq (4ac - b^2)/4a$, and that the graph crosses the $X$-axis in two distinct points and extends indefinitely downward. Draw two typical graphs.

**35.** Make an analysis similar to that of Exercise 34 for the quadratic function $y = ax^2 + bx + c$ when $b^2 - 4ac < 0$, and show that the curve lies entirely on one side of the $X$-axis for both $a > 0$ and $a < 0$. Draw two typical graphs.

**64. Inverse trigonometric functions.** We consider now the inverses of the trigonometric functions. These inverses are of considerable importance in calculus and other more advanced subjects.

The relation inverse to $y = \sin x$ is denoted symbolically in either of two ways:

$$x = \sin^{-1} y \qquad \text{or} \qquad x = \arcsin y. \tag{1}$$

These may be read either "$x$ is the inverse sine of $y$" or "$x$ equals arc sine of $y$." However, the most informative way of speaking or thinking about this inverse function is to say: "$x$ is the angle whose sine is $y$," for then the primary fact that the variable $x$ represents an angle is clearly exhibited.

Similarly, we designate the inverses of the other five trigonometric functions. Thus, we have

$$y = \cos x: \quad x = \cos^{-1} y, \quad x = \arccos y; \tag{2}$$

$$y = \tan x: \quad x = \tan^{-1} y, \quad x = \arctan y; \tag{3}$$

etc. Note that the symbols $\sin^{-1} y$, $\cos^{-1} y$, and so on, always denote inverse trigonometric functions. If we wish to use the exponent $-1$ to signify the reciprocal of a trigonometric function, we must use parentheses; for example, $1/\sin x = (\sin x)^{-1}$ (Art. 15).

Corresponding to each value of the angle $x$, there exists one and only one value of the trigonometric function $y = \sin x$. On the other hand, if $y$ is given a value (which must be in the range $-1 \leqq y \leqq 1$), there will be indefinitely many corresponding values of $x = \arcsin y$. Thus, if $y = 0$, we get $x = 0$, $\pm\pi$, $\pm2\pi$, $\cdots$. A similar indefiniteness occurs also for the other inverse trigonometric functions.

These ambiguities are undesirable in many connections, and it is therefore customary to assign restricted values to the inverse trigonometric functions. If we examine the graph of the function $y = \sin x$ (Fig. 25), we see that, as $x$ increases from $-\pi/2$ to $\pi/2$, $y$ assumes each value from −1 to 1 once and only once. Hence we agree to the convention that the inverse sine function shall be restricted to the range

$$-\frac{\pi}{2} \leqq \arcsin y \leqq \frac{\pi}{2}.$$  (4)

We call these the **principal values** of the inverse sine function.

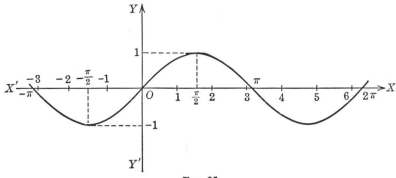

FIG. 25

The graph of $y = \cos x$ (Fig. 26) indicates that the same range, from $-\pi/2$ to $\pi/2$, will not serve for this inverse function also, for there are two values of $x$ corresponding to each permissible positive $y$-value, and

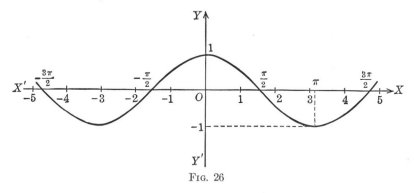

FIG. 26

no $x$-values for $y$ negative, in that range. However, we may take, as the range of principal values of the inverse cosine function,

$$0 \leqq \arccos y \leqq \pi,$$  (5)

for the graph shows that there is then one and only one value of arccos $y$ for each value of $y$ from −1 to 1.

With regard to the inverse tangent function, the graph of $y = \tan x$ (Fig. 27) indicates that a convenient range of principal values is

$$-\frac{\pi}{2} < \arctan y < \frac{\pi}{2}, \tag{6}$$

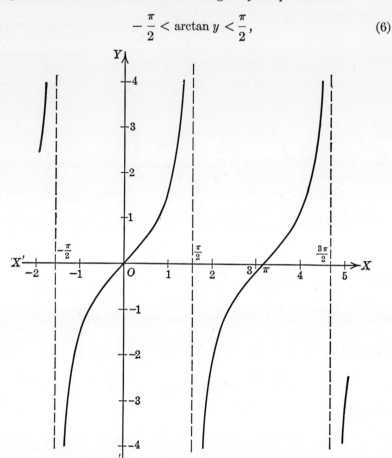

FIG. 27

the same as that for the inverse sine function, except that the end points, $-\pi/2$ and $\pi/2$, are not included here since these two angles have no tangents.

Since the inverse functions arccot $y$, arcsec $y$, and arccsc $y$ arise comparatively rarely, we shall not discuss principal values for these three functions here. (See Exercises 36–38, below.)

Hereafter in this book it will be understood that all inverse trigonometric functions are to be restricted to their principal values, as given in (4)–(6). With this agreement, we have, for example, arcsin $(-1) =$ $-\pi/2$ (not $3\pi/2$), arctan $(-1) = -\pi/4$ (not $3\pi/4$), etc.

*Example 1.* Evaluate tan $[\frac{1}{2} \arcsin (-\frac{8}{17})]$.

*Solution.* When dealing with an inverse function, it is good practice to designate it by an angle symbol and then determine necessary values of the trigonometric functions of that angle. Consequently we set $\theta = \arcsin (-\frac{8}{17})$, so that $\sin \theta = -\frac{8}{17}$, and we have to evaluate tan $(\theta/2)$. We have (Art. 38)

$$\tan \frac{\theta}{2} = \frac{1 - \cos \theta}{\sin \theta},$$

and it is therefore necessary to find, in addition to $\sin \theta = -\frac{8}{17}$, the corresponding value of $\cos \theta$. Now, when $\sin \theta$ is negative, restriction to the principal range (4) requires that $\theta$ be a negative angle in the fourth quadrant. Then $\cos \theta$ will be positive, and we find

$$\cos \theta = \sqrt{1 - \sin^2 \theta} = \frac{15}{17}.$$

Therefore the desired value is

$$\tan \frac{\theta}{2} = \frac{1 - \frac{15}{17}}{-\frac{8}{17}} = -\frac{1}{4}.$$

*Example 2.* Evaluate arctan $\frac{5}{12}$ − arccos $\frac{3}{5}$.

*Solution.* Let $\alpha = \arctan \frac{5}{12}$, $\beta = \arccos \frac{3}{5}$. We are to evaluate the angle $\alpha - \beta$, where, by (5) and (6), both $\alpha$ and $\beta$ are acute angles. We first find some function of $\alpha - \beta$, say $\sin (\alpha - \beta)$. Since $\tan \alpha = \frac{5}{12}$, we readily get $\sin \alpha = \frac{5}{13}$ and $\cos \alpha = \frac{12}{13}$; also, since $\cos \beta = \frac{3}{5}$, $\sin \beta = \frac{4}{5}$. Then

$$\sin (\alpha - \beta) = \sin \alpha \cos \beta - \cos \alpha \sin \beta$$

$$= \frac{5}{13} \cdot \frac{3}{5} - \frac{12}{13} \cdot \frac{4}{5} = -\frac{33}{65} = -0.5077$$

approximately. Now it is easy to see that $\alpha$ is less than $\pi/4$ and that $\beta$ is greater than $\pi/4$; hence $\alpha - \beta$ is a negative angle. Reference to tables consequently gives us

$$\alpha - \beta = - \arcsin 0.5077 = -0.5325$$

approximately.

### EXERCISES

Evaluate each of the expressions in Exercises 1–35.

**1.** arcsin 0.

**2.** arccos 1.

**3.** arctan 0.

**4.** arcsin $\dfrac{\sqrt{3}}{2}$.

**5.** arccos $\frac{1}{2}$.

**6.** arctan 1.

**7.** arcsin $(-\frac{1}{2})$.

**8.** arccos $\left(-\dfrac{\sqrt{3}}{2}\right)$.

**9.** arctan $(-1)$.

**10.** cos (arcsin $\frac{1}{2}$).

**11.** sin (arctan $\sqrt{3}$).

**12.** $\csc\left(\arcsin\dfrac{\sqrt{2}}{2}\right).$        **13.** $\cot\left[\arccos\left(-\dfrac{\sqrt{3}}{2}\right)\right].$

**14.** $\sin\left[\arctan\left(-\sqrt{3}\right)\right].$        **15.** $\sec\left[\arccos\left(-\tfrac{1}{2}\right)\right].$

**16.** $\sin\left(\arccos 1 + \arccos 0\right).$        **17.** $\cos\left(\arcsin 1 - \arcsin 0\right).$

**18.** $\sin\left(\arcsin\tfrac{1}{2} - \arcsin 1\right).$        **19.** $\cos\left(\arccos\tfrac{1}{2} - \arccos 0\right).$

**20.** $\tan\left(\arccos 1 + \arcsin 0\right).$        **21.** $\cot\left(\arccos\tfrac{1}{2} - \arcsin\tfrac{1}{2}\right).$

**22.** $\sin\left[\arccos\left(-1\right) - \arcsin\left(-1\right)\right].$        **23.** $\cos\left[\arctan 1 - \arctan\left(-1\right)\right].$

**24.** $\cos\left(\arcsin\tfrac{1}{4} + \arcsin\tfrac{3}{4}\right).$        **25.** $\sin\left(\arccos\tfrac{1}{4} - \arccos\tfrac{3}{4}\right).$

**26.** $\cos\left(2\arcsin\tfrac{1}{2}\right).$        **27.** $\sin\left[2\arccos\left(-\tfrac{1}{2}\right)\right].$

**28.** $\sin\left(2\arcsin\tfrac{4}{5}\right).$        **29.** $\tan\left(2\arccos\tfrac{4}{5}\right).$

**30.** $\sin\left(\tfrac{1}{2}\arccos\tfrac{4}{5}\right).$        **31.** $\cos\left(\tfrac{1}{2}\arccos\tfrac{5}{13}\right).$

**32.** $\arcsin\dfrac{\sqrt{2}}{2} - \arccos\left(-\tfrac{1}{2}\right).$        **33.** $\arctan\dfrac{\sqrt{3}}{3} + \arccos\left(-\dfrac{\sqrt{3}}{2}\right).$

**34.** $\arcsin\tfrac{1}{5} - \arcsin\left(-\tfrac{1}{5}\right).$        **35.** $\arctan 5 - \arctan 4.$

**36.** Plot the graph of the function $y = \cot x$, and show that $-\pi/2 \leqq \text{arccot } y < 0$ and $0 < \text{arccot } y \leqq \pi/2$ are suitable ranges of principal values.

**37.** Plot the graph of the function $y = \sec x$, and show that $-\pi \leqq \text{arcsec } y < -\pi/2$ and $0 \leqq \text{arcsec } y < \pi/2$ are suitable ranges of principal values.

**38.** Plot the graph of the function $y = \csc x$, and show that $-\pi < \text{arccsc } y \leqq -\pi/2$ and $0 < \text{arccsc } y \leqq \pi/2$ are suitable ranges of principal values.

**39.** Show that $\arctan\tfrac{1}{3} + \arctan\tfrac{1}{4} + \arctan\tfrac{2}{9} = \pi/4.$

**40.** Show that $\arctan\sqrt{2} + \arctan 2\sqrt{2} + \arctan\left(3 - 2\sqrt{2}\right) = 3\pi/4.$

Under the restriction that only principal values are to be used, show that the relations of Exercises 41–50 hold whether $x$ is positive, negative, or zero.

**41.** $\arcsin\left(-x\right) = -\arcsin x.$        **42.** $\arccos\left(-x\right) = \pi - \arccos x.$

**43.** $\arctan\left(-x\right) = -\arctan x.$        **44.** $\arccos x = \dfrac{\pi}{2} - \arcsin x.$

**45.** $\arcsin x = \arctan\dfrac{x}{\sqrt{1 - x^2}}.$        **46.** $\arctan x = \arcsin\dfrac{x}{\sqrt{1 + x^2}}.$

**47.** $\sin\left(\arccos x\right) = \sqrt{1 - x^2}.$        **48.** $\cos\left(\arctan x\right) = \dfrac{1}{\sqrt{1 + x^2}}.$

**49.** $\sin\left(2\arccos x\right) = 2x\sqrt{1 - x^2}.$        **50.** $\cos\left(2\arcsin x\right) = 1 - 2x^2.$

**65. Trigonometric equations.** We sometimes have to solve an equation in which the unknown is involved in one or more inverse trigonometric functions. The general procedure for solving such an equation is to identify each inverse function with an angle and then to transform the given relation into an algebraic equation by means of trigonometric functions of the various angles.

Since we are restricting ourselves to principal values, it is essential that each solution be checked in the original equation. Moreover, when an irrationality is introduced, as is often necessary, care must be taken with the attached algebraic signs, and when rationalizing processes are used, the possibility of thereby introducing extraneous solutions should be kept in mind. Consequently all solutions should be checked.

*Example.* Solve the equation

$$\arcsin x + \arccos (1 - x) = 0.$$

*Solution.* Let $\alpha = \arcsin x$, $\beta = \arccos (1 - x)$. Then we have to solve the equation

$$\alpha + \beta = 0,$$

where $\sin \alpha = x$ and $\cos \beta = 1 - x$. A simple relation may be obtained from

$$\sin (\alpha + \beta) = \sin \alpha \cos \beta + \cos \alpha \sin \beta = 0.$$

Since $\cos \alpha = \pm \sqrt{1 - x^2}$ and $\sin \beta = \pm \sqrt{1 - (1 - x)^2} = \pm \sqrt{2x - x^2}$, we therefore get

$$x(1 - x) \pm \sqrt{1 - x^2} \sqrt{2x - x^2} = 0,$$

$$x^2(1 - 2x + x^2) = (1 - x^2)(2x - x^2).$$

Evidently $x = 0$ satisfies this equation, and, since $\arcsin 0 = 0$ and $\arccos 1 = 0$, this value of $x$ also satisfies the original equation. The factor $x$ being removed, the preceding relation then yields

$$x(1 - 2x + x^2) = (1 - x^2)(2 - x),$$

$$x - 2x^2 + x^3 = 2 - x - 2x^2 + x^3,$$

$$x = 1.$$

But $\arcsin 1 = \pi/2$ and $\arccos 0 = \pi/2$, so that the value $x = 1$ does not satisfy the given equation. (Note, however, that outside the range of principal values we have $\arccos 0 = -\pi/2$ also, which, together with $\arcsin 1 = \pi/2$, would make $x = 1$ a possible solution.)

Hence $x = 0$ is the only solution of the original equation when only principal values are permitted.

This problem can be solved by a verbal analysis, without the above algebraic manipulations, as follows. In the first place, $x$ is restricted to the range $0 \leq x \leq 1$. For, if $x < 0$, $1 - x > 1$, and $\arccos (1 - x)$ becomes meaningless; and if $x > 1$, $\arcsin x$ has no significance. But for values of $x$ between 0 and 1, both $\arcsin x$ and $\arccos (1 - x)$ are positive angles, whence their sum cannot be zero. When $x = 1$, $\arcsin 1 + \arccos 0 = \pi$ instead of 0, as we have seen, and therefore $x = 0$ is the only possible solution.

### EXERCISES

Using only principal values, solve the following equations.

**1.** $\arcsin x + \arcsin 1 = \pi/2$.
**2.** $\arccos x + \arccos \frac{1}{2} = \pi/2$.
**3.** $\arctan x + \arctan \sqrt{3} = \pi/6$.

**4.** $2 \arcsin x + \arccos 0 = \arccos (-1)$.

**5.** $\arccos x - \arcsin 1 = \arccos (-1)$.

**6.** $\arcsin (1 + x) + \arcsin (1 - x) = \pi$.

**7.** $\arccos x + \arccos (1 - x) = \pi/2$.

**8.** $\arctan x + \arctan (1 - x) = \pi/4$.

**9.** $\arctan x + \arccos \sqrt{1 - x^2} = 0$.

**10.** $\arccos 2x - \arcsin x = \pi/2$.

**11.** $\arcsin (1 - x) + \arccos x = \pi$.

**12.** $\arcsin x + \arccos (1 - x) = \pi/2$.

**13.** $2 \arctan x - \arcsin x = 0$.

**14.** $\arcsin x + \arcsin \dfrac{1}{x} = \pi$.

**15.** $2 \arcsin x - \arccos x = \pi$.

**16.** $2 \arccos \sqrt{x} + \arcsin \sqrt{x} = \pi$.

**17.** $2 \arctan x + \arccos x = \pi/2$.

**18.** $2 \arcsin \sqrt{x} + \arccos \sqrt{1 - x} = \pi$.

**19.** $2 \arccos x + \arcsin (1 - 2x^2) = \pi/2$.

**20.** $\arctan \sqrt{x} + 2 \arctan \sqrt{1 - x} = \pi/2$.

### SUPPLEMENTARY EXERCISES

Discuss and plot the graph of each equation in Exercises 1–8.

**1.** $xy = 1$.                **2.** $xy^2 = 1$.

**3.** $x^3 y = 1$.              **4.** $x^2 y + y = 2$.

**5.** $x^2 y^2 - x^2 + y^2 = 0$.     **6.** $xy^2 - y^2 + x + 1 = 0$.

**7.** $x^2 y^2 - x^2 - y = 0$.      **8.** $x^2 y + xy^2 = 2$.

Find the inverse of each of the functions in Exercises 9–15. Restricting $x$ and $y$ to real values, and using only principal values of inverse trigonometric functions, find the permissible ranges for $x$ and for $y$ in each case.

**9.** $y = 2 \arcsin (x - 1) + 3$.

**10.** $y = \arccos (2x - 1) - 2$.

**11.** $y = \arcsin \sqrt{x} + \arccos \sqrt{1 - x}$.

**12.** $y = \arctan x + \arctan 2x$.

**13.** $y = \arctan 3x - \arctan 2x$.

**14.** $y = \arcsin x + \arccos 2x$.

**15.** $y = \sqrt{2 \sin x} + \sin x$

# XIII———————— Functional Variation

**66. Direct and inverse variation.** When two variables $x$ and $y$ are connected by some functional relation, the variation of $x$ will in general imply a variation in $y$. Although the study of such variations usually requires more advanced methods than we now have at our command, it is possible here to consider a few fundamental and important types of functional relations.

One of the simplest of dependencies between two variables $x$ and $y$ is that in which their ratio is always the same number $k$:

$$\frac{y}{x} = k \qquad \text{or} \qquad y = kx. \tag{1}$$

We say then that **$y$ varies directly as $x$,** and $k$ is referred to as the **constant of proportionality.** Sometimes the symbolism $y \propto x$ is used to denote the fact that $y$ varies as $x$.

Similarly, if $y = kx^2$, $y$ is said to vary as the square of $x$; if $y = kx^3$, $y$ varies as the cube of $x$; and so on.

When

$$y = \frac{k}{x}, \tag{2}$$

we say that **$y$ varies inversely as $x$.** In similar fashion, $y$ may vary inversely as the square of $x$, etc.

As illustrations, we have the following: (1) The distance $s$ traversed by a freely falling body varies directly as the square of the time $t$ in motion: $s = kt^2$. (2) The gravitational force of attraction $F$ between two bodies varies inversely as the square of the distance $x$ between them: $F = k/x^2$. (3) The volume $V$ of a sphere varies directly as the cube of the radius $r$: $V = kr^3$.

**67. Combined variation.** Frequently, as we have seen, one variable depends upon two or more other variables. We then have **combined variation.** Thus, the volume $V$ of a right circular cylinder varies with both the radius $r$ of the base and the altitude $h$: $V = \pi r^2 h$. If $h$ is held fixed, we may say that $V$ varies directly as the square of $r$. Likewise, if $r$ remains constant, $V$ varies directly as $h$.

Suppose that a variable $z$ depends upon two quantities, $x$ and $y$, in the following manner. If $y$ is held constant, $z$ varies directly as $x$, and if $x$ remains fixed in value, $z$ varies directly as $y$. Then we have both

$$z = f(y) \cdot x, \qquad (1)$$

and

$$z = g(x) \cdot y, \qquad (2)$$

where, when $y$ is constant, the function $f(y)$ serves as a constant of proportionality in (1), and, if $x$ is constant, $g(x)$ is a constant of proportionality in (2). Relations (1) and (2) may be combined to yield

$$f(y)x = g(x)y,$$

or

$$\frac{f(y)}{y} = \frac{g(x)}{x}. \qquad (3)$$

Now let $x$ vary while $y$ remains fixed. Then the left member of (3) is constant, and therefore the right member must be a constant also. Consequently the common value of the two members of (3) must be a constant $k$, whence

$$f(y) = ky \qquad \text{and} \qquad g(x) = kx. \qquad (4)$$

Replacing $f(y)$ in (1) by $ky$, or replacing $g(x)$ in (2) by $kx$, we see that

$$z = kxy. \qquad (5)$$

The variation represented by a relation of the form (5) is sometimes referred to as **joint variation**.

*Example.* A certain beam $L$ ft. long has a rectangular cross section $b$ in. in horizontal breadth and $d$ in. in vertical depth. It is found that, when the beam is supported at the ends, the deflection $D$ at the center varies directly as the fourth power of $L$, inversely as $b$, and inversely as the cube of $d$. If the length is decreased by 10 per cent but the breadth kept the same, by how much should the depth be changed in order that the same deflection $D$ be obtained?

*Solution.* From the statement of the problem, we see that the combined variation is given by

$$D = \frac{kL^4}{bd^3}.$$

Since corresponding values of the four variables are not known, nor are other equivalent data available, we cannot determine the value of the constant of proportionality $k$. But if one set of variables is designated with the subscript 1, and the new set with the subscript 2, we have

$$D_1 = \frac{kL_1^4}{b_1 d_1^3}, \qquad D_2 = \frac{kL_2^4}{b_2 d_2^3},$$

whence

$$\frac{D_2}{D_1} = \frac{L_2^4 b_1 d_1^3}{L_1^4 b_2 d_2^3}.$$

In this problem we have $D_2 = D_1$, $L_2 = 0.9L_1$, and $b_2 = b_1$. Therefore we get

$$d_2^3 = (0.9)^4 d_1^3,$$

$$d_2/d_1 = (0.9)^{\frac{4}{3}} = 0.869$$

approximately. Hence $d_2 = 0.869 d_1$, so that the depth must be decreased by about 13.1 per cent.

### EXERCISES

**1.** If the base and altitude of a triangle are respectively doubled and tripled, by what percentage does the area increase?

**2.** If the area of a circle is to be reduced by 25 per cent, by what percentage must the radius be decreased?

**3.** If the radius of a sphere is increased by 20 per cent, by what percentage does the surface area increase?

**4.** By what percentage does the volume of the sphere of Exercise 3 increase?

**5.** The distance traversed by a freely falling body during the first second of its motion is 4.90 meters. How far does the body move in the next second?

**6.** The kinetic energy of a moving body varies directly as its weight and as the square of its speed. If the weight is halved, what must be the ratio of the new speed to the original if the kinetic energy is to remain the same?

**7.** When an electric current flows through a wire, the resistance to the flow varies directly as the length and inversely as the cross-sectional area of the wire. If the length and diameter are respectively tripled and doubled, by what percentage does the resistance change?

**8.** Ohm's law states that the electric current flowing in a circuit varies directly as the applied voltage and inversely as the resistance. Combine this law with the conditions stated in Exercise 7, and hence show that the same current will be obtained if the voltage is decreased by 25 per cent.

**9.** The pressure exerted by a confined gas varies jointly as its density and its absolute temperature. If the density is decreased by 10 per cent while its absolute temperature is increased by 10 per cent, by what percentage does the pressure change?

**10.** Boyle's law states that the product of pressure and volume of a confined gas is a constant. If the radius of a spherical balloon expands by 5 per cent, by what percentage does the pressure of the enclosed gas change?

**11.** The volume of a cone varies directly as the square of the base radius and as the altitude. If the altitude is decreased by 20 per cent, by what percentage must the base radius be changed in order that the same volume be obtained?

**12.** The force of attraction between two bodies varies directly as the product of their masses and inversely as the square of the distance between them. If one mass is decreased by 25 per cent and the force is to be twice as large, by what percentage must the distance between the bodies be changed?

**13.** The maximum safe load for a beam varies directly as the breadth and as the square of the depth, and inversely as the length of the beam. If the breadth is decreased by 10 per cent, the depth increased by 10 per cent, and the length increased by 25 per cent, by what percentage must the load be decreased?

**14.** The horizontal range of a projectile varies directly as the square of the initial velocity and as the sine of twice the angle of elevation. If the initial velocity is decreased by 10 per cent, by how much must the original angle of 25° be increased to achieve the same range?

**15.** The force of attraction between a thin spherical shell and a particle at a distance $x$ from the center of the shell varies directly as the surface area of the shell and inversely as $x^2$. If both the volume of the shell and $x$ are halved, by what percentage is the force changed?

**16.** The time required to empty a vertical cylindrical tank varies directly as the square of the radius and as the square root of the height of the tank. If the radius and height are each decreased by 10 per cent, by what percentage does the time required to empty decrease?

**17.** The available power in a jet of water varies as the cube of the velocity and as the cross-sectional area of the jet. If the velocity and the nozzle diameter are both increased by 10 per cent, by what percentage is the power increased?

**18.** The quantity of water flowing over a weir varies as the width of the weir and as the three-halves power of the head of water available. If the width is halved, by what percentage must the head be increased to obtain the same rate of flow?

**19.** The velocity of efflux of a gas through a small opening varies directly as the square root of the difference of pressure on the two sides of the opening and inversely as the square root of the density of the gas. If the pressure difference is decreased by 10 per cent and the density is increased by 5 per cent, by what percentage does the velocity decrease?

**20.** The force of attraction between a right circular cone of altitude $h$ and semi-vertical angle $\theta$ and a particle at the vertex of the cone varies jointly as the altitude and the versed sine of $\theta$. (See Exercise 20, following Art. 15.) If the altitude is decreased by 20 per cent, and the force is to remain the same, by how much must the original angle of 60° be changed?

**21.** A law due to Kepler states that the square of the period of revolution of a planet about the sun varies as the cube of the mean distance between them. Using 12 months as the earth's period, 93,000,000 miles as the distance between earth and sun, and 22.9 months as Mars's period, find the distance from Mars to the sun.

**22.** The maximum deflection of a circular disc carrying a uniform load varies directly as the fourth power of the radius and inversely as the cube of the thickness of the disc. If the deflection is to be halved when the thickness is doubled, by what percentage must the radius be increased?

**23.** The resistance of two resistors connected in parallel varies directly as the product and inversely as the sum of the individual resistances. If one resistance is increased by an amount $x$ and the other is decreased by $x$, show that the combined resistance will remain the same only if $x$ is equal to the difference between the original resistances.

**24.** In a tangent galvanometer, the current flowing through the coil varies jointly as the horizontal component of the earth's magnetic force and the tangent of the angle through which the needle turns. If the force decreases by 1 per cent and the angle decreases from 15° to 12°, by what percentage does the current decrease?

**25.** A jet of water impinging on a curved vane is deflected through an angle $\theta$. The resultant force on the vane varies as the square of the velocity of the jet and as the sine of $\theta/2$. If the velocity of the jet is increased by 10 per cent and $\theta$ is decreased from $30°$ to $20°$, by what percentage does the force change?

**68. Variation of algebraic functions.** For the remainder of this chapter we shall be concerned with functions of a single independent variable $x$. The variation of such a function, as the independent variable increases, can be exhibited geometrically by means of a graph. Although a graph can be plotted point by point, the computation of the values of the dependent variable $y$ corresponding to the chosen values of $x$ is often laborious; moreover, in merely drawing a curve through isolated plotted points, one is apt to be somewhat uncertain about the behavior of the functional variation for intermediate values of $x$.

It is therefore desirable to establish procedures for the determination of the important characteristics of a given functional relation. The development of general methods of analysis requires the techniques of analytic geometry and calculus, and consequently we cannot make extensive analyses here. We shall restrict ourselves to the examination of a few important types of functions and to some of their salient characteristics.

Consider first the power function (Art. 21),

$$y = x^p, \tag{1}$$

where $p$ is a rational number. If $p = 1$, equation (1) is a simple linear relation, $y = x$, the graph of which is a straight line bisecting the first and third quadrants; if $p = 2$, we have a simple quadratic function, $y = x^2$, whose graph is a parabola (Fig. 28). The graphs of both $y = x$ and $y = x^2$ pass through the origin $O$ and the point $(1, 1)$; when $0 < x < 1$ the parabola lies below the line, and when $x > 1$ the parabola is above the line, as shown. For, the difference between the ordinates on the parabola and straight line respectively is $x^2 - x = x(x - 1)$, which is evidently negative when $0 < x < 1$ and positive when $x > 1$.

More generally, since $x^p - x = x(x^{p-1} - 1)$, we see that, for any rational value of $p$ greater than unity, so that the exponent $p - 1$ is positive, $x^{p-1} < 1$ and hence $x^p < x$ when $0 < x < 1$, whereas $x^{p-1} > 1$ and $x^p > x$ when $x > 1$. Graphs of equation (1) corresponding to $p = 3$ and $p = \frac{7}{2}$ are also shown in Fig. 28; these two curves likewise exhibit the stated inequalities.

Since an even power of any real number is non-negative, the graphs corresponding to $p = 2, 4, 6, \cdots$ will not extend below the $X$-axis. When $p$ is an odd positive integer, $x^p$ has the same sign as $x$, and consequently the corresponding curves lie in the first and third quadrants. If $p$ is half an odd positive integer greater than unity, as $\frac{7}{2}$, only non-negative values of $x$ yield real values of $y$, and $y$ is then non-negative (Art. 4); hence such graphs lie in only the first quadrant.

Now if $p$ is a positive rational number less than unity, $x^{p-1} \equiv 1/x^{1-p}$ will be greater than 1 when $0 < x < 1$ and will be less than 1 when $x > 1$. Consequently $x^p - x = x(x^{p-1} - 1) = x(1/x^{1-p} - 1) > 0$ when

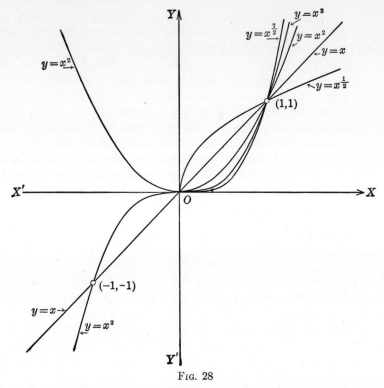

Fig. 28

$0 < x < 1$, and $x^p - x < 0$ when $x > 1$. The variation of $x^p$ as compared to that of $x$, for $0 < p < 1$, is exemplified by the graph of $y = x^{\frac{1}{2}}$ shown in Fig. 28; thus the curves $y = x^p$, $0 < p < 1$, lie above the line $y = x$ when $0 < x < 1$, and below that line when $x > 1$.

To summarize, we see that, whenever $p > 0$, the power function $x^p$ increases as $x$ increases from zero. In the range $0 < x < 1$, $x^p$ is greater or less than $x$ according as $p < 1$ or $p > 1$, and when $x > 1$, $x^p < x$ for $p < 1$ and $x^p > x$ for $p > 1$.

Consider next the power function (1) when $p$ is negative. It is immediately apparent that $x$ cannot then be assigned the value zero, and, as $x$ approaches zero, $x^p$ will become numerically very large. On the other hand, as $x$ increases through positive values, $x^p$ will decrease and approach zero for each negative value of $p$. Some typical graphs are shown in Fig. 29. All curves again pass through the point $(1, 1)$. If $p$ is a negative odd integer, the graph lies in the first and third quadrants; if $p$ is a negative even integer, the graph is in the first and second quadrants. For negative fractional values of $p$, the graph may lie entirely

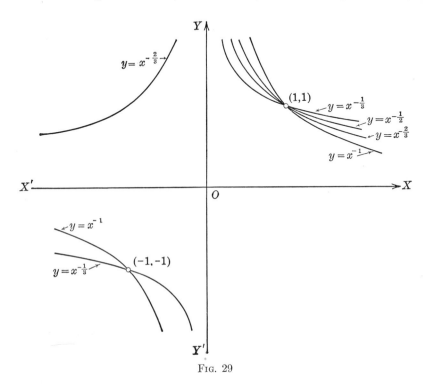

FIG. 29

in the first quadrant, as does that of $y = x^{-\frac{1}{2}}$, or in the first and second quadrants (when $p = -\frac{2}{3}$, for example), or in the first and third quadrants (as when $p = -\frac{1}{3}$).

Suppose now that we have, instead of (1), the power-function relation

$$y = cx^p, \tag{2}$$

where $c$ is any real constant. For each particular value of $p$, the variation of $y$ will evidently be similar to that already considered. If $c$ is positive, the graph of (2) for any chosen index $p$ will be like the corresponding graph of (1); the only effect will be to multiply each ordinate $y$ by the number $c$, so that the graph is vertically "stretched" if $c > 1$ or "compressed" if $c < 1$. If $c$ is negative, the effect on the graph is that of vertical distortion, as in the case of $c$ positive, and, in addition,

the graph is turned upside down by a 180°-rotation about the $X$-axis—
the first and second quadrants respectively change places, in effect, with
the fourth and third quadrants.

If we have, instead of $x^p$, the function $(x + k)^p$, where $k$ is a real constant, the graph is shifted $k$ units horizontally. For, each abscissa $x$ is
thereby changed by the number $k$, so that the origin $O$ is in effect moved
to the point $(-k, 0)$. Consequently, if $k$ is positive, the graph is moved
to the left; and, if $k$ is negative, the shift is to the right by an amount $|k|$.

The results of the above analysis of simple power functions enable one
to determine the variational behavior of many other kinds of algebraic
functions, as illustrated in the following examples.

*Example 1.* Discuss and sketch the graph of the equation $y^2 = x^3 - 3x^2 + 2x$.
*Solution.* Writing this equation in the form

$$y = \pm \sqrt{x(x - 1)(x - 2)}, \tag{3}$$

we see that, when $x = 0$, 1, or 2, we have $y = 0$, and that $y$ has two distinct
values for every other permissible value of $x$. Now it was found in Example 2
of Art. 61 that $y$ is real for $0 \leqq x \leqq 1$ and for $x \geqq 2$; these are therefore the
permissible ranges for $x$.

For small positive values of $x$, the factors $x - 1$ and $x - 2$ differ respectively
from $-1$ and $-2$ by very little. Hence the behavior of the function (3) for
small positive $x$ resembles that of the function $\pm \sqrt{x(-1)(-2)} = \pm \sqrt{2} \, x^{\frac{1}{2}}$.
Accordingly, we may expect the graph of (3) to rise and fall sharply away from
the $X$-axis as it proceeds from the origin $O$ into the first and fourth quadrants,
just as the graph of $y = x^{\frac{1}{2}}$ rises sharply in Fig. 28. Similarly, if $x$ is nearly
equal to 1, the function (3) resembles

$$\pm \sqrt{(1)(x - 1)(1 - 2)} = \pm (1 - x)^{\frac{1}{2}},$$

wherein we again have a power function with exponent $\frac{1}{2}$, this time of $1 - x$
instead of $x$ itself; thus the two branches of our curves come back sharply toward
the $X$-axis to meet at the point $(1, 0)$. The graph of equation (3) for the range
$0 \leqq x \leqq 1$ is therefore a closed loop, as shown in Fig. 30.

For values of $x$ slightly greater than 2, an approximation to (3) is

$$\pm \sqrt{2(2 - 1)(x - 2)} = \pm \sqrt{2} \, (x - 2)^{\frac{1}{2}}.$$

Consequently the behavior of the graph in this neighborhood is like that near
the origin: $y$ sharply increases numerically, as indicated in Fig. 30, and the
curve tends to flatten out as it proceeds toward the right. But for large values
of $x$, relative to which 1 and 2 are negligible, the function (3) has much the
same characteristics as

$$\pm \sqrt{x(x)(x)} = \pm x^{\frac{3}{2}}.$$

Hence $y$ will ultimately increase more rapidly than $x$, and the graph of (3) must
recede sharply from the $X$-axis for large values of $x$, just as do the curves of

Fig. 28 for other values of the exponent $p$ greater than 1.  This geometric behavior is also shown in Fig. 30.

   *Example 2.*   Discuss and sketch the graph of the equation $(x^2 - 1)y = x$.
   *Solution.*   When the equation is written

$$y = \frac{x}{x^2 - 1},\tag{4}$$

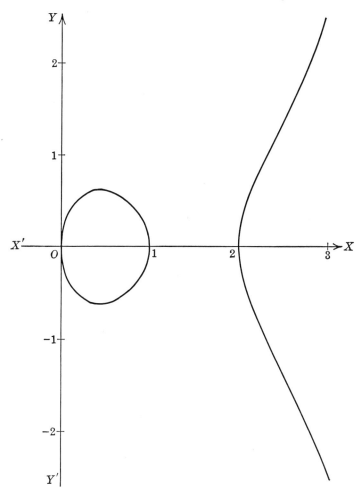

FIG. 30

it is seen that $x$ may be assigned any value except 1 and $-1$.  As $x$ approaches either of these excluded values, $y$ becomes numerically large.  When $-1 < x < 1$, $x^2 - 1 < 0$ and the sign of $y$ is opposite that of $x$; using also the fact that $y = 0$ for $x = 0$, we find that, when $-1 < x < 1$, the graph has the form shown in Fig. 31.

If $x > 1$, $y > 0$, and if $x < -1$, $y < 0$. For large positive values of $x$, $x^2 - 1$ differs from $x^2$ by a small amount, so that the function (4) has the

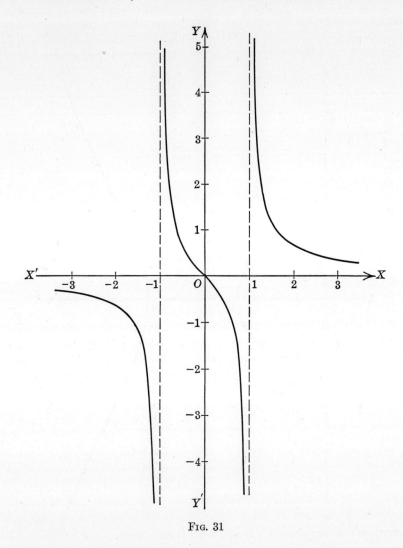

FIG. 31

characteristics of $x/x^2 = 1/x$ when $x$ is large, and $y$ will approach zero as $x$ becomes infinite. Similarly, for $x$ negative and numerically large, the function $1/x$ is again an approximation to (4). Therefore there are two additional parts to the graph, corresponding respectively to $x > 1$ and $x < -1$, as shown in Fig. 31.

## EXERCISES

Discuss the variation of each of the functions defined by the following equations, and sketch the graphs.

1. $y = x^4$.
2. $y = x^5$.
3. $y^3 = x$.
4. $y^3 = x^2$.
5. $x^2 y = 1$.
6. $xy^3 = 1$.
7. $x^3 y^2 = 1$.
8. $y = (x + 1)^2$.
9. $y^2 = x + 1$.
10. $y^2 = 4 - x$.
11. $xy = x + 1$.
12. $(x + 1)y = x$.
13. $y^2 = x(x - 2)$.
14. $y^2 = x^2(x - 2)$.
15. $xy^2 = x + 1$.
16. $x^2 y^2 = x + 1$.
17. $(x - 2)y^2 = x$.
18. $(x - 2)y^2 = x^2$.
19. $y^2 = -x^3 + 3x^2 - 2x$.
20. $y^2 = x^4 - x^2$.
21. $(x^2 + 1)y = 2$.
22. $(x^2 + 1)y = 2x$.
23. $(x^2 + 1)y = 2x^2$.
24. $(x^2 + 1)y^2 = 2x$.
25. $(x^2 + 1)y^2 = 4x^2$.
26. $(2 - x)y^2 = x^3$.
27. $x^2 + y^2 = 4$.
28. $x^3 + y^3 = 2$.
29. $x^4 + y^4 = 16$.
30. $x^{\frac{1}{2}} + y^{\frac{1}{2}} = 2$.
31. $x^{\frac{2}{3}} + y^{\frac{2}{3}} = 4$.
32. $x^2 y^2 = 2x^2 + y^2$.
33. $(x^2 - 4)y = 4$.
34. $(x^2 - 4)y = x^3$.
35. $(x^2 - 4)y^2 = 4$.
36. $(x^2 - 4)y^2 = x^3$.
37. $(4 - x^2)y^2 = x^4$.
38. $(x + 1)y^2 = x^3 - x^2$.
39. $y^2 = (1 - x^2)(4 - x^2)^2$.
40. $y^2 = (4 - x^2)(1 - x^2)^2$.

## 69. Variation of trigonometric functions.

In connection with our discussion of inverse trigonometric functions in Art. 64, we exhibited the graphs of $y = \sin x$, $y = \cos x$, and $y = \tan x$ (Figs. 25–27). These graphs indicate certain facts concerning the respective trigonometric functions. We may now examine these results from the standpoint of the variation of the trigonometric functions, and we shall extend the analyses to the consideration of additional functional relations of trigonometric type.

The graphs of $y = \sin x$ and $y = \cos x$ are seen to have the same form; in fact, one may be obtained from the other by a shift in the $x$-direction through a distance of $\pi/2$ units. This result is verified analytically by means of the identity $\sin (x + \pi/2) \equiv \cos x$ (Art. 18), which shows that, when $x$ is increased by $\pi/2$, the sine of the resulting angle is equal to the cosine of the original angle $x$ for every value of $x$. Consequently we need discuss the variation of only the sine function.

We know that $\sin x$ varies between $-1$ and $1$, and that, when the variable $x$ is changed by $2n\pi$, where $n$ is any integer, the same value of the sine is obtained.   That is, we have

$$-1 \leqq \sin x \leqq 1, \tag{1}$$

$$\sin (x + 2n\pi) \equiv \sin x, \tag{2}$$

for every $x$ and every integer $n$.   We call the maximum variation of $\sin x$ from zero the **amplitude** of this sine function; then the amplitude of $\sin x$ is 1.   By (2), the variation of $\sin x$ is seen to be periodic, and consequently $2n\pi$ is called **a period** of $\sin x$.   When $n = 1$, the period has the least value it may have; accordingly, $2\pi$ is called **the period** of $\sin x$.   A variation of $x$ over a range of length equal to the period, $2\pi$, is called a **cycle** of the function $\sin x$; any cycle of the graph of $y = \sin x$ is evidently a representative portion of the graph, and this graphical cycle is repeated indefinitely often on both sides of the chosen portion.

If $x$ is replaced by $x + h$, where $h$ is any real number, the function $\sin x$ becomes $\sin (x + h)$.   In particular, as we have seen, when $h = \pi/2$, the function $\sin x$ becomes $\cos x$.   The number $h$ is called a **phase displacement.**   Thus, $\sin x$ and $\cos x$ differ in phase by the amount $\pi/2$.

We now consider the above concepts in relation to the more general sine function,

$$y = a \sin (kx + b), \tag{3}$$

where $a$, $b$, and $k$ are any real constants, except that $a \neq 0$ and $k \neq 0$ to avoid trivial cases.   The maximum value attained by $y$, namely, $|a|$, is called the **amplitude** of the function (3).   Since $\sin (kx + b + 2\pi)$ $\equiv \sin (kx + b)$ and $kx + b + 2\pi \equiv k(x + 2\pi/k + b/k)$, the positive number $|2\pi/k|$, measuring the additive change in $x$ that produces the identity of the sine functions, is called **the period** of the function (3).   We also say that $b/k$ is the **phase displacement** or **phase difference,** and that the reciprocal of the period, $|k/2\pi|$, is the **frequency** of the function (3).

The nature of the graph of equation (3) is easily deduced.   The curve will be similar in form to that of Fig. 25, with the following differences. (1) There will be an elongation or compression in the $y$-direction in accordance with the proportionality factor $a$.   (2) The period of function (3), $|2\pi/k|$, will be greater or less than that of $\sin x$, according as $|k| < 1$ or $|k| > 1$; in effect, this changes the scale on the $x$-axis. (3) There will be a displacement in the $x$-direction by the phase difference $b/k$, to the right or left according as $b/k < 0$ or $b/k > 0$.

Before illustrating these ideas by means of a particular example, we shall establish a useful identity, namely,

$$A \sin \theta + B \cos \theta = \sqrt{A^2 + B^2} \sin \left( \theta + \arctan \frac{B}{A} \right), \tag{4}$$

where $A > 0$.* This identity is useful because it enables us to replace each expression of the form $A \sin \theta + B \cos \theta$ by a function of the form (3), whose amplitude, period, and phase angle are all easily determined.

To prove the truth of relation (4), we proceed as follows (cf. Example 1, Art. 62). In the expression

$$\frac{A}{\sqrt{A^2 + B^2}} \sin \theta + \frac{B}{\sqrt{A^2 + B^2}} \cos \theta,$$

we may identify the coefficients of $\sin \theta$ and $\cos \theta$ respectively with the cosine and sine of some angle $\alpha$, since neither can be greater than unity in absolute value and the sum of their squares is unity. Hence

$$\frac{A}{\sqrt{A^2 + B^2}} \sin \theta + \frac{B}{\sqrt{A^2 + B^2}} \cos \theta = \sin \theta \cos \alpha + \cos \theta \sin \alpha$$
$$= \sin (\theta + \alpha),$$

and

$$A \sin \theta + B \cos \theta = \sqrt{A^2 + B^2} \sin (\theta + \alpha),$$

where

$$\tan \alpha = \frac{\sin \alpha}{\cos \alpha} = \frac{B}{A}.$$

Now since, by supposition, $A > 0$, $\cos \alpha = A/\sqrt{A^2 + B^2} > 0$, so that $\alpha$ is an angle in either the first or fourth quadrant. But the principal values of $\arctan (B/A)$ are between $-\pi/2$ and $\pi/2$ (Art. 64), so that this angle is also in either the first or fourth quadrant. Hence

$$\alpha = \arctan \frac{B}{A}$$

is correct not only in magnitude but also with regard to principal values. Thus identity (4) holds, and the angle $\arctan (B/A)$ is uniquely given through our choice of principal values.

We now illustrate the use of identity (4) in connection with our study of variation.

*Example.* Discuss the variation of the function

$$10y = 3 \sin 2x - 4 \cos 2x,$$

and sketch the graph.

---

* If $A = 0$, (4) is replaced by the obviously correct relation, $B \cos \theta = B \sin (\theta + \pi/2)$. The restriction to positive values of $A$ is made in order to avoid the ambiguous double sign before the radical $\sqrt{A^2 + B^2}$; if, in a given case, $A < 0$, we use the identity obtained from (4) by multiplying both members by $-1$.

*Solution.* We first apply (4), with $A = 3$, $B = -4$, and $\theta = 2x$. This gives us the equivalent functional relation,

$$10y = 5 \sin [2x + \arctan (-\tfrac{4}{3})],$$

or, since $\arctan (-\tfrac{4}{3}) = - \arctan \tfrac{4}{3} = -0.9273$ approximately,

$$y = \tfrac{1}{2} \sin (2x - 0.9273).$$

We therefore have a sine function with amplitude $\tfrac{1}{2}$, period $2\pi/2 = \pi$, and phase angle $-0.9273/2 = -0.464$ approximately. If $2x = 0.9273$, or $x = 0.464$, $y = 5 \sin 0 = 0$; the point $(0.464, 0)$ may therefore be conveniently chosen as the beginning of a cycle, the graph of which is shown in Fig. 32.

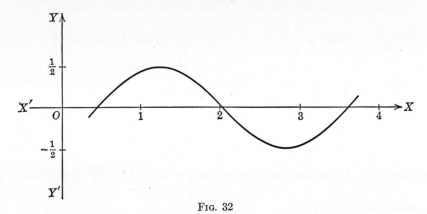

Fig. 32

We have discussed the sine function in some detail because of its importance in various applications. Problems in dynamics such as those involving simple harmonic motion and periodic vibratory motion, electric circuits and machines, and many other types of physical phenomena entail sine functions.

We now consider briefly the tangent function. Since $\tan x$ can assume all real values (Fig. 27), a constant of proportionality merely serves to change the scale on the $Y$-axis. Since $\tan (x + \pi) \equiv \tan x$ (Art. 18), the function $\tan x$ is periodic and its period is $\pi$. All values of $x$ with the exception of $(2n + 1)\pi/2$, where $n$ is an integer or zero, are permissible; as $x$ approaches any of these values, $\tan x$ becomes numerically large. Knowledge of these facts makes it easy to discuss and draw a graph of the function

$$y = a \tan (kx + b), \quad a \neq 0, \quad k \neq 0, \tag{5}$$

whose period is $| \pi/k |$ and which has a phase displacement of $b/k$.

The three remaining trigonometric functions, cot $x$, sec $x$, and csc $x$, are not of sufficiently frequent occurrence to warrant discussion here. The fact that each is equal to the reciprocal of a function considered above enables one to discuss the variation of functions of the types $a \cot (kx + b)$, $a \sec (kx + b)$, $a \csc (kx + b)$ with no difficulty. Instances of these three functions, as well as of the tangent function (5), will be found in the exercises.

The general inverse trigonometric functions likewise require no separate examination. When conventions concerning principal values are adopted, as was done in Art. 64, each becomes a single-valued function whose variation may be determined from a knowledge of the behavior of the direct trigonometric functions.

It will sometimes be found that a trigonometric expression may be transformed, as was $A \sin \theta + B \cos \theta$, into another form whose variation can be more readily determined. Thus, the equation

$$y = \sin^2 x$$

may be replaced by the equivalent one (Art. 38)

$$y = \tfrac{1}{2} - \tfrac{1}{2} \cos 2x;$$

the characteristics of this function are easily ascertained.

### EXERCISES

Discuss the variation of each of the functions defined by the equations of Exercises 1–30, and sketch the graphs.

1. $y = 3 \sin 2x$.
2. $y = 2 \sin 3x$.
3. $y = 2 \sin \dfrac{x}{4}$.
4. $y = 3 \cos 2x$.
5. $y = 2 \sin (x - 2)$.
6. $y = 3 \sin (2x - 1)$.
7. $y = \sin x + \cos x$.
8. $y = \sin x - \cos x$.
9. $y = \sqrt{3} \cos x - \sin x$.
10. $y = 2 \cos \dfrac{x}{2} - \sin \dfrac{x}{2}$.
11. $y = \tan 2x$.
12. $y = - \tan \dfrac{x - 1}{2}$.
13. $y = 3 \cot \left( x - \dfrac{\pi}{4} \right)$.
14. $y = 2 \cot \left( 2x - \dfrac{\pi}{6} \right)$.
15. $y = 2 \sec 3x$.
16. $y = -3 \sec \dfrac{x}{2}$.
17. $y = \csc \left( x - \dfrac{\pi}{3} \right)$.
18. $y = 2 \csc \dfrac{x}{2}$.
19. $y = 2 \sin^2 x$.
20. $y = 2 \cos^2 x$.

**21.** $y = 4 \sin^3 x.$

**22.** $y = \cos^3 2x.$

**23.** $y = 2 \sin^4 x.$

**24.** $y = \cos^4 (1 - x).$

**25.** $y^2 = 4 \sin x.$

**26.** $y^2 = -4 \cos 2x.$

**27.** $y^3 = \sin 3x.$

**28.** $y^4 = \cos x.$

**29.** $y = x \sin x.$

**30.** $y = x \cos x.$

Discuss each of the function types in Exercises 31–34 with regard to variation, periodicity, phase angles, and excluded values.

**31.** $y = a \tan (kx + b).$

**32.** $y = a \cot (kx + b).$

**33.** $y = a \sec (kx + b).$

**34.** $y = a \csc (kx + b).$

**35.** If $B > 0$, prove the identity

$$A \sin \theta + B \cos \theta = \sqrt{A^2 + B^2} \cos \left( \theta - \arctan \frac{A}{B} \right).$$

## SUPPLEMENTARY EXERCISES

**1.** The period of a pendulum varies directly as the square root of its length and inversely as the square root of a gravitational quantity $g$. If the length is increased by 1 per cent due to temperature changes when the pendulum is taken to another location where $g$ is 1 per cent less, by what percentage is the period increased?

**2.** The friction loss in a pipe through which a fluid flows varies directly as the length of the pipe and as the square of the velocity of flow, and inversely as the diameter of the pipe. If the length is decreased by 10 per cent, the velocity is increased by 20 per cent, and the diameter is increased by 25 per cent, by what percentage is the friction loss changed?

**3.** The angle of twist of a circular shaft varies directly as the applied torque and as the length of the shaft, and inversely as the fourth power of the shaft diameter. If the torque is doubled, the length is decreased by 20 per cent, and the diameter is increased by 25 per cent, by what percentage is the angle of twist changed?

**4.** Ampere's law states that the magnetic field intensity at a point $P$, due to a current flowing in a circular loop, varies directly as the current, inversely as the square of the distance $r$ from $P$ to a point $Q$ on the loop, and directly as the sine of the angle $\theta$ between the radius vector $PQ$ and the direction of flow through $Q$. If the current is increased by 10 per cent and $r$ by 20 per cent while $\theta$ decreases from $60°$ to $50°$, by what percentage does the field intensity change?

**5.** The pressure of saturated steam varies inversely approximately as the 1.06 power of the volume. If the volume is increased by 10 per cent, by what percentage does the pressure decrease?

Discuss the variation of each of the functions defined by the equations of Exercises 6–15, and sketch the graphs.

**6.** $(x^2 + 1)y = x^3.$

**7.** $(x^2 + 1)y = x^4.$

**8.** $(x^2 + 1)y^2 = x^3.$

**9.** $(x^2 + 1)y^2 = x^4.$

**10.** $y^2 = x^2(1 + x^2).$

**11.** $y^2 = x^2(1 - x^2).$

**12.** $y = x + \sin x.$

**13.** $y = x - \cos x.$

**14.** $y = x \tan x.$

**15.** $y = x + \tan x.$

# XIV——— Exponential and Logarithmic Functions

**70. Definitions and properties.** Up to this point, all the functions under consideration have been either algebraic, trigonometric, or inverse trigonometric. Two other types of transcendental functions mentioned in our classification of functions (Art. 21) are the exponential functions and their inverses, logarithmic functions. In this chapter we shall examine these functions and functional relations involving them.

In the algebraic power function, $x^p$, the variable $x$ appears as base and the exponent $p$ is a constant. If, on the other hand, we have a function $a^x$ in which the variable $x$ appears as an exponent while the base is a constant $a$, the function is said to be an **exponential function**.

In Art. 4 we formulated certain laws of exponents. If the base $a$ is a positive number, it follows that $a^x$ has meaning and may be subjected to algebraic operations whenever $x$ is a rational number. To broaden the realm of existence of the exponential function $y = a^x$, so that it has meaning for all real values of $x$, we proceed as follows. If $x = x_1$ is an irrational number, we think of $x$ as successively assuming rational values approaching $x_1$, and we form the sequence of corresponding values of $y = a^x$. It is possible to show, by more advanced methods, that the latter sequence approaches a limiting value $y_1$. We then define $a^{x_1}$ to be equal to $y_1$:

$$y_1 = \lim_{x \to x_1} a^x = a^{x_1}.$$

As a consequence, the exponential function

$$y = a^x, \qquad a > 0, \tag{1}$$

exists for all real values of $x$ and is represented by a smooth continuous graph. Figure 33 shows a typical graph of equation (1) in which the base $a$ has been taken equal to 2.

It is found that the most important of the exponential functions are those in which $a > 1$; accordingly, we shall restrict ourselves to such values of $a$ in what follows. Our discussion will therefore be concerned with the function

$$y = a^x, \qquad a > 1. \tag{2}$$

We see that the graph of the exponential function (2) lies entirely above the X-axis; that is, $a^x$ is positive for every real value of $x$. As $x$

245

increases, $a^x$ does likewise: when $x < 0$, $a^x < 1$; and, when $x > 0$, $a^x > 1$. As $x$ decreases algebraically, $a^x$ approaches but never attains the value zero. Corresponding to each real value of $x$, there is one and only one value of $y = a^x$; thus the exponential function $a^x$ is a single-valued function.

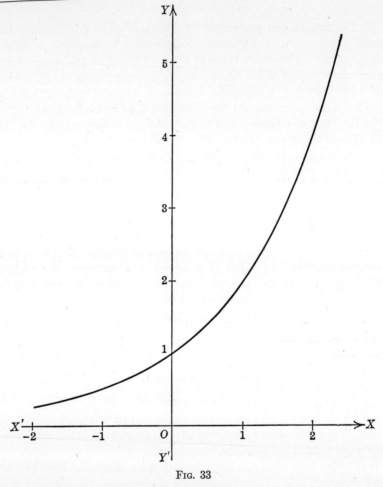

Fig. 33

The inverse of the exponential function (2) is called a **logarithmic function** and is denoted by the symbolism

$$x_1 = \log_a y, \qquad a > 1. \tag{3}$$

This is read "$x$ is equal to the logarithm of $y$ to the base $a$."

From the viewpoint of the inverse relationship (3), the graph (Fig. 33) gives us the following facts concerning logarithmic functions with base $a > 1$, when only real values of the variables are concerned. Logarithms of negative numbers and of zero do not exist. The logarithm of a number between 0 and 1 is negative, that of unity is zero, and logarithms of numbers greater than 1 are positive. As the number $y$ increases, its logarithm does likewise, and as $y$ approaches zero, its logarithm becomes negatively infinite.

Our functional definition of a logarithm enables us to frame the following verbal definition: The logarithm $(x)$ of a number $(y)$ to the base $a$ is the power to which the base must be raised to produce the number. Relation (3) corresponds to the subject of this defining sentence; relation (2) corresponds to the predicate.

If we replace $x$ in (2) by the expression (3), we get the identity

$$y \equiv a^{\log_a y}. \tag{4}$$

Similarly, if $y$ is replaced in (3) by its expression (2), we obtain the identity

$$x \equiv \log_a a^x. \tag{5}$$

These relations have frequent utility in changing a functional relation from exponential to logarithmic form, and vice versa.

We now consider some basic and important properties of logarithms. Let $s = \log_a u$ and $t = \log_a v$, so that $a^s = u$ and $a^t = v$. Then we have $uv = a^{s+t}$, whence $\log_a uv = s + t$, or

$$\log_a uv = \log_a u + \log_a v. \tag{6}$$

That is, *the logarithm of the product of two quantities is equal to the sum of their separate logarithms.* Likewise, since $u/v = a^s/a^t = a^{s-t}$, we find *

$$\log_a \frac{u}{v} = \log_a u - \log_a v. \tag{7}$$

If $p$ is any real number, $u^p = (a^s)^p = a^{sp}$, whence

$$\log_a u^p = p \log_a u. \tag{8}$$

Now if we take the logarithm to the base $b$, where $b > 1$ and $b \neq a$, of both members of identity (4), we get

$$\log_b y = \log_b a^{\log_a y},$$

or

$$\log_b y = (\log_a y)(\log_b a), \tag{9}$$

* The student should frame verbal statements of relation (7) and subsequent properties, as was done for relation (6).

by property (8). If, in particular, we set $y = b$, then, since $\log_b b = 1$ by definition, relation (9) yields

$$\log_a b = \frac{1}{\log_b a} \cdot \tag{10}$$

Relations (9) and (10) are useful in changing from one base to another, as we shall see in later work.

The following numerical examples illustrate the manner in which the above properties (6)–(8) of logarithms may be applied:

$$\log_a 370 = \log_a 37 + \log_a 10,$$

$$\log_a \tfrac{1}{7} = \log_a 1 - \log_a 7 = -\log_a 7,$$

$$\log_a \sqrt{3} = \log_a 3^{\frac{1}{2}} = \tfrac{1}{2} \log_a 3,$$

$$\log_a \frac{4\sqrt{2}}{125} = \log_a 4 + \log_a \sqrt{2} - \log_a 125$$

$$= \log_a 2^2 + \log_a 2^{\frac{1}{2}} - \log_a 5^3$$

$$= \tfrac{5}{2} \log_a 2 - 3 \log_a 5.$$

Although any positive number $a$ different from unity may be taken as the base of a system of logarithms, only two numbers are widely used in practice. For ordinary computations, the base 10 is most frequently employed; the system of logarithms with base 10 is called the common or Briggs's system. In analytical work, dealing with functional relations, the natural or Napierian system is found to be most useful; this system employs a certain irrational number, denoted by $e$ or $\epsilon$, as base. This number $e$ is defined as a limit:

$$e = \lim_{z \to \infty} \left( 1 + \frac{1}{z} \right)^z = 2.71828 \cdots. \tag{11}$$

The reason that this limit, having the peculiar value $2.71828 \cdots$, is chosen as the base of a system of logarithms cannot be discussed here; it must suffice now to say that the application of the concepts of differential calculus to the logarithmic function (3) leads quite naturally to the limit (11) and to its adoption as a convenient base.

We cannot even prove here that the limit (11) exists, but it is of interest to show how its existence may be made plausible and to indicate that its value may then be approximated. If the quantity $z$ in (11) is allowed to become infinite by assuming successively larger and larger positive integral values, then for any such value of $z$ we get from the binomial theorem (Art. 43),

$$\left(1 + \frac{1}{z}\right)^z = 1 + z\left(\frac{1}{z}\right) + \frac{z(z-1)}{2!}\left(\frac{1}{z}\right)^2 + \cdots + \frac{z(z-1)\cdots 1}{z!}\left(\frac{1}{z}\right)^z$$

$$= 1 + 1 + \frac{1}{2!}\left(1 - \frac{1}{z}\right) + \frac{1}{3!}\left(1 - \frac{1}{z}\right)\left(1 - \frac{2}{z}\right) + \cdots$$

$$+ \frac{1}{z!}\left(1 - \frac{1}{z}\right)\left(1 - \frac{2}{z}\right)\cdots\left(1 - \frac{z-1}{z}\right).$$

Now each term of this expansion is positive; also, as $z$ increases, the number $(z + 1)$ of terms increases and each term, after the second, likewise increases. But since $n! \geqq 2^{n-1}$ for $n = 2, 3, 4, \cdots$, we have also

$$\left(1 + \frac{1}{z}\right)^z < 1 + 1 + \frac{1}{2} + \frac{1}{2^2} + \cdots + \frac{1}{2^{z-1}}.$$

Summing the geometric progression that starts with the second term on the right, we get (Art. 55), $2 - (\frac{1}{2})^{z-1}$, whence

$$\left(1 + \frac{1}{z}\right)^z < 3 - \frac{1}{2^{z-1}} < 3.$$

Consequently the expression $(1 + 1/z)^z$, which increases with $z$, cannot increase indefinitely, for it must always be less than 3. It is therefore reasonable to conclude that $(1 + 1/z)^z$ approaches a limit, which by the above relations lies between 2 and 3.

Direct computation yields the following table, from which it may be inferred that the value of $e$ is slightly more than the last entry:

| $z$ | 10 | 100 | 1000 | 10,000 |
|---|---|---|---|---|
| $\left(1 + \frac{1}{z}\right)^z$ | 2.5937 | 2.7048 | 2.7169 | 2.7181 |

In elementary work such as this, in which the common base 10 arises more frequently than the natural base $e$, it is usual to write log $u$ in the place of $\log_{10} u$, the base 10 then being understood. Also, instead of $\log_e u$, the notation ln $u$ (obtained from the Latin for "natural logarithm") is frequently used. We shall adopt these conventions, for brevity in writing, for all subsequent work.

**71. Exponential equations.** An equation in which one or more variables appear in exponential functions will be called an exponential equation. Thus, the equation

$$2^{3x} = 4^{x+1}$$

is an exponential equation involving one variable, and

$$y = \frac{e^x + e^{-x}}{2}$$

is an exponential equation since one variable, $x$, is involved exponentially.

In connection with exponential equations containing only one variable, such as the first example, the principal problem is usually to solve the equation. When an exponential equation involves two variables, as does our second example, we are often concerned with the variation of one variable regarded as a function of the other.

In both types of problems, we shall restrict ourselves to real values of the variables. An equation may then fail to have a solution; this statement is exemplified by the simple equation $2^x = 0$, for the exponential function $2^x$ is positive for every real value of $x$.

*Example 1.* Solve the equation

$$2^{3x} = 4^{x+1}. \tag{1}$$

*Solution.* If two quantities are equal, their logarithms (to any base) must also be equal since the exponential function $a^x$ and its inverse are single-valued (Art. 70). Taking logarithms of both members of (1) to the base 10, say, we therefore have

$$\log 2^{3x} = \log 4^{x+1}, \qquad \text{log } 2^{3+x} = \text{log } 4^{x+1}$$

whence

$$3x \log 2 = (x + 1) \log 4. \qquad 2^{3+2} = 4^{2+1}$$

Now $\log 4 = \log 2^2 = 2 \log 2$, and consequently

$$3x \log 2 = 2(x + 1) \log 2, \qquad 2^6 = 4^3$$

$$3x = 2x + 2, \qquad 2\cdot2\cdot2\cdot2\cdot2\cdot2 \qquad 4\cdot4\cdot4$$

$$x = 2. \qquad\qquad 64 \qquad\qquad 64$$

This is the only solution of equation (1); it is easy to verify its correctness since each member of (1) has the value 64 when $x = 2$.

*Example 2.* Discuss the variation of the function

$$y = \frac{e^x + e^{-x}}{2} \tag{2}$$

and sketch the graph.

*Solution.* We first note that $y = 1$ when $x = 0$. Now $e^x$ is positive for every real value of $x$ (Art. 70), and $e^{-x}$ is the reciprocal of $e^x$. Hence (Example, Art. 60), $e^x + e^{-x} \geq 2$, so that $y \geq 1$. Since $e^{-x}$ is small in comparison with $e^x$ when $x$ is large, $y$ is approximately equal to $\frac{1}{2}e^x$ for large values of $x$; thus $y$ increases as $x$ increases through positive values. Inasmuch as the replacement of $x$ by $-x$ in (2) leaves the function unaltered, $y$ likewise increases when $x$ decreases through negative values. Moreover, if $y_1$ is the value of $y$ corresponding to $x = x_1$, then $y_1$ is also obtained when $x = -x_1$.

We next try to get the function inverse to (2), that is, we wish to solve (2) for $x$ in terms of $y$. If we replace $e^{-x}$ by $1/e^x$ and simplify, equation (2) becomes

$$e^{2x} - 2ye^x + 1 = 0.$$

Since $e^{2x} = (e^x)^2$, this is an equation in quadratic form. Solving for $e^x$ by means of the quadratic formula, we find

$$e^x = y \pm \sqrt{y^2 - 1}.$$

Taking the natural logarithm of each member yields

$$x = \ln \left( y \pm \sqrt{y^2 - 1} \right). \tag{3}$$

Now $y$ is not less than unity, and, since $\sqrt{y^2 - 1} < y$ whenever $y$ is positive, both $y + \sqrt{y^2 - 1}$ and $y - \sqrt{y^2 - 1}$ will be positive. Hence the logarithm of each expression is real, so that we get two values of $x$ for every $y > 1$.

At the close of our discussion of the direct function (2), it was noted that two values of $x$, numerically equal but opposite in sign, correspond to each permissible value of $y$. This implies that the two logarithmic expressions (3) are equal in absolute value but opposite in sign. That this is true may be shown as follows; we have

$$\ln \left( y - \sqrt{y^2 - 1} \right) = \ln \left( \frac{(y - \sqrt{y^2 - 1})(y + \sqrt{y^2 - 1})}{y + \sqrt{y^2 - 1}} \right)$$

$$= \ln \left( \frac{1}{y + \sqrt{y^2 - 1}} \right) = \ln \left( y + \sqrt{y^2 - 1} \right)^{-1}$$

$$= -\ln \left( y + \sqrt{y^2 - 1} \right).$$

Therefore (3) becomes

$$x = \pm \ln \left( y + \sqrt{y^2 - 1} \right), \tag{4}$$

where the two signs correspond respectively to the two signs in (3).

Making use of the various facts determined above, we can easily sketch the graph of equation (2). The curve, shown in Fig. 34, is called a catenary. It may be shown by more advanced methods that a flexible uniform cable or chain suspended from two points assumes the form of a catenary.

The exponential function (2), yielding the catenary, is one of a group of six functions called hyperbolic functions; the function (2) is named the hyperbolic cosine of $x$, denoted by cosh $x$. Other hyperbolic functions appear in the following exercises; it will be found that these expo-

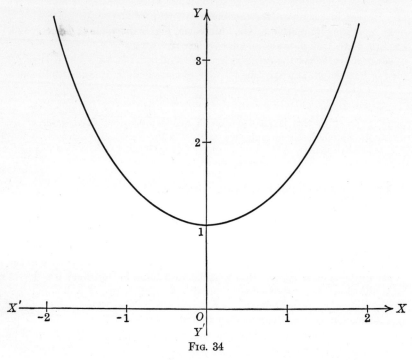

FIG. 34

nential functions are connected by identities bearing a strong resemblance to the trigonometric identities previously discussed.

### EXERCISES

Solve each of the equations in Exercises 1–10.

1. $3^{4x} = 9^{x+3}$.
2. $125^{2x} = 5^{x^2}$.
3. $6^{2x^2} = 36^{x+6}$.
4. $4^{x+4} = 32^{x^2+1}$.
5. $10^{3x} = 2(10^{2x})$.
6. $e^{5x} = 3e^x$.
7. $e^{2x} - 5e^x + 6 = 0$.
8. $e^{2x} - e^{-2x} = 4$.
9. $e^x + e^{-x} = 2$.
10. $e^{2x} + e^{-2x} = 4$.

Find the inverse of each of the functions in Exercises 11–20.

11. $y = e^{2x} - e^{-2x}$.
12. $y = e^x + e^{-x}$.
13. $y = 2e^x + e^{-x}$.
14. $y = e^{2x} - 3e^{-2x}$.
15. $y = \dfrac{2}{e^x + e^{-x}}$.
16. $y = \dfrac{2}{e^x - e^{-x}}$.

**17.** $y = \dfrac{e^{2x}}{e^x + 3}.$

**13.** $y = \dfrac{2e^x - e^{-x}}{2e^x + e^{-x}}.$

**19.** $y = e^{x-2} + 3e^{2-x}.$

**20.** $y = 2\sqrt{e^x} - \sqrt{e^{-x}}.$

Discuss the variation of each of the hyperbolic functions defined in Exercises 21–25 and sketch their graphs.

**21.** $y = \dfrac{e^x - e^{-x}}{2}$ (hyperbolic sine).

$cosh = Y = \dfrac{e^x + e^{-x}}{2}$

**22.** $y = \dfrac{e^x - e^{-x}}{e^x + e^{-x}}$ (hyperbolic tangent).

**23.** $y = \dfrac{e^x + e^{-x}}{e^x - e^{-x}}$ (hyperbolic cotangent).

**24.** $y = \dfrac{2}{e^x + e^{-x}}$ (hyperbolic secant).

**25.** $y = \dfrac{2}{e^x - e^{-x}}$ (hyperbolic cosecant).

**26–30.** Using the definitions of the five hyperbolic functions given in Exercises 21–25, find their inverses.

Prove the identities in Exercises 31–40.

**31.** $\sinh x \operatorname{csch} x = 1.$              **32.** $\cosh x \operatorname{sech} x = 1.$
**33.** $\tanh x \coth x = 1.$              **34.** $\tanh x \cosh x = \sinh x.$
**35.** $\cosh^2 x - \sinh^2 x = 1.$              **36.** $\operatorname{sech}^2 x = 1 - \tanh^2 x.$
**37.** $\operatorname{csch}^2 x = \coth^2 x - 1.$              **38.** $\sinh 2x = 2 \sinh x \cosh x.$

**39.** $\cosh 2x = \cosh^2 x + \sinh^2 x.$              **40.** $\tanh 2x = \dfrac{2 \tanh x}{1 + \tanh^2 x}.$

**72. Logarithmic equations.** When an equation involves logarithmic functions of one or more variables, we call it a logarithmic equation. As in working with exponential equations, the principal problems are to find solutions of a logarithmic equation containing a single variable and to study functional variations when two variables are present.

Sometimes a logarithmic equation can readily be transformed into an equation free of logarithms. The resulting equation may contain algebraic functions, or exponential functions, or both. We illustrate some of the possible modes of procedure by means of examples.

*Example 1.* Solve the equation

$$2 \log x - \log (30 - 2x) = 1. \tag{1}$$

*Solution.* The essential point in solving an equation such as (1) is to combine all logarithmic expressions into a single logarithm with coefficient unity, by means of the properties discussed in Art. 70, so that the relation takes the form $\log_a u = v$. This form can then be immediately changed into the equivalent exponential form $u = a^v$.

Accordingly, we first replace $2 \log x$ by $\log x^2$. Then, since the difference of two logarithms, each with the coefficient unity, is equal to the logarithm of a quotient, we have

$$\log \frac{x^2}{30 - 2x} = 1.$$

This equation now transforms into

$$\frac{x^2}{30 - 2x} = 10,$$

whence we get

$$x^2 + 20x - 300 = 0.$$

Solving this quadratic equation, we find

$$x = -30 \quad \text{and} \quad x = 10.$$

It is important that all solutions of a logarithmic equation be checked. Here we see that the negative number $x = -30$ is not permissible, for the first term of equation (1) has no meaning if $x$ is negative. The value $x = 10$, however, when substituted in the left member of (1), gives us $2 \log 10 - \log 10 = 2 - 1 = 1$, so that this is a valid solution.

*Example 2.*   Find the inverse of the function

$$y = \ln \left(1 + \sqrt{1 - e^2 x^4}\right) - 2 \ln x - 1. \tag{2}$$

*Solution.*   Employing the same principle as in Example 1, we write, in the place of (2),

$$y + 1 = \ln \frac{1 + \sqrt{1 - e^2 x^4}}{x^2},$$

whence

$$e^{y+1} = \frac{1 + \sqrt{1 - e^2 x^4}}{x^2}.$$

Then

$$x^2 e^{y+1} - 1 = \sqrt{1 - e^2 x^4}.$$

Rationalizing this equation, we get

$$x^4 e^{2y+2} - 2x^2 e^{y+1} + 1 = 1 - e^2 x^4.$$

Now $x$ must be positive in order that the term involving $\ln x$, in equation (2), have meaning. In particular, $x$ cannot be zero; hence, after subtracting 1 from each member of the last equation, we may further simplify by dividing by $ex^2$. This gives us

$$x^2 e^{2y+1} - 2e^y = -ex^2,$$

$$ex^2(e^{2y} + 1) = 2e^y,$$

$$x^2 = \frac{2e^y}{e(e^{2y} + 1)} = \frac{2}{e(e^y + e^{-y})}.$$

Remembering that $x$ must be positive, we extract only the positive square root to obtain

$$x = \sqrt{\frac{2}{e(e^y + e^{-y})}}.$$ (3)

This is the required inverse function.

The form of relation (3) would seem to indicate that, if $x = x_1$ is the value corresponding to $y = y_1$, then $y = -y_1$ will also yield $x = x_1$. However, equation (2) shows that $y$ cannot be replaced by $-y$ without creating thereby a different functional relation. In fact, as the student can show without much difficulty, $y$ as given by (2) will be non-negative for every real value of $x$ in its permissible range, $0 < x \le e^{-\frac{1}{2}}$. The student should also show that the functional relation $y = \ln(1 - \sqrt{1 - e^2 x^4}) - 2\ln x - 1$ yields only non-positive values of $y$ and likewise leads to the same inverse relation (3).

Our example thus illustrates the fact that all conclusions drawn from a deduced inverse function must be checked against the original relation.

*Jan 6*

### EXERCISES

Solve each of the equations in Exercises 1–10.

**1.** $\log(2x + 8) = 2.$         **2.** $\log(x^2 - 3x) = 1.$
**3.** $2\log(3 - x) = 1.$         **4.** $2\log x - 1 = \log(1 - 2x).$
**5.** $\ln x + \ln(2e - x) = 2.$    **6.** $3\log x - 3\log(x - 2) = \log 27.$

**7.** $\log(2\sqrt{x} - 4) + \log(2\sqrt{x} + 4) = 2.$
**8.** $\log(x^3 - 8) - 1 = \log(x - 2).$
**9.** $\ln 3x + \ln(2x - e) - 2 = \ln\frac{2}{3}.$
**10.** $\log(\sqrt{x + 1} + 5) + \log(\sqrt{x + 1} - 2) = 3\log 2.$

Transform each of the equations in Exercises 11–20 into an equation free of logarithms.

**11.** $\log y - 1 = 2\log x.$         **12.** $2\log(x + 2) = 3\log y.$
**13.** $\ln y - 2x = 3\ln x.$         **14.** $\ln y + 3x = \ln \cos x.$
**15.** $2\log x + 1 = \log(x^2 - y).$    **16.** $\ln y + \ln x = \ln(\ln x).$

**17.** $\ln 2x + y - \ln 3 = \ln(\cos 2x).$
**18.** $\ln(x + y) - \ln x = \ln y + \ln 3 - \ln(x^2 - xy + y^2).$
**19.** $\log(x^2 + 4y^2) + \log(x + 2y) - 2\log y = 2\log x - \log(x - 2y).$
**20.** $\ln \sin x - 2x + \ln \cos x - \ln y + \ln 6 = 0.$

Find the inverse of each of the functions in Exercises 21–30.

**21.** $y = \ln 2x - \ln(2 - x).$         **22.** $y = \frac{1}{2}\ln x - \frac{1}{2}\ln(2x - 1).$
**23.** $y = \ln x + \ln(x + 4).$         **24.** $y = 2\ln 2x - \ln(4x - 3).$
**25.** $y = \ln(2x + \sqrt{4x^2 + 1}).$    **26.** $y = \ln(x - \sqrt{x^2 - 4}).$
**27.** $y = \ln(1 - \sqrt{1 - x^2}) - \ln x.$    **28.** $y = \ln(x - \sqrt{x^2 - 4x}).$

**29.** $y = \ln(\sqrt{4 + x} + 2) - \ln(\sqrt{4 + x} - 2).$
**30.** $y = \log(x + \sqrt{4x - 2}).$

**73. Logarithmic computation.** As has been stated (Art. 70), the system of logarithms usually employed in computation is the common or Briggs's system, the base of which is 10. In order to see how tables of logarithms may be constructed, and how such tables may be used, we shall therefore consider common logarithms, although the first part of our discussion will apply to other systems of logarithms also.

The invention of logarithms (by Napier in the early seventeenth century) had its basis in the comparison of two sequences of numbers, one in arithmetic and the other in geometric progression. If a geometric progression is denoted as usual (Art. 55), by

$$a_1, a_2 = a_1 r, a_3 = a_1 r^2, \cdots, a_n = a_1 r^{n-1}, \cdots, \tag{1}$$

then the logarithms of these numbers will be

$$\log a_1, \log a_2 = \log a_1 + \log r, \log a_3 = \log a_1 + 2 \log r, \cdots,$$

$$\log a_n = \log a_1 + (n-1) \log r, \cdots. \tag{2}$$

Consequently the sequence (2) of logarithms is an arithmetic progression, with first term $\log a_1$ and common difference $\log r$ (Art. 54). In order that this arithmetic progression exist as real numbers, it is of course necessary that $a_1$ and $r$ be positive.

If, in particular, $a_1 = 1$ and $r = 10$ (the base of the system of logarithms), sequence (1) becomes

$$1, 10, 10^2, \cdots, 10^{n-1}, \cdots, \tag{3}$$

and the corresponding sequence (2) is

$$0, 1, 2, \cdots, n-1, \cdots. \tag{4}$$

We thus have the sequence of positive integers as the common logarithms of the sequence of positive integral powers of the base 10.

We may start to fill in the gaps in the corresponding sequences (3) and (4) in the following manner. Let $10^s$ and $10^{s+1}$ be any two adjacent members of (3); the corresponding logarithms of these numbers are then $s$ and $s+1$, adjacent members of (4). Now the geometric mean of $10^s$ and $10^{s+1}$ is (Art. 55)

$$\sqrt{(10^s)(10^{s+1})} = 10^{s+\frac{1}{2}},$$

and the arithmetic mean of $s$ and $s+1$ is (Art. 54)

$$\frac{s + (s+1)}{2} = s + \frac{1}{2}.$$

Consequently the logarithm of the geometric mean of two numbers is the arithmetic mean of their logarithms. We therefore augment sequence (3) by inserting, between each adjacent pair of members, their geometric mean; and we get the corresponding sequence of logarithms by inserting the proper arithmetic means in (4). This gives us a new geometric progression

$$1, \quad 10^{\frac{1}{2}} = 3.162, \quad 10, \quad 10^{\frac{3}{2}} = 31.62, \quad 10^2 = 100, \cdots,$$

whose logarithms are the respective members of the new arithmetic progression

$$0, \quad \tfrac{1}{2}, \quad 1, \quad \tfrac{3}{2}, \quad 2, \cdots.$$

Evidently this process of inserting geometric means in one sequence and, at the same time, inserting their respective logarithms as arithmetic means in the corresponding sequence may be carried through as many stages as desired.

A more effective way of computing logarithms is by means of certain infinite series that are obtained by the methods of calculus. One such series yields the logarithm of any positive integer $n$ when log $(n - 1)$ is known, so that the logarithms of all positive integers may be found successively. Actually, the logarithms of only prime numbers * need be computed. For, the logarithm of a composite number is expressible in terms of the logarithms of its prime factors; thus, log 45 = 2 log 3 + log 5. Moreover, any non-integral positive number may be expressed as the product of a positive integer and some power of 10. Thus, $4.5 = 45 \times 10^{-1}$ and $450{,}000 = 45 \times 10^4$, so that log 4.5 = log 45 $-1$ = 2 log 3 + log 5 $- 1$, and log 450,000 = log 45 + 4 = 2 log 3 + log 5 + 4.

From the definition of a logarithm, it is evident that the only numbers whose logarithms are integers are integral powers of 10. We have log 1 = 0,

$$\log \quad 10 = 1, \qquad \log 0.1 \quad = -1,$$

$$\log \quad 100 = 2, \qquad \log 0.01 \quad = -2,$$

$$\log 1000 = 3, \qquad \log 0.001 = -3,$$

---

* A prime number is an integer greater than unity which has no integral divisors other than unity and itself. The first few primes are 2, 3, 5, 7, 11, 13, $\cdots$. A positive integer that is not a prime is called composite; thus $6 = 2 \cdot 3$ and $45 = 3^2 \cdot 5$ are composite.

and so on. Since the logarithm of a number $p$ increases as $p$ increases (Art. 70), we have the following tabulation for non-integral powers of 10:

| $p$ BETWEEN | | LOG $p$ BETWEEN |
|---|---|---|
| · · · · · · · | | · · · · · |
| 0.001 and 0.01 | | −3 and −2 |
| 0.01 and 0.1 | | −2 and −1 |
| 0.1 and 1 | | −1 and 0 |
| 1 and 10 | | 0 and 1 |
| 10 and 100 | | 1 and 2 |
| · · · · · · · | | · · · · · |

For example, we have, correct to four decimal places,

$$\log 0.002 = \log 2 - 3 = 0.3010 - 3(= -2.6990),$$

$$\log 0.02 \ \ = \log 2 - 2 = 0.3010 - 2(= -1.6990),$$

$$\log 0.2 \ \ \ = \log 2 - 1 = 0.3010 - 1(= -0.6990),$$

$$\log 2 \qquad\qquad\qquad = 0.3010,$$

$$\log 20 \ \ \ = \log 2 + 1 = 1.3010,$$

etc. In the first three of these cases, where the logarithms are negative, these negative results have been explicitly given to show how they fit into the above tabulation. However, ignoring the numbers enclosed in parentheses, we see that every common logarithm may be expressed as a *positive* decimal part (between 0 and 1) plus an integer (positive or negative) or zero. The positive decimal part is called the mantissa, and the integral part is known as the characteristic; a common logarithm thus consists of the sum of a mantissa and a characteristic.

From what has been said, we see that all numbers having the same significant figures, such as 230,400, 2.304, 0.002304, have the same mantissa, and the position of the decimal point affects only the characteristic. Consequently only the mantissa is given in a table of logarithms; the characteristic must be determined in each case from the position of the decimal point. Thus, we have

$$\log 230,400 \ \ = 0.3625 + 5,$$

$$\log 2.304 \ \ \ \ \ = 0.3625,$$

$$\log 0.002304 = 0.3625 - 3.$$

In more compact form, we write these as

$$\log 230{,}400 \;\; = 5.3625,$$

$$\log 2.304 \;\;\;\;\; = 0.3625,$$

$$\log 0.002304 = 7.3625 \, - \, 10.^*$$

In the last case, the characteristic $-3$ has been expressed as $7 - 10$. Similarly we have

$$\log 0.002 \; = 7.3010 \, - \, 10,$$

$$\log 0.02 \;\; = 8.3010 \, - \, 10,$$

$$\log 0.2 \;\;\; = 9.3010 \, - \, 10,$$

etc.

Rules for determining the characteristic in a given case can be variously stated. One way is the following: When the number exceeds unity, the positive characteristic is one less than the number of digits to the left of the decimal point; when the number is a positive decimal less than unity, the negative characteristic is numerically one more than the number of zeros between the decimal point and the first significant figure of the number. As a working method, the student may wish to adopt the following procedure: Since the characteristic is zero for the decimal point just to the right of the first significant figure, count off from this position to the actual decimal-point location—positive if to the right, negative if to the left.

The characteristic having been found for a given number, the mantissa may be determined from the tables in the Appendix in the following manner. If there are three or fewer significant digits, the first two are found in the left-hand column and the third at the top of the page. The mantissa (apart from the decimal point understood to be before it) is then found in the row of the first two digits of the number and in the column of the third digit. Thus, $\log 12.3 = 1.0899$. If there is a fourth significant figure in the number, interpolation is necessary; the procedure, based on the assumption that the change in the logarithm is proportional to that in the number, when these changes are small, is like that employed in Chapter III in connection with trigonometric functions. For example, $\log 12{,}340 = 4.0913$.

---

* Sometimes $\log 0.002304$ is written $\overline{3}.3625$, the minus sign being written above the characteristic to show that it alone, and not the entire logarithm including the mantissa, is negative.

Conversely, the number corresponding to a given logarithm, called the *antilogarithm*, may be found by referring to the tables. Thus, if $\log x = 8.4276 - 10$, we get $x = 0.02677$.

The following example will illustrate the above points and indicate how logarithms are used in computation.

*Example.*   Evaluate
$$\frac{542.3\sqrt{0.1383}}{32.72}.$$

*Solution.*   Letting $x$ denote the above expression, we have (Art. 70)

$$\log x = \log 542.3 + \tfrac{1}{2}\log 0.1383 - \log 32.72.$$

We find $\log 542.3 = 2.7342$, $\log 0.1383 = 9.1408 - 10$, and $\log 32.72 = 1.5148$. Hence

$$\tfrac{1}{2}\log 0.1383 = \tfrac{1}{2}(19.1408 - 20) = 9.5704 - 10,$$

| | |
|---|---|
| $\log 542.3$ | $= 2.7342$ |
| $\tfrac{1}{2}\log 0.1383 + \log 542.3$ | $= 2.3046$ |
| $\log 32.72$ | $= 1.5148$ |
| $\log x$ | $= 0.7898$ |
| | $x = 6.163$ |

If a number to be computed is negative, logarithms may be used to find its absolute value; the negative sign should then be attached to the antilogarithm. Thus, if $x = \sqrt[3]{-2} = -\sqrt[3]{2}$, we find $\log |x| = \tfrac{1}{3}\log 2 = 0.1003$, whence $|x| = 1.260$, and $x = -1.260$.

When natural logarithms are required, they may be easily obtained from the corresponding common logarithms. For, relation (9) of Art. 70 gives us, with $a = e$ and $b = 10$,

$$\log y = (\ln y)(\log e),$$

whence

$$\ln y = \frac{\log y}{\log e} = \frac{\log y}{0.4343} = 2.303 \log y.$$

The number $\log e = 0.4343$ (correct to four significant figures) is called the **modulus** of common logarithms with respect to natural logarithms. Its reciprocal [relation (10), Art. 70], namely, $\ln 10 = 2.303$, is then the modulus of natural logarithms with respect to common logarithms.

It should be noted that natural logarithms cannot be regarded as the sum of a characteristic and a mantissa. Consequently tables of natural logarithms must contain the entire logarithm. For example, ln 1.5 = 0.4055 and ln 15 = ln 1.5 + ln 10 = 0.4055 + 2.3026 = 2.7081 bear no simple relation to one another.

Jan 7

### EXERCISES

Using logarithms, evaluate each of the expressions in Exercises 1–20.

1. $\dfrac{7.290 \times 19.49}{625.0}$.

2. $\dfrac{0.8273 \times 0.1546}{0.03617}$.

3. $82.47\sqrt{13.54}$.

4. $\dfrac{\sqrt{73.72 \times 0.0428}}{51.64}$.

5. $432.7(5.486)^{\frac{3}{2}}$.

6. $(-0.1892)^{\frac{2}{3}}$.

7. $\pi(14.93)^2$.

8. $2.953\sqrt{74.35(2.904)^3}$.

9. $(3.629)^{1.4}$.

10. $4275e^{1.7}$.

11. $2\pi\sqrt{3.281/32.17}$.

12. $\frac{4}{3}\pi(6.592)^3$.

13. $\frac{1}{3}\pi(522.5)^2 \times 1743$.

14. $336.2e^{-2.05}$.

15. $448(1 - e^{-0.329})$.

16. $8243(517)^{-2.3}$.

17. $\dfrac{2\pi \times 8.40 \times 10^{-3}}{\ln 2.5}$.

18. $758(\ln 3.14)^2$.

19. $7270(\ln 11.5)^{1.3}$.

20. $3485 \ln (\ln 4.326)$.

21. The velocity of light is approximately 186,000 miles per second. Find the equivalent value in centimeters per second. (1 in. = 2.540 cm.)

22. A circular mil, used in measuring the cross-sectional area of wire, is the area of a circle 0.001 in. in diameter. If a certain gauge of wire has an area of 21,000 circular mils, what is its diameter in inches?

23. If 1 cc. of water weighs 1 gram, how many pounds does a cubic foot of water weigh? (453.6 grams = 1 lb.)

24. One atmosphere is the air pressure that will support 76.0 cm. of mercury in a barometer. If the density of mercury is 849 lb./cu. ft., how many feet of water will one atmosphere support?

25. The period $T$ (seconds) of a simple pendulum is given approximately by the formula $T = 2\pi\sqrt{L/g}$, where $L$ (feet) is the length of the pendulum and $g = 32.17$ ft./sec.[2] Find the period of a pendulum 16 in. long.

26. Under certain assumptions, atmospheric pressure $p$ (pounds per square inch) is given by $p = 14.7(12/14.7)^h$, where $h$ (miles) is the altitude above sea level. Find the pressure at a height of 1.5 miles.

27. The density $d$ (pounds per cubic foot) of sea water is approximately given by $d = 64e^{0.00676h}$, where $h$ (miles) is the depth below the surface. Find the density at a depth of 2 miles.

28. The velocity $v$ (feet per second) of a body moving under the action of certain forces, including air resistance, is given by $v = 173(1 - e^{-0.161t})$, where $t$ (seconds) is time. Find the velocity at the end of 10 seconds.

29. The quantity $q$ (calories per second) of heat lost from a certain insulated steam pipe is given by $q = 6.42/\ln r$, where $r$ is the ratio of outside to inside diameter. Find the heat loss per day when $r = 1.8$.

30. When an inductance $L$ (henries) and a resistance $R$ (ohms) are connected in

series with a constant electromotive force $E$ (volts), the current $I$ (amperes) flowing after time $t$ (seconds) is given by $I = E(1 - e^{-Rt/L})/R$. If $E = 110$ volts, $R = 6$ ohms, and $L = 0.1$ henry, find the current when $t = 0.01$ second.

**31.** When a resistance $R$ (ohms) and a capacitance $C$ (farads) are connected in series with a constant electromotive force, the current $I$ (amperes) is given by $I = I_0 e^{-t/RC}$, where $I_0$ is the initial current and $t$ is time (seconds). If $R = 1000$ ohms, $C = 10^{-6}$ farad, and $I_0 = 5$ amperes, find the time required for the current to decrease to 1 ampere.

**32.** If one end of a piece of rope is at the level of the axis of a rough horizontal cylinder of radius $a$ (feet), and the other hangs down a distance $L$ (feet) below the axis, then $L = 2fa(1 + e^{\pi f})/(1 + f^2)$ when the coefficient of friction $f$ is such that the rope is just about to slip. If $a = 8$ in. and $f = 0.37$, find $L$.

**33.** Under the action of a force of attraction and a resisting force, a particle moves in a straight line. Its displacement $x$ (feet) from the center of attraction is given by $x = 3e^{-t} - e^{-3t}$, where $t$ is time (seconds). Find $x$ when $t = 0.8$ second.

**34.** The pressure $p$ (pounds per square inch) and volume $v$ (cubic feet) of saturated steam are such that the expression $pv^{1.06}$ is nearly constant. If $v = 3.286$ cu. ft. when $p = 50$ lb./in.$^2$, find $v$ when $p$ is doubled.

**35.** In problems involving the flow of water from one pipe into a larger one, the formula for loss of head involves a coefficient $K$, the value of which may be computed from the relation $K = 1.098(1 - r^2)^{1.919}/v^{0.081}$, where $r$ is the ratio of the pipe diameters and $v$ is the speed of flow in the smaller pipe. Find $K$ if $r = 0.45$ and $v = 12$ ft./sec.

**74. Logarithmic solution of triangles.** In Art. 41 we discussed the solution of problems involving oblique triangles. Of the four cases considered, two, (a) and (c), may be solved with the help of the law of sines (Art. 40). Since the application of the sine law entails only multiplication and division, it is possible to carry out the necessary computations by means of logarithms. For this purpose, the logarithms of the trigonometric functions are given in the tables in the back of this book; the use of these tables is illustrated later in this article.

With regard to case (b), Art. 41, in which two sides and the included angle are known, it was stated that the law of cosines could be used to find the third side, after which a second angle could be determined by means of the sine law. Now, since the cosine law entails additions and subtractions, it is not best suited to logarithmic computation. Accordingly, we give here an alternative method of treating this case, in which logarithms may be used to advantage.

As before, we denote the three sides of the triangle by $a$, $b$, and $c$, and the respective angles opposite these sides by $A$, $B$, and $C$. Suppose the given two sides and included angle to be labeled $a$, $b$, and $C$; then for any possible value of $C$ between $0°$ and $180°$ we have (see Fig. 20, Art. 40)

$$\cot B = \frac{BD}{h} = \frac{a - b \cos C}{b \sin C} = \frac{a}{b \sin C} - \cot C. \qquad (1)$$

Angle $B$ may thus be determined when $a$, $b$, and $C$ are known. The computation of $a/(b \sin C)$ may be effected by means of logarithms, for this is just the sort of expression that arises when dealing with the sine law. Two references to the table of cotangent values then complete the work of finding $B$, after which $A = 180° - (B + C)$ and $c = (b \sin C)/\sin B$ may be determined.

*Example.* It is required to find the distance between two points, $A$ and $B$. Since an obstacle between $A$ and $B$ prevents direct measurement, a point $C$ accessible to both $A$ and $B$ is chosen, whence the data $CB = a = 472$ ft., $CA = b = 386$ ft., angle $C = 38° 42'$ are found. Determine $AB = c$.

*Solution.* Here relation (1) yields

$$\cot B = \frac{472}{386 \sin 38° 42'} - \cot 38° 42',$$

and we also have

$$c = \frac{386 \sin 38° 42'}{\sin B}.$$

The computation of these two quantities is given in tabular form below. Note that $\log 386 \sin 38° 42'$, obtained in the determination of $\cot B$, is applicable directly to the computation of $c$. The student should verify each step in the computation by independent reference to the tables.

| | |
|---|---|
| $\log 472$ | $= 2.6739$ |
| $\log 386$ | $= 2.5866$ |
| $\log \sin 38° 42'$ | $= 9.7960 - 10$ |
| $\log 386 \sin 38° 42'$ | $= 2.3826$ |

$$\log \frac{472}{386 \sin 38° 42'} = 0.2913$$

$$\frac{472}{386 \sin 38° 42'} = 1.956$$

| | |
|---|---|
| $\log 386 \sin 38° 42'$ | $= 2.3826$ |
| $\log \sin 54° 42'$ | $= 9.9118 - 10$ |
| $\log c$ | $= 2.4708$ |
| $c$ | $= 295.7$ ft. |

$\cot B = 1.956 - 1.248 = 0.708$

$B = 54° 42'$

We now develop formulas, adaptable to logarithmic computation, for use in connection with case $(d)$, Art. 41, where the three sides $a$, $b$, and $c$ are known. We have (Art. 38)

$$\tan^2 \frac{A}{2} = \frac{1 - \cos A}{1 + \cos A}.$$

Now $a^2 = b^2 + c^2 - 2bc \cos A$ by the cosine law (Art. 40), whence

$\cos A = (b^2 + c^2 - a^2)/2bc$.   Therefore

$$1 - \cos A = 1 - \frac{b^2 + c^2 - a^2}{2bc} = \frac{a^2 - (b - c)^2}{2bc}$$

$$= \frac{(a + b - c)(a - b + c)}{2bc},$$

and

$$1 + \cos A = 1 + \frac{b^2 + c^2 - a^2}{2bc} = \frac{(b + c)^2 - a^2}{2bc}$$

$$= \frac{(b + c + a)(b + c - a)}{2bc}.$$

Consequently we get

$$\tan^2 \frac{A}{2} = \frac{(a + b - c)(a - b + c)}{(b + c + a)(b + c - a)}.$$

For brevity, denote the perimeter of the triangle by $2s = a + b + c$; then $a + b - c = 2s - 2c = 2(s - c)$, $a - b + c = 2(s - b)$, and $b + c - a = 2(s - a)$.   Hence the preceding relation yields

$$\tan \frac{A}{2} = \sqrt{\frac{(s - c)(s - b)}{s(s - a)}}. \tag{2}$$

Only the positive square root has significance here, since $A/2$ must be less than $90°$.   By a cyclic interchange of letters, we likewise have

$$\tan \frac{B}{2} = \sqrt{\frac{(s - a)(s - c)}{s(s - b)}}, \tag{3}$$

$$\tan \frac{C}{2} = \sqrt{\frac{(s - b)(s - a)}{s(s - c)}}. \tag{4}$$

Any two of these formulas, together with $A + B + C = 180°$, may be used to determine the three angles.   If desired, all three formulas may be employed, and the results checked by means of $A + B + C = 180°$.

### EXERCISES

**1.** Using the notation of Art. 74, show that $\sin^2 (A/2) = (s - b)(s - c)/bc$.

**2.** Show that $\cos^2 (A/2) = s(s - a)/bc$.

**3.** Using the results of Exercises 1 and 2 and the fact that the area of a triangle is $K = \frac{1}{2}bc \sin A = bc \sin (A/2) \cos (A/2)$, show that

$$K = \sqrt{s(s - a)(s - b)(s - c)}.$$

**4.** If $r$ is the radius of the inscribed circle of a triangle, show that the area of the triangle is equal to $rs$. Hence, from the result of Exercise 3, show that $r^2 = (s - a)(s - b)(s - c)/s$.

**5.** Using relation (1) and the sine law, show that

$$\cot B + \cot C = \frac{\sin A}{\sin B \sin C}.$$

**6.** Using the result of Exercise 5 and the fact that $\sin A = \sin [180° - (B + C)]$ $= \sin (B + C)$, derive the formula $\sin (B + C) = \sin B \cos C + \cos B \sin C$.

**7.** If the three sides of a triangle are respectively 729, 1113, and 654, find the angles.

**8.** Find the area of the triangle of Exercise **7.**

**9.** Find the radius of the inscribed circle of the triangle of Exercise **7.**

The following exercises refer to the correspondingly numbered exercises of Art. 41. In each case, compute the quantities required in the exercises of Art. 41, using the data given here.

**10.** $a = 3.52$, $b = 2.17$, $\alpha = 58°$, $\beta = 36°$.
**11.** $h = 5.76$, $\alpha = 18° 20'$, $\beta = 7° 27'$.
**12.** $a = 108$ ft., $\alpha = 53° 8'$, $\beta = 29° 7'$.
**13.** $a = 64.5$ ft., $\alpha = 26° 4'$, $\phi = 32° 10'$, $\theta = 47° 45'$.
**14.** $a = 72.5$ ft., $\alpha = 42° 12'$, $\beta = 36° 24'$.
**15.** $a = 8.36$, $\theta = 72° 10'$, $\alpha = 18° 50'$, $\beta = 24° 15'$.
**16.** $a = 44.5$ ft., $\alpha = 62° 20'$, $\beta = 56° 50'$, $\theta = 15° 8'$, $\phi = 21° 32'$.
**17.** $a = 5.62$, $b = 8.49$, $\theta = 75° 5'$.
**18.** $A = 41° 19'$, $\alpha = 84° 16'$.
**19.** $a = 12.68$, $d = 8.39$, $\alpha = 62° 12'$, $\beta = 9° 37'$.
**20.** $c = 2.77$, $A = 38° 17'$, $B = 18° 43'$.

## SUPPLEMENTARY EXERCISES

Solve each of the equations in Exercises 1–5.

**1.** $e^x - 28e^{-x} - 3 = 0$.          **2.** $e^{2x} = 8e^{-x}$.
**3.** $7e^{-2x} + 2e^{-x} - 1 = 0$.          **4.** $\log (x - 2) + \log (x + 4) = 1$.
**5.** $\ln (e^x - 1) + \ln (e^x + 3) = 2$.

Find the inverse of each of the functions in Exercises 6–10.

**6.** $y = e^x - 3e^{-x}$.          **7.** $y = 2e^x - e^{-x} + 1$.
**8.** $y = \ln 3x - \frac{1}{2} \ln x$.          **9.** $y = 2 \ln x - \ln (x + 1)$.
**10.** $y = \ln \sin x + \ln \cos x + \ln e^2$.

**11.** Show that an alternative expression for the distance $x = PQ$ of Exercise 16 Art. 41, is given by

$$x^2 = \frac{a^2 \sin^2 \theta}{\sin^2 (\beta + \theta)} + \frac{a^2 \sin^2 \alpha}{\sin^2 (\alpha + \phi)} - \frac{2a^2 \sin \alpha \sin \theta \cos (\beta - \phi)}{\sin (\beta + \theta) \sin (\alpha + \phi)}.$$

Using this formula with the data of Exercise 16, Art. 74, redetermine the value of $x$.

**12.** A body is subjected to two forces of magnitudes 3.75 and 4.25 pounds, respectively, the angle between the directions of these forces being 45°.   Find the magnitude and direction of the resultant force.

**13.** A body is to be subjected to two forces, of magnitudes 8.625 and 12.5 pounds, respectively, and such that their resultant is to be 15 pounds.   Find the angle between the directions of the given forces.

**14.** A picture 4 feet in height is hung on a wall with its lower edge 2 feet above the level of an observer's eye.   At what distance from the wall should the observer stand in order that the vertical angle subtended by the picture at his eye shall be equal to the angle of elevation of the lower edge?

**15.** (a) Show that the radius $R$ of the circumscribed circle of the triangle $ABC$ is given by

$$2R = \frac{a}{\sin A} = \frac{b}{\sin B} = \frac{c}{\sin C}.$$

(b) Using also the formula $K = \frac{1}{2}bc \sin A$ for the area of the triangle, show that $4RK = abc$.   (c) Using the result of Exercise 3, Art. 74, show that the radius $R$ is therefore given, in terms of the three sides $a$, $b$, and $c$, by

$$R = \frac{abc}{4\sqrt{s(s-a)(s-b)(s-c)}}.$$

(d) Find the radius of the circle circumscribed about the triangle whose sides are 2.74, 3.95, and 4.68 feet long, respectively.

# XV——————————  Rational Integral Equations

**75. Remainder and factor theorems.** In Art. 21 we defined a rational integral equation in one variable $x$ as an equation of the form

$$a_0x^n + a_1x^{n-1} + \cdots + a_{n-1}x + a_n = 0, \tag{1}$$

where $n$ is a positive integer and the $a$'s are quantities independent of $x$. In Chapter IX the quadratic equation, of the form (1) with $n = 2$, was considered. The subject of this chapter is the study of rational integral equations, and relations reducible to the form (1), when $n$ is greater than 2.

For brevity, we shall denote the polynomial forming the left member of (1) by the functional notation $P(x)$. Throughout the chapter, the symbol $P(x)$ shall be understood to have this meaning.

If $P(x)$ is divided by the linear expression $x - r$, where $r$, like the $a$'s, is independent of $x$, the quotient, $Q(x)$, is another polynomial, of degree $n - 1$. In general there will also be a remainder $R$, which does not involve $x$, so that

$$\frac{P(x)}{x - r} = Q(x) + \frac{R}{x - r}. \tag{2}$$

For example, we have

$$\frac{x^3 + 3ax^2 + 3a^2x + b}{x + a} = x^2 + 2ax + a^2 + \frac{b - a^3}{x + a},$$

$$\frac{2x^4 - 5x^2 - 7x + 3}{x - 2} = 2x^3 + 4x^2 + 3x - 1 + \frac{1}{x - 2}.$$

If we multiply both members of (2) by $x - r$, we get the identity

$$P(x) \equiv Q(x) \cdot (x - r) + R. \tag{3}$$

If we now set $x = r$, (3) yields

$$P(r) = R. \tag{4}$$

267

Expressed verbally, this result is the **remainder theorem:**

*If a polynomial $P(x)$ is divided by $x - r$, the remainder is equal to the quantity obtained by replacing $x$ by $r$ in the polynomial.*

The above two examples illustrate this theorem. For, if $P(x) = x^3 + 3ax^2 + 3a^2x + b$, then $P(-a) = -a^3 + 3a^3 - 3a^3 + b = b - a^3$, which is the remainder found when $P(x)$ is divided by $x + a$. Likewise, if $P(x) = 2x^4 - 5x^2 - 7x + 3$, then $P(2) = 32 - 20 - 14 + 3 = 1$, the remainder obtained when $P(x)$ is divided by $x - 2$.

Suppose now that $r$ is a solution of the equation $P(x) = 0$, so that $P(r) \equiv 0$. From the remainder theorem, it follows that $R \equiv 0$, whence (3) becomes $P(x) = Q(x) \cdot (x - r)$. This gives us the **factor theorem:**

*If $r$ is a solution of the rational integral equation $P(x) = 0$, then $x - r$ is a factor of $P(x)$.*

Conversely, if $x - r$ is a factor of $P(x)$, so that the remainder $R = 0$, the remainder theorem tells us that $P(r) = 0$, whence $r$ is a solution of the equation $P(x) = 0$.

To illustrate the factor theorem, let $b$ be replaced by $a^3$ in the first example, so that $P(x) = x^3 + 3ax^2 + 3a^2x + a^3$. Then $P(-a) = 0$, and $P(x) \equiv (x^2 + 2ax + a^2)(x + a)$.

**76. Synthetic division.** In order to make use of the remainder and factor theorems as working tools in the subsequent discussion, we now consider a rapid and compactly written method of performing the necessary divisions. To illustrate the procedure, let us examine the usual way of carrying out the division involved in the second example of Art. 75:

$$
\begin{array}{r}
2x^4 \phantom{xxx} - 5x^2 - 7x + 3 \\
2x^4 - 4x^3 \\
\hline
4x^3 - 5x^2 \\
4x^3 - 8x^2 \\
\hline
3x^2 - 7x \\
3x^2 - 6x \\
\hline
-x + 3 \\
-x + 2 \\
\hline
1
\end{array}
\quad
\begin{array}{|l}
x - 2 \\
\hline
2x^3 + 4x^2 + 3x - 1 \\
\end{array}
$$

To begin with, we see that we can easily dispense with everything except the coefficients, for the terms of dividend, divisor, and quotient are all ordered according to descending powers of $x$. To avoid confusion, we supply a zero coefficient for a missing term. Thus, our dividend is represented by the coefficients $2 + 0 - 5 - 7 + 3$.

Further simplifications are made possible as a result of the fact that the divisor, $x - r$, is always linear, and the coefficient of $x$ in it is always unity. We may, for example, write merely $-r$ in the divisor's place, $x$'s coefficient unity being understood. Moreover, the coefficient of any particular term in the quotient must be the coefficient of the first term in the corresponding partial remainder, and consequently the quotient need not be represented separately. In addition, the first term in each subtrahend is always the same as the first term of the corresponding minuend, and hence the former numbers need not be written; and it is unnecessary to recopy the successive terms of the dividend in the corresponding minuends.

When we omit all these superfluities, the above division reduces to the following form:

$$
\begin{array}{r}
2 + 0 - 5 - 7 + 3 \underline{\;\lvert -2} \\
- 4 \phantom{aaaaaaaaaaaa} \\
\hline
4 \phantom{aaaaaaaaaa} \\
- 8 \phantom{aaaaaa} \\
\hline
3 \phantom{aaaaaa} \\
- 6 \phantom{aa} \\
\hline
- 1 \phantom{aa} \\
2 \\
\hline
1
\end{array}
$$

This may be written compactly as follows:

$$
\begin{array}{r}
2 + 0 - 5 - 7 + 3 \underline{\;\lvert -2} \\
- 4 - 8 - 6 + 2 \\
\hline
2 + 4 + 3 - 1 + 1
\end{array}
$$

Here the last line exhibits both the ordered coefficients of the quotient, $2x^3 + 4x^2 + 3x - 1$, and the remainder, 1.

Finally, since addition is performed more easily than subtraction, we replace $-2$ in the divisor's place by its negative, 2, and add the partial products in the second line to the corresponding coefficients of the dividend to get the successive terms of quotient and remainder; that is, we employ the fundamental properties VI and IV of Art. 3. The resulting **synthetic division** therefore takes the form:

$$
\begin{array}{r}
2 + 0 - 5 - 7 + 3 \underline{\;\lvert\, 2} \\
+ 4 + 8 + 6 - 2 \\
\hline
2 + 4 + 3 - 1 + 1
\end{array}
$$

It is apparent that the process of synthetic division described above is applicable whenever a polynomial $P(x)$ is to be divided by a linear expression of the form $x - r$. The steps in the procedure are as follows:

1. In the first line, write the coefficients of the dividend $P(x)$ in the normal order of descending powers of $x$, supplying any missing terms with zero coefficients, and to the right place the number $r$ to represent the divisor, $x - r$.

2. Bring the leading coefficient $a_0$ of $P(x)$ down into the third line, multiply it by $r$, and place the product $a_0 r$ in the second line under the coefficient $a_1$ of $P(x)$. Bring down the sum, $a_0 r + a_1$, into the third line, multiply by $r$, and continue as in the preceding step.

3. When this process has been completed, through $n + 1$ stages, the first $n$ numbers in the third line represent, in order, the coefficients of the quotient (of degree $n - 1$), and the last number is the remainder.

As another example, we divide $x^5 + 2x^4 - 7x^3 - 8x^2 + 14x + 11$ by $x + 3$. Here, since $x + 3 = x - (-3)$, we have $r = -3$. Hence the synthetic division proceeds as shown below:

$$
\begin{array}{r}
1 + 2 - 7 - \phantom{0}8 + 14 + 11 \ \underline{\phantom{|}\ -3} \\
- 3 + 3 + 12 - 12 - \phantom{0}6 \\
\hline
1 - 1 - 4 + \phantom{0}4 + \phantom{0}2 + \phantom{0}5
\end{array}
$$

Therefore the quotient is $x^4 - x^3 - 4x^2 + 4x + 2$, and the remainder is 5.

### EXERCISES

**1.** Using the remainder theorem, show that $x^n - a^n$ is divisible by $x - a$ for every positive integer $n$.

**2.** Show that $x^{2n} - a^{2n}$ is divisible by $x + a$ for every positive integer $n$.

**3.** Show that $x^{2n-1} + a^{2n-1}$ is divisible by $x + a$ for every positive integer $n$.

**4.** By means of the remainder theorem, determine the values of $k$ for which $3x^4 + k^2 x^3 - 2kx + 5 = 0$ is divisible by $x + 1$.

**5.** Prove the remainder theorem by forming a suitable expression for $P(x) - P(r)$ and using the result of Exercise 1.

Using synthetic division and the remainder theorem, find $P(r)$ in each of Exercises 6–15.

**6.** $P(x) = x^2 - 5x + 2$; $r = 4$.

**7.** $P(x) = x^3 - 2x^2 + 4x + 1$; $r = -2$.

**8.** $P(x) = x^3 + 3ax^2 + 3a^2 x + a^3$; $r = -a$.

**9.** $P(x) = 8x^4 - 4x^3 + 2x - 1$; $r = \frac{1}{2}$.

**10.** $P(x) = 81x^4 - a^4$; $r = a/3$.

**11.** $P(x) = x^5 + 32$; $r = 2$.

**12.** $P(x) = a^5 + a^4 x + a^3 x^2 + a^2 x^3 + ax^4 + x^5$; $r = -a$.

**13.** $P(x) = 3x^4 + x^3 + 2x^2 + x - 1$; $r = i$.

**14.** $P(x) = 2x^4 - 4x^3 + 9x^2 + 2x - 5; r = 1 + 2i.$
**15.** $P(x) = x^4 + 4x^3 + 8x^2 + 4x + 7; r = \sqrt{3}\, i - 2.$

Using synthetic division and the factor theorem, determine whether the given numbers are solutions of the corresponding equations in Exercises 16–25.

**16.** $x^3 - x^2 - 5x - 3 = 0; x = 3.$
**17.** $4x^3 - 6x^2 + 2x + 1 = 0; x = \frac{1}{2}.$
**18.** $16x^4 + 16x^3 + 31x^2 - x - 2 = 0; x = -\frac{1}{4}.$
**19.** $2x^4 + 6x^3 + 6x^2 - 12x - 20 = 0; x = -\sqrt{2}.$
**20.** $3x^4 + x^3 - 17x^2 - 5x + 10 = 0; x = -\sqrt{5}.$
**21.** $4x^4 - 16x^3 + 5x^2 - 4x + 1 = 0; x = 2 + \sqrt{3}.$
**22.** $3x^4 - x^3 + 32x^2 - 9x + 45 = 0; x = 3i.$
**23.** $2x^5 + 13x^3 - 2x^2 + 6x - 12 = 0; x = \sqrt{6}\, i.$
**24.** $x^4 - 2x^2 + 25 = 0; x = \sqrt{3} - \sqrt{2}\, i.$
**25.** $2x^5 + x^4 - 2x^3 - 4x^2 - 2x + 4 = 0; x = 2^{\frac{1}{3}}.$

**77. Number and nature of roots.** We begin now our discussion of the rational integral equation,

$$P(x) \equiv a_0 x^n + a_1 x^{n-1} + \cdots + a_{n-1}x + a_n = 0, \qquad (1)$$

and of its solutions, or roots. We shall assume that the leading coefficient, $a_0$, is different from zero, so that $P(x)$ is actually of degree $n$.

As we have seen (Chapter IX), it is possible to solve equation (1) for $x$ in terms of the coefficients when $n = 2$, and the quadratic formula shows that this second-degree equation has two roots. The questions that naturally arise are: Can equation (1) be solved for $x$ in terms of the coefficients $a_0, a_1, \cdots, a_n$ when $n$ is greater than 2, and will there always be $n$ roots of an equation of degree $n$?

The answer to the first question is a rather surprising one. When $n$ is equal to 3 or 4, as well as when $n$ is 1 or 2, it is possible to find formulas for the roots in terms of the coefficients, but when $n > 4$, such algebraic formulas do not exist. Algebraic solutions of the general cubic and quartic equations ($n = 3$ and $n = 4$, respectively) can be obtained without much difficulty; * the proof that the general equation of degree greater than 4 is not solvable algebraically requires more advanced methods. Since there is no general method of solving rational integral equations, and since the formulas for the solutions of the cubic and quartic equations have but limited practical value, we shall not consider these formulas here.

We consider now our second question, relative to the number of roots of equation (1). We shall assume that every equation of the form (1) has at least one root; it is possible to prove this fact, but again the method of proof is too advanced for a book such as this. If $r_1$ is a

---
* See, for example, Barnard and Child, *Higher Algebra*, Chapter XII.

root whose existence is assumed, then by the factor theorem (Art. 75), we have

$$P(x) = Q_1(x) \cdot (x - r_1),$$

where $Q_1(x)$ is a rational integral function of degree $n - 1$. By our assumption, the equation $Q_1(x) = 0$ has a root, say $r_2$, whence $Q_1(x) = Q_2(x) \cdot (x - r_2)$, and

$$P(x) = Q_2(x) \cdot (x - r_1)(x - r_2),$$

where $Q_2(x)$ is of degree $n - 2$. Proceeding in this way, we get $n$ linear factors of $P(x)$, namely $x - r_1$, $x - r_2$, $\cdots$, $x - r_n$. Since the term of highest degree in the product $(x - r_1)(x - r_2) \cdots (x - r_n)$ is $x^n$, the final quotient $Q_n(x)$ will be the constant $a_0$ which serves as leading coefficient in $P(x)$. That is, we have

$$P(x) \equiv a_0(x - r_1)(x - r_2) \cdots (x - r_n), \tag{2}$$

and $r_1, r_2, \cdots, r_n$ are $n$ roots of the equation $P(x) = 0$ of degree $n$.

There cannot be more than $n$ roots, for, if there were, $P(x)$ would have more than $n$ linear factors, one corresponding to each root, and the degree of the product of these linear factors would be greater than $n$, contrary to supposition. We therefore have the following theorem:

*A rational integral equation of degree $n$ possesses $n$ and only $n$ solutions.*

Two or more of the roots $r_1, r_2, \cdots, r_n$ may sometimes be equal; we say then that equation (1) has repeated or multiple roots. Thus, if $(x - r_k)^m$ is a factor of $P(x)$, where $m$ is a positive integer greater than unity, then $r_k$ is a root, of multiplicity $m$, of $P(x) = 0$.

Consider now an equation of the form (1) in which all the coefficients $a_0, a_1, \cdots, a_n$ are real numbers. We have seen that, in the case of the quadratic equation whose discriminant is negative, both roots are complex and conjugate to each other (Art. 50). This is a particular instance of a more general result:

*Complex roots of a rational integral equation of any degree $n$ and with real coefficients occur in conjugate pairs.*

This theorem may be proved in the following manner. Suppose that equation (1), in which $a_0, a_1, \cdots, a_n$ are all real, has a complex root, which we designate in polar form (Art. 44) by $r(\cos \theta + i \sin \theta)$. Then we get

$$P[r(\cos \theta + i \sin \theta)] \equiv a_0[r(\cos \theta + i \sin \theta)]^n + a_1[r(\cos \theta + i \sin \theta)]^{n-1}$$
$$+ \cdots + a_{n-1}[r(\cos \theta + i \sin \theta)] + a_n = 0.$$

By De Moivre's theorem (Art. 46), this relation becomes

$$a_0 r^n(\cos n\theta + i \sin n\theta) + a_1 r^{n-1}[\cos (n - 1)\theta + i \sin (n - 1)\theta] + \cdots$$
$$+ a_{n-1} r(\cos \theta + i \sin \theta) + a_n = 0,$$

or

$$a_0 r^n \cos n\theta + a_1 r^{n-1} \cos (n - 1)\theta + \cdots + a_{n-1} r \cos \theta + a_n$$
$$+ i[a_0 r^n \sin n\theta + a_1 r^{n-1} \sin (n - 1)\theta + \cdots + a_{n-1} r \sin \theta] = 0. \quad (3)$$

Since a complex number $a + bi$ is equal to zero only if $a = 0$ and $b = 0$, we have

$$a_0 r^n \cos n\theta + a_1 r^{n-1} \cos (n - 1)\theta + \cdots + a_{n-1} r \cos \theta + a_n = 0, \quad (4)$$
$$a_0 r^n \sin n\theta + a_1 r^{n-1} \sin (n - 1)\theta + \cdots + a_{n-1} r \sin \theta \quad\quad = 0. \quad (5)$$

Now the number conjugate to $r \cos \theta + ir \sin \theta$ is, by definition, $r \cos \theta - ir \sin \theta$. For any positive integer $m$,

$$(r \cos \theta - ir \sin \theta)^m = r^m[\cos (-\theta) + i \sin (-\theta)]^m$$
$$= r^m[\cos (-m\theta) + i \sin (-m\theta)]$$
$$= r^m (\cos m\theta - i \sin m\theta).$$

Hence, if $x$ is replaced by $r(\cos \theta - i \sin \theta)$ in $P(x)$, the expression obtained is the conjugate of the left member of relation (3). By virtue of relations (4) and (5), we then get $P[r(\cos \theta - i \sin \theta)] = 0$, so that $r(\cos \theta - i \sin \theta)$ is a solution provided that its conjugate, $r(\cos \theta + i \sin \theta)$, is a solution. Thus our equation with real coefficients will have no or an even number of complex roots.

As a corollary of the theorem just proved, it follows that a rational integral equation of odd degree and with real coefficients will have at least one real solution.

Corresponding to the conjugate complex roots $a + bi$ and $a - bi$, there must be the factors $x - a - bi$ and $x - a + bi$ of $P(x)$. Now

$$(x - a - bi)(x - a + bi) = (x - a)^2 + b^2$$
$$= x^2 - 2ax + a^2 + b^2,$$

and consequently $P(x)$ has a quadratic factor with real coefficients corresponding to each pair of conjugate complex solutions. Therefore $P(x)$ may be expressed as the product of real linear and quadratic factors whenever $P(x)$ has real coefficients. For example, the equation

$x^3 + x^2 - 7x - 15 = 0$ has one real root, 3, and the conjugate complex roots, $-2 \pm i$, as may be checked by synthetic division; then we have

$$x^3 + x^2 - 7x - 15 \equiv (x - 3)(x + 2 - i)(x + 2 + i)$$

$$\equiv (x - 3)(x^2 + 4x + 5).$$

**78. Graphs of polynomials.** In this and the following three articles, our principal concern will be with the determination of the solutions of a rational integral equation with real coefficients.

Consider, then, the equation

$$P(x) \equiv a_0 x^n + a_1 x^{n-1} + \cdots + a_{n-1} x + a_n = 0, \tag{1}$$

where $a_0, a_1, \cdots, a_n$ are real numbers. Using synthetic division and the remainder theorem, we can construct a table of real values of $x$ and the corresponding real values of $P(x)$. With these number pairs as coordinates, the graph of the function $P(x)$ may be plotted. Such a graph can be very helpful in determining the variation of the function and the number and approximate values of its real zeros.

Evidently there will exist one and only one real value of $P(x)$ corresponding to every real value assigned to $x$. Also, corresponding to a small change in $x$, we should expect a small variation in $P(x)$. To substantiate the latter statement, let $x$ be changed from any particular value $x_1$ to a value $x_1 + h$, where $h$ is numerically small; then we have

$$P(x_1 + h) = a_0(x_1 + h)^n + a_1(x_1 + h)^{n-1} + \cdots + a_{n-1}(x_1 + h) + a_n$$

$$= a_0[x_1^n + nhx_1^{n-1} + \cdots + h^n] + a_1[x_1^{n-1} + (n - 1)hx_1^{n-2}$$

$$+ \cdots + h^{n-1}] + \cdots + a_{n-1}(x_1 + h) + a_n$$

$$= a_0 x_1^n + a_1 x_1^{n-1} + \cdots + a_{n-1} x_1 + a_n + h[a_0 n x_1^{n-1}$$

$$+ \cdots + a_0 h^{n-1} + a_1(n - 1)x_1^{n-2} + \cdots + a_1 h^{n-2}$$

$$+ \cdots + a_{n-1}]$$

$$= P(x_1) + hP_1(x_1),$$

say. Therefore the change in $P(x)$, namely $P(x_1 + h) - P(x_1)$, is a number having $h$ as a factor, so that this change can be made as small numerically as we please by taking $h$ sufficiently small. Consequently the graph of $P(x)$ will be a smooth continuous curve, that is, one without any abrupt changes.

This result has the following important consequence: If $x_1$ and $x_2$ are two real values of $x$ such that $P(x_1)$ and $P(x_2)$ have opposite signs, then the graph of $P(x)$ must cross the $X$-axis at least once in the interval between $x_1$ and $x_2$. For, the points on the graph corresponding to $x_1$ and $x_2$ will lie on opposite sides of the $X$-axis, and a continuous curve connecting them must therefore cross that axis an odd number of times. Hence, since a point at which the graph cuts the $X$-axis corresponds to a real zero of the function $P(x)$, there will exist an odd number of real roots of equation (1) between $x_1$ and $x_2$.

In the preceding article, we found that a polynomial $P(x)$ with real coefficients can be expressed as the product of real linear and quadratic factors. Let us now examine the effect of each type of factor of $P(x)$ on the graph of the function, using the ideas of functional variation discussed in Art. 68.

Suppose first that $x = r$ is a real non-repeated root. Then $x - r$ is a factor of $P(x)$, and the product of the remaining factors, a polynomial of degree $n - 1$, will be different from zero for $x = r$. For values of $x$ near $r$, the function $P(x)$ then varies somewhat like the linear function $c(x - r)$, where $c$ is a constant; that is, the graph will cut the $X$-axis at $x = r$ at a non-zero angle.

Next suppose that $x = r$ is a real repeated root, of multiplicity $m$, so that $(x - r)^m$ is a factor of $P(x)$, where $m$ is a positive integer greater than unity. The character of the graph of $P(x)$ near $x = r$ will then resemble that of $c(x - r)^m$. If $m$ is even, $(x - r)^m$ will be positive on either side of and close to $x = r$; thus the curve will be tangent to the $X$-axis at $x = r$ and will remain on one side of the axis in the vicinity of that point. If $m$ is odd, $(x - r)^m$ will change from negative to positive as $x$ increases from a value less than $r$ to a value greater than $r$; however, the graph of $P(x)$ will not cross the $X$-axis at a sharp angle, but instead will be tangent to the $X$-axis at $x = r$ (cf. the graph of $y = x^3$, Fig. 28, Art. 68).

Finally, suppose that equation (1) has a pair of conjugate complex solutions, $x = a + bi$ and $x = a - bi$. Then the real quadratic factor of $P(x)$ corresponding to these roots will be $(x - a)^2 + b^2$, which is always positive. Hence the algebraic sign of $P(x)$ for each real value of $x$ will be independent of the possible presence of quadratic factors corresponding to complex zeros of the function, but will be determined only by the real linear factors and the constant $a_0$.

These matters are illustrated by the following example.

*Example.*   Plot the rational integral function

$$P(x) = x^8 - 5x^7 + 9x^6 - 9x^5 + 8x^4 - 4x^3.$$

*Solution.* We see immediately that the equation $P(x) = 0$ has the triple root zero, since $x^3$ is a factor of $P(x)$. If we divide the remaining factor of fifth degree by $x - 1$,* synthetically, we get:

$$1 - 5 + 9 - 9 + 8 - 4 \,\underline{\,| \, 1}$$
$$\underline{\;\;\;+ 1 - 4 + 5 - 4 + 4\;\;\;\;}$$
$$1 - 4 + 5 - 4 + 4 + 0$$

Hence $P(x) = x^3(x - 1)(x^4 - 4x^3 + 5x^2 - 4x + 4)$. The last factor, of fourth degree, is not again divisible by $x - 1$, and consequently unity is a non-repeated root. Dividing the fourth-degree expression by $x - 2$, we find:

$$1 - 4 + 5 - 4 + 4 \,\underline{\,| \, 2}$$
$$\underline{\;\;\;+ 2 - 4 + 2 - 4\;\;\;\;}$$
$$1 - 2 + 1 - 2 + 0$$

Therefore $P(x) = x^3(x - 1)(x - 2)(x^3 - 2x^2 + x - 2)$. The cubic factor, $x^3 - 2x^2 + x - 2$, is again divisible by $x - 2$:

$$1 - 2 + 1 - 2 \,\underline{\,| \, 2}$$
$$\underline{\;\;\;+ 2 + 0 + 2\;\;\;\;}$$
$$1 + 0 + 1 + 0$$

Consequently

$$P(x) = x^3(x - 1)(x - 2)^2(x^2 + 1).$$

Thus the equation $P(x) = 0$ has 0 as a triple root, 1 as a single root, 2 as a double root, and the conjugate pair $\pm i$ as non-repeated roots.

We further find that:

$$P(x) > 0 \quad \text{for} \quad x < 0,$$

$$P(x) < 0 \quad \text{for} \quad 0 < x < 1,$$

$$P(x) > 0 \quad \text{for} \quad 1 < x < 2,$$

$$P(x) > 0 \quad \text{for} \quad x > 2.$$

To get greater accuracy in our graph, we also compute

$$P(\tfrac{1}{2}) = -\tfrac{45}{256}, \qquad P(\tfrac{3}{2}) = \tfrac{351}{256}.$$

The given function is shown plotted in Fig. 35. The nature of the graph in the vicinity of a single, double, or triple zero of the function is indicated, and our general discussion is thereby exemplified.

---

\* The fact that $x = 1$ is a root is easily seen by noting that the sum of the coeffi cients of $P(x)$ is zero.

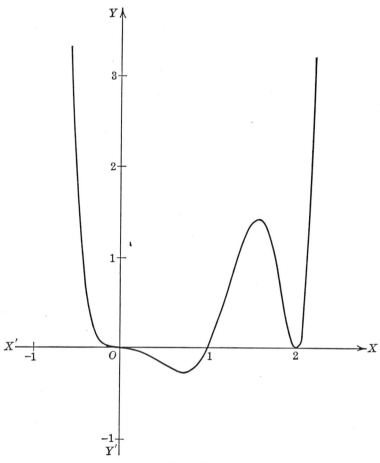

FIG. 35

### EXERCISES

**1.** Prove that, if two rational integral functions of degrees $n$ or less are equal for more than $n$ values of the variable $x$, they are equal for all values of $x$; that is, the equality is an identity.

**2.** Show that the function $x^6 + x^2 + 1$ has no real zeros, and draw its graph.

**3.** Divide $x^3 + x - 1$ by $x - 1$ synthetically, and show that the coefficients of the quotient and also the remainder are all positive. Since division of this cubic expression by $x - r$, where $r > 1$, would produce still greater positive coefficients and a positive remainder, deduce the fact that this function can have no zero greater than unity.

**4.** Show that the function of Exercise 3 has a positive zero between 0 and 1 and that it has no negative zeros. Draw the graph of the function.

**5.** Show that the function $x^3 - 2ax^2 + (a^2 + 3)x$ has 0 and $a \pm \sqrt{3}\, i$ as its zeros. On one set of axes, draw the graphs of this function when $a = 0$, $a = 3$, and $a = 5$. It will be found that the first curve sharply cuts each horizontal line in only one point; that the second crosses the line $y = 8$ tangentially; and that the third sharply cuts the line $y = 20$ in three distinct points. These three examples illustrate the fact that, although the presence of complex zeros does not affect the real zeros of a rational integral function, the nature of the functional variation may be markedly altered by changing the values of the complex zeros alone.

Sketch the graph of each of the functions in Exercises 6–25.

**6.** $x^3 - 4x$.

**7.** $x^4 - 9x^2$.

**8.** $x^3 + 4x^2 + 4x$.

**9.** $x^4 - 2x^3 + x^2$.

**10.** $x^4 - 3x^3$.

**11.** $x^4 - 6x^3 + 12x^2 - 8x$.

**12.** $x^5 + 2x^4 + x^3$.

**13.** $2x^5 - 5x^4$.

**14.** $x^3 + 1$.

**15.** $x^3 - 8$.

**16.** $x^4 - 1$.

**17.** $x^5 + 32$.

**18.** $x^6 - 64$.

**19.** $x^4 - 2x^3 + 2x^2$.

**20.** $x^5 + 2x^4 + 5x^3$.

**21.** $243 - x^5$.

**22.** $x^4 - x^3 + 2x^2 - x + 1$.

**23.** $x^3 - 7x - 6$.

**24.** $2x^3 + x^2 - 9$.

**25.** $16x^4 - 16x^3 - 12x - 9$.

**79. Rule of signs.**  Let there be given a rational integral equation, $P(x) = 0$, all of whose coefficients are real numbers. In an attempt to determine all the real solutions of this equation, it would manifestly be desirable to know how many of the $n$ roots are positive, how many are negative, and how many are complex.

Although we cannot always determine the exact number of roots of each of these three classes, we can establish a criterion for the maximum possible number of positive roots and the maximum possible number of negative roots. The criterion is the so-called rule of signs, which we shall develop in this article.

When two successive terms of a polynomial, written according to descending powers of the variable, have like signs, we say that there is a **permanence** of sign, and when two successive terms have unlike signs, there is said to be a **variation** of sign. Thus, the polynomial

$$P(x) \equiv x^5 - 2x^4 - 2x^3 + 7x^2 - 8x + 4$$

has one permanence and four variations of sign. We may now state the **rule of signs,**[*] as follows:

*If a rational integral equation $P(x) = 0$, with real coefficients, has $m$ variations of sign, then the number of positive roots of $P(x) = 0$ will be $m - 2k$, where $k$ is a positive integer or zero.*

[*] Often referred to as Descartes's rule of signs, after the French mathematician and philosopher, René Descartes (1596–1650).

Thus the number of positive roots cannot exceed the number $m$ of variations of sign; the number of positive roots must either be equal to $m$ or less by an even integer.

Since the polynomial in the above example has four variations of sign, this function, according to the rule of signs, may have four, two, or no positive zeros.

To establish this rule for a typical case, suppose that the signs of the terms of $P(x)$ vary in the following way:

$$+ \cdots\cdots + - \cdots\cdots - + \cdots\cdots + - \cdots\cdots -$$

Here we have assumed three variations and an indefinite number of permanences, the latter being represented by the dots in each of the four groups of like signs. We shall show first that, if $P(x)$ is multiplied by $x - r$, where $r$ is a positive number, so that the product has one more positive zero than $P(x)$ has, then the number of variations of signs in the product must exceed the number in $P(x)$ by an odd number.

When $P(x)$ is multiplied first by $x$ and then by $-r$, and the results added in the usual way, the signs involved will be arranged as follows:

$$
\begin{array}{l}
+ \quad \cdots\cdots + - \quad\ \cdots\cdots - + \quad\ \cdots\cdots + - \quad\ \cdots\cdots - \\
\ - \ \ \cdots\ \ - - + \ \ \cdots\ \ + + - \ \ \cdots\ \ - - + \ \ \cdots\ \ + + \\
\hline
+ \pm \ \ \cdots\ \ \pm - \pm \ \ \cdots\ \ \pm + \pm \ \ \cdots\ \ \pm - \pm \ \ \cdots\ \ \pm +
\end{array}
$$

The double signs indicate an ambiguity; the actual sign in each of these positions will depend upon the relative magnitudes of the two terms of opposite sign immediately above. Likewise, the positions represented by dots in the sum are occupied by terms with ambiguous signs. Thus each permanence of sign in $P(x)$ is replaced in the product $(x - r)P(x)$ by an ambiguity.

However, we see that there is a variation of sign in the product, corresponding to each variation of sign in $P(x)$, and an additional variation at the end. Therefore the product must have at least one more variation than $P(x)$ has. If the number of variations in the product exceeds the number in $P(x)$ by more than one, the excess must be an odd number. For, consider a complete group $G$ of permanences in $P(x)$, say of positive signs, followed by a minus sign (which begins the following group). In the product $(x - r)P(x)$, the group corresponding to $G$ must start with a plus sign and there must be a minus sign beginning the next corresponding group. If there is a variation from plus to minus within the group corresponding to $G$ in $(x - r)P(x)$, either this is maintained into the next group or each additional variation to a plus within the first group must be followed by a second variation to minus in order that the next group begin with a minus sign.

Consequently the total number of variations in the product $(x - r)P(x)$ exceeds that in $P(x)$ by an odd positive integer.

Now let $r_1, r_2, \cdots, r_p$ denote all the positive zeros of $P(x)$, and let $Q(x)$ denote the product of all the factors of $P(x)$ corresponding to its $n - p$ negative and complex zeros. The first and last terms of $Q(x)$ must have the same sign; for, if they were of opposite sign, a sufficiently large positive value $x_1$ would make $Q(x_1)$ and $Q(0)$ unlike in sign, whence $Q(x)$ would have a positive zero (Art. 78), contrary to supposition. Hence $Q(x)$ will have an even number $2h$ of variations of sign. When $Q(x)$ is multiplied by $x - r_1$, an odd number $(2k_1 + 1)$ of variations of sign is introduced, as shown above. Multiplying $(x - r_1)Q(x)$ by $x - r_2$, we introduce $2k_2 + 1$ additional variations of sign, and so on. Hence $P(x)$ will involve

$$2h + (2k_1 + 1) + (2k_2 + 1) + \cdots + (2k_p + 1)$$
$$= 2(h + k_1 + k_2 + \cdots + k_p) + p$$

variations of sign. That is, the number of variations of sign in $P(x)$ will be equal to the number $p$ of its positive zeros, or will be greater by an even number, and the rule of signs is established.

Having determined the maximum possible number of positive zeros of $P(x)$, we can find the maximum possible number of negative zeros in the following way. If we replace $x$ in $P(x)$ by $-x$, we get a function $P(-x)$ whose zeros are the negatives of those of $P(x)$. Consequently, by the rule of signs, the number of positive zeros of $P(-x)$, and therefore the number of negative zeros of $P(x)$, must be equal to the number of variations in sign of $P(-x)$ or less than this number by an even positive integer.

Thus, in connection with our previous examples, $P(x) \equiv x^5 - 2x^4 -2x^3 + 7x^2 - 8x + 4$, we have $P(-x) \equiv -x^5 - 2x^4 + 2x^3 + 7x^2 + 8x + 4$, in which there is only one variation of sign. Hence there can be no more than one negative zero of $P(x)$, and since one minus an even number is impossible here, there will actually be one negative zero of $P(x)$.

### EXERCISES

Apply the rule of signs to each of the polynomials in Exercises 1–16, and give all possible information concerning the nature of their zeros.

1. $x^3 - 2x^2 - 1$.     2. $x^4 + 2$.
3. $x^3 + 3x + 1$.       4. $x^3 + 3x^2 + 5x + 1$.

**5.** $x^5 - 2$.

**6.** $x^5 + 2x^3 + x$.

**7.** $x^6 - 3$.

**8.** $x^7 + x^3 - 3$.

**9.** $2x^6 + x^4 + 3$.

**10.** $x^8 + 2x^4 + 1$.

**11.** $3x^5 - x + 4$.

**12.** $5 - 2x^3 - x^8$.

**13.** $4 + x^2 - 3x^6$.

**14.** $x^5 + 6x^4 + 2x^2 - 3x - 5$.

**15.** $x^4 - x^3 + x^2 - x + 1$.

**16.** $x^9 + x^5 + x$.

**17.** Show that a polynomial all of whose coefficients are positive cannot have a positive zero, and that, if the number of variations is odd, the polynomial has at least one positive zero.

**18.** Show that a polynomial which involves only even powers of the variable, and whose coefficients, including the constant term, are all positive, has no real zeros.

**19.** Show that a polynomial containing only odd powers of the variable and no constant term, for which the coefficients are all positive, has zero as its only real zero.

**20.** Show that, if a polynomial has only real zeros and if all its coefficients $a_0$, $a_1$, $\cdots$, $a_n$ are different from zero, then the number of positive zeros is equal to the number of variations, and the number of negative zeros is equal to the number of permanences.

**21.** Show that a polynomial all of whose coefficients are different from zero and of alternating signs cannot have a negative zero.

**22.** Show that the equation $x^{2m} + a^2 = 0$, where $m$ is a positive integer and $a$ is a positive number, has $2m$ complex roots.

**23.** Show that the equation $x^{2m} - a^2 = 0$, where $m$ is a positive integer and $a$ is a positive number, has $2m - 2$ complex roots.

**24.** Show that the equation $x^{2m+1} - a^2 = 0$, where $m$ is a positive integer and $a$ is a positive number, has one positive root and $2m$ complex roots.

**25.** Show that the equation $x^{2m+1} + a^2 = 0$, where $m$ is a positive integer and $a$ is a positive number, has one negative root and $2m$ complex roots.

## 80. Rational roots.

We consider now a rational integral equation,

$$P(x) \equiv a_0 x^n + a_1 x^{n-1} + \cdots + a_{n-1} x + a_n = 0, \tag{1}$$

in which the coefficients are rational numbers. If any coefficients are fractional, we may multiply both members of (1) by a suitable integer so as to obtain an equivalent equation all of whose coefficients are integers (or zero) with no common integral factor. Also, if equation (1) has zero as an $m$-fold solution, we may set this aside by dividing by $x^m$.

Suppose these two matters to be thus taken care of, so that (1) is now an equation in which all coefficients are integers or zero, and in which $a_0$ and $a_n$ are both different from zero. A given equation of this form may or may not have rational roots; if it does possess a rational root $p/q$, where $p$ and $q$ are integers that may be supposed to have no common integral divisor, then the following theorem applies:

*Let $P(x) = 0$ be a rational integral equation with integral coefficients, $a_0 \neq 0$ and $a_n \neq 0$. If $P(p/q) = 0$, where $p$ and $q$ are positive or negative* *integers with no common integral divisor, then p is a divisor of $a_n$ and q is a divisor of $a_0$.*

This theorem is easily proved. By supposition we have

$$P\left(\frac{p}{q}\right) = a_0\left(\frac{p}{q}\right)^n + a_1\left(\frac{p}{q}\right)^{n-1} + \cdots + a_{n-1}\left(\frac{p}{q}\right) + a_n = 0. \quad (2)$$

If we multiply both members of this equation by $q^{n-1}$, we get

$$\frac{a_0 p^n}{q} + a_1 p^{n-1} + \cdots + a_{n-1}pq^{n-2} + a_n q^{n-1} = 0.$$

Now each term beyond the first in the left member of this relation is an integer, so that their sum is integral. Hence the quantity $-a_0 p^n/q$, equal to that sum, must be an integer. Since $p$ and $q$ have no common integral factor, it follows that $a_0$ must be divisible by $q$.

Similarly, if we multiply both members of (2) by $q^n/p$, we find

$$a_0 p^{n-1} + a_1 p^{n-2}q + \cdots + a_{n-1}q^{n-1} + \frac{a_n q^n}{p} = 0.$$

Since all but the last term in this expression are integers, $a_n q^n/p$ must be integral, whence it follows that $a_n$ must have $p$ as a factor.

This theorem enables us to limit our search for rational roots of a given equation to a definite number of possibilities, as in the examples below. Having exhausted all these possibilities, we can be certain that all remaining roots are either irrational or complex.

*Example 1.* Find all rational roots of the equation

$$2x^4 + 5x^3 - x^2 + 5x - 3 = 0.$$

*Solution.* This equation is of the stipulated form, with $a_0 = 2$ and $a_n = -3$. Thus possible values of $p$ are $\pm 1$ and $\pm 3$; possible values of $q$ are $\pm 1$ and $\pm 2$. Hence there are eight possible rational roots:

$$\pm 1, \quad \pm 3, \quad \pm\tfrac{1}{2}, \quad \pm\tfrac{3}{2}.$$

If we try each of the above eight possibilities in turn, we find that $-3$ and $\tfrac{1}{2}$ are roots:

$$
\begin{array}{l}
2 + 5 - 1 + 5 - 3 \underline{\,|\,-3} \\
\ \ \ \ -6 + 3 - 6 + 3 \\
\hline
2 - 1 + 2 - 1 \underline{\,|\,\tfrac{1}{2}} \\
\ \ \ \ + 1 + 0 + 1 \\
\hline
2 + 0 + 2
\end{array}
$$

Consequently the given equation may be written in the form

$$(x + 3)(2x - 1)(x^2 + 1) = 0,$$

whence all four roots are in this case obtainable; they are

$$x = -3, \quad x = \tfrac{1}{2}, \quad x = \pm i.$$

It should be noted that, after having found $-3$ as one root, we deal thereafter with the polynomial $2x^3 - x^2 + 2x - 1$, obtained as the quotient of the given polynomial by $x + 3$. If, as here, there are rational roots, the removal of the factors corresponding to these roots yields a polynomial that is easier to treat. When the quotient has been reduced to a quadratic, the remaining two roots are, of course, easily obtained by the methods of Chapter IX.

An important corollary of our theorem on rational roots may be stated as follows:

*If $a_0 = 1$, and the remaining coefficients of $P(x)$ are integers, with $a_n \neq 0$, then any rational root of $P(x) = 0$ must be an integer and a divisor of $a_n$.*

For, if $p/q$ is a root of such an equation, $q$ will be a divisor of $a_0 = 1$, and therefore $q$ must be 1 or $-1$, so that $p/q$ is an integral root.

*Example 2.* Find all rational roots of the equation

$$x^4 - 4x^3 + x^2 - 5x + 4 = 0.$$

*Solution.* By the above corollary, the only possible rational roots are $\pm 1$, $\pm 2$, and $\pm 4$. Now the rule of signs shows that this equation can have no negative root, and consequently we need test only 1, 2, and 4. When this is done, it is found that 4 is the only rational root, and our equation may then be written as

$$(x - 4)(x^3 + x - 1) = 0.$$

From this relation we find that the given equation must have, in addition to the rational solution $x = 4$, an irrational root between 0 and 1 and two conjugate complex roots.

### EXERCISES

Determine all rational zeros of each of the following functions.

1. $x^3 + 2x + 3$.

2. $x^3 + 2x^2 - x - 2$.

3. $x^4 - 3x^3 + 2x^2 - 6x$.

4. $2x^3 + x^2 + 8x + 4$.

5. $2x^3 - 3x^2 - 10x + 15$.

6. $x^6 - 2x^4 + 4x^2 - 8$.

7. $4x^3 - 14x^2 - 6x + 21$.

8. $x^3 - 8x^2 + 20x - 16$.

9. $25x^3 - 5x^2 - 10x + 2$.

10. $64x^3 - 16x^2 - 4x + 1$.

11. $x^4 - x^3 - 5x^2 - x - 6$.

12. $6x^3 - 5x^2 - 3x + 2$.

13. $3x^4 - 2x^3 + 3x^2 + x - 2$.

14. $x^6 - 2x^4 + 2x^2 - 4$.

15. $x^5 - 3x^3 + 2x^2 + 2x - 2$.

16. $x^5 + 4x^4 - 3x - 12$.

17. $x^5 + 4x^3 - 3x^2 - 12$.

18. $4x^5 - x^3 + 12x^2 - 3$.

19. $4x^6 - 17x^4 + 20x^2 - 4$.

20. $x^5 - 2x^3 - 27x^2 + 54$.

**81. Irrational roots.** Suppose now that all rational roots of the equation $P(x) = 0$ have been determined, and that the linear factors corresponding to these roots have been removed. In general, there will remain a rational integral equation of degree $m$, say, where $m \leqq n$, having integral coefficients and such that all $m$ of its roots are either irrational real numbers or complex numbers.

There are various methods for determining the irrational and complex zeros of a polynomial.* We shall consider here only one process, which involves no new concepts or theory, and which applies to irrational algebraic and transcendental functions as well as to rational integral functions. This is the method of successive approximations, which was briefly referred to and applied to a simple equation in Art. 11. We illustrate the process as part of a general problem in the determination of roots; this example will serve also to summarize the techniques previously developed.

*Example 1.*   Find all real roots of the equation

$$P(x) \equiv x^4 + 2x^3 + x^2 - x - 6 = 0, \tag{1}$$

correct to five significant figures.

*Solution.*   The rule of signs tells us that equation (1) has just one positive root. In addition, there may be three negative roots or one negative root and two conjugate complex roots.

Applying the corollary to the theorem of Art. 80, we find that the only possible rational roots are $\pm 1$, $\pm 2$, $\pm 3$, and $\pm 6$. Testing all eight of these possibilities, we get only $x = -2$ as a solution:

$$
\begin{array}{r}
1 + 2 + 1 - 1 - 6 \ \underline{\big|\, -2} \\
-2 + 0 - 2 + 6 \\
\hline
1 + 0 + 1 - 3 + 0
\end{array}
$$

Hence

$$P(x) \equiv (x + 2)(x^3 + x - 3) = 0. \tag{2}$$

Putting aside the solution $x = -2$, we then have to consider the equation

$$Q(x) \equiv x^3 + x - 3 = 0. \tag{3}$$

The rule of signs, applied to this equation, shows that (3) has one positive and no negative roots. Thus the original equation (1) has the negative rational root $x = -2$, a positive irrational root, and two conjugate complex roots.

* See, for example, Conkwright's *Introduction to the Theory of Equations.* Graeffe's method (Chapter XII) may be used to find both irrational and complex zeros of polynomials; Horner's method (Art. 50) serves to determine only irrational real zeros of polynomials; Newton's method (Art. 53), which applies concepts from calculus, may be used to find real zeros of other types of functions as well as of polynomials.

It remains to determine the positive irrational root of equation (3). Since $Q(1) = -1$ and $Q(2) = 7$, the solution sought must have a value between 1 and 2. The graph of the function $Q(x)$ (Fig. 36) indicates that the root is approximately equal to 1.2; we take this as our first approximation. By syn-

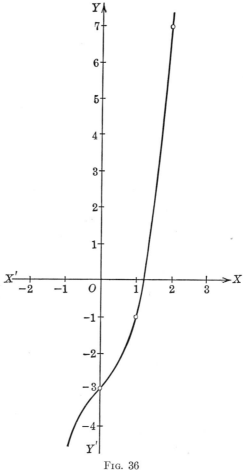

Fig. 36

thetic division and the remainder theorem, we find $Q(1.2) = -0.072$; since this is negative, the required root must be slightly greater than 1.2.

To get our next approximation, we also compute $Q(1.3) = 0.497$ by means of synthetic division. We then see that the function $Q(x)$ varies by the amount $0.497 - (-0.072) = 0.569$ when $x$ changes, by 0.1, from 1.2 to 1.3. For the second approximation, we use the principle of interpolation; that is, although the variation of $Q(x)$ is not linear, the assumption of proportionality is justified, in the small interval $1.2 < x < 1.3$, for approximation purposes. We therefore get, as our second approximation,

$$x = 1.2 + 0.1 \frac{0.072}{0.569} = 1.213^-.$$

Synthetic division yields $Q(1.213) = -0.002$ approximately, and consequently the desired root is a little larger than 1.213. We then compute $Q(1.214) = 0.003$ approximately, whence it appears that the actual root is a little less than midway between 1.213 and 1.214. Synthetic division gives us $Q(1.2135) = 0.0005$, so that 1.2135 is slightly too large, and when we find $Q(1.2134) = -0.0001$, we conclude that the required root is $x = 1.2134^+$, correct to five significant figures.

We therefore have, to four decimal places,

$$P(x) = (x + 2)(x - 1.2134)(x^2 + 1.2134x + 2.4723),$$

and it is possible here to find the approximate values of the two complex roots, using the quadratic formula. The final result is that the four roots of equation (1) are given very nearly by

$$x = -2, \quad x = 1.2134, \quad x = -0.6067 \pm 1.4506i.$$

Successive approximations beyond the third would, if desired, give us still greater accuracy.

As previously stated, the process illustrated by the above example is quite general in its application to the determination of irrational zeros of functions—rational or irrational, algebraic or transcendental—provided merely that the coefficients are real. When complex zeros are required, and in particular when the function at hand involves complex numbers, the following device is sometimes useful. We replace $x$ in the equation by $y + iz$, say, where $y$ and $z$ are to be real; since we are seeking complex values of $x$, we stipulate that $z \neq 0$. The resulting equation then involves two real variables with complex coefficients. If this equation can be written in the form $f(y, z) + ig(y, z) = 0$, where $f(y, z)$ and $g(y, z)$ are real functions,* we thereby get a system of two equations, involving two variables,

$$f(y, z) = 0, \qquad g(y, z) = 0. \tag{4}$$

Real values of $y$ and $z$ satisfying these equations simultaneously yield complex zeros, $x = y + iz$, of the given equation. The problem of finding real solutions of the system (4) may present practical difficulties, but sometimes one of the variables, $y$ or $z$, may be eliminated between

---

* This can surely be done with little trouble in the case of rational integral equations, if we expand each integral power of $y + iz$ by means of the binomial theorem

the two equations, and the resulting relation, containing one unknown, can then be solved by successive approximations. This is illustrated in the following example.

*Example 2.* Using the above method, find the complex solutions of the equation of Example 1.

*Solution.* After the real rational solution, $x = -2$, of equation (1) was removed, we were left in Example 1 with the cubic equation (3),

$$x^3 + x - 3 = 0.$$

Following the procedure outlined above, we get with the substitution $x = y + iz$,

$$(y + iz)^3 + (y + iz) - 3 = 0,$$

$$y^3 + 3iy^2z - 3yz^2 - iz^3 + y + iz - 3 = 0,$$

whence we have the system

$$y^3 - 3yz^2 + y - 3 = 0, \quad 3y^2z - z^3 + z = 0. \tag{5}$$

The second of these equations yields $z = 0$; this value inserted in the first equation gives us merely $y^3 + y - 3 = 0$, the original cubic equation with $y$ replacing $x$. But the second of equations (5) also gives us

$$z^2 = 3y^2 + 1. \tag{6}$$

Substituting this into the first of equations (5), there is obtained

$$y^3 - 9y^3 - 3y + y - 3 = 0,$$

or

$$8y^3 + 2y + 3 = 0. \tag{7}$$

This equation has, by the rule of signs, no positive root, one negative root, and two complex roots. Since, by supposition, $y$ is real, only the single negative solution of (7) is relevant. By the method of successive approximations we get $y = -0.6067$, whence (6) gives us

$$z = \pm\sqrt{3y^2 + 1} = \pm 1.4506.$$

Hence the only complex solutions of equation (1) are the conjugate pair

$$x = y + iz = -0.6067 \pm 1.4506i.$$

These values agree with those obtained in Example 1.

### EXERCISES

For each of the equations of Exercises 1–10, find, correct to four significant figures, the irrational root lying in the indicated range.

**1.** $3x^3 - 2x^2 - 6x + 4 = 0,$    $1 < x < 2.$
**2.** $x^4 + x^3 - 3x^2 - 7x - 28 = 0,$    $2 < x < 3.$
**3.** $x^4 - 2x^3 - 6x^2 + 24x - 72 = 0,$    $-4 < x < -3.$

**4.** $x^4 - x^3 - x^2 - 2x - 6 = 0,$     $2 < x < 3.$
**5.** $3x^4 + 6x^3 - x^2 + 4x - 2 = 0,$     $-3 < x < -2.$
**6.** $x^4 + 3x^3 + 6x + 4 = 0,$     $-1 < x < 0.$
**7.** $4x^4 + 2x^3 - 8x^2 + x - 5 = 0,$     $1 < x < 2.$
**8.** $x^4 - 9x^2 + 6x - 1 = 0,$     $2 < x < 3.$
**9.** $2x^4 - x^2 - 18x - 4 = 0,$     $2 < x < 3.$
**10.** $x^5 + x^4 + 2x^3 - 4x^2 - 4x - 8 = 0,$     $1 < x < 2.$

**11–15.** Find, correct to four significant figures, the complex roots of the equations of Exercises 2, 3, 5, 6, 9.

**16.** The length of a rectangular box is twice its depth, and its width is 3 in. more than its depth. The volume of the box is 200 cu. in. Find the depth to the nearest $\frac{1}{16}$ in.

**17.** The depth $h$ to which a sphere of radius $R$ and specific gravity $s < 1$ will sink in water is given by $h^3 - 3Rh^2 + 4R^3s = 0$. Find $h$ to the nearest $\frac{1}{16}$ in. if $R = 4$ in. and $s = 0.75$.

**18.** A rectangular box has the dimensions 4, 8, and 16 in. By increasing each dimension by the same amount $x$, the capacity of the box is doubled. Find $x$ to the nearest $\frac{1}{8}$ in.

**19.** A 12-ft. ladder, leaning against a wall, just touches a bench 3 ft. high and with its touching edge 3 ft. from the wall. How high up the wall (to the nearest inch) does the ladder reach?

**20.** Using the trigonometric identity $\sin 3\theta = 3 \sin \theta - 4 \sin^3 \theta$, find $\sin 10°$ correct to five decimal places.

**21.** Using the relation $\cos 3\theta = 4 \cos^3 \theta - 3 \cos \theta$, find $\cos 20°$ correct to five decimal places.

**22.** Using the relation $(1 - 3 \tan^2 \theta) \tan 3\theta = 3 \tan \theta - \tan^3 \theta$, find $\tan 15°$ correct to five decimal places.

**23.** The deflection $y$ at a distance $x$ from one end of a simply supported beam, $L$ ft. long and carrying only a load of $P$ lb. at its midpoint, is given by the equation $48EIy = P(3L^2x - 4x^3)$ for $0 \leq x \leq L/2$. Find, correct to the nearest inch, the distance $x$ at which the deflection is half that at the midpoint, taking $L = 12$ ft.

**24.** The deflection $y$ at a distance $x$ from one end of a simply supported beam, $L$ ft. long and carrying a uniform load of $w$ lb./ft., is given by the equation $24EIy = w(x^4 - 2Lx^3 + L^3x)$ for $0 \leq x \leq L$. Find, correct to the nearest inch, the smaller distance $x$ at which the deflection is half that at the midpoint, taking $L = 12$ ft.

**25.** A right circular cone is to be inscribed in a sphere of radius 3 in. and is to have a volume of 30 cu. in. Find, correct to the nearest hundredth of an inch, the two possible values of the altitude of the cone.

## 82. Relations between coefficients and roots.

In Art. 50 we found that there exist certain relations connecting the coefficients of a quadratic equation and the roots of the equation. These are particular instances of general relations connected with rational integral equations of any degree $n$.

Let the rational integral equation be written

$$x^n + \frac{a_1}{a_0} x^{n-1} + \cdots + \frac{a_{n-1}}{a_0} x + \frac{a_n}{a_0} = 0, \tag{1}$$

obtained from the general form by dividing by $a_0$, so that the leading coefficient is unity. If $r_1, r_2, \cdots, r_n$ are the $n$ roots of equation (1), then $(x - r_1)$, $(x - r_2)$, $\cdots$, $(x - r_n)$ are factors of the left member of (1), and the product of these $n$ linear factors will be identical with the above polynomial of degree $n$ and with unity as leading coefficient. Now by actual multiplication we find

$$(x - r_1)(x - r_2) \cdots (x - r_n) \equiv x^n - (r_1 + r_2 + \cdots + r_n)x^{n-1}$$

$$+ (r_1 r_2 + r_1 r_3 + \cdots + r_{n-1} r_n)x^{n-2} - \cdots + (-1)^n r_1 r_2 \cdots r_n. \quad (2)$$

This is another way of writing equation (1), so as to exhibit the coefficients as functions of the roots. Here the coefficient of $x^{n-1}$ is the negative of the sum of all the roots, that of $x^{n-2}$ is the sum of the products of the roots taken two at a time, that of $x^{n-3}$ is the negative of the sum of the products of the roots taken three at a time, and so on, until we get to the constant term, which is $(-1)^n$ times the product of the $n$ roots.

By comparison of (1) and (2) we then get

$$-\frac{a_1}{a_0} = r_1 + r_2 + \cdots + r_n$$

$$\frac{a_2}{a_0} = r_1 r_2 + r_1 r_3 + \cdots + r_{n-1} r_n,$$

$$-\frac{a_3}{a_0} = r_1 r_2 r_3 + r_1 r_2 r_4 + \cdots + r_{n-2} r_{n-1} r_n, \qquad (3)$$

$$\cdots \cdots \cdots \cdots \cdots,$$

$$(-1)^n \frac{a_n}{a_0} = r_1 r_2 r_3 \cdots r_n.$$

These relations are sometimes useful in solving an equation when the roots are known to be connected in a specific manner, as in the following example.

*Example 1.* It is known that the roots of the equation

$$x^3 - 3\sqrt{5}x^2 + 11x - \sqrt{5} = 0$$

are in arithmetic progression. Find the roots.

*Solution.* Let the three roots in arithmetic progression be denoted by $a - d$, $a$, and $a + d$, so that their sum is $3a$. Since we have $a_0 = 1$, $a_1 = -3\sqrt{5}$, $a_2 = 11$, $a_3 = -\sqrt{5}$, the first of relations (3) gives us

$$3\sqrt{5} = 3a,$$

whence
$$a = \sqrt{5}.$$

Hence the roots are $\sqrt{5} - d$, $\sqrt{5}$, and $\sqrt{5} + d$. Then the last of equations (3) yields

$$\sqrt{5} = (\sqrt{5} - d)\sqrt{5}(\sqrt{5} + d) = \sqrt{5}(5 - d^2),$$
$$1 = 5 - d^2,$$
$$d^2 = 4,$$
$$d = \pm 2.$$

Taking $d = 2$, we get as the required roots

$$\sqrt{5} - 2, \quad \sqrt{5}, \quad \sqrt{5} + 2;$$

with $d = -2$, we get the same three values in reverse order. We may check either by direct substitution or by using the second of relations (3); by the latter procedure, we have $a_2/a_0 = 11$, and $r_1 r_2 + r_1 r_3 + r_2 r_3 = (\sqrt{5} - 2)\sqrt{5} + (\sqrt{5} - 2)(\sqrt{5} + 2) + \sqrt{5}(\sqrt{5} + 2) = (5 - 2\sqrt{5}) + (5 - 4) + (5 + 2\sqrt{5}) = 11$.

We now regard the coefficients $a_0, a_1, \cdots, a_n$ as variable quantities. These variables may be independent or they may in turn be functions of other variables. As the coefficients vary, the roots of the equation

$$a_0 x^n + a_1 x^{n-1} + \cdots + a_{n-1} x + a_n = 0 \qquad (4)$$

will likewise vary, and conversely.

Suppose first that $a_n$ is allowed to approach zero, the other coefficients remaining constant. Then the last of relations (3), and equation (4) itself, show that one of the roots must likewise approach zero. If $a_n$ and $a_{n-1}$ both approach zero, the other coefficients remaining fixed, then two roots will approach zero. More generally, if

$$a_n \to 0, \ a_{n-1} \to 0, \ \cdots, \ a_{n-p+1} \to 0,$$

while $a_0, a_1, \cdots, a_{n-p}$ remain fixed, then just $p$ of the roots will approach zero.

In certain problems of analytic geometry, and elsewhere, it is necessary to determine the effect upon the coefficients when one or more roots increase beyond all bound, that is, become infinite. To examine this question, let $x$ be replaced in equation (4) by $1/z$, so that we have, after clearing of fractions,

$$a_0 + a_1 z + \cdots + a_{n-1} z^{n-1} + a_n z^n = 0 \qquad (5)$$

Then, as $z$ approaches zero, $x = 1/z$ will become infinite. The preceding discussion now leads to the following conclusions: If only $a_0 \to 0$, one root of (5) approaches zero, whence one root of (4) becomes infinite; if $a_0 \to 0$ and $a_1 \to 0$, all other coefficients remaining constant, two roots of (5) approach zero, so that two roots of (4) become infinite; and so on. In general, if $a_0 \to 0$, $a_1 \to 0$, $\cdots$, $a_{p-1} \to 0$, but $a_p$, $a_{p+1}$, $\cdots$, $a_n$ remain fixed, then just $p$ roots of equation (4) will become infinite.

*Example 2.* If, in the equation

$$4x^2 - 3xy - y^2 + 5x = 0, \tag{6}$$

$y$ is replaced by $mx + b$, there is obtained a quadratic equation in $x$ with coefficients that are functions of the quantities $m$ and $b$. Determine the values of $m$ and $b$ that make both roots of the quadratic infinite.

*Solution.* The quadratic equation in question is

$$4x^2 - 3x(mx + b) - (mx + b)^2 + 5x = 0,$$

or

$$(4 - 3m - m^2)x^2 - (3b + 2bm - 5)x - b^2 = 0. \tag{7}$$

Both roots of this equation will be infinite if $a_0 = 4 - 3m - m^2 = 0$ and $a_1 = -(3b + 2bm - 5) = 0$. From the first of these relations we get $m = 1$ and $m = -4$. When $m = 1$, the second relation yields $b = 1$; when $m = -4$, we get $b = -1$. Thus there are two pairs of values yielding two infinite roots:

$$m = 1, \qquad b = 1;$$

$$m = -4, \qquad b = -1.$$

This problem has the following geometric interpretation. The graph of the equation $4x^2 - 3xy - y^2 + 5x = 0$ is a curve called a hyperbola, and the equation $y = mx + b$ represents, for each chosen pair of values of $m$ and $b$, a straight line. Among all the straight lines thus obtainable, some may intersect the hyperbola (6) in two distinct points, some may yield only one point of intersection, and others may have no point in common with the hyperbola. The abscissa $x$ of a point of intersection will be a real solution of equation (7), and when both roots become infinite the points of intersection recede indefinitely from the origin. The straight lines $y = x + 1$ and $y = -4x - 1$ corresponding to the values found for $m$ and $b$ are called the asymptotes of the hyperbola. The student should plot the hyperbola and these two lines; it will be found that, as a point on the hyperbola recedes from the origin, it gets closer and closer to one or the other of these lines but that the curve and the lines never intersect.

### EXERCISES

**1.** If the sum of two of the roots of the equation $x^3 + 2x^2 - 5x - 6 = 0$ is 1, find the three roots.

**2.** Solve the equation $x^3 + 2x^2 - 12x - 24 = 0$, given that one root is the negative of a second root.

**3.** Solve the equation $4x^3 - 29x^2 + 55x - 12 = 0$, given that one root is the reciprocal of a second one.

**4.** If two roots of the equation $x^3 - 6x + 4\sqrt{2} = 0$ are equal, find all the roots.

**5.** Solve the equation $x^4 + 4x^3 - 2x^2 - 12x + 9 = 0$, given that it has two double roots.

**6.** Solve the equation $x^4 + 16x^3 + 86x^2 + 176x + 105 = 0$, given that the roots are in arithmetic progression.

**7.** Solve the equation $64x^3 - 280x^2 + 350x - 125 = 0$, given that the roots are in geometric progression.

**8.** Solve the equation $8x^4 - 20x^3 - 42x^2 - 23x - 4 = 0$, given that it has a triple root.

**9.** If the sum of two of the roots of the equation $4x^3 + kx^2 + 10x - 25 = 0$ is zero, find $k$.

**10.** If the roots of the equation $8x^3 + ax^2 + 46x + b = 0$ are in the ratio $1:3:5$, find $a$ and $b$.

**11.** Find, correct to three decimal places, the positive root of the equation $x^3 + x^2 + x - k = 0$ when (a) $k = 1$; (b) $k = 0.1$; (c) $k = 0.01$. What inference may be made on the basis of these results?

**12.** Find, correct to two decimal places, the positive root of the equation $kx^3 - x^2 - x - 1 = 0$ when (a) $k = 1$; (b) $k = 0.1$; (c) $k = 0.01$. What inference may be made on the basis of these results?

**13.** In the linear equation $Ax + By + C = 0$, where $B \neq 0$, substitute $mx$ for $y$ and determine $m$ so that the resulting equation shall have an infinite root. What is the geometric interpretation of this problem?

**14.** The general quadratic equation in two variables, $Ax^2 + Bxy + Cy^2 + Dx + Ey + F = 0$, represents an ellipse, a parabola, or a hyperbola * according as $B^2 - 4AC$ is negative, zero, or positive. Replace $y$ by $mx + b$, and show that the resulting quadratic equation can have one or two infinite roots corresponding to real values of $m$ and $b$ only in the case of the hyperbola. Hence deduce the fact that the hyperbola is the only one of these three types of curves that possesses asymptotes.

**15.** Consider the power function $y = x^n$, where $n$ is an integer. Replace $y$ by $mx + b$, and show that the graph of $y = x^n$ can have an asymptote only if $n$ is a negative integer. Find the equation of this asymptote, and compare your result with the findings of Art. 68.

In each of the equations of Exercises 16–20, use the method of Example 2, Art. 82, to determine asymptotes. Draw the graph of each curve, and verify your results geometrically.

**16.** $y^2 - 4x^2 = 1$.      **17.** $3x^2 - 4xy + y^2 = 2$.

**18.** $y^3 - x^2y + x^2 = 0$.      **19.** $x^3 + y^3 = 3xy$.

**20.** $y^3 + 4xy^2 + 3x^2y - 24x^2 = 3$.

**83. Transcendental equations.** As the final topic of this chapter, we consider equations that, although not rational integral with respect to the variable $x$ itself, are in rational integral form, so that they can be

---

* Except for the special cases in which the graph degenerates into straight lines or when there is no geometric representation.

treated by the methods previously discussed. In other words, we shall be concerned here with equations that are in, or can be made to assume, the form

$$a_0 y^n + a_1 y^{n-1} + \cdots + a_{n-1} y + a_n = 0, \tag{1}$$

where $y$ is some specific function of the variable $x$ whose solution values are desired.

We have already considered this type of problem when $n = 2$ (Arts. 51–52). The student should review the methods of solving equations in quadratic form, as we shall apply similar techniques to the cases where $n > 2$.

*Example 1.* Solve the trigonometric equation

$$2 \sin^4 x - 5 \sin x \cos^2 x - 4 \cos^2 x + 10 \sin x + 6 = 0 \tag{2}$$

for non-negative values of $x$ less than $2\pi$.

*Solution.* This equation involves two trigonometric functions of $x$, $\sin x$ and $\cos x$. If we replace $\cos^2 x$ by $1 - \sin^2 x$, we get

$$2 \sin^4 x - 5(\sin x)(1 - \sin^2 x) - 4(1 - \sin^2 x) + 10 \sin x + 6 = 0,$$

or

$$2 \sin^4 x + 5 \sin^3 x + 4 \sin^2 x + 5 \sin x + 2 = 0,$$

which is evidently of the form (1), with $y = \sin x$. For simplicity and brevity, we therefore write our equation as

$$2y^4 + 5y^3 + 4y^2 + 5y + 2 = 0, \tag{3}$$

where $y = \sin x$.

By the rule of signs, this equation can have no positive roots. By the theorem of Art. 80, the only possible negative rational roots are $-\frac{1}{2}$, $-1$, and $-2$. Using synthetic division and the remainder theorem, we find that $y = -\frac{1}{2}$ and $y = -2$ satisfy equation (3), and that the equation may be written in factored form as

$$(2y + 1)(y + 2)(y^2 + 1) = 0.$$

Hence the four roots of (3) are

$$y = -\tfrac{1}{2}, \qquad y = -2, \qquad y = \pm i.$$

Since $y$ denotes $\sin x$, the conjugate complex roots $\pm i$ have no significance, nor has the value $-2$ since $\sin x$ cannot be less than $-1$. Consequently the only relevant solution is

$$\sin x = -\tfrac{1}{2},$$

from which we get

$$x = \frac{7\pi}{6} \quad \text{and} \quad x = \frac{11\pi}{6}$$

as the only solutions of equation (2) in the specified range.

*Example 2.* Find the real solutions of the equation

$$e^{5x} + 2e^{4x} - 4e^{2x} - 9e^x - 6 = 0. \tag{4}$$

*Solution.* This equation is already in the form (1); if we set $y = e^x$, we get the rational integral equation

$$y^5 + 2y^4 - 4y^2 - 9y - 6 = 0. \tag{5}$$

Now, since $e^x$ is positive for all real values of $x$ (Art. 70), we need seek only positive roots of equation (5). The rule of signs shows that there is just one positive root.

The corollary to the theorem of Art. 80 indicates that the only possible rational roots of equation (5) are $\pm1, \pm2, \pm3, \pm6$. Of these eight possibilities, only $y = -1$ is found to satisfy the equation. Dividing both members of (5) by $y + 1$, we then have

$$y^4 + y^3 - y^2 - 3y - 6 = 0, \tag{6}$$

and this equation possesses the single positive solution we are seeking.

Since the desired positive root of equation (6) is irrational, we use the method of Art. 81. The root, correct to four significant figures, is found to be

$$y = 1.732.$$

Thus we have

$$e^x = 1.732,$$

whence we get

$$x = \ln 1.732 = 0.5493$$

approximately.

## EXERCISES

Solve each of the equations in Exercises 1–10 for non-negative values of $x$ less than $2\pi$.

1. $\sin^3 x + 3 \sin^2 x - 4 = 0$.
2. $2 \cos^3 x - 3 \cos^2 x - 3 \cos x + 2 = 0$.
3. $\cos^3 x - 3 \sin^2 x - \cos x = 0$.
4. $2 \sin^3 x - 3 \cos^2 x - 11 \sin x - 3 = 0$.
5. $\tan^3 x - \sec^2 x - \tan x + 2 = 0$.
6. $12 \csc^3 x + 17 \cot^2 x + 2 \csc x + 14 = 0$.
7. $6 \sec^3 x - 7 \tan^2 x - 9 \sec x - 9 = 0$.
8. $\cos^4 x + \sin^3 x - \cos^2 x - 2 \sin x - 2 = 0$.
9. $\sec^3 x - 7 \tan^2 x + 15 \sec x - 16 = 0$.
10. $4 \sin^4 x - 7 \sin x \cos^2 x - 6 \cos^2 x + 21 \sin x + 2 = 0$.

Find the real values of $x$ satisfying each of the equations in Exercises 11–20.

11. $e^{3x} + e^x - 2 = 0$.
12. $e^{3x} - 2e^{2x} + 4e^x - 8 = 0$.
13. $e^{2x} + 4e^x - 1 - 4e^{-x} = 0$.
14. $8e^{-3x} + 4e^{-2x} + 1 = 0$.
15. $e^{-4x} - 4e^{-3x} - 5e^{-2x} + 36e^{-x} - 36 = 0$.
16. $\log (3x + 5) + \log (2x - 5) = 3 - \log (x + 5)$.

**17.** $\log (3x + 4) + 2 \log (3x - 5) = 1$.

**18.** $\log (10 - x^2) + \log (2x - 5) = 0$.

**19.** $2 \log (x + 6) + \log (x^2 - 6) = 3$.

**20.** $3 \log (x - 1) + \log (3 - x) = 0$.

Using principal values, solve each of the following equations.

**21.** $2 \arcsin x - \arcsin \sqrt{x} = \pi/2$.

**22.** $2 \arccos \sqrt{1 - x^2} + \arccos \sqrt{1 - x} = \pi/2$.

**23.** $\arccos (1 - 2x) - 2 \arcsin x = 0$.

**24.** $\arctan 2x + \arccos \sqrt{1 - x} = \pi/2$.

**25.** $2 \arctan x - \arcsin (1 - x) = \pi/2$.

## SUPPLEMENTARY EXERCISES

Find the smallest positive value of $x$ satisfying each of the equations in Exercises 1–6.

**1.** $8 \cos^4 x - 20 \cos^3 x - 2 \sin^2 x + 15 \cos x - 4 = 0$.

**2.** $2 \tan^5 x + 5 \sec^4 x + 2 \tan^3 x - 8 \sec^2 x + 5 \tan x + 5 = 0$.

**3.** $4e^{4x} - 4e^{3x} + 5e^{2x} - 8e^x - 6 = 0$.

**4.** $40e^{-4x} + 46e^{-3x} + 9e^{-2x} - 4e^{-x} - 1 = 0$.

**5.** $\log (6x + 2) + \log (4x^2 + 1) = 1$.

**6.** $2 \log x + \log (x^4 - 5) = 2$.

**7.** Let $P(x)$ be a polynomial of degree $n$. (a) If $P(-x) = P(x)$ identically, show that the coefficients of the odd powers of $x$ in $P(x)$ are all zero; (b) if $P(-x) = -P(x)$ identically, show that the coefficients of the even powers of $x$ and the constant term are all zero.

**8.** If 1 is a root of the equation $3x^4 - 2kx^3 + (k - 2)x^2 + 1 = 0$ show that it must be a double root.

**9.** For what real values of $k$ is $k$ a root of the equation $4x^4 - 4kx^3 - 3k^2x^2 + 2k^3x + 8k = 0$? What is the multiplicity of the root $k$ for each of its permissible values?

**10.** Show that $-1$ is a root of the equation $x^4 + kx^3 + 2kx^2 + kx - 1 = 0$ for all values of $k$, but that no value of $k$ will make $-1$ a double root.

**11.** Determine values of $a$ and $b$ such that $x^4 + ax^2 + bx + 12 = 0$ shall have 2 as a double root, and find the other two roots.

**12.** Show that $k$ will be a root of the equation $x^4 + 3kx^3 - 3k^2x^2 - 7k^3x + 6k^4 + c = 0$ if and only if $c = 0$, and that $k$ will then be a double root.

**13.** Let $P(x)$ be a polynomial of degree $n \geq 2$. If $P(x)$ is divided by $(x - a)(x - b)$, where $a$ and $b$ are constants, $a \neq b$, show that the remainder is

$$\frac{P(a) - P(b)}{a - b} x + \frac{aP(b) - bP(a)}{a - b}.$$

**14.** Show that one root of the equation $x^3 + ax^2 + bx + c = 0$ is the negative of another root if and only if $ab = c$.

**15.** Show that the equation $x^3 + ax + b = 0$ has a multiple root if and only if $4a^3 + 27b^2 = 0$.

**84. Permutations.** In Art. 30 we found that the expansion of a determinant of order $n$ contains $n!$ terms since there are $n!$ ways in which the numbers $1, 2, \cdots, n$ can be ordered or arranged. The reasoning used in that connection is an instance of the following fundamental principle:

Suppose that there are $n$ acts to be performed successively. Let $m_1$ be the number of ways in which the first act can be done. After the first act has been completed, let $m_2$ be the number of ways in which the second can be done. In general, let $m_k$ ($k = 1, 2, \cdots, n$) be the number of ways in which the $k$th act can be performed after the preceding $k - 1$ have been completed. Then the total number of ways in which the $n$ acts can be done, in order, is the product $m_1 m_2 \cdots m_n$.

For, corresponding to each of the $m_1$ ways of making the first choice, there are $m_2$ ways for the second, so that the first two can be done in $m_1 m_2$ ways. For each of these $m_1 m_2$ ways, there are then $m_3$ choices for the third, so that the first three can be done in $m_1 m_2 m_3$ ways, and so on.

The things to be done successively may be referred to as acts to be performed, choices to be made, or objects to be arranged, according to circumstances. With the last viewpoint, we speak of each arrangement of objects as a **permutation** of the objects. For example, the letters $a$, $b$, $c$, taken two at a time, yield six permutations:

$$ab, \quad ba, \quad ac, \quad ca, \quad bc, \quad cb.$$

If there were four letters, $a$, $b$, $c$, and $d$, there would be twelve permutations taking two at a time. For, the first place can be filled by any one of the four letters, and, after this has been done, the second place can be filled by any one of the three remaining letters, whence there are $4 \cdot 3 = 12$ permutations.

The number of permutations of $n$ different things taken $r$ at a time is the number of possible arrangements of any $r$ things that can be obtained from the $n$ things. We denote this by the functional notation * $P(n, r)$.

* Other symbols sometimes used are $_nP_r$ and $^nP_r$.

It is easy to find the functional form of $P(n, r)$. The first of the $r$ objects can be chosen in any one of $n$ ways, the second may then be taken as any one of the remaining $n - 1$ things, the third as any one of the remaining $n - 2$ things, and so on, until the $r$th one is chosen from among the $n - r + 1$ things then left. Hence the fundamental principle gives us

$$P(n, r) = n(n - 1)(n - 2) \cdots (n - r + 1). \qquad (1)$$

In the particular case in which $r = n$, that is, when all $n$ of the things are to be chosen in turn, the number of permutations is

$$P(n, n) = n(n - 1)(n - 2) \cdots 1 = n! \qquad (2)$$

*Example 1.* How many different five-letter "words" can be made from the 26 letters of the alphabet, no repetitions being allowed?

*Solution.* Here we have $n = 26$ things, of which $r = 5$ are to be chosen in turn. Since the first letter of our "word" may be any one of 26, the second any one of 25 remaining, and so on for five letters, we have

$$P(26, 5) = 26 \cdot 25 \cdot 24 \cdot 23 \cdot 22 = 7,893,600$$

possible permutations.

In the above discussion we have restricted ourselves to permutations of $n$ different objects. We consider now the situation in which not all the $n$ objects are distinct. Before we examine the general case, let us consider the following example.

*Example 2.* Find the number of permutations of the seven letters of the word *algebra*.

*Solution.* Temporarily place subscripts, 1 and 2, on the $a$'s to distinguish them, so that we now have $7! = 5040$ possible permutations of the seven distinct objects. Of these 5040 arrangements, half will contain the $a$'s in the order $a_1, a_2$ and the other half will contain them in the order $a_2, a_1$. Without the subscripts on the $a$'s, the two groups would coincide, pair by pair. Hence there are actually $7!/2! = 2520$ permutations of the letters when the $a$'s are indistinguishable.

Similar reasoning enables us to treat the general case in which $n$ objects are to be permuted, when $n_1$ are alike, $n_2$ others are alike, $n_3$ others alike, and so on. Let $P$ denote the required number of permutations. If we replace the $n_1$ like objects by $n_1$ unlike ones, there would be $n_1!P$ permutations, obtained from the original $P$ permutations, in each of which there are $n_2$ alike, $n_3$ alike, etc. Likewise, if we replace the $n_2$ like ones by $n_2$ unlike ones, we find $n_1!n_2!P$ permutations in each of which there are $n_3$ like objects, etc. Continuing in this way, we finally get $(n_1!n_2!n_3! \cdots)P$ permutations of $n$ different things. But this last number must be equal to $n!$. Hence we have

$$P = \frac{n!}{n_1!n_2!n_3! \cdots}. \tag{3}$$

A **circular permutation** of $n$ objects is an arrangement of the $n$ objects around the circumference of a circle. Here we take into account only the arrangement of the $n$ things relative to one another, and not the position of a circular arrangement relative to its surroundings. Consequently any one object may be thought of as fixed in one position, and the other $n - 1$ arranged with respect to that fixed thing, whence it follows that there are $(n - 1)!$ circular permutations of $n$ different things taken all at a time.

*Example 3.* In how many ways may a party of four women and four men be seated at a round table if the women and men are to occupy alternate seats?

*Solution.* We may suppose one person, say a woman, seated in a particular place, and have then to arrange the remaining three women and four men relative to her. Because of the alternate seating scheme, there are three possible places for the remaining three women, so that there are $3! = 6$ ways of seating them. There are four possible places for the four men, whence there are $4! = 24$ ways in which the men may be seated. Hence the total number of arrangements is $6 \cdot 24 = 144$.

### EXERCISES

**1.** There are five roads between towns A and B, and four roads between towns B and C. In how many different ways may one travel from A to C by way of B?

**2.** How many five-letter words can be formed from the 26 letters of the alphabet if no repetitions are allowed and if the second and fourth letters are to be chosen from the vowels a, e, i, o, u and the letter y while the other three positions are to be filled from the remaining 20 consonants?

**3.** Solve the problem of Exercise 2 if vowels or y are to occupy the first, third, and fifth places while the other two letters are chosen from the 20 consonants.

**4.** How many four-letter words can be formed from the 5 vowels and 21 consonants if repetitions are allowed and if vowels and consonants are to alternate?

**5.** A president, a vice-president, a secretary, and a treasurer are to be elected from a membership of 25. How many sets of officers are possible?

**6.** Solve Exercise 5 if only ten of the members are eligible for the presidency and vice-presidency.

**7.** Find the number of different signals that can be made by displaying five flags in a vertical line.

**8.** Solve Exercise 7 if one or more of the five flags may be used.

**9.** How many different arrangements can be made of the seven letters in *college?*

**10.** Four men, A, B, C, and D, are to address a club. If A must speak before B, in how many orders can the speeches be arranged?

**11.** If $17P(n, 2) = 5P(2n - 2, 2)$, find $n$.

**12.** If $7P(2n - 3, 3) = 45P(n, 3)$, find $n$.

**13.** If $91P(n + 2, 3) = 2P(4n + 3, 3)$, find $n$.

**14.** How many even numbers containing all five of the digits 1, 2, 3, 4, 5 can be found?

**15.** Solve Exercise 14 if one or more of the five digits may be used.

**16.** How many different positive integers can be formed from the digits 0, 1, 2, 3, 4, the left-hand digit being different from zero?

**17.** In how many ways can five people sit in a row if two particular ones are to sit next each other?

**18.** In how many ways may five people sit in a row if two particular ones are not to sit next each other?

**19.** In how many ways can five people be seated in consecutive chairs of a row containing nine chairs?

**20.** There are four sets of books, one set consisting of two volumes and the other three sets of three volumes each. If the books of each set are to be together, in how many ways may the books be arranged on a shelf?

**21.** How many five-digit numbers can be formed from the digits 1, 1, 2, 2, and 3?

**22.** How many of the numbers of Exercise 21 are more than 20,000?

**23.** There are six boys and six girls. In how many ways may all twelve be arranged if the boys form a straight line and the girls form a circle (without regard to the relative positions of straight line and circle)?

**24.** Solve Exercise 23 if the boys and girls form concentric circles, boys in one circle and girls in the other, relative positions being taken into account.

**25.** How many positive integers can be formed from the digits 0, 0, 1, 2, 3?

**85. Combinations.** In the preceding article we were concerned with arrangement, or permutation, problems. We now consider problems in which a choice is made on the basis of an entire group of $r$ objects from among $n$ objects, without regard to the order of the $r$ things within the group. A group or set of things thus chosen as a whole, regardless of order, is called a **combination.**

For example, there are three combinations of the three letters $a$, $b$, $c$ taken two at a time, namely

$$ab, \qquad ac, \qquad bc.$$

We denote the number of combinations of $n$ things taken $r$ at a time by $C(n, r)$. Corresponding to each combination of $r$ things, $r!$ permutations can be formed. Hence we have $r!\, C(n, r) = P(n, r)$, and since $P(n, r) = n(n - 1) \cdots (n - r + 1)$, we have

$$C(n, r) = \frac{n(n - 1) \cdots (n - r + 1)}{r!}. \qquad (1)$$

Thus the number of combinations of $n$ things taken $r$ at a time is identical with the coefficient of the $(r + 1)$th term in the expansion of $(a + b)^n$

(Art. 43).   Another way of writing $C(n, r)$ was found to be

$$C(n, r) = \frac{n!}{r!(n - r)!},$$    (2)

from which it follows that

$$C(n, n - r) = C(n, r).$$    (3)

*Example 1.*   How many baseball teams of nine members can be chosen from among twelve boys, without regard to the position played by each member?

*Solution.*   We have to find the number of combinations of 12 things taken 9 at a time.   By relation (3), we may equally well find the number of combinations of 12 things taken $12 - 9 = 3$ at a time.   Hence we have

$$C(12, 9) = C(12, 3) = \frac{12 \cdot 11 \cdot 10}{1 \cdot 2 \cdot 3} = 220$$

possible teams.

We sometimes have occasion to find the total number of combinations of $n$ things taken one at a time, two at a time, $\cdots$, or $n$ at a time. The binomial expansion of $(a + b)^n$, written in terms of combination symbols, is of aid in this connection.   For,

$$(a + b)^n = a^n + C(n, 1)a^{n-1}b + C(n, 2)a^{n-2}b^2 + \cdots$$
$$+ C(n, r)a^{n-r}b^r + \cdots + C(n, n)b^n.$$

If we set $a = 1$ and $b = 1$ in this identity, we get

$$2^n = 1 + C(n, 1) + C(n, 2) + \cdots + C(n, r) + \cdots + C(n, n).$$

Therefore the total number of combinations of $n$ things taken 1, 2, $\cdots$, or $n$ at a time is

$$C(n, 1) + C(n, 2) + \cdots + C(n, n) = 2^n - 1.$$    (4)

*Example 2.*   How many groups can be formed from ten objects taking at least three at a time?

*Solution.*   Relation (4), with $n = 10$, yields

$$C(10, 1) + C(10, 2) + C(10, 3) + \cdots + C(10, 10) = 2^{10} - 1.$$

Hence the desired number is

$$C(10, 3) + C(10, 4) + \cdots + C(10, 10) = 2^{10} - 1 - C(10, 1) - C(10, 2)$$
$$= 1024 - 1 - 10 - 45$$
$$= 968.$$

Certain problems involve both permutations and combinations, like the following example.

*Example 3.* How many "words," each consisting of two vowels and three consonants, can be formed from the letters of the word *integral?*

*Solution.* We first select the two vowels to be used, from among the three vowels in *integral;* this can be done in $C(3, 2) = 3$ ways. Next, we select the three consonants from the five in *integral;* this yields $C(5, 3) = 10$ possible choices. Finally, we permute the five chosen letters in all possible ways, of which there are $P(5, 5) = 5! = 120$ arrangements. Hence the total number of possible words is, by the fundamental principle of Art. 84,

$$C(3, 2)C(5, 3)P(5, 5) = 3 \cdot 10 \cdot 120 = 3600.$$

### EXERCISES

**1.** In how many ways may a bridge party of four players be chosen from among twelve people?

**2.** Solve Exercise 1 if the choice of two pairs of partners is taken into account for each choice of four players.

**3.** In how many ways may a sextet of three men and three women be chosen from among ten men and twelve women?

**4.** How many straight lines can be drawn through pairs of points selected from $n$ points no three of which are collinear?

**5.** How many diagonals has a regular polygon of $n$ sides?

**6.** If $C(n, 3) = 455$, find $n$.

**7.** If $P(n, r) = 1680$ and $C(n, r) = 70$, find $n$ and $r$.

**8.** How many committees of five people can be made from a group of twelve men and nine women if there are to be just three men and two women on the committee?

**9.** Solve Exercise 8 if there are to be no more than three men on the committee.

**10.** How many different sums of money can be made from a cent, a nickel, a dime, a quarter, a half-dollar, and a dollar?

**11.** How many different planes are determined by three of fifteen points in space, if no four of the points are coplanar?

**12.** How many of the planes of Exercise 11 pass through one specified point, and how many pass through two specified points?

**13.** Six men and six women are to make a certain trip. Five of the party can go in one automobile, five in a second automobile, and the remaining two will go by rail. In how many ways can the party be distributed for the trip?

**14.** Solve Exercise 13 if all the women are to go by automobile.

**15.** How many circular permutations can be made of twelve things taken five at a time?

**16.** In how many ways may twelve objects be put into six groups of two each?

**17.** Solve Exercise 16 if the six groups of objects are to be distributed among six people.

**18.** In how many ways can four hands of thirteen cards each be dealt to four players from a deck of fifty-two cards? (Express your answer in terms of factorial numbers.)

**19.** A coin is tossed eight times in succession. How many distributions of heads and tails are possible?

**20.** How many of the distributions in Exercise 19 will entail just four heads and four tails?

**21.** From the nine digits 1, 2, $\cdots$, 9, how many groups of five digits can be formed, regardless of order, in which all are greater than 2?

**22.** Solve Exercise 21 if at least one of the five digits is to be greater than 6.

**23.** Using the identity $C(n, r) + C(n, r - 1) = C(n + 1, r)$ (Art. 43), find in two ways the number of groups that can be formed from fifty objects taken either two or three at a time.

**24.** Show that the number of ways in which $2m$ objects can be divided into two equal groups is equal to the number of ways in which $2m - 1$ objects can be divided into groups of $m$ and $m - 1$ objects.

**25.** Show that $rC(n, r) = (n - r + 1)C(n, r - 1)$. Using this result, show that if $n$ is even the greatest value of $C(n, r)$ occurs when $2r = n$, and that if $n$ is odd the greatest value of $C(n, r)$ occurs either when $2r = n - 1$ or when $2r = n + 1$.

**86. Probability.** In order to evaluate the chance or probability that a certain event will occur, we may adopt either one of two procedures. On the one hand, we may rely on past experience with similar situations, and assume that future results will be approximately the same; on the other, we may analyze the various ways in which the event can happen or fail to happen, and thereby compute a theoretical probability.

The former method is that of **empirical or statistical probability,** and the latter gives rise to **mathematical probability.**

Empirical probability has considerable value and utility in connection with statistics and insurance. The guiding principle of empirical probability may be stated as follows. If it has been found, in a large number $n$ of possible cases, that a certain event has occurred $h$ times, then it is assumed that the event will happen approximately $h$ times in $n$ future cases. It should be noted that $n$ is supposed to be a large number; for example, insurance companies can rely on the American Experience Table of Mortality, which is based on a very great number of observations.

We now consider the elements of mathematical probability. Suppose that a certain event can happen in $h$ different ways and that it can fail to occur in $f$ different ways, and suppose further that all the $h + f$ ways are equally likely. Then the probability that the event will occur in a given trial is defined as the fraction

$$p = \frac{h}{h + f}. \tag{1}$$

The probability that it will fail to occur is

$$q = \frac{f}{h + f}. \tag{2}$$

It is apparent that $p \leqq 1$ and $q \leqq 1$, and that $p + q = 1$. The value $p = 1$, which implies $q = 0$, denotes certainty of the occurrence of the event; the value $p = 0$, implying $q = 1$, denotes certainty that the event will fail to occur. When $p > \frac{1}{2}$, we say that the odds are $h$ to $f$ in favor of the event; when $p < \frac{1}{2}$, the odds are said to be $h$ to $f$ against the event.

*Example 1.* A bag contains five white balls and ten black balls. If three balls are drawn at random, what is the probability of drawing just one white and two black balls?

*Solution.* We first determine the total number of ways in which three balls may be selected from fifteen balls. This will be $C(15, 3) = 455$, the total number $(h + f)$ of ways in which the desired event can happen or fail. Next we find the number $h$ of ways in which one white ball and two black balls can be selected from five white and ten black balls; we get $h = C(5, 1) \cdot C(10, 2) = 225$. Hence the probability that the event in question will occur is

$$p = \frac{h}{h + f} = \frac{225}{455} = \frac{45}{91}.$$

We see that the desired probability is slightly less than one-half; the odds against the event are 45 to 46.

A set of two or more events may be any one of three kinds: **mutually exclusive, dependent, or independent.** If the occurrence of one event precludes the possibility of occurrence of the other events, the events are said to be mutually exclusive. If the events are not mutually exclusive, they are dependent or independent according as the occurrence of any one does or does not affect the occurrence of others in the set.

Let $p_1, p_2, \cdots, p_n$ denote the individual probabilities of occurrence of a set of $n$ mutually exclusive events, all of which are equally likely. If there are altogether $w$ ways in which these $n$ events can happen or fail to happen, and if the number of ways in which the $k$th event $(k = 1, 2, \cdots, n)$ can occur is $h_k$, then $p_k = h_k/w$. Since the $n$ events are mutually exclusive, the $h_1$ ways, $h_2$ ways, $\cdots$, $h_n$ ways are all different. Hence the probability that one of the $n$ events will occur is

$$p = \frac{h_1 + h_2 + \cdots + h_n}{w} = \frac{h_1}{w} + \frac{h_2}{w} + \cdots + \frac{h_n}{w}$$
$$= p_1 + p_2 + \cdots + p_n. \qquad (3)$$

We thus have the following theorem:

*The probability that some one of $n$ mutually exclusive events will occur in a certain trial is the sum of the $n$ individual probabilities.*

*Example 2.* A bag contains five white balls and ten black balls. If three balls are drawn at random, what is the probability that they will be all of one color?

*Solution.* As in Example 1, the total number of ways in which three balls can be drawn from the fifteen in the bag is $C(15, 3) = 455$. Now the desired event in the present problem occurs either if all three balls are white or if all three are black, and these two events are mutually exclusive. The number of ways in which three white balls can be drawn is $C(5, 3) = 10$, so that the probability for this case is $p_1 = \frac{10}{455} = \frac{2}{91}$. The number of ways of drawing three black balls is $C(10, 3) = 120$, and consequently the probability for this case is $p_2 = \frac{120}{455} = \frac{24}{91}$. Hence the probability of getting all three balls of one color is

$$p = p_1 + p_2 = \tfrac{2}{91} + \tfrac{24}{91} = \tfrac{2}{7}.$$

Now consider $n$ events that are not mutually exclusive. Let the number of ways in which the $k$th event $(k = 1, 2, \cdots, n)$ can happen be $h_k$, and let $w_k$ be the number of ways in which this event can either occur or fail to occur, so that $p_k = h_k/w_k$ is the probability of occurrence of the $k$th event. For any particular event, the numbers $h_k$ and $w_k$ will or will not depend upon the preceding $h$'s and $w$'s according as the events are dependent or independent. Now by the fundamental principle (Art. 84), the $n$ events can happen together in $h_1 h_2 \cdots h_n$ ways out of $w_1 w_2 \cdots w_n$ possible ways of occurring or failing to occur. Therefore the probability that all $n$ events will happen is

$$p = \frac{h_1 h_2 \cdots h_n}{w_1 w_2 \cdots w_n} = p_1 p_2 \cdots p_n. \tag{4}$$

Thus we have the following theorem:

*The probability that n dependent or independent events will occur—in turn if they are dependent, either simultaneously or in turn if they are independent—is the product of the n individual probabilities.*

*Example 3.* One bag contains three white and four black balls, and a second bag contains five white and six black balls. A ball is drawn from the first bag and then, without replacing the ball drawn, a second ball is drawn. Similarly, two balls are drawn in turn from the second bag. What is the probability that there be drawn first a white ball and then a black ball from each bag?

*Solution.* The drawing of two balls in turn from a particular bag involves dependent events, whereas the drawing of a pair of balls from each of two bags involves independent events.

With regard to the first bag, the probability that the first ball drawn will be white is $\frac{3}{7}$; *if* the first ball is white, the probability that the second is black is $\frac{4}{6} = \frac{2}{3}$. Hence the probability that we draw first a white and then a black ball from the first bag is

$$p_1 = \tfrac{3}{7} \cdot \tfrac{2}{3} = \tfrac{2}{7}.$$

Similarly, the probability of getting a white ball on the first draw from the second bag is $\frac{5}{11}$; *if* the first ball is white, the probability that the second will be black is $\frac{6}{10} = \frac{3}{5}$. Consequently the probability of drawing a white and a black ball, in that order, from the second bag is

$$p_2 = \tfrac{5}{11} \cdot \tfrac{3}{5} = \tfrac{3}{11}.$$

Therefore the probability of success for both bags at the same time is

$$p = p_1 p_2 = \tfrac{2}{7} \cdot \tfrac{3}{11} = \tfrac{6}{77}.$$

We next consider the question of repeated or successive trials of an event. Let $p$ denote the probability that a certain event will occur in a given trial, so that $q = 1 - p$ is the probability that the event will fail to occur in a single trial. Suppose that $n$ trials are made. The occurrence of the event in exactly $r$ particular trials and its failure to occur in the remaining $n - r$ trials are independent events, and consequently the probability that this situation will prevail is, by the preceding theorem, $p^r q^{n-r}$. Now $r$ trials can be selected from the $n$ trials in $C(n, r)$ ways, and these ways are mutually exclusive. Hence the probability that the event will happen in exactly $r$ trials and fail to occur in the other $n - r$ trials is

$$C(n, r)p^r q^{n-r}. \tag{5}$$

We observe that this expression is the $(n - r + 1)$th term in the expansion of $(p + q)^n$ (Art. 43).

The event will occur at least $m$ times in $n$ trials if it occurs $n$, $n - 1$, $\cdots$, $m + 1$, or $m$ times. Since these situations are mutually exclusive, the probability that the event will happen at least $m$ times in $n$ trials is the sum of terms of the form (5), with $r = n$, $n - 1$, $\cdots$, $m + 1$, $m$ in turn:

$$p^n + C(n, n - 1)p^{n-1}q + \cdots + C(n, m)p^m q^{n-m}. \tag{6}$$

This expression constitutes the first $n - m + 1$ terms of the expansion of $(p + q)^n$.

*Example 4.* A die is tossed five times. What is the probability that an ace will appear: (*a*) at least twice; (*b*) at least once?

*Solution.* Since the six numbers, any one of which may appear in a single toss, are equally likely, the probability that an ace will appear in a given trial is $p = \frac{1}{6}$, and the probability that it will not be an ace is $q = 1 - p = \frac{5}{6}$. With $n = 5$ and $m = 2$ in expression (6), we then get

$$(\tfrac{1}{6})^5 + C(5, 4)(\tfrac{1}{6})^4(\tfrac{5}{6}) + C(5, 3)(\tfrac{1}{6})^3(\tfrac{5}{6})^2 + C(5, 2)(\tfrac{1}{6})^2(\tfrac{5}{6})^3$$

$$= \frac{1}{6^5} + \frac{5}{1} \cdot \frac{5}{6^5} + \frac{5 \cdot 4}{1 \cdot 2} \cdot \frac{5^2}{6^5} + \frac{5 \cdot 4}{1 \cdot 2} \cdot \frac{5^3}{6^5} = \frac{1 + 25 + 250 + 1250}{6^5}$$

$$= \tfrac{1526}{7776} = \tfrac{763}{3888}.$$

This is the probability that an ace will appear at least twice.

To answer part (*b*) of our question, we may similarly use formula (6) with $m = 1$. Alternatively, we may reason as follows. The probability of *not* getting an ace in five throws is $(\frac{5}{6})^5$, and therefore the probability of getting at least one ace is

$$1 - (\tfrac{5}{6})^5 = 1 - \tfrac{3125}{7776} = \tfrac{4651}{7776}.$$

*Jan 1⁰*

### EXERCISES

**1.** A ball is drawn from a bag containing five white and eight black balls. What is the probability that the ball drawn is white?

**2.** A ball is drawn from a bag containing four white, ten black, and six red balls. What is the probability that the ball drawn is either white or black?

**3.** If five coins are tossed, what is the probability of getting just three heads?

**4.** If two dice are thrown, what is the probability of getting a sum of 9?

**5.** If two dice are thrown, what is the probability of getting either 6 or 10?

**6.** If two dice are thrown, what is the probability of getting more than 8?

**7.** A bag contains five white and ten black balls. If two balls are drawn together, what is the probability that both are black?

**8.** A bag contains four white and nine black balls. If two balls are drawn together, what is the probability of getting at least one white ball?

**9.** A box contains nine tickets, numbered from 1 to 9. If two tickets are drawn together, what is the probability that both are even numbers?

**10.** What is the probability that the sum of the two numbers drawn in Exercise 9 is even?

**11.** What is the probability that the sum of the two numbers drawn in Exercise 9 exceeds 10?

**12.** Eight books are placed at random on a shelf. What is the probability that two particular books will be adjacent?

**13.** Eight objects are placed at random in a circle. What is the probability that two particular objects will be adjacent?

**14.** Four men and four women are seated at random in a row of eight chairs. What is the probability that the men and women alternate?

**15.** Four men and four women are seated at random at a round table. What is the probability that the men and women alternate?

**16.** If four dice are thrown, what is the probability that the same number appears on all four?

**17.** If four cards are drawn from a pack of fifty-two cards, what is the probability that all are of the same denomination?

**18.** What is the probability that the four cards drawn in Exercise 17 are all of the same suit?

**19.** What is the probability that the four cards drawn in Exercise 17 are all of one color?

**20.** A bag contains five white and ten black balls. Three balls are drawn in turn, without replacing any balls already drawn at the time of each drawing. What is the probability that all three are white?

**21.** What is the probability that just two of the three balls drawn in Exercise 20 are white?

**22.** One bag contains six white balls, and a second bag contains four white and two black balls. If a bag is selected at random, and a ball is drawn from it, what is the probability that it is black?

**23.** A bag contains four white, five black, and six red balls. Three drawings are made of one ball each, the ball drawn being replaced each time before the next is drawn. What is the probability that all three balls are red?

**24.** What is the probability that the three balls drawn in Exercise 23 are white, black, and red in that order?

**25.** What is the probability that the three balls drawn in Exercise 23 are all of the same color?

**26.** A box contains ten tickets, numbered from 1 to 10. If three tickets are drawn together, what is the probability that the sum of the numbers will be even?

**27.** Three bags respectively contain three white and four black balls, four white and five black balls, and five white and six black balls. Two bags are selected at random, and one ball is drawn from each. What is the probability that both balls will be white?

**28.** The probability that a man of a certain age will die within the next twenty years is 0.25, and the probability that his wife will die within that interval is 0.20. Find the probability that at least one of the two will still be living at the end of twenty years.

**29.** If six coins are tossed, what is the probability that at least two will be heads?

**30.** If $p$ is the probability of occurrence of a certain event in a single trial, find the probability that the event will occur at least once in $n$ trials.

**31.** Show that the probability of throwing at least one head in two tosses of a coin is greater than the probability of throwing at least one ace in six casts of a die.

**32.** If a sum $s$ of money is at stake, and if the probability that a certain person will win the money is $p$, then $ps$ is said to be that person's *mathematical expectation*. If three men toss a coin, in turn, and if the first to toss a head wins seven dollars, what are the respective mathematical expectations of the three men?

**33.** Statistics indicate that the probability of an accident on any particular day is approximately 0.001 for a certain job. Show that the probability of avoiding an accident in 100 working days is about 0.91.

**34.** A bag contains five balls. If one or more are drawn at random, what is the probability of drawing an odd number of balls?

**35.** Show that $C(n,r)p^r(1-p)^{n-r}$ is greater or less than $C(n,r-1)p^{r-1}(1-p)^{n-r+1}$ according as $r$ is less or greater than $p(n+1)$. Hence show that, if $p$ is the probability that an event will occur in a given trial, the most probable number of occurrences of the event in $n$ trials is the largest integer that does not exceed $pn$.

## SUPPLEMENTARY EXERCISES

**1.** How many four-digit numbers can be made from the nine digits $1, 2, \cdots, 9$, if repetitions are allowed but no two adjacent digits are to be alike?

**2.** A set of dominoes runs from double blank to double $n$. How many dominoes are in the set?

**3.** A business organization has nine officers. Every day the president invites five other officers to lunch with him. How many different parties may be formed, and how many luncheons will each of the other officers attend?

**4.** In how many ways may six men and four women be seated in a row so that no two women sit together?

**5.** Solve Exercise 4 if there are $m$ men and $w$ women. What inequality must $m$ and $w$ satisfy?

**6.** A set of $m$ parallel lines is cut at right angles by another set of $n$ parallel lines. How many rectangles are formed?

**7.** In how many ways may one go from one corner of the largest rectangle of Exercise 6 to the opposite corner, taking the shortest path along lines of the two sets?

**8.** If a marksman hits a target nine times out of ten, on the average, what is the probability that he hits it just nine times in ten shots?

**9.** Let $p_1$ be the probability of drawing two black and two red cards when four cards are drawn from a pack of fifty-two, and let $p_2$ be the probability of drawing two black and two red cards when one card is drawn from each of four packs. Show that $p_1$ exceeds $p_2$, and determine the difference.

**10.** Determine the minimum number of throws of two dice such that there will be better than an even chance of getting a double six.

**11.** A set of dominoes runs from double blank to double $n$. If two dominoes are drawn, what is the probability that a blank appears on neither of them?

**12.** Two players take turns drawing a ball from a bag containing three white and five black balls, each ball withdrawn remaining outside the bag. What is the probability that the first player is the first to draw a white ball?

**13.** What is the maximum number of dice that may be simultaneously thrown such that there will be at least an even chance of all coming up alike in one hundred throws?

**14.** Ten coins are tossed. Those falling heads up are removed and the remainder are tossed. The process is repeated until all the coins are removed. How many tosses are necessary to yield favorable odds for the removal of all the coins?

**15.** Each of a number of bags contains $m$ white and $n$ black balls. A ball is drawn from the first bag and put into the second bag, then a ball is drawn from the second bag and put into the third, and so on. Show that the probability of drawing a white ball is the same at each stage of this process, and equal to $m/(m + n)$.

# APPENDIX A

## MEANINGS OF SYMBOLS

$+$, read *plus*, meaning *addition*

$-$, read *minus*, meaning *subtraction*

$\times$ or $\cdot$, read *times*, meaning *multiplication*

$\div$ or $/$, read *divided by*, meaning *division*

$=$, read *equals* or *is equal to*

$\pm$, read *plus or minus*

$\mp$, read *minus or plus*

$\equiv$, read *is identical with*

$\neq$, read *is not equal to*

$>$, read *is greater than*

$<$, read *is less than*

$\geqq$, read *is greater than or equal* **to**

$\leqq$, read *is less than or equal to*

$a^n$, read *a to the nth power*

$\sqrt[n]{a}$, read *nth root of a*

$\sqrt{a}$, read (positive) *square root of a*

$x_1$, read *x sub one*

$x'$, $x''$, $\cdots$ read *x prime, x second,* $\cdots$

$|\,a\,|$, read *absolute value of a*.  If $a \geqq 0$, $|\,a\,| = a$; if $a < 0$, $|\,a\,| = -a$.

$f(x)$, read *f function of x*

$(x, y)$, read *point whose coordinates are x and y* (in plane)

$n!$, read *factorial n*, meaning, $1 \cdot 2 \cdot 3 \cdots n$.

$\log_a x$, read *logarithm of x to the base a*

$\log x$, read *common logarithm of x* (base 10)

$\ln x$, read *natural logarithm of x* (base $e = 2.718\cdots$)

$x \to a$, read *x approaches a*

$x \to \infty$, read *x becomes infinite*, or *x increases beyond all bound*

$\lim\limits_{x \to a} y$, read *limit of y as x approaches a*

## APPENDIX B

### GREEK ALPHABET

| | | | | | | | | |
|---|---|---|---|---|---|---|---|---|
| A | $\alpha$ | alpha | I | $\iota$ | iota | P | $\rho$ | rho |
| B | $\beta$ | beta | K | $\kappa$ | kappa | $\Sigma$ | $\sigma$ | sigma |
| $\Gamma$ | $\gamma$ | gamma | $\Lambda$ | $\lambda$ | lambda | T | $\tau$ | tau |
| $\Delta$ | $\delta$ | delta | M | $\mu$ | mu | U | $\upsilon$ | upsilon |
| E | $\epsilon$ | epsilon | N | $\nu$ | nu | $\Phi$ | $\phi$ | phi |
| Z | $\zeta$ | zeta | $\Xi$ | $\xi$ | xi | X | $\chi$ | chi |
| H | $\eta$ | eta | O | $o$ | omicron | $\Psi$ | $\psi$ | psi |
| $\Theta$ | $\theta$ | theta | $\Pi$ | $\pi$ | pi | $\Omega$ | $\omega$ | omega |

## APPENDIX C

### ANGLE CONVERSION TABLES

#### SEXAGESIMAL EQUIVALENTS OF RADIAN MEASURE

| | | | |
|---|---|---|---|
| 0.0001 | 21 ″ | 0.0600 | 3° 26′ 16″ |
| 0.0002 | 41 ″ | 0.0700 | 4° 0′ 39″ |
| 0.0003 | 1′ 2″ | 0.0800 | 4° 35′ 1″ |
| 0.0004 | 1′ 23″ | 0.0900 | 5° 9′ 24″ |
| 0.0005 | 1′ 43″ | 0.1000 | 5° 43′ 46″ |
| 0.0006 | 2′ 4″ | 0.2000 | 11° 27′ 33″ |
| 0.0007 | 2′ 24″ | 0.3000 | 17° 11′ 19″ |
| 0.0008 | 2′ 45″ | 0.4000 | 22° 55′ 6″ |
| 0.0009 | 3′ 6″ | 0.5000 | 28° 38′ 52″ |
| 0.0010 | 3′ 26″ | 0.6000 | 34° 22′ 39″ |
| 0.0020 | 6′ 53″ | 0.7000 | 40° 6′ 25″ |
| 0.0030 | 10′ 19″ | 0.8000 | 45° 50′ 12″ |
| 0.0040 | 13′ 45″ | 0.9000 | 51° 33′ 58″ |
| 0.0050 | 17′ 11″ | 1.0000 | 57° 17′ 45″ |
| 0.0060 | 20′ 38″ | 2.0000 | 114° 35′ 30″ |
| 0.0070 | 24′ 4″ | 3.0000 | 171° 53′ 14″ |
| 0.0080 | 27′ 30″ | 4.0000 | 229° 10′ 59″ |
| 0.0090 | 30′ 56″ | 5.0000 | 286° 28′ 44″ |
| 0.0100 | 34′ 23″ | 6.0000 | 343° 46′ 29″ |
| 0.0200 | 1° 8′ 45″ | 7.0000 | 401° 4′ 14″ |
| 0.0300 | 1° 43′ 8″ | 8.0000 | 458° 21′ 58″ |
| 0.0400 | 2° 17′ 31″ | 9.0000 | 515° 39′ 43″ |
| 0.0500 | 2° 51′ 53″ | 10.0000 | 572° 57′ 28″ |

$\pi$ radians $= 180°$

#### RADIAN EQUIVALENTS OF SEXAGESIMAL MEASURE

| | | | | | | | |
|---|---|---|---|---|---|---|---|
| 1′ | 0.0003 | 9′ | 0.0026 | 3° | 0.0524 | 20° | 0.3491 |
| 2′ | 0.0006 | 10′ | 0.0029 | 4° | 0.0698 | 30° | 0.5236 |
| 3′ | 0.0009 | 20′ | 0.0058 | 5° | 0.0873 | 40° | 0.6981 |
| 4′ | 0.0012 | 30′ | 0.0087 | 6° | 0.1047 | 50° | 0.8727 |
| 5′ | 0.0015 | 40′ | 0.0116 | 7° | 0.1222 | 60° | 1.0472 |
| 6′ | 0.0017 | 50′ | 0.0145 | 8° | 0.1396 | 70° | 1.2217 |
| 7′ | 0.0020 | 1° | 0.0175 | 9° | 0.1571 | 80° | 1.3963 |
| 8′ | 0.0023 | 2° | 0.0349 | 10° | 0.1745 | 90° | 1.5708 |

APPENDIX D

## COMMON LOGARITHMS

|    | 0 | 1 | 2 | 3 | 4 | 5 | 6 | 7 | 8 | 9 |
|----|------|------|------|------|------|------|------|------|------|------|
| 10 | 0000 | 0043 | 0086 | 0128 | 0170 | 0212 | 0253 | 0294 | 0334 | 0374 |
| 11 | 0414 | 0453 | 0492 | 0531 | 0569 | 0607 | 0645 | 0682 | 0719 | 0755 |
| 12 | 0792 | 0828 | 0864 | 0899 | 0934 | 0969 | 1004 | 1038 | 1072 | 1106 |
| 13 | 1139 | 1173 | 1206 | 1239 | 1271 | 1303 | 1335 | 1367 | 1399 | 1430 |
| 14 | 1461 | 1492 | 1523 | 1553 | 1584 | 1614 | 1644 | 1673 | 1703 | 1732 |
| 15 | 1761 | 1790 | 1818 | 1847 | 1875 | 1903 | 1931 | 1959 | 1987 | 2014 |
| 16 | 2041 | 2068 | 2095 | 2122 | 2148 | 2175 | 2201 | 2227 | 2253 | 2279 |
| 17 | 2304 | 2330 | 2355 | 2380 | 2405 | 2430 | 2455 | 2480 | 2504 | 2529 |
| 18 | 2553 | 2577 | 2601 | 2625 | 2648 | 2672 | 2695 | 2718 | 2742 | 2765 |
| 19 | 2788 | 2810 | 2833 | 2856 | 2878 | 2900 | 2923 | 2945 | 2967 | 2989 |
| 20 | 3010 | 3032 | 3054 | 3075 | 3096 | 3118 | 3139 | 3160 | 3181 | 3201 |
| 21 | 3222 | 3243 | 3263 | 3284 | 3304 | 3324 | 3345 | 3365 | 3385 | 3404 |
| 22 | 3424 | 3444 | 3464 | 3483 | 3502 | 3522 | 3541 | 3560 | 3579 | 3598 |
| 23 | 3617 | 3636 | 3655 | 3674 | 3692 | 3711 | 3729 | 3747 | 3766 | 3784 |
| 24 | 3802 | 3820 | 3838 | 3856 | 3874 | 3892 | 3909 | 3927 | 3945 | 3962 |
| 25 | 3979 | 3997 | 4014 | 4031 | 4048 | 4065 | 4082 | 4099 | 4116 | 4133 |
| 26 | 4150 | 4166 | 4183 | 4200 | 4216 | 4232 | 4249 | 4265 | 4281 | 4298 |
| 27 | 4314 | 4330 | 4346 | 4362 | 4378 | 4393 | 4409 | 4425 | 4440 | 4456 |
| 28 | 4472 | 4487 | 4502 | 4518 | 4533 | 4548 | 4564 | 4579 | 4594 | 4609 |
| 29 | 4624 | 4639 | 4654 | 4669 | 4683 | 4698 | 4713 | 4728 | 4742 | 4757 |
| 30 | 4771 | 4786 | 4800 | 4814 | 4829 | 4843 | 4857 | 4871 | 4886 | 4900 |
| 31 | 4914 | 4928 | 4942 | 4955 | 4969 | 4983 | 4997 | 5011 | 5024 | 5038 |
| 32 | 5051 | 5065 | 5079 | 5092 | 5105 | 5119 | 5132 | 5145 | 5159 | 5172 |
| 33 | 5185 | 5198 | 5211 | 5224 | 5237 | 5250 | 5263 | 5276 | 5289 | 5302 |
| 34 | 5315 | 5328 | 5340 | 5353 | 5366 | 5378 | 5391 | 5403 | 5416 | 5428 |
| 35 | 5441 | 5453 | 5465 | 5478 | 5490 | 5502 | 5514 | 5527 | 5539 | 5551 |
| 36 | 5563 | 5575 | 5587 | 5599. | 5611 | 5623 | 5635 | 5647 | 5658 | 5670 |
| 37 | 5682 | 5694 | 5705 | 5717 | 5729 | 5740 | 5752 | 5763 | 5775 | 5786 |
| 38 | 5798 | 5809 | 5821 | 5832 | 5843 | 5855 | 5866 | 5877 | 5888 | 5899 |
| 39 | 5911 | 5922 | 5933 | 5944 | 5955 | 5966 | 5977 | 5988 | 5999 | 6010 |
| 40 | 6021 | 6031 | 6042 | 6053 | 6064 | 6075 | 6085 | 6096 | 6107 | 6117 |
| 41 | 6128 | 6138 | 6149 | 6160 | 6170 | 6180 | 6191 | 6201 | 6212 | 6222 |
| 42 | 6232 | 6243 | 6253 | 6263 | 6274 | 6284 | 6294 | 6304 | 6314 | 6325 |
| 43 | 6335 | 6345 | 6355 | 6365 | 6375 | 6385 | 6395 | 6405 | 6415 | 6425 |
| 44 | 6435 | 6444 | 6454 | 6464 | 6474 | 6484 | 6493 | 6503 | 6513 | 6522 |
| 45 | 6532 | 6542 | 6551 | 6561 | 6571 | 6580 | 6590 | 6599 | 6609 | 6618 |
| 46 | 6628 | 6637 | 6646 | 6656 | 6665 | 6675 | 6684 | 6693 | 6702 | 6712 |
| 47 | 6721 | 6730 | 6739 | 6749 | 6758 | 6767 | 6776 | 6785 | 6794 | 6803 |
| 48 | 6812 | 6821 | 6830 | 6839 | 6848 | 6857 | 6866 | 6875 | 6884 | 6893 |
| 49 | 6902 | 6911 | 6920 | 6928 | 6937 | 6946 | 6955 | 6964 | 6972 | 6981 |
| 50 | 6990 | 6998 | 7007 | 7016 | 7024 | 7033 | 7042 | 7050 | 7059 | 7067 |
| 51 | 7076 | 7084 | 7093 | 7101 | 7110 | 7118 | 7126 | 7135 | 7143 | 7152 |
| 52 | 7160 | 7168 | 7177 | 7185 | 7193 | 7202 | 7210 | 7218 | 7226 | 7235 |
| 53 | 7243 | 7251 | 7259 | 7267 | 7275 | 7284 | 7292 | 7300 | 7308 | 7316 |
| 54 | 7324 | 7332 | 7340 | 7348 | 7356 | 7364 | 7372 | 7380 | 7388 | 7396 |

# Appendix D

## COMMON LOGARITHMS (*Continued*)

|    | 0 | 1 | 2 | 3 | 4 | 5 | 6 | 7 | 8 | 9 |
|----|------|------|------|------|------|------|------|------|------|------|
| 55 | 7404 | 7412 | 7419 | 7427 | 7435 | 7443 | 7451 | 7459 | 7466 | 7474 |
| 56 | 7482 | 7490 | 7497 | 7505 | 7513 | 7520 | 7528 | 7536 | 7543 | 7551 |
| 57 | 7559 | 7566 | 7574 | 7582 | 7589 | 7597 | 7604 | 7612 | 7619 | 7627 |
| 58 | 7634 | 7642 | 7649 | 7657 | 7664 | 7672 | 7679 | 7686 | 7694 | 7701 |
| 59 | 7709 | 7716 | 7723 | 7731 | 7738 | 7745 | 7752 | 7760 | 7767 | 7774 |
| 60 | 7782 | 7789 | 7796 | 7803 | 7810 | 7818 | 7825 | 7832 | 7839 | 7846 |
| 61 | 7853 | 7860 | 7868 | 7875 | 7882 | 7889 | 7896 | 7903 | 7910 | 7917 |
| 62 | 7924 | 7931 | 7938 | 7945 | 7952 | 7959 | 7966 | 7973 | 7980 | 7987 |
| 63 | 7993 | 8000 | 8007 | 8014 | 8021 | 8028 | 8035 | 8041 | 8048 | 8055 |
| 64 | 8062 | 8069 | 8075 | 8082 | 8089 | 8096 | 8102 | 8109 | 8116 | 8122 |
| 65 | 8129 | 8136 | 8142 | 8149 | 8156 | 8162 | 8169 | 8176 | 8182 | 8189 |
| 66 | 8195 | 8202 | 8209 | 8215 | 8222 | 8228 | 8235 | 8241 | 8248 | 8254 |
| 67 | 8261 | 8267 | 8274 | 8280 | 8287 | 8293 | 8299 | 8306 | 8312 | 8319 |
| 68 | 8325 | 8331 | 8338 | 8344 | 8351 | 8357 | 8363 | 8370 | 8376 | 8382 |
| 69 | 8388 | 8395 | 8401 | 8407 | 8414 | 8420 | 8426 | 8432 | 8439 | 8445 |
| 70 | 8451 | 8457 | 8463 | 8470 | 8476 | 8482 | 8488 | 8494 | 8500 | 8506 |
| 71 | 8513 | 8519 | 8525 | 8531 | 8537 | 8543 | 8549 | 8555 | 8561 | 8567 |
| 72 | 8573 | 8579 | 8585 | 8591 | 8597 | 8603 | 8609 | 8615 | 8621 | 8627 |
| 73 | 8633 | 8639 | 8645 | 8651 | 8657 | 8663 | 8669 | 8675 | 8681 | 8686 |
| 74 | 8692 | 8698 | 8704 | 8710 | 8716 | 8722 | 8727 | 8733 | 8739 | 8745 |
| 75 | 8751 | 8756 | 8762 | 8768 | 8774 | 8779 | 8785 | 8791 | 8797 | 8802 |
| 76 | 8808 | 8814 | 8820 | 8825 | 8831 | 8837 | 8842 | 8848 | 8854 | 8859 |
| 77 | 8865 | 8871 | 8876 | 8882 | 8887 | 8893 | 8899 | 8904 | 8910 | 8915 |
| 78 | 8921 | 8927 | 8932 | 8938 | 8943 | 8949 | 8954 | 8960 | 8965 | 8971 |
| 79 | 8976 | 8982 | 8987 | 8993 | 8998 | 9004 | 9009 | 9015 | 9020 | 9025 |
| 80 | 9031 | 9036 | 9042 | 9047 | 9053 | 9058 | 9063 | 9069 | 9074 | 9079 |
| 81 | 9085 | 9090 | 9096 | 9101 | 9106 | 9112 | 9117 | 9122 | 9128 | 9133 |
| 82 | 9138 | 9143 | 9149 | 9154 | 9159 | 9165 | 9170 | 9175 | 9180 | 9186 |
| 83 | 9191 | 9196 | 9201 | 9206 | 9212 | 9217 | 9222 | 9227 | 9232 | 9238 |
| 84 | 9243 | 9248 | 9253 | 9258 | 9263 | 9269 | 9274 | 9279 | 9284 | 9289 |
| 85 | 9294 | 9299 | 9304 | 9309 | 9315 | 9320 | 9325 | 9330 | 9335 | 9340 |
| 86 | 9345 | 9350 | 9355 | 9360 | 9365 | 9370 | 9375 | 9380 | 9385 | 9390 |
| 87 | 9395 | 9400 | 9405 | 9410 | 9415 | 9420 | 9425 | 9430 | 9435 | 9440 |
| 88 | 9445 | 9450 | 9455 | 9460 | 9465 | 9469 | 9474 | 9479 | 9484 | 9489 |
| 89 | 9494 | 9499 | 9504 | 9509 | 9513 | 9518 | 9523 | 9528 | 9533 | 9538 |
| 90 | 9542 | 9547 | 9552 | 9557 | 9562 | 9566 | 9571 | 9576 | 9581 | 9586 |
| 91 | 9590 | 9595 | 9600 | 9605 | 9609 | 9614 | 9619 | 9624 | 9628 | 9633 |
| 92 | 9638 | 9643 | 9647 | 9652 | 9657 | 9661 | 9666 | 9671 | 9675 | 9680 |
| 93 | 9685 | 9689 | 9694 | 9699 | 9703 | 9708 | 9713 | 9717 | 9722 | 9727 |
| 94 | 9731 | 9736 | 9741 | 9745 | 9750 | 9754 | 9759 | 9763 | 9768 | 9773 |
| 95 | 9777 | 9782 | 9786 | 9791 | 9795 | 9800 | 9805 | 9809 | 9814 | 9818 |
| 96 | 9823 | 9827 | 9832 | 9836 | 9841 | 9845 | 9850 | 9854 | 9859 | 9863 |
| 97 | 9868 | 9872 | 9877 | 9881 | 9886 | 9890 | 9894 | 9899 | 9903 | 9908 |
| 98 | 9912 | 9917 | 9921 | 9926 | 9930 | 9934 | 9939 | 9943 | 9948 | 9952 |
| 99 | 9956 | 9961 | 9965 | 9969 | 9974 | 9978 | 9983 | 9987 | 9991 | 9996 |

## APPENDIX E

### TRIGONOMETRIC FUNCTIONS AND THEIR LOGARITHMS

| Angles | Sines | | Cosines | | Tangents | | Cotangents | | |
|---|---|---|---|---|---|---|---|---|---|
| | Func. | Log. | Func. | Log. | Func. | Log. | Func. | Log. | |
| 0° 00′ | .0000 | | 1.0000 | 0.0000 | .0000 | | | | 90° 00′ |
| 10 | .0029 | 7.4637 | 1.0000 | .0000 | .0029 | 7.4637 | 343.77 | 2.5363 | 50 |
| 20 | .0058 | .7648 | 1.0000 | .0000 | .0058 | .7648 | 171.89 | .2352 | 40 |
| 30 | .0087 | .9408 | 1.0000 | .0000 | .0087 | .9409 | 114.59 | .0591 | 30 |
| 40 | .0116 | 8.0658 | .9999 | .0000 | .0116 | 8.0658 | 85.940 | 1.9342 | 20 |
| 50 | .0145 | .1627 | .9999 | .0000 | .0145 | .1627 | 68.750 | .8373 | 10 |
| 1° 00′ | .0175 | 8.2419 | .9998 | 9.9999 | .0175 | 8.2419 | 57.290 | 1.7581 | 89° 00′ |
| 10 | .0204 | .3088 | .9998 | .9999 | .0204 | .3089 | 49.104 | .6911 | 50 |
| 20 | .0233 | .3668 | .9997 | .9999 | .0233 | .3669 | 42.964 | .6331 | 40 |
| 30 | .0262 | .4179 | .9997 | .9999 | .0262 | .4181 | 38.188 | .5819 | 30 |
| 40 | .0291 | .4637 | .9996 | .9998 | .0291 | .4638 | 34.368 | .5362 | 20 |
| 50 | .0320 | .5050 | .9995 | .9998 | .0320 | .5053 | 31.242 | .4947 | 10 |
| 2° 00′ | .0349 | 8.5428 | .9994 | 9.9997 | .0349 | 8.5431 | 28.636 | 1.4569 | 88° 00′ |
| 10 | .0378 | .5776 | .9993 | .9997 | .0378 | .5779 | 26.432 | .4221 | 50 |
| 20 | .0407 | .6097 | .9992 | .9996 | .0407 | .6101 | 24.542 | .3899 | 40 |
| 30 | .0436 | .6397 | .9990 | .9996 | .0437 | .6401 | 22.904 | .3599 | 30 |
| 40 | .0465 | .6677 | .9989 | .9995 | .0466 | .6682 | 21.470 | .3318 | 20 |
| 50 | .0494 | .6940 | .9988 | .9995 | .0495 | .6945 | 20.206 | .3055 | 10 |
| 3° 00′ | .0523 | 8.7188 | .9986 | 9.9994 | .0524 | 8.7194 | 19.081 | 1.2806 | 87° 00′ |
| 10 | .0552 | .7423 | .9985 | .9993 | .0553 | .7429 | 18.075 | .2571 | 50 |
| 20 | .0581 | .7645 | .9983 | .9993 | .0582 | .7652 | 17.169 | .2348 | 40 |
| 30 | .0610 | .7857 | .9981 | .9992 | .0612 | .7865 | 16.350 | .2135 | 30 |
| 40 | .0640 | .8059 | .9980 | .9991 | .0641 | .8067 | 15.605 | .1933 | 20 |
| 50 | .0669 | .8251 | .9978 | .9990 | .0670 | .8261 | 14.924 | .1739 | 10 |
| 4° 00′ | .0698 | 8.8436 | .9976 | 9.9989 | .0699 | 8.8446 | 14.301 | 1.1554 | 86° 00′ |
| 10 | .0727 | .8613 | .9974 | .9989 | .0729 | .8624 | 13.727 | .1376 | 50 |
| 20 | .0756 | .8783 | .9971 | .9988 | .0758 | .8795 | 13.197 | .1205 | 40 |
| 30 | .0785 | .8946 | .9969 | .9987 | .0787 | .8960 | 12.706 | .1040 | 30 |
| 40 | .0814 | .9104 | .9967 | .9986 | .0816 | .9118 | 12.251 | .0882 | 20 |
| 50 | .0843 | .9256 | .9964 | .9985 | .0846 | .9272 | 11.826 | .0728 | 10 |
| 5° 00′ | .0872 | 8.9403 | .9962 | 9.9983 | .0875 | 8.9420 | 11.430 | 1.0580 | 85° 00′ |
| 10 | .0901 | .9545 | .9959 | .9982 | .0904 | .9563 | 11.059 | .0437 | 50 |
| 20 | .0929 | .9682 | .9957 | .9981 | .0934 | .9701 | 10.712 | .0299 | 40 |
| 30 | .0958 | .9816 | .9954 | .9980 | .0963 | .9836 | 10.385 | .0164 | 30 |
| 40 | .0987 | .9945 | .9951 | .9979 | .0992 | .9966 | 10.078 | .0034 | 20 |
| 50 | .1016 | 9.0070 | .9948 | .9977 | .1022 | 9.0093 | 9.7882 | 0.9907 | 10 |
| 6° 00′ | .1045 | 9.0192 | .9945 | 9.9976 | .1051 | 9.0216 | 9.5144 | 0.9784 | 84° 00′ |
| 10 | .1074 | .0311 | .9942 | .9975 | .1080 | .0336 | 9.2553 | .9664 | 50 |
| 20 | .1103 | .0426 | .9939 | .9973 | .1110 | .0453 | 9.0098 | .9547 | 40 |
| 30 | .1132 | .0539 | .9936 | .9972 | .1139 | .0567 | 8.7769 | .9433 | 30 |
| 40 | .1161 | .0648 | .9932 | .9971 | .1169 | .0678 | 8.5555 | .9322 | 20 |
| 50 | .1190 | .0755 | .9929 | .9969 | .1198 | .0786 | 8.3450 | .9214 | 10 |
| 7° 00′ | .1219 | 9.0859 | .9925 | 9.9968 | .1228 | 9.0891 | 8.1443 | 0.9109 | 83° 00′ |
| | Func. | Log. | Func. | Log. | Func. | Log. | Func. | Log. | |
| | Cosines | | Sines | | Cotangents | | Tangents | | Angles |

Appendix E

**TRIGONOMETRIC FUNCTIONS** (*Continued*)

| Angles | Sines | | Cosines | | Tangents | | Cotangents | | |
|---|---|---|---|---|---|---|---|---|---|
| | Func. | Log. | Func. | Log. | Func. | Log. | Func. | Log. | |
| 7° 00′ | .1219 | 9.0859 | .9925 | 9.9968 | .1228 | 9.0891 | 8.1443 | 0.9109 | 83° 00′ |
| 10 | .1248 | .0961 | .9922 | .9966 | .1257 | .0995 | 7.9530 | .9005 | 50 |
| 20 | .1276 | .1060 | .9918 | .9964 | .1287 | .1096 | 7.7704 | .8904 | 40 |
| 30 | .1305 | .1157 | .9914 | .9963 | .1317 | .1194 | 7.5958 | .8806 | 30 |
| 40 | .1334 | .1252 | .9911 | .9961 | .1346 | .1291 | 7.4287 | .8709 | 20 |
| 50 | .1363 | .1345 | .9907 | .9959 | .1376 | .1385 | 7.2687 | .8615 | 10 |
| 8° 00′ | .1392 | 9.1436 | .9903 | 9.9958 | .1405 | 9.1478 | 7.1154 | 0.8522 | 82° 00′ |
| 10 | .1421 | .1525 | .9899 | .9956 | .1435 | .1569 | 6.9682 | .8431 | 50 |
| 20 | .1449 | .1612 | .9894 | .9954 | .1465 | .1658 | 6.8269 | .8342 | 40 |
| 30 | .1478 | .1697 | .9890 | .9952 | .1495 | .1745 | 6.6912 | .8255 | 30 |
| 40 | .1507 | .1781 | .9886 | .9950 | .1524 | .1831 | 6.5606 | .8169 | 20 |
| 50 | .1536 | .1863 | .9881 | .9948 | .1554 | .1915 | 6.4348 | .8085 | 10 |
| 9° 00′ | .1564 | 9.1943 | .9877 | 9.9946 | .1584 | 9.1997 | 6.3138 | 0.8003 | 81° 00′ |
| 10 | .1593 | .2022 | .9872 | .9944 | .1614 | .2078 | 6.1970 | .7922 | 50 |
| 20 | .1622 | .2100 | .9868 | .9942 | .1644 | .2158 | 6.0844 | .7842 | 40 |
| 30 | .1650 | .2176 | .9863 | .9940 | .1673 | .2236 | 5.9758 | .7764 | 30 |
| 40 | .1679 | .2251 | .9858 | .9938 | .1703 | .2313 | 5.8708 | .7687 | 20 |
| 50 | .1708 | .2324 | .9853 | .9936 | .1733 | .2389 | 5.7694 | .7611 | 10 |
| 10° 00′ | .1736 | 9.2397 | .9848 | 9.9934 | .1763 | 9.2463 | 5.6713 | 0.7537 | 80° 00′ |
| 10 | .1765 | .2468 | .9843 | .9931 | .1793 | .2536 | 5.5764 | .7464 | 50 |
| 20 | .1794 | .2538 | .9838 | .9929 | .1823 | .2609 | 5.4845 | .7391 | 40 |
| 30 | .1822 | .2606 | .9833 | .9927 | .1853 | .2680 | 5.3955 | .7320 | 30 |
| 40 | .1851 | .2674 | .9827 | .9924 | .1883 | .2750 | 5.3093 | .7250 | 20 |
| 50 | .1880 | .2740 | .9822 | .9922 | .1914 | .2819 | 5.2257 | .7181 | 10 |
| 11° 00′ | .1908 | 9.2806 | .9816 | 9.9919 | .1944 | 9.2887 | 5.1446 | 0.7113 | 79° 00′ |
| 10 | .1937 | .2870 | .9811 | .9917 | .1974 | .2953 | 5.0658 | .7047 | 50 |
| 20 | .1965 | .2934 | .9805 | .9914 | .2004 | .3020 | 4.9894 | .6980 | 40 |
| 30 | .1994 | .2997 | .9799 | .9912 | .2035 | .3085 | 4.9152 | .6915 | 30 |
| 40 | .2022 | .3058 | .9793 | .9909 | .2065 | .3149 | 4.8430 | .6851 | 20 |
| 50 | .2051 | .3119 | .9787 | .9907 | .2095 | .3212 | 4.7729 | .6788 | 10 |
| 12° 00′ | .2079 | 9.3179 | .9781 | 9.9904 | .2126 | 9.3275 | 4.7046 | 0.6725 | 78° 00′ |
| 10 | .2108 | .3238 | .9775 | .9901 | .2156 | .3336 | 4.6382 | .6664 | 50 |
| 20 | .2136 | .3296 | .9769 | .9899 | .2186 | .3397 | 4.5736 | .6603 | 40 |
| 30 | .2164 | .3353 | .9763 | .9896 | .2217 | .3458 | 4.5107 | .6542 | 30 |
| 40 | .2193 | .3410 | .9757 | .9893 | .2247 | .3517 | 4.4494 | .6483 | 20 |
| 50 | .2221 | .3466 | .9750 | .9890 | .2278 | .3576 | 4.3897 | .6424 | 10 |
| 13° 00′ | .2250 | 9.3521 | .9744 | 9.9887 | .2309 | 9.3634 | 4.3315 | 0.6366 | 77° 00′ |
| 10 | .2278 | .3575 | .9737 | .9884 | .2339 | .3691 | 4.2747 | .6309 | 50 |
| 20 | .2306 | .3629 | .9730 | .9881 | .2370 | .3748 | 4.2193 | .6252 | 40 |
| 30 | .2334 | .3682 | .9724 | .9878 | .2401 | .3804 | 4.1653 | .6196 | 30 |
| 40 | .2363 | .3734 | .9717 | .9875 | .2432 | .3859 | 4.1126 | .6141 | 20 |
| 50 | .2391 | .3786 | .9710 | .9872 | .2462 | .3914 | 4.0611 | .6086 | 10 |
| 14° 00′ | .2419 | 9.3837 | .9703 | 9.9869 | .2493 | 9.3968 | 4.0108 | 0.6032 | 76° 00′ |
| | Func. | Log. | Func. | Log. | Func. | Log. | Func. | Log. | |
| | Cosines | | Sines | | Cotangents | | Tangents | | Angles |

## TRIGONOMETRIC FUNCTIONS (*Continued*)

| Angles | Sines | | Cosines | | Tangents | | Cotangents | | |
|--------|-------|-------|---------|-------|----------|-------|------------|-------|---|
| | Func. | Log. | Func. | Log. | Func. | Log. | Func. | Log. | |
| 14° 00′ | .2419 | 9.3837 | .9703 | 9.9869 | .2493 | 9.3968 | 4.0108 | 0.6032 | 76° 00′ |
| 10 | .2447 | .3887 | .9696 | .9866 | .2524 | .4021 | 3.9617 | .5979 | 50 |
| 20 | .2476 | .3937 | .9689 | .9863 | .2555 | .4074 | 3.9136 | .5926 | 40 |
| 30 | .2504 | .3986 | .9681 | .9859 | .2586 | .4127 | 3.8667 | .5873 | 30 |
| 40 | .2532 | .4035 | .9674 | .9856 | .2617 | .4178 | 3.8208 | .5822 | 20 |
| 50 | .2560 | .4083 | .9667 | .9853 | .2648 | .4230 | 3.7760 | .5770 | 10 |
| 15° 00′ | .2588 | 9.4130 | .9659 | 9.9849 | .2679 | 9.4281 | 3.7321 | 0.5719 | 75° 00′ |
| 10 | .2616 | .4177 | .9652 | .9846 | .2711 | .4331 | 3.6891 | .5669 | 50 |
| 20 | .2644 | .4223 | .9644 | .9843 | .2742 | .4381 | 3.6470 | .5619 | 40 |
| 30 | .2672 | .4269 | .9636 | .9839 | .2773 | .4430 | 3.6059 | .5570 | 30 |
| 40 | .2700 | .4314 | .9628 | .9836 | .2805 | .4479 | 3.5656 | .5521 | 20 |
| 50 | .2728 | .4359 | .9621 | .9832 | .2836 | .4527 | 3.5261 | .5473 | 10 |
| 16° 00′ | .2756 | 9.4403 | .9613 | 9.9828 | .2867 | 9.4575 | 3.4874 | 0.5425 | 74° 00′ |
| 10 | .2784 | .4447 | .9605 | .9825 | .2899 | .4622 | 3.4495 | .5378 | 50 |
| 20 | .2812 | .4491 | .9596 | .9821 | .2931 | .4669 | 3.4124 | .5331 | 40 |
| 30 | .2840 | .4533 | .9588 | .9817 | .2962 | .4716 | 3.3759 | .5284 | 30 |
| 40 | .2868 | .4576 | .9580 | .9814 | .2994 | .4762 | 3.3402 | .5238 | 20 |
| 50 | .2896 | .4618 | .9572 | .9810 | .3026 | .4808 | 3.3052 | .5192 | 10 |
| 17° 00′ | .2924 | 9.4659 | .9563 | 9.9806 | .3057 | 9.4853 | 3.2709 | 0.5147 | 73° 00′ |
| 10 | .2952 | .4700 | .9555 | .9802 | .3089 | .4898 | 3.2371 | .5102 | 50 |
| 20 | .2979 | .4741 | .9546 | .9798 | .3121 | .4943 | 3.2041 | .5057 | 40 |
| 30 | .3007 | .4781 | .9537 | .9794 | .3153 | .4987 | 3.1716 | .5013 | 30 |
| 40 | .3035 | .4821 | .9528 | .9790 | .3185 | .5031 | 3.1397 | .4969 | 20 |
| 50 | .3062 | .4861 | .9520 | .9786 | .3217 | .5075 | 3.1084 | .4925 | 10 |
| 18° 00′ | .3090 | 9.4900 | .9511 | 9.9782 | .3249 | 9.5118 | 3.0777 | 0.4882 | 72° 00′ |
| 10 | .3118 | .4939 | .9502 | .9778 | .3281 | .5161 | 3.0475 | .4839 | 50 |
| 20 | .3145 | .4977 | .9492 | .9774 | .3314 | .5203 | 3.0178 | .4797 | 40 |
| 30 | .3173 | .5015 | .9483 | .9770 | .3346 | .5245 | 2.9887 | .4755 | 30 |
| 40 | .3201 | .5052 | .9474 | .9765 | .3378 | .5287 | 2.9600 | .4713 | 20 |
| 50 | .3228 | .5090 | .9465 | .9761 | .3411 | .5329 | 2.9319 | .4671 | 10 |
| 19° 00′ | .3256 | 9.5126 | .9455 | 9.9757 | .3443 | 9.5370 | 2.9042 | 0.4630 | 71° 00′ |
| 10 | .3283 | .5163 | .9446 | .9752 | .3476 | .5411 | 2.8770 | .4589 | 50 |
| 20 | .3311 | .5199 | .9436 | .9748 | .3508 | .5451 | 2.8502 | .4549 | 40 |
| 30 | .3338 | .5235 | .9426 | .9743 | .3541 | .5491 | 2.8239 | .4509 | 30 |
| 40 | .3365 | .5270 | .9417 | .9739 | .3574 | .5531 | 2.7980 | .4469 | 20 |
| 50 | .3393 | .5306 | .9407 | .9734 | .3607 | .5571 | 2.7725 | .4429 | 10 |
| 20° 00′ | .3420 | 9.5341 | .9397 | 9.9730 | .3640 | 9.5611 | 2.7475 | 0.4389 | 70° 00′ |
| 10 | .3448 | .5375 | .9387 | .9725 | .3673 | .5650 | 2.7228 | .4350 | 50 |
| 20 | .3475 | .5409 | .9377 | .9721 | .3706 | .5689 | 2.6985 | .4311 | 40 |
| 30 | .3502 | .5443 | .9367 | .9716 | .3739 | .5727 | 2.6746 | .4273 | 30 |
| 40 | .3529 | .5477 | .9356 | .9711 | .3772 | .5766 | 2.6511 | .4234 | 20 |
| 50 | .3557 | .5510 | .9346 | .9706 | .3805 | .5804 | 2.6279 | .4196 | 10 |
| 21° 00′ | .3584 | 9.5543 | .9336 | 9.9702 | .3839 | 9.5842 | 2.6051 | 0.4158 | 69° 00′ |
| | Func. | Log. | Func. | Log. | Func. | Log. | Func. | Log. | |
| | Cosines | | Sines | | Cotangents | | Tangents | | Angles |

## TRIGONOMETRIC FUNCTIONS (*Continued*)

| Angles | Sines | | Cosines | | Tangents | | Cotangents | | |
|---|---|---|---|---|---|---|---|---|---|
| | Func. | Log. | Func. | Log. | Func. | Log. | Func. | Log. | |
| 21° 00′ | .3584 | 9.5543 | .9336 | 9.9702 | .3839 | 9.5842 | 2.6051 | 0.4158 | 69° 00′ |
| 10 | .3611 | .5576 | .9325 | .9697 | .3872 | .5879 | 2.5826 | .4121 | 50 |
| 20 | .3638 | .5609 | .9315 | .9692 | .3906 | .5917 | 2.5605 | .4083 | 40 |
| 30 | .3665 | .5641 | .9304 | .9687 | .3939 | .5954 | 2.5386 | .4046 | 30 |
| 40 | .3692 | .5673 | .9293 | .9682 | .3973 | .5991 | 2.5172 | .4009 | 20 |
| 50 | .3719 | .5704 | .9283 | .9677 | .4006 | .6028 | 2.4960 | .3972 | 10 |
| 22° 00′ | .3746 | 9.5736 | .9272 | 9.9672 | .4040 | 9.6064 | 2.4751 | 0.3936 | 68° 00′ |
| 10 | .3773 | .5767 | .9261 | .9667 | .4074 | .6100 | 2.4545 | .3900 | 50 |
| 20 | .3800 | .5798 | .9250 | .9661 | .4108 | .6136 | 2.4342 | .3864 | 40 |
| 30 | .3827 | .5828 | .9239 | .9656 | .4142 | .6172 | 2.4142 | .3828 | 30 |
| 40 | .3854 | .5859 | .9228 | .9651 | .4176 | .6208 | 2.3945 | .3792 | 20 |
| 50 | .3881 | .5889 | .9216 | .9646 | .4210 | .6243 | 2.3750 | .3757 | 10 |
| 23° 00′ | .3907 | 9.5919 | .9205 | 9.9640 | .4245 | 9.6279 | 2.3559 | 0.3721 | 67° 00′ |
| 10 | .3934 | .5948 | .9194 | .9635 | .4279 | .6314 | 2.3369 | .3686 | 50 |
| 20 | .3961 | .5978 | .9182 | .9629 | .4314 | .6348 | 2.3183 | .3652 | 40 |
| 30 | .3987 | .6007 | .9171 | .9624 | .4348 | .6383 | 2.2998 | .3617 | 30 |
| 40 | .4014 | .6036 | .9159 | .9618 | .4383 | .6417 | 2.2817 | .3583 | 20 |
| 50 | .4041 | .6065 | .9147 | .9613 | .4417 | .6452 | 2.2637 | .3548 | 10 |
| 24° 00′ | .4067 | 9.6093 | .9135 | 9.9607 | .4452 | 9.6486 | 2.2460 | 0.3514 | 66° 00′ |
| 10 | .4094 | .6121 | .9124 | .9602 | .4487 | .6520 | 2.2286 | .3480 | 50 |
| 20 | .4120 | .6149 | .9112 | .9596 | .4522 | .6553 | 2.2113 | .3447 | 40 |
| 30 | .4147 | .6177 | .9100 | .9590 | .4557 | .6587 | 2.1943 | .3413 | 30 |
| 40 | .4173 | .6205 | .9088 | .9584 | .4592 | .6620 | 2.1775 | .3380 | 20 |
| 50 | .4200 | .6232 | .9075 | .9579 | .4628 | .6654 | 2.1609 | .3346 | 10 |
| 25° 00′ | .4226 | 9.6259 | .9063 | 9.9573 | .4663 | 9.6687 | 2.1445 | 0.3313 | 65° 00′ |
| 10 | .4253 | .6286 | .9051 | .9567 | .4699 | .6720 | 2.1283 | .3280 | 50 |
| 20 | .4279 | .6313 | .9038 | .9561 | .4734 | .6752 | 2.1123 | .3248 | 40 |
| 30 | .4305 | .6340 | .9026 | .9555 | .4770 | .6785 | 2.0965 | .3215 | 30 |
| 40 | .4331 | .6366 | .9013 | .9549 | .4806 | .6817 | 2.0809 | .3183 | 20 |
| 50 | .4358 | .6392 | .9001 | .9543 | .4841 | .6850 | 2.0655 | .3150 | 10 |
| 26° 00′ | .4384 | 9.6418 | .8988 | 9.9537 | .4877 | 9.6882 | 2.0503 | 0.3118 | 64° 00′ |
| 10 | .4410 | .6444 | .8975 | .9530 | .4913 | .6914 | 2.0353 | .3086 | 50 |
| 20 | .4436 | .6470 | .8962 | .9524 | .4950 | .6946 | 2.0204 | .3054 | 40 |
| 30 | .4462 | .6495 | .8949 | .9518 | .4986 | .6977 | 2.0057 | .3023 | 30 |
| 40 | .4488 | .6521 | .8936 | .9512 | .5022 | .7009 | 1.9912 | .2991 | 20 |
| 50 | .4514 | .6546 | .8923 | .9505 | .5059 | .7040 | 1.9768 | .2960 | 10 |
| 27° 00′ | .4540 | 9.6570 | .8910 | 9.9499 | .5095 | 9.7072 | 1.9626 | 0.2928 | 63° 00′ |
| 10 | .4566 | .6595 | .8897 | .9492 | .5132 | .7103 | 1.9486 | .2897 | 50 |
| 20 | .4592 | .6620 | .8884 | .9486 | .5169 | .7134 | 1.9347 | .2866 | 40 |
| 30 | .4617 | .6644 | .8870 | .9479 | .5206 | .7165 | 1.9210 | .2835 | 30 |
| 40 | .4643 | .6668 | .8857 | .9473 | .5243 | .7196 | 1.9074 | .2804 | 20 |
| 50 | .4669 | .6692 | .8843 | .9466 | .5280 | .7226 | 1.8940 | .2774 | 10 |
| 28° 00′ | .4695 | 9.6716 | .8829 | 9.9459 | .5317 | 9.7257 | 1.8807 | 0.2743 | 62° 00′ |
| | Func. | Log. | Func. | Log. | Func. | Log. | Func. | Log. | |
| | Cosines | | Sines | | Cotangents | | Tangents | | Angles |

## TRIGONOMETRIC FUNCTIONS (*Continued*)

| Angles | Sines | | Cosines | | Tangents | | Cotangents | | |
|---|---|---|---|---|---|---|---|---|---|
| | Func. | Log. | Func. | Log. | Func. | Log. | Func. | Log. | |
| 28° 00′ | .4695 | 9.6716 | .8829 | 9.9459 | .5317 | 9.7257 | 1.8807 | 0.2743 | 62° 00′ |
| 10 | .4720 | .6740 | .8816 | .9453 | .5354 | .7287 | 1.8676 | .2713 | 50 |
| 20 | .4746 | .6763 | .8802 | .9446 | .5392 | .7317 | 1.8546 | .2683 | 40 |
| 30 | .4772 | .6787 | .8788 | .9439 | .5430 | .7348 | 1.8418 | .2652 | 30 |
| 40 | .4797 | .6810 | .8774 | .9432 | .5467 | .7378 | 1.8291 | .2622 | 20 |
| 50 | .4823 | .6833 | .8760 | .9425 | .5505 | .7408 | 1.8165 | .2592 | 10 |
| 29° 00′ | .4848 | 9.6856 | .8746 | 9.9418 | .5543 | 9.7438 | 1.8040 | 0.2562 | 61° 00′ |
| 10 | .4874 | .6878 | .8732 | .9411 | .5581 | .7467 | 1.7917 | .2533 | 50 |
| 20 | .4899 | .6901 | .8718 | .9404 | .5619 | .7497 | 1.7796 | .2503 | 40 |
| 30 | .4924 | .6923 | .8704 | .9397 | .5658 | .7526 | 1.7675 | .2474 | 30 |
| 40 | .4950 | .6946 | .8689 | .9390 | .5696 | .7556 | 1.7556 | .2444 | 20 |
| 50 | .4975 | .6968 | .8675 | .9383 | .5735 | .7585 | 1.7437 | .2415 | 10 |
| 30° 00′ | .5000 | 9.6990 | .8660 | 9.9375 | .5774 | 9.7614 | 1.7321 | 0.2386 | 60° 00′ |
| 10 | .5025 | .7012 | .8646 | .9368 | .5812 | .7644 | 1.7205 | .2356 | 50 |
| 20 | .5050 | .7033 | .8631 | .9361 | .5851 | .7673 | 1.7090 | .2327 | 40 |
| 30 | .5075 | .7055 | .8616 | .9353 | .5890 | .7701 | 1.6977 | .2299 | 30 |
| 40 | .5100 | .7076 | .8601 | .9346 | .5930 | .7730 | 1.6864 | .2270 | 20 |
| 50 | .5125 | .7097 | .8587 | .9338 | .5969 | .7759 | 1.6753 | .2241 | 10 |
| 31° 00′ | .5150 | 9.7118 | .8572 | 9.9331 | .6009 | 9.7788 | 1.6643 | 0.2212 | 59° 00′ |
| 10 | .5175 | .7139 | .8557 | .9323 | .6048 | .7816 | 1.6534 | .2184 | 50 |
| 20 | .5200 | .7160 | .8542 | .9315 | .6088 | .7845 | 1.6426 | .2155 | 40 |
| 30 | .5225 | .7181 | .8526 | .9308 | .6128 | .7873 | 1.6319 | .2127 | 30 |
| 40 | .5250 | .7201 | .8511 | .9300 | .6168 | .7902 | 1.6212 | .2098 | 20 |
| 50 | .5275 | .7222 | .8496 | .9292 | .6208 | .7930 | 1.6107 | .2070 | 10 |
| 32° 00′ | .5299 | 9.7242 | .8480 | 9.9284 | .6249 | 9.7958 | 1.6003 | 0.2042 | 58° 00′ |
| 10 | .5324 | .7262 | .8465 | .9276 | .6289 | .7986 | 1.5900 | .2014 | 50 |
| 20 | .5348 | .7282 | .8450 | .9268 | .6330 | .8014 | 1.5798 | .1986 | 40 |
| 30 | .5373 | .7302 | .8434 | .9260 | .6371 | .8042 | 1.5697 | .1958 | 30 |
| 40 | .5398 | .7322 | .8418 | .9252 | .6412 | .8070 | 1.5597 | .1930 | 20 |
| 50 | .5422 | .7342 | .8403 | .9244 | .6453 | .8097 | 1.5497 | .1903 | 10 |
| 33° 00′ | .5446 | 9.7361 | .8387 | 9.9236 | .6494 | 9.8125 | 1.5399 | 0.1875 | 57° 00′ |
| 10 | .5471 | .7380 | .8371 | .9228 | .6536 | .8153 | 1.5301 | .1847 | 50 |
| 20 | .5495 | .7400 | .8355 | .9219 | .6577 | .8180 | 1.5204 | .1820 | 40 |
| 30 | .5519 | .7419 | .8339 | .9211 | .6619 | .8208 | 1.5108 | .1792 | 30 |
| 40 | .5544 | .7438 | .8323 | .9203 | .6661 | .8235 | 1.5013 | .1765 | 20 |
| 50 | .5568 | .7457 | .8307 | .9194 | .6703 | .8263 | 1.4919 | .1737 | 10 |
| 34° 00′ | .5592 | 9.7476 | .8290 | 9.9186 | .6745 | 9.8290 | 1.4826 | 0.1710 | 56° 00′ |
| 10 | .5616 | .7494 | .8274 | .9177 | .6787 | .8317 | 1.4733 | .1683 | 50 |
| 20 | .5640 | .7513 | .8258 | .9169 | .6830 | .8344 | 1.4641 | .1656 | 40 |
| 30 | .5664 | .7531 | .8241 | .9160 | .6873 | .8371 | 1.4550 | .1629 | 30 |
| 40 | .5688 | .7550 | .8225 | .9151 | .6916 | .8398 | 1.4460 | .1602 | 20 |
| 50 | .5712 | .7568 | .8208 | .9142 | .6959 | .8425 | 1.4370 | .1575 | 10 |
| 35° 00′ | .5736 | 9.7586 | .8192 | 9.9134 | .7002 | 9.8452 | 1.4281 | 0.1548 | 55° 00′ |
| | Func. | Log. | Func. | Log. | Func. | Log. | Func. | Log. | |
| | Cosines | | Sines | | Cotangents | | Tangents | | Angles |

## TRIGONOMETRIC FUNCTIONS (*Continued*)

| Angles | Sines | | Cosines | | Tangents | | Cotangents | | |
|---|---|---|---|---|---|---|---|---|---|
| | Func. | Log. | Func. | Log. | Func. | Log. | Func. | Log. | |
| 35° 00′ | .5736 | 9.7586 | .8192 | 9.9134 | .7002 | 9.8452 | 1.4281 | 0.1548 | 55° 00′ |
| 10 | .5760 | .7604 | .8175 | .9125 | .7046 | .8479 | 1.4193 | .1521 | 50 |
| 20 | .5783 | .7622 | .8158 | .9116 | .7089 | .8506 | 1.4106 | .1494 | 40 |
| 30 | .5807 | .7640 | .8141 | .9107 | .7133 | .8533 | 1.4019 | .1467 | 30 |
| 40 | .5831 | .7657 | .8124 | .9098 | .7177 | .8559 | 1.3934 | .1441 | 20 |
| 50 | .5854 | .7675 | .8107 | .9089 | .7221 | .8586 | 1.3848 | .1414 | 10 |
| 36° 00′ | .5878 | 9.7692 | .8090 | 9.9080 | .7265 | 9.8613 | 1.3764 | 0.1387 | 54° 00′ |
| 10 | .5901 | .7710 | .8073 | .9070 | .7310 | .8639 | 1.3680 | .1361 | 50 |
| 20 | .5925 | .7727 | .8056 | .9061 | .7355 | .8666 | 1.3597 | .1334 | 40 |
| 30 | .5948 | .7744 | .8039 | .9052 | .7400 | .8692 | 1.3514 | .1308 | 30 |
| 40 | .5972 | .7761 | .8021 | .9042 | .7445 | .8718 | 1.3432 | .1282 | 20 |
| 50 | .5995 | .7778 | .8004 | .9033 | .7490 | .8745 | 1.3351 | .1255 | 10 |
| 37° 00′ | .6018 | 9.7795 | .7986 | 9.9023 | .7536 | 9.8771 | 1.3270 | 0.1229 | 53° 00′ |
| 10 | .6041 | .7811 | .7969 | .9014 | .7581 | .8797 | 1.3190 | .1203 | 50 |
| 20 | .6065 | .7828 | .7951 | .9004 | .7627 | .8824 | 1.3111 | .1176 | 40 |
| 30 | .6088 | .7844 | .7934 | .8995 | .7673 | .8850 | 1.3032 | .1150 | 30 |
| 40 | .6111 | .7861 | .7916 | .8985 | .7720 | .8876 | 1.2954 | .1124 | 20 |
| 50 | .6134 | .7877 | .7898 | .8975 | .7766 | .8902 | 1.2876 | .1098 | 10 |
| 38° 00′ | .6157 | 9.7893 | .7880 | 9.8965 | .7813 | 9.8928 | 1.2799 | 0.1072 | 52° 00′ |
| 10 | .6180 | .7910 | .7862 | .8955 | .7860 | .8954 | 1.2723 | .1046 | 50 |
| 20 | .6202 | .7926 | .7844 | .8945 | .7907 | .8980 | 1.2647 | .1020 | 40 |
| 30 | .6225 | .7941 | .7826 | .8935 | .7954 | .9006 | 1.2572 | .0994 | 30 |
| 40 | .6248 | .7957 | .7808 | .8925 | .8002 | .9032 | 1.2497 | .0968 | 20 |
| 50 | .6271 | .7973 | .7790 | .8915 | .8050 | .9058 | 1.2423 | .0942 | 10 |
| 39° 00′ | .6293 | 9.7989 | .7771 | 9.8905 | .8098 | 9.9084 | 1.2349 | 0.0916 | 51° 00′ |
| 10 | .6316 | .8004 | .7753 | .8895 | .8146 | .9110 | 1.2276 | .0890 | 50 |
| 20 | .6338 | .8020 | .7735 | .8884 | .8195 | .9135 | 1.2203 | .0865 | 40 |
| 30 | .6361 | .8035 | .7716 | .8874 | .8243 | .9161 | 1.2131 | .0839 | 30 |
| 40 | .6383 | .8050 | .7698 | .8864 | .8292 | .9187 | 1.2059 | .0813 | 20 |
| 50 | .6406 | .8066 | .7679 | .8853 | .8342 | .9212 | 1.1988 | .0788 | 10 |
| 40° 00′ | .6428 | 9.8081 | .7660 | 9.8843 | .8391 | 9.9238 | 1.1918 | 0.0762 | 50° 00′ |
| 10 | .6450 | .8096 | .7642 | .8832 | .8441 | .9264 | 1.1847 | .0736 | 50 |
| 20 | .6472 | .8111 | .7623 | .8821 | .8491 | .9289 | 1.1778 | .0711 | 40 |
| 30 | .6494 | .8125 | .7604 | .8810 | .8541 | .9315 | 1.1708 | .0685 | 30 |
| 40 | .6517 | .8140 | .7585 | .8800 | .8591 | .9341 | 1.1640 | .0659 | 20 |
| 50 | .6539 | .8155 | .7566 | .8789 | .8642 | .9366 | 1.1571 | .0634 | 10 |
| 41° 00′ | .6561 | 9.8169 | .7547 | 9.8778 | .8693 | 9.9392 | 1.1504 | 0.0608 | 49° 00′ |
| 10 | .6583 | .8184 | .7528 | .8767 | .8744 | .9417 | 1.1436 | .0583 | 50 |
| 20 | .6604 | .8198 | .7509 | .8756 | .8796 | .9443 | 1.1369 | .0557 | 40 |
| 30 | .6626 | .8213 | .7490 | .8745 | .8847 | .9468 | 1.1303 | .0532 | 30 |
| 40 | .6648 | .8227 | .7470 | .8733 | .8899 | .9494 | 1.1237 | .0506 | 20 |
| 50 | .6670 | .8241 | .7451 | .8722 | .8952 | .9519 | 1.1171 | .0481 | 10 |
| 42° 00′ | .6691 | 9.8255 | .7431 | 9.8711 | .9004 | 9.9544 | 1.1106 | 0.0456 | 48° 00′ |
| | Func. | Log. | Func. | Log. | Func. | Log. | Func. | Log. | |
| | Cosines | | Sines | | Cotangents | | Tangents | | Angles |

**TRIGONOMETRIC FUNCTIONS** (*Continued*)

| Angles | Sines | | Cosines | | Tangents | | Cotangents | | |
|---|---|---|---|---|---|---|---|---|---|
| | Func. | Log. | Func. | Log. | Func. | Log. | Func. | Log. | |
| 42° 00′ | .6691 | 9.8255 | .7431 | 9.8711 | .9004 | 9.9544 | 1.1106 | 0.0456 | 48° 00′ |
| 10 | .6713 | .8269 | .7412 | .8699 | .9057 | .9570 | 1.1041 | .0430 | 50 |
| 20 | .6734 | .8283 | .7392 | .8688 | .9110 | .9595 | 1.0977 | .0405 | 40 |
| 30 | .6756 | .8297 | .7373 | .8676 | .9163 | .9621 | 1.0913 | .0379 | 30 |
| 40 | .6777 | .8311 | .7353 | .8665 | .9217 | .9646 | 1.0850 | .0354 | 20 |
| 50 | .6799 | .8324 | .7333 | .8653 | .9271 | .9671 | 1.0786 | .0329 | 10 |
| 43° 00′ | .6820 | 9.8338 | .7314 | 9.8641 | .9325 | 9.9697 | 1.0724 | 0.0303 | 47° 00′ |
| 10 | .6841 | .8351 | .7294 | .8629 | .9380 | .9722 | 1.0661 | .0278 | 50 |
| 20 | .6862 | .8365 | .7274 | .8618 | .9435 | .9747 | 1.0599 | .0253 | 40 |
| 30 | .6884 | .8378 | .7254 | .8606 | .9490 | .9772 | 1.0538 | .0228 | 30 |
| 40 | .6905 | .8391 | .7234 | .8594 | .9545 | .9798 | 1.0477 | .0202 | 20 |
| 50 | .6926 | .8405 | .7214 | .8582 | .9601 | .9823 | 1.0416 | .0177 | 10 |
| 44° 00′ | .6947 | 9.8418 | .7193 | 9.8569 | .9657 | 9.9848 | 1.0355 | 0.0152 | 46° 00′ |
| 10 | .6967 | .8431 | .7173 | .8557 | .9713 | .9874 | 1.0295 | .0126 | 50 |
| 20 | .6988 | .8444 | .7153 | .8545 | .9770 | .9899 | 1.0235 | .0101 | 40 |
| 30 | .7009 | .8457 | .7133 | .8532 | .9827 | .9924 | 1.0176 | .0076 | 30 |
| 40 | .7030 | .8469 | .7112 | .8520 | .9884 | .9949 | 1.0117 | .0051 | 20 |
| 50 | .7050 | .8482 | .7092 | .8507 | .9942 | .9975 | 1.0058 | .0025 | 10 |
| 45° 00′ | .7071 | 9.8495 | .7071 | 9.8495 | 1.0000 | 0.0000 | 1.0000 | 0.0000 | 45° 00′ |
| | Func. | Log. | Func. | Log. | Func. | Log. | Func. | Log. | |
| | Cosines | | Sines | | Cotangents | | Tangents | | Angles |

# ANSWERS TO EXERCISES

## Art. 1. Page 6

**1.** 10, 12, 14.    **2.** 16, 19, 22.    **3.** $\frac{5}{6}, \frac{6}{7}, \frac{7}{8}$.    **4.** 13, $-15$, 17.
**5.** $\frac{1}{243}, \frac{1}{729}, \frac{1}{2187}$.    **6.** 144, 196, 256.    **7.** $\frac{25}{6}, \frac{36}{7}, \frac{49}{8}$.    **8.** $\frac{4}{9}, \frac{5}{10}, \frac{6}{11}$.
**9.** 17, 19, 23.    **10.** 34, 55, 89.    **11.** i, ii, iii; ii, iii; ii, iii; i, ii, iii; iii; ii, iii; iii.
**12.** $-4$, 0.1949, $1/(\sqrt{2}+1)$, $\frac{11}{5}$, $\pi$, $\sqrt{729}$, 29.

## Arts. 4–5. Pages 18–19

**1.** $a^5$.   **2.** $a^{-1}$.   **3.** 1.   **4.** $ab^{-2}$.   **5.** $a^{-2}b$.   **6.** $a^8b^{-1}$.   **7.** $a^4b^{-2}$.
**8.** $a^6b^{-1}$.   **9.** $a^{p-2}b^{q-4}$.   **10.** $a^3b^{-3}$.   **11.** $a^{p+2}b^{p+1}$.   **12.** $a^{3p-12}b^{3q-6}$.
**13.** $-a^pb^{3p-6}$.   **14.** $a^{-2p}b^{3-p}$.   **15.** $ab^5$.   **16.** $a^{-3}b^3$.   **17.** $18b^4$.
**18.** $a^{-\frac{3}{2}}b^{-\frac{5}{3}}$.   **19.** $a^{\frac{1}{3}}$.   **20.** $a^{\frac{7}{2}}b^{-\frac{11}{3}}$.   **21.** $a^{\frac{5}{2}}b^{-\frac{7}{2}}$.   **22.** $a^{-\frac{p}{2}}b^{-\frac{p}{2}}$.
**23.** $a^{1-4p}b^{2q}$.   **24.** $a^{\frac{1}{2}}b$.   **25.** $a^5b^{-5}$.   **26.** $b$.   **27.** $a^{\frac{3}{2}}b^{-\frac{7}{2}}$.   **28.** $a^{\frac{29}{10}}$.
**29.** $a^{\frac{5}{2}}b^{-\frac{7}{2}}$.   **30.** $a^{\frac{1}{2}}b^{-\frac{1}{3}}$.   **31.** $a^6-4$.   **32.** $1+a^2$.   **33.** $a^{-2}-b^{-4}$.
**34.** $a^9-b^9$.   **35.** $a^2b^2-a^{-2}b^{-2}$.   **36.** $ab^2-2a^{\frac{3}{2}}b^{\frac{3}{2}}+a^2b$.
**37.** $a^{-p}b^{-q}-a^pb^q$.   **38.** $a^{\frac{1}{2}}-a^{-\frac{1}{2}}$.   **39.** $a^{\frac{2}{3}}-a^{\frac{1}{2}}$.
**40.** $a+6a^{\frac{2}{3}}b^{\frac{1}{3}}+12a^{\frac{1}{3}}b^{\frac{2}{3}}+8b$.   **41.** $a^{-\frac{p}{2}}b^{-\frac{p}{2}}-a^{\frac{p}{2}}b^{\frac{p}{2}}$.   **42.** $a-2a^{\frac{1}{2}}+1$.
**43.** $(a^2-b)^{\frac{3}{4}}$.   **44.** 2.   **45.** $a^{-1}b^{-2}-a^{-1}b^{-\frac{1}{2}}$.   **46.** 1.   **47.** $a^{4p}-b^{4p}$.
**48.** $a+b^{-4}+c^{-2}$.   **49.** $a^{-8}-b^{\frac{8}{3}}$.   **50.** $a^{-4p}$.

## Art. 6. Pages 21–22

**1.** $4a^2b(1-3ab)$.    **2.** $3a^4(7a^2-11+15a^3)$.    **3.** $(a^2+3b)(a^2-3b)$.
**4.** $(4-5a^2)(16+20a^2+25a^4)$.    **5.** $(2x+3y^3)(4x^2-6xy^3+9y^6)$.
**6.** $3(r-4s)(r+4s)$.    **7.** $(x+y)(x-y)(x^2-xy+y^2)(x^2+xy+y^2)$.
**8.** $(3a+b)^2$.    **9.** $(3+x)(x+3y)$.    **10.** $(a-b+2)^2$.
**11.** $(a-2b)(a-3b)$.    **12.** $(x+3y)(x-2y)$.    **13.** $mn^2(n+3m)(n-3m)$.
**14.** $(a^2+b)(a^2+3b)$.    **15.** $a^2(a^2-2b^2)(a^4+2a^2b^2+4b^4)$.
**16.** $3y(x+2y)(x^2-2xy+4y^2)$.    **17.** $(2x-5)(3x+1)$.
**18.** $(a-2b)(x+3y)$.    **19.** $(a+2b)(a+2b-3)$.    **20.** $3(r+3s)(r+s)$.
**21.** $(x-y-2)(x-y-3)$.    **22.** $(a+2b)(3a^2+2c^2)$.
**23.** $(2ab-c^2)(4a^2b^2+2abc^2+c^4)$.    **24.** $(m-3n+2mn)(m-3n-2mn)$.
**25.** $(x+2y)(x-2y+4z)$.    **26.** $2(a-b^2)(2a+3b^2)$.
**27.** $(x^2+4x+8)(x^2-4x+8)$.    **28.** $(a+3)(a-3)(2a^2+3)$.
**29.** $3(x-y)(x+y)$.    **30.** $-9y(x^2+xy+y^2)$.
**31.** $-(a+b)(7a^2-13ab+7b^2)$.    **32.** $(r^4+2\sqrt{2}\,r^2s+4s^2)(r^4-2\sqrt{2}\,r^2s+4s^2)$.
**33.** $(a^2+2ab-2b^2)(a^2-2ab-2b^2)$.    **34.** $(x+y)^2(x-y)(x^2-xy+y^2)$.
**35.** $(a^4+9b^2)(a^2+3b)(a^2-3b)$.
**36.** $4b(a+b)(a^2+2ab+4b^2)(3a^2+6ab+4b^2)$.
**37.** $(2m+n)(2m-n)(m+2n)(m-2n)$.
**38.** $(a+2b^2)(a-2b^2)(a+2b)(a^2-2ab+4b^2)$.
**39.** $(x+2y+1)(x-y+1)$.    **40.** $(2a-b+1)(a+3b-1)$.

321

## Art. 7.  Pages 24–26

**1.** $2 - 5a$.    **2.** $5a^3 - 6$.    **3.** $xy(2y - x)$.    **4.** $(15x - 7)/3x^2$.
**5.** $(2b^2 + 3ab - 4a^2)/ab^2$.    **6.** $2/x(3 - x)$.    **7.** $3a^2/(a^3 - b^3)$.
**8.** $4/(9 - 4x^2)$.    **9.** $4a/(4a^2 - b^2)$.    **10.** $2/(y - x)$.    **11.** $4ab/(2b + c)$.
**12.** $b^2/(a^3 - b^3)$.    **13.** $1/(x - 2)^2$.    **14.** $a - 2$.    **15.** $1$.
**16.** $25x^3/(3x - 2y)$.    **17.** $(x + 3)(x + 1)^2$.
**18.** $7(y - 1)/(x - 2y)(3x + y)$.    **19.** $0$.    **20.** $-1$.    **21.** $2(x + 2)/x$.
**22.** $-(2x + y)/2x$.    **23.** $(a - 1)/2(a + 1)$.    **24.** $2(a + 2b)/(a - 2b)$.
**25.** $-6x^2/(3x - 2)^2$.    **26.** $-1/2x(x + h)$.    **27.** $-3/(x + 1)(x + h + 1)$.
**28.** $-4/(x - 4)(x + h - 4)$.    **29.** $-2/x(2 + 3x)$.    **30.** $4/(4 - x^2)$.
**31.** $-30x(3 + 2x)^{\frac{1}{2}}$.    **32.** $6x/\sqrt{3 - 2x}$.    **33.** $1/(1 - x^2)^{\frac{3}{2}}$.    **34.** $1/\sqrt{x^2 + 4}$.
**35.** $1/x\sqrt{x^2 - 1}$.    **36.** $-3/(x^2 - 3)^{\frac{3}{2}}$.    **37.** $2\sqrt{a^2 - x^2}$.
**38.** $-a/x^2\sqrt{a^2 + x^2}$.    **39.** $6/x(3 + 4x^2)$.    **40.** $1/2x\sqrt{bx - a}$.
**41.** $x^2/(a^2 - x^2)^{\frac{3}{2}}$.    **42.** $\sqrt{a^2 - x^2}/x$.    **43.** $8x^2\sqrt{a^2 - x^2}$.
**44.** $2x^2/\sqrt{a^2 - x^2}$.    **45.** $x^2/(x^2 + a^2)^{\frac{3}{2}}$.    **46.** $2\sqrt{x^2 + a^2}$.    **47.** $2\sqrt{2ax - x^2}$.
**48.** $-nx^n/\sqrt{2ax - x^2}$.    **49.** $a(1 - 2n)/x^n\sqrt{2ax - x^2}$.    **50.** $8(a^2 - x^2)^{\frac{3}{2}}$.

## Arts. 8–9.  Page 29

**1.** $V = \frac{4}{3}\pi r^3$.    **2.** $V = \frac{1}{3}\pi r^2 h$.    **3.** $A = \frac{1}{4}\sqrt{3}\, s^2$.
**4.** $(a)$ $x > 0$, all $y$; $(b)$ $x < 0$, all $y$; $(c)$ $x = 0$, $y \neq 0$.    **6.** $V = 2\pi r^2\sqrt{25 - r^2}$.
**7.** $V = \frac{1}{3}\pi r^2(10 \pm \sqrt{100 - r^2}\,)$.    **8.** $V = 4\pi r^4/(r^2 - 36)$.
**9.** One value; $x \neq 2$ and $x \neq -2$.    **10.** Two values; $y < 0$, $y = 0$, and $y > 1$.

## Art. 10.  Page 30

**1.** $-5, 1, -9$.    **2.** $\sqrt{13}, 5, \sqrt{21}$; $g(0) = 3$.    **3.** $0, 1, -\frac{2}{3}$; $x = -2$.
**4.** $-F(x, y)$.    **5.** $19, 2x - y + x^4 y^2$.    **6.** $-1, F(x, y)$.    **10.** $a + d = 0$.

## Art. 11.  Page 35

**1.** $-\frac{3}{4}$.    **2.** $\frac{7}{5}$.    **3.** $-1, 2$.    **4.** $-2, -\frac{1}{3}$.    **5.** $-2, -1, 2$.    **6.** $1$.
**7.** $\pm\sqrt{3}, \pm 2$.    **8.** $\pm\sqrt{2}$.    **9.** $\pm\frac{3}{2}$.    **10.** $\pm 1$.    **17.** $(0, 0), (1, 1)$.
**18.** $(a)$ I, II; $(b)$ I, III.    **19.** $(1, 1)$.    **20.** $(a)$ I, II; $(b)$ I, III.

## Supplementary Exercises, Chapter II.  Pages 35–36

**1.** $10x - 2x^2$ in.$^2$    **2.** $360x - 78x^2 + 4x^3$ in.$^3$    **3.** $\frac{1}{4}x\sqrt{256 - x^2}$ in.$^2$
**4.** $\frac{1}{4}(8 + x)\sqrt{192 + 16x - x^2}$ in.$^2$    **5.** $12x^2 - 12x + 2$; $27x^4 - 18x^2 + 2$.
**6.** $2x^4$; $4x^4 - 16x^3 + 24x^2 - 16x + 5$.    **7.** $2.5$.    **8.** $3$.    **10.** $16$.

## Arts. 12–13.  Pages 40–41

**1.** $\pi/6$, $-\pi/4$, $2\pi/3$, $7\pi/4$, $5\pi/3$, $7\pi/6$, $-3\pi/4$, $3\pi/2$, $3\pi$, $10\pi/3$.
**2.** $60°, 270°, 150°, -135°, 540°, 420°, 330°, 405°, 390°, 1440°$.
**3.** $(a)$ $\pi/3$; $(b)$ $\pi/4$, $\pi/4$, $\pi/2$; $(c)$ $3\pi/5$.

**4.** (a) $17\pi/30$; (b) $34\pi/5$.    **5.** 1.178, 1.833, 12.72, 0.01425.    **6.** $97°\,24'$.
**7.** $240°\,39'$.    **8.** $21°\,12'$.    **9.** $14°\,19'$.    **10.** $25°\,43'$.    **11.** $2°\,0'$.
**12.** $359°\,49'$.    **13.** $658°\,54'$.    **14.** $1°\,0'$.    **15.** $180°\,1'$.    **16.** 0.4189.
**17.** 0.9250.    **18.** 0.6516.    **19.** 0.1934.    **20.** 0.1815.    **21.** 1.521.
**22.** 1.000.    **23.** 0.1303.    **24.** 0.1614.    **25.** 10.77.    **26.** $365\pi/3$.
**27.** $\pi/4$, $\pi/3$, $5\pi/12$.    **29.** $(2n+1)\pi/4$.    **30.** $(3n+1)\pi/3$, $(6n+1)\pi/6$.

### Art. 14.   Page 42

**1.** 20 in.$^2$    **2.** 47.8 in.$^2$    **3.** $s = \sqrt{2\theta A}$.    **4.** 16 in.    **5.** 31.4 in.
**6.** 84.0 rpm.    **7.** 31.4 ft./sec.    **8.** 1520 ft./sec.    **9.** 101 ft.    **10.** 6 in.
**11.** 18.5 mi./sec.    **12.** 31'.    **13.** 2750 rpm.    **14.** $2\pi r/\sqrt{r^2 + h^2}$.
**15.** $\pi r\sqrt{r^2 + h^2}$.

### Art. 15.   Pages 46–47

**1.** II.    **2.** IV.    **3.** I.    **4.** IV.    **5.** I.    **6.** III.    **7.** I.    **8.** II.
**9.** III.    **10.** I.    **11.** III.    **12.** I.    **13.** I.    **14.** IV.    **15.** II.
**16.** cot 0, csc 0; tan $(\pi/2)$, sec $(\pi/2)$; cot $\pi$, csc $\pi$; tan $(3\pi/2)$, sec $(3\pi/2)$.
**20.** $0 \leqq \text{vers}\,\theta \leqq 2$; $0 \leqq \text{covers}\,\theta \leqq 2$; $0 \leqq \text{hav}\,\theta \leqq 1$.

### Art. 16.   Page 51

**13.** $\sqrt{3}+1$.    **14.** 1.    **15.** 0.    **16.** 0.    **17.** $-1$.    **18.** $-\frac{1}{2}$.    **19.** 1.
**20.** $\sqrt{3}$.    **21.** $-2$.    **22.** $\sqrt{6}$.    **23.** 1.    **24.** 3.    **25.** 1.    **26.** 0.
**27.** 1.    **28.** 1.    **29.** 1.    **30.** $\sqrt{2}-1$.

### Art. 17.   Pages 57–59

**1.** 8.00, 10.00.    **2.** 2.65, 4.80.    **3.** 3.33, 6.01.    **4.** 8.00, 8.94.
**5.** 4.20, 5.60.    **6.** 7.63, 13.8.    **7.** 7.02, 7.98.    **8.** 6.55, 3.21.
**9.** $\sqrt{2mn/(m+n)}$.    **10.** $2mn/(m^2+n^2)$.    **11.** $63°$.    **12.** $15°$.    **13.** $20°$.
**14.** $25°$.    **15.** $2°$.    **16.** 14.1, 16.6.    **17.** 16.4, 36.1.    **18.** 1.75, 5.37.
**19.** 0.224, 0.530.    **20.** 159, 237.    **21.** 49.0, 89.2.    **22.** 2.90, 4.70.
**23.** $37°\,53'$, 8.55.    **24.** $45°\,1'$, 447.    **25.** $40°\,23'$, 12.1.    **26.** 14.0 ft.
**27.** $86°\,52'$.    **28.** $35°\,50'$.    **29.** 1.55 in.    **30.** 1.50, 2.60, 3.00 in.
**31.** 91 ft. 3 in.    **32.** 115 in.$^2$    **33.** 24.4 ft.    **34.** $4\frac{1}{2}$ in.    **36.** 10.5 in.
**37.** 9.66 in.    **38.** 309 in.$^2$    **39.** $\frac{1}{2}r^2(\theta - \sin\theta)$.    **40.** 109 ft.    **41.** 21 ft. 3 in.
**44.** 11.8 in.$^2$    **45.** $a(\tan\alpha)[\tan(\beta+\theta) - \tan\beta]/(\tan\alpha - \tan\beta)$.
**46.** $\frac{1}{6}a^3\tan\theta$.    **47.** $a^2(1+\sec\theta)$.    **48.** $a - 2b\cot\theta$.    **49.** $a\tan\alpha\csc\beta$.

### Art. 18.   Page 63

**7.** 0.9781.    **8.** $-0.9063$.    **9.** $-2.2460$.    **10.** 0.9781.    **11.** 0.7660.
**12.** $-0.4040$.    **13.** $-0.6428$.    **14.** 0.4226.    **15.** $-0.2079$.    **16.** $-0.7604$.
**17.** $-4.4494$.    **18.** 0.8711.    **19.** 0.6442.    **20.** 0.1304.    **21.** $-0.8573$.
**22.** 0.    **23.** 0.    **24.** sec $\theta$.    **25.** cos $\theta$ − sin $\theta$.    **26.** 0.    **27.** 0.    **28.** 0.
**29.** $-\cos^2\theta - \sin^2\theta$.    **30.** 0.

### Art. 19. Page 67

**31.** $\rho \cos \theta = 2$.    **32.** $\rho \sin \theta + 4 = 0$.    **33.** $\rho(2 \cos \theta + \sin \theta) = 3$.
**34.** $2\rho(\cos \theta - 2 \sin \theta) = 1$.    **35.** $\rho = 3$.    **36.** $\rho = 4 \sin \theta$.
**37.** $\rho + 2 \cos \theta = 0$.    **38.** $\rho^2 - 2\rho(2 \cos \theta + \sin \theta) + 4 = 0$.
**39.** $\sin \theta = \rho \cos^2 \theta$.    **40.** $\cos \theta = \rho^2 \sin^3 \theta$.    **41.** $x^2 + y^2 = 16$.
**42.** $x^2 + y^2 = 3y$.    **43.** $x + 2 = 0$.    **44.** $y + 3x = 1$.
**45.** $x^2 + y^2 + 4x = 5$.    **46.** $x^2 + y^2 - 2y = 8$.    **47.** $x^3 + xy^2 - 2y = 3x$.
**48.** $y^2 = 8(x + 2)$.    **49.** $3x^2 + 4y^2 + 6x = 9$.    **50.** $x^2 - 3y^2 + 20y = 25$.

### Supplementary Exercises, Chapter III. Pages 67–68

**1.** $A = s^2/2\theta$ in.$^2$    **2.** 3.37 in.    **3.** 19 in.
**4.** $P = 2(r_2 - r_1) + 2A/(r_2 - r_1)$.    **5.** 0.    **6.** 0.    **7.** 0.    **8.** −1.    **9.** 2.
**10.** 2.    **11.** 29.4 in.    **12.** $t = \frac{1}{3}b \sec \theta + \frac{1}{4}(a - b \tan \theta)$ hr.
**13.** $L = a \csc \theta + b \sec \theta$ ft.    **14.** 4940 mi.    **15.** $35° 16'$.    **16.** 0.    **17.** 0.
**18.** 0.    **19.** $-2 \sin \theta \cos \theta$.

### Arts. 20–21. Page 74

**1.** Rational integral.    **2.** Rational fractional.    **3.** Rational fractional.
**4.** Irrational.    **5.** Rational integral.    **6.** Rational fractional.
**7.** Rational fractional.    **8.** Transcendental.    **9.** Transcendental.
**10.** Transcendental.    **14.** 1; 1, 1, 1.    **15.** 2; 2, 1, 2.    **16.** 2; 2, 2, 2.
**17.** 4; 2, 2, 2.    **18.** 4; 2, 2.    **19.** 6; 3, 3.    **20.** 11; 11, 5.

### Art. 22. Page 78

**1.** $\pm\sqrt{1 - \cos^2 \theta}$, $\pm(\tan \theta)/\sqrt{1 + \tan^2 \theta}$, $\pm 1/\sqrt{1 + \cot^2 \theta}$, $\pm\sqrt{\sec^2 \theta - 1}/\sec \theta$,
$1/\csc \theta$.    **2.** $\pm(\sin \theta)/\sqrt{1 - \sin^2 \theta}$, $\pm\sqrt{1 - \cos^2 \theta}/\cos \theta$, $1/\cot \theta$,
$\pm\sqrt{\sec^2 \theta - 1}$, $\pm 1/\sqrt{\csc^2 \theta - 1}$.    **3.** $\pm\sqrt{1 - \sin^2 \theta}/\sin \theta$,
$\pm(\cos \theta)/\sqrt{1 - \cos^2 \theta}$, $1/\tan \theta$, $\pm 1/\sqrt{\sec^2 \theta - 1}$, $\pm\sqrt{\csc^2 \theta - 1}$.
**4.** $\pm 1/\sqrt{1 - \sin^2 \theta}$, $1/\cos \theta$, $\pm\sqrt{1 + \tan^2 \theta}$, $\pm\sqrt{1 + \cot^2 \theta}/\cot \theta$,
$\pm(\csc \theta)/\sqrt{\csc^2 \theta - 1}$.    **5.** $1/\sin \theta$, $\pm 1/\sqrt{1 - \cos^2 \theta}$, $\pm\sqrt{1 + \tan^2 \theta}/\tan \theta$,
$\pm\sqrt{1 + \cot^2 \theta}$, $\pm(\sec \theta)/\sqrt{\sec^2 \theta - 1}$.    **6.** $\sin \theta = \frac{12}{13}$, $\tan \theta = \frac{12}{5}$.
**7.** $\cos \theta = -\frac{1}{2}\sqrt{2}$, $\tan \theta = -1$.    **8.** $\sin \theta = -\frac{1}{4}\sqrt{15}$, $\cos \theta = -\frac{1}{4}$.
**9.** $\sin \theta = -\frac{2}{5}\sqrt{5}$, $\cos \theta = \frac{1}{5}\sqrt{5}$.    **10.** $\sin \theta = \frac{3}{10}\sqrt{10}$, $\cos \theta = -\frac{1}{10}\sqrt{10}$.
**11.** $\sin \theta = -\frac{1}{2}$, $\cos \theta = -\frac{1}{2}\sqrt{3}$.    **14.** $\pm\sqrt{(m^2 + n^2)/2mn}$.
**15.** $\pm(m^2 + n^2)/2mn$.

### Arts. 24–25. Page 87

**1.** Yes.    **2.** Yes.    **3.** Yes.    **4.** Yes.    **5.** Yes.    **6.** Yes.    **7.** Yes.
**8.** Yes.    **9.** Yes.    **10.** Yes.    **11.** Yes.    **12.** No.    **13.** No.    **14.** Yes.
**15.** No.    **17.** $x = 1$.    **18.** $x = -2$.    **19.** $x = \pm 2$.

### Art. 26. Page 91

**1.** $\pi/6$, $5\pi/6$.    **2.** $0$, $\pi/2$, $3\pi/2$.    **3.** $\pi$.    **4.** $7\pi/6$, $3\pi/2$, $11\pi/6$.
**5.** $\pi/3$, $5\pi/3$.    **6.** $0$, $\pi$, $3\pi/2$.    **7.** $0$, $\pi/12$, $5\pi/12$, $\pi/2$, $\pi$, $13\pi/12$, $3\pi/2$, $17\pi/12$.

**8.** $\pi/12$, $5\pi/12$, $7\pi/12$, $11\pi/12$, $13\pi/12$, $17\pi/12$, $19\pi/12$, $23\pi/12$.
**9.** $\pi/2$, $5\pi/6$, $7\pi/6$, $3\pi/2$.  **10.** $7\pi/6$, $3\pi/2$, $11\pi/6$.  **11.** $3\pi/4$, $5\pi/4$.
**12.** $\pi/3$, $4\pi/3$.  **13.** $\pi/6$, $\pi/3$, $7\pi/6$, $4\pi/3$.  **14.** $0$, $2\pi/3$, $4\pi/3$.
**15.** $0$, $3\pi/8$, $\pi/2$, $7\pi/8$, $\pi$, $11\pi/8$, $3\pi/2$, $15\pi/8$.  **16.** $7\pi/6$, $11\pi/6$.
**17.** $\pi/2$, $2\pi/3$, $3\pi/2$, $5\pi/3$.  **18.** $2\pi/3$, $5\pi/3$.  **19.** $\pi/3$, $5\pi/3$.  **20.** $0$.
**21.** $0$, $\pi/6$, $\pi$, $11\pi/6$.  **22.** $\pi/4$, $3\pi/4$, $5\pi/4$, $7\pi/4$.  **23.** $\pi/2$, $7\pi/6$, $3\pi/2$, $11\pi/6$.
**24.** $0$, $0.464$, $\pi$, $3.605$.  **25.** $\pi/2$.  **26.** $0.927$, $\pi$, $5.356$.
**27.** $\pi/6$, $5\pi/6$, $7\pi/6$, $11\pi/6$.  **28.** $\pi/2$, $3\pi/2$.  **29.** $0.643$.  **30.** $4.069$.
**31.** No solution.  **32.** No solution.  **33.** $0$, $\pi/4$, $3\pi/4$, $\pi$, $5\pi/4$, $7\pi/4$.
**34.** $\pi/4$, $5\pi/4$.  **35.** $0$, $\pi$.  **36.** $0$, $\pi/2$, $\pi$, $3\pi/2$.  **37.** $0$, $0.464$, $\pi$, $3.605$.
**38.** $2\pi/3$, $4\pi/3$.  **39.** $2.034$, $5.176$.  **40.** No solution.

## Supplementary Exercises, Chapter IV. Pages 91–92

**1.** Rational fractional.  **2.** Transcendental.  **3.** Rational integral.
**4.** Rational integral.  **13.** $\pi$.  **14.** $\pi/6$.  **15.** $\pi/4$.  **16.** $3\pi/4$.
**17.** $0.6434$.  **18.** $\pi/2$.  **19.** $\pi$.  **20.** $5\pi/4$.

## Arts. 27–28. Pages 98–99

**1.** $x = 1$, $y = 2$.  **2.** $x = 2$, $y = -3$.  **3.** Incompatible.  **4.** Dependent.
**5.** $x = 2$, $y = -1$, $z = 1$.  **6.** Dependent.  **7.** Incompatible.
**8.** $x = 1$, $y = 0$, $z = -6$.  **9.** $x = \frac{1}{2}$, $y = -3$, $z = 0$.
**10.** $x = 3$, $y = 7$, $z = -5$.  **11.** $k = 7$.  **12.** $c = 5$; $y = 1$, $z = -3$.
**13.** $a = 1$; $x = 1$, $y = 1$.  **14.** $5F - 9C = 160$.  **15.** $32$.  **16.** $40°$, $20°$, $120°$.
**17.** $7, 27, 49$.  **18.** $365$.  **19.** $3$.  **20.** $\pi/4$, $\pi/12$.  **24.** $617$.

## Art. 29. Page 103

**1.** $x = 3$, $y = -4$.  **2.** $x = -3$, $y = -8$.
**3.** $x = \pm 2$, $y = \pm 3$; $x = \pm 2$, $y = \mp 3$.  **4.** $x = -4$, $y = 2$.
**5.** $x = 0$, $y = 0$; $x = 1$, $y = 2$.  **6.** $x = 4$, $y = -2$, $z = -1$.
**7.** $x = 3$, $y = 3$, $z = -3$.  **8.** $x = -2$, $y = -5$, $z = -1$.
**9.** $x = 1$, $y = 2$, $z = 3$.
**10.** $x = 1$, $y = -1$, $z = -1$; $x = k$, $y = 0$, $z = 0$; $x = 0$, $y = k$, $z = 0$; $x = 0$, $y = 0$, $z = k$.

## Art. 30. Page 111

**1.** $-23$.  **2.** $30$.  **3.** $450$.  **4.** $-906$.  **5.** $0$.  **6.** $0$.
**8.** $ab(a - 1)(b - 1)(b - a)$.  **9.** $abc(a + b)(a - b)(b + c)(b - c)(c + a)(c - a)$.

## Arts. 31–34. Pages 119–120

**1.** $1, 0, 1, -1$.  **2.** $1, 2, -1, -2$.  **3.** $0, 2, -1, 3$.  **4.** $2, 1, -3, 1$.
**5.** $-1, -3, 2, 5$.  **6.** $1, 4, \frac{1}{2}, 3$.  **7.** $1, 0, 0, -1, 1$.  **8.** $0, -1, 1, 2, 0$.
**9.** $-4, -8, 8, 4, -8$.  **10.** $2$.  **11.** $-1, -8$.
**12.** $x = (5w - 1)/7$, $y = (64 - 47w)/77$, $z = (w + 74)/77$.
**13.** $x = 2z - w + 1$, $y = 3w - z - 5$.  **14.** $x = 2$, $y = -1$, $z = 3$.
**15.** $K = -1$; $x = 4$, $y = -2$, $z = -3$.

## Supplementary Exercises, Chapter V.　Pages 120-122

**1.** $K = (2n - 1)/(3n - 2)$.　　**4.** $a, b$.　　**5.** 0.

## Art. 35.　Pages 128-129

**6.** $\frac{63}{65}, \frac{16}{65}$.　　**7.** $-\frac{16}{65}, \frac{63}{65}$.　　**8.** $(\sqrt{5} + 10\sqrt{3})/20, (5\sqrt{3} + 2\sqrt{5})/20$.
**9.** $\sqrt{2}/2, -\sqrt{2}/10$.　　**10.** $-(2\sqrt{6} + \sqrt{15})/20, -(6\sqrt{10} - 1)/20$.
**18.** $6°, 30°, 78°$.　　**19.** $5°, 85°$.　　**20.** $28°, 62°$.　　**21.** $114° 40', 125° 20'$.

## Art. 36.　Page 131

**3.** $\sqrt{3} - 2$.　　**4.** $-\frac{63}{16}, -\frac{33}{56}$.　　**5.** $-\frac{7}{11}, -\frac{1}{13}$.　　**6.** $5\sqrt{2}/4, \sqrt{2}/8$.
**7.** $(54 + 25\sqrt{2})/28, -(54 - 25\sqrt{2})/28$.

## Art. 37.　Pages 134-135

**1.** $\frac{120}{169}, -\frac{119}{169}, -\frac{120}{119}$.　　**2.** $-\frac{24}{25}, \frac{7}{25}, -\frac{24}{7}$.　　**3.** $\frac{120}{169}, -\frac{119}{169}, -\frac{120}{119}$.
**4.** $-\frac{24}{25}, -\frac{7}{25}, \frac{24}{7}$.　　**5.** $\frac{3}{5}, -\frac{4}{5}, -\frac{3}{4}$.　　**26.** $0, \pi/3, \pi, 5\pi/3$.
**27.** $0, 2\pi/3, 4\pi/3$.　　**28.** $\pi/6, \pi/2, 5\pi/6, 3\pi/2$.　　**29.** $\pi/6, 5\pi/6, 3\pi/2$.
**30.** $0, \pi/3, \pi/2, 2\pi/3, \pi, 4\pi/3, 3\pi/2, 5\pi/3$.　　**31.** $0, \pi$.　　**32.** $0, \pi$.
**33.** $0, \pi/4, \pi, 5\pi/4$.　　**34.** $0, 0.643, \pi, 3\pi/2$.　　**35.** $\pi/3, 3\pi/4, 5\pi/3, 7\pi/4$.

## Art. 38.　Pages 137-138

**1.** $\frac{1}{2}\sqrt{2 + \sqrt{3}}, \frac{1}{2}\sqrt{2 - \sqrt{3}}, 2 + \sqrt{3}$.
**2.** $\frac{1}{2}\sqrt{2 + \sqrt{2}}, \frac{1}{2}\sqrt{2 - \sqrt{2}}, \sqrt{2} + 1$.
**3.** $\frac{1}{2}\sqrt{2 + \sqrt{2}}, -\frac{1}{2}\sqrt{2 - \sqrt{2}}, -(\sqrt{2} + 1)$.
**4.** $\frac{1}{2}\sqrt{2 - \sqrt{2}}, -\frac{1}{2}\sqrt{2 + \sqrt{2}}, -(\sqrt{2} - 1)$.　　**5.** $\frac{1}{4}\sqrt{6}, \frac{1}{4}\sqrt{10}, \frac{1}{5}\sqrt{15}$.
**6.** $\frac{1}{3}\sqrt{6}, \frac{1}{3}\sqrt{3}, \sqrt{2}$.　　**7.** $\frac{3}{10}\sqrt{10}, -\frac{1}{10}\sqrt{10}, -3$.　　**8.** $\frac{1}{26}\sqrt{26}, -\frac{5}{26}\sqrt{26}, -\frac{1}{5}$.
**9.** $\frac{1}{5}\sqrt{5}$.　　**10.** $-\frac{7}{10}\sqrt{2}$.　　**11.** $\frac{1}{5}$.　　**12.** $\frac{1}{4}\sqrt{10}$.　　**13.** $-(\sqrt{10} - 3)$.
**25.** $\pi$.　　**26.** $\pi/2, 3\pi/2$.　　**27.** $0, 2\pi/3, 4\pi/3$.　　**28.** $0, \pi, 3\pi/2$.　　**29.** 1.066.
**30.** 2.696, 5.158.

## Art. 39.　Pages 140-141

**1.** $\frac{1}{4}(\sqrt{3} - 1)$.　　**2.** $\frac{1}{4}\sqrt{2}$.　　**3.** $-\frac{1}{4}(\sqrt{3} + 2)$.　　**4.** $-\frac{1}{4}(\sqrt{3} - \sqrt{2})$.
**5.** $-\frac{1}{4}(\sqrt{2} + \sqrt{3})$.　　**6.** $\frac{1}{2}\sqrt{6}$.　　**7.** $\frac{1}{2}\sqrt{2}$.　　**8.** $-\frac{1}{2}\sqrt{6}$.　　**9.** $-\frac{1}{2}\sqrt{6}$.
**10.** $\sqrt{2}$.　　**36.** $0, \pi/4, 3\pi/4, \pi, 5\pi/4, 7\pi/4$.　　**37.** $0, \pi/2, \pi, 3\pi/2$.
**38.** $0, \pi/2, \pi, 3\pi/2$.　　**39.** $\pi/4, \pi/2, 3\pi/4, 5\pi/4, 3\pi/2, 7\pi/4$.
**40.** $0, \pi/4, \pi/2, 3\pi/4, \pi, 5\pi/4, 3\pi/2, 7\pi/4$.
**41.** $\pi/8, 3\pi/8, \pi/2, 5\pi/8, 7\pi/8, 9\pi/8, 11\pi/8, 3\pi/2, 13\pi/8, 15\pi/8$.
**42.** $0, \pi/3, \pi/2, \pi, 3\pi/2, 5\pi/3$.　　**43.** $\pi/4, \pi/3, 3\pi/4, 5\pi/4, 5\pi/3, 7\pi/4$.
**44.** $0, \pi/3, 2\pi/3, \pi, 4\pi/3, 5\pi/3$.　　**45.** $\pi/6, \pi/2, 2\pi/3, 5\pi/6, 7\pi/6, 4\pi/3, 3\pi/2, 11\pi/6$.

## Supplementary Exercises, Chapter VI.　Page 149

**1.** $\pi/4, 3\pi/4, 5\pi/4, 7\pi/4$.　　**2.** $0, \pi/4, 3\pi/4, \pi, 5\pi/4, 7\pi/4$.
**3.** $\pi/2, 7\pi/12, 11\pi/12, 3\pi/2, 19\pi/12, 23\pi/12$.

**4.** $\pi/6$, $\pi/4$, $3\pi/4$, $5\pi/6$, $5\pi/4$, $7\pi/4$.     **5.** 0, $7\pi/12$, $11\pi/12$, $\pi$, $19\pi/12$, $23\pi/12$.

**6.** 0, $\pi/6$, $\pi/2$, $5\pi/6$, $\pi$, $3\pi/2$.     **7.** $\pi/8$, $\pi/2$, $5\pi/8$, $9\pi/8$, $3\pi/2$, $13\pi/8$.

**8.** 0, $3\pi/8$, $7\pi/8$, $\pi$, $11\pi/8$, $15\pi/8$.

### Art. 43. Pages 158–159

**1.** $a^6 - 6a^5b + 15a^4b^2 - 20a^3b^3 + 15a^2b^4 - 6ab^5 + b^6$.

**2.** $a^5 + 10a^4b + 40a^3b^2 + 80a^2b^3 + 80ab^4 + 32b^5$.

**3.** $x^7 + 14x^6 + 84x^5 + 280x^4 + 560x^3 + 672x^2 + 448x + 128$.

**4.** $a^6 + 6a^4 + 15a^2 + 20 + 15a^{-2} + 6a^{-4} + a^{-6}$.

**5.** $x^{10} - 5x^8y + 10x^6y^2 - 10x^4y^3 + 5x^2y^4 - y^5$.

**6.** $a^{18} - 12a^{15}b^2 + 60a^{12}b^4 - 160a^9b^6 + 240a^6b^8 - 192a^3b^{10} + 64b^{12}$.

**7.** $a^3 - 6a^{\frac{5}{2}}x^{\frac{1}{2}} + 15a^2x - 20a^{\frac{3}{2}}x^{\frac{3}{2}} + 15ax^2 - 6a^{\frac{1}{2}}x^{\frac{5}{2}} + x^3$.

**8.** $a^{\frac{8}{3}} - 4a^2x^{\frac{2}{3}} + 6a^{\frac{4}{3}}x^{\frac{4}{3}} - 4a^{\frac{2}{3}}x^2 + x^{\frac{8}{3}}$.

**9.** $729/x^6 - 486/x^4 + 135/x^2 - 20 + 5x^2/3 - 2x^4/27 + x^6/729$.

**10.** $x^5/y^{10} - 5x^2/y^7 + 10/xy^4 + 10/x^4y + 5y^2/x^7 - y^5/x^{10}$.

**11.** $a^{-5} - 5a^{-4}b^{-2} + 10a^{-3}b^{-4} - 10a^{-2}b^{-6} + 5a^{-1}b^{-8} - b^{-10}$.

**12.** $64a^{12} + 96a^{\frac{19}{2}} + 60a^7 + 20a^{\frac{9}{2}} + 15a^2/4 + 3/8a^{\frac{1}{2}} + 1/64a^3$.

**13.** $a^5d^5 - 5a^4bcd^4 + 10a^3b^2c^2d^3 - 10a^2b^3c^3d^2 + 5ab^4c^4d - b^5c^5$.

**14.** $a^{-5} - 5a^{-3} + 10a^{-1} - 10a + 5a^3 - a^5$.

**15.** $x^3/y^9 + 6x^2/y^6 + 15x/y^3 + 20 + 15y^3/x + 6y^6/x^2 + y^9/x^3$.

**16.** $a^4/b^2 - 4a^{\frac{5}{2}}/b^{\frac{1}{2}} + 6ab - 4b^{\frac{3}{2}}/a^{\frac{1}{2}} + b^4/a^2$.

**17.** $12a + 40a^3 + 12a^5$.     **18.** $2x^7 + 42x^5y^2 + 70x^3y^4 + 14xy^6$.

**19.** $a^3 - 3a^2b + 3ab^2 - b^3 + 3a^2c - 6abc + 3b^2c + 3ac^2 - 3bc^2 + c^3$.

**20.** $a^4 - 4a^3 + 10a^2 - 16a + 19 - 16a^{-1} + 10a^{-2} - 4a^{-3} + a^{-4}$.

**21.** $280x^3y^4$.    **22.** $126a^5b^5$.    **23.** $-252a^{10}b^5$.    **24.** $-48{,}384x^{10}y^3$.

**25.** $792a^{-2}$.    **26.** $45a^6b^9$.    **27.** $-252$.    **28.** 70.    **29.** $1120a^4$.

**30.** $960a^{12}$.    **31.** 1,030,301.    **32.** 96,059,601.    **33.** 1.1040808032.

**34.** 85,873.40257.    **35.** 0.262144.    **36.** 1.9487171.    **37.** 6.    **38.** 255.

**39.** 7.    **40.** 3.

### Supplementary Exercises, Chapter VII. Page 159

**3.** $1 + 4x + 10x^2 + 20x^3 + 31x^4 + 40x^5 + 44x^6 + 40x^7 + 31x^8 + 20x^9 + 10x^{10} + 4x^{11} + x^{12}$.

### Art. 44. Page 163

**1.** $\sqrt{2}$, $7\pi/4$.    **2.** $3\sqrt{2}$, $\pi/4$.    **3.** $2\sqrt{2}$, $3\pi/4$.    **4.** $2\sqrt{2}$, $5\pi/4$.

**5.** 2, $11\pi/6$.    **6.** 4, $4\pi/3$.    **7.** 5, $\pi/2$.    **8.** 4, $\pi$.    **9.** 5, 0.6434.

**10.** 5, 4.069.    **11.** $\sqrt{5}$, 1.107.    **12.** 13, 2.747.    **13.** $\frac{1}{2} + \frac{1}{2}\sqrt{3}\,i$.

**14.** $-2\sqrt{2} + 2\sqrt{2}\,i$.    **15.** $2i$.    **16.** 3.    **17.** $-5$.    **18.** $-\frac{1}{2} + \frac{1}{2}\sqrt{3}\,i$.

**19.** $-3i$.    **20.** $0.5403 + 0.8415i$.

### Art. 45. Page 167

**1.** $5 + 5i$.    **2.** $11 + i$.    **3.** $6 - 9i$.    **4.** $-2 + 3i$.    **5.** $7 + 3i$.

**6.** $-5 + 2i$.    **7.** $10 + 10i$.    **8.** $38 - 8i$.    **9.** $15 - 29i$.    **10.** $52 + 36i$.

**11.** $28 + 16i$.    **12.** 7.    **13.** $2\sqrt{15} - 2i$.    **14.** $18 - 5\sqrt{3}\,i$.    **15.** $-2 - 2i$.

**16.** $-4$.    **17.** $3 - 2i$.    **18.** $-i$.    **19.** $\frac{1}{2} + \frac{1}{2}i$.    **20.** $\frac{1}{2}\sqrt{3} - \frac{1}{2}i$.

**21.** $-1$.  **22.** $-1 - i$.  **23.** $-\frac{3}{4}$.  **24.** $-\frac{1}{64}(a^2 + b^2)$.  **25.** $x = 1, y = 1$.
**26.** $x = 2, y = -1$.  **27.** $x = 3, y = 2$.
**28.** $x = \pm 1, y = \pm\sqrt{2}; x = \pm 1, y = \mp\sqrt{2}$.  **29.** $x = -1, y = \pm 2$.
**30.** $x = 0, y = 0; x = \frac{1}{2}, y = -\frac{1}{4}$.  **32.** 0.  **33.** 1.

### Arts. 46–47.  Page 170

**1.** $\frac{1}{2}\sqrt{2} + \frac{1}{2}\sqrt{2}\, i$.  **2.** $\frac{1}{2}\sqrt{2} - \frac{1}{2}\sqrt{2}\, i$.  **3.** $-2i$.  **4.** $-4$.  **5.** $-8$.
**6.** $-8i$.  **7.** $-\frac{1}{2} + \frac{1}{2}\sqrt{3}\, i$.  **8.** 512.  **9.** $i$.  **10.** $\frac{1}{2} + \frac{1}{2}\sqrt{3}\, i$.
**11.** $\frac{1}{2} + \frac{1}{2}\sqrt{3}\, i$.  **12.** $-1024i$.  **13.** $7776i$.  **14.** $-128 + 128\sqrt{3}\, i$.

### Art. 48.  Page 172

**1.** $2, -1, \pm\sqrt{3}\, i$.  **2.** $\pm 2, \pm 2i$.  **3.** $-3, \frac{3}{2} \pm \frac{3}{2}\sqrt{3}\, i$.
**4.** $2, 0.6180 \pm 1.902i, -1.618 \pm 1.176i$.
**5.** $-1, 0.8090 \pm 0.5878i, -0.3090 \pm 0.9511i$.
**6.** $\pm 1, \frac{1}{2} \pm \frac{1}{2}\sqrt{3}\, i, -\frac{1}{2} \pm \frac{1}{2}\sqrt{3}\, i$.  **7.** $\sqrt{2} \pm \sqrt{2}\, i, -\sqrt{2} \pm \sqrt{2}\, i$.
**8.** $\pm 2i, \sqrt{3} \pm i, -\sqrt{3} \pm i$.  **9.** $\pm\frac{1}{2}(\sqrt{3} + i), \pm\frac{1}{2}(1 - \sqrt{3}\, i)$.
**10.** $\pm(1 + \sqrt{3}\, i), \pm(\sqrt{3} - i)$.
**11.** $-\sqrt{2} - \sqrt{2}\, i, -1.035 + 3.864i, 3.864 - 1.035i$.
**12.** $\pm(0.8315 + 0.5556i), \pm(0.5556 - 0.8315i)$.
**13.** $\sqrt{2} - \sqrt{2}\, i, 0.5176 + 1.932i, -1.932 - 0.5176i$.
**14.** $\frac{1}{2}\sqrt{2} + \frac{1}{2}\sqrt{2}\, i, -0.9659 + 0.2588i, 0.2588 - 0.9659i$.
**15.** $i, \pm 0.9511 + 0.3090i, \pm 0.5878 - 0.8090i$.
**16.** $-i, \pm 0.5878 + 0.8090i, \pm 0.9511 - 0.3090i$.
**17.** $\pm\frac{1}{2}\sqrt{2}\,(1 - i), \pm(0.9659 + 0.2588i), \pm(0.2588 + 0.9659i)$.
**18.** $\pm\frac{1}{2}\sqrt{2}\,(1 + i), \pm(0.2588 - 0.9659i), \pm(0.9659 - 0.2588i)$.
**19.** $\pm\frac{1}{2}\sqrt{2}\,(3 + i)$.  **20.** $1.292 + 0.2012i, -0.8203 + 1.018i, -0.4718 - 1.220i$.

### Supplementary Exercises, Chapter VIII.  Page 173

**9.** $u = x + a, v = y + b$.  **10.** $u = ax - by, v = bx + ay$.
**11.** $u = x^2 - y^2, v = 2xy$.  **12.** $u = x^3 - 3xy^2, v = 3x^2y - y^3$.
**13.** $u = x^4 - 6x^2y^2 + y^4, v = 4x^3y - 4xy^3$.
**14.** $u = x/(x^2 + y^2), v = -y/(x^2 + y^2)$.
**15.** $u = (ax + by)/(x^2 + y^2), v = (bx - ay)/(x^2 + y^2)$.

### Art. 49.  Page 176

**1.** $2, 3$.  **2.** $3, 4$.  **3.** $1, -2$.  **4.** $3, \frac{1}{2}$.  **5.** $-3, -\frac{1}{4}$.  **6.** $1 \pm 2i$.
**7.** $-2 \pm \sqrt{2}$.  **8.** $1 \pm \frac{1}{3}\sqrt{3}$.  **9.** $\frac{1}{5}(-1 \pm \sqrt{6})$.  **10.** $\sqrt{3}, \frac{1}{3}\sqrt{3}$.
**11.** $-1 \pm \frac{1}{2}\sqrt{14}$.  **12.** $\frac{1}{16}(3 \pm \sqrt{73})$.  **13.** $9a, -5a$.  **14.** $3, 2a$.
**15.** $\sqrt{a}, \sqrt{a}$.  **16.** $\frac{1}{2}(-c \pm \sqrt{c^2 - 4k})$.  **17.** $(2b \pm \sqrt{4b^2 - 6ac})/2a$.
**18.** $(-c \pm \sqrt{c^2 - 4ab})/2b$.  **19.** $(-a \pm \sqrt{a^2 - 4bc})/2c$.
**20.** $(b \pm \sqrt{b^2 + 4ac})/2a$.  **21.** $(s \pm \sqrt{s^2 - 4rt^2})/2r$.
**22.** $(-n^2 \pm \sqrt{n^4 - 4mp^3})/2m$.  **23.** $2i, 3i$.  **24.** $\frac{1}{2}i, -2i$.
**25.** $-a \pm \sqrt{a^2 - b^2}$.  **26.** $(-Kg \pm \sqrt{K^2g^2 - 4mk^2g})/2m$.  **27.** $\pm 1, \pm 2$.
**28.** $\pm\sqrt{2}, \pm 2i$.  **29.** $1 - i, -2 + i$.  **30.** $3 - 4i, 4 - 3i$.

## Art. 50.  Pages 179–181

1. $x^2 - 10x + 21 = 0$.  2. $x^2 - 2x - 24 = 0$.  3. $x^2 + 4 = 0$.
4. $x^2 - 2x - 1 = 0$.  5. $x^2 - 4x + 13 = 0$.
6. $x^2 - (7 + i)x + 14 + 2i = 0$.  7. $x^2 + ax - 12a^2 = 0$.
8. $x^2 - 2ax + a^2 - b^2 = 0$.  9. $x^2 - 2\sqrt{a}x + a - b^2 = 0$.
10. $x^2 - 2ax + a^2 + b^2 = 0$.  11. $2, -4$.  12. $a = -3, b = -6$.  13. $1$.
14. $-1$.  15. $1, -2$.  16. $1, -\frac{9}{4}$.  17. $5, -3$.  18. $\pm 4$.  19. $1, 64$.
20. $-2, -\frac{1}{4}$.  21. 8 in., 5 in.  22. 24 in., 12 in.  23. 9.32 sec.
24. 37.3 ft.  25. 1.61 or 7.70 sec.  30. 1728 cu. in.  31. 12.

## Art. 51.  Pages 183–184

1. $\pm 2, \pm \sqrt{3}$.  2. $\pm \frac{1}{2}\sqrt{2}, \pm 3i$.  3. $4$.  4. $64, -8$.  5. $5, -2$.
6. $18$.  7. $2, -1, -1 \pm \sqrt{3}\,i, \frac{1}{2} \pm \frac{1}{2}\sqrt{3}\,i$.  8. $626$.  9. $\pm 3, \pm \sqrt{14}$.
10. $4, \frac{1}{4}$.  11. $\frac{1}{2}, -2$.  12. $0, -\frac{217}{216}$.  13. $0, 4$.  14. $0, 4, -6$.
15. $1, -\frac{5}{9}$.  16. $6, \frac{2}{5}$.  17. $\frac{1}{9}, \frac{25}{4}$.  18. $\frac{64}{121}$.  19. $1, -2 \pm \sqrt{3}$.
20. $2, \pm 3, \frac{1}{2}$.  21. $9$.  22. $3, \frac{1}{2} \pm \frac{1}{2}\sqrt{5}$.  23. $2, \frac{17}{10}, -\frac{1}{2}, -\frac{4}{5}$.
24. $1, \pm 2, -3$.  25. $-2 \pm \sqrt{5}, -2 \pm i$.

## Art. 52.  Page 185

1. No solution.  2. No solution.  3. No solution.  4. No solution.
5. No solution.  6. No solution.  7. $90°$.  8. $150°$.  9. $70°\,32'$.
10. $194°\,29'$.  11. No solution.  12. No solution.  13. $135°$.  14. $64°\,16'$.
15. $360°$.  16. No solution.  17. $45°$.  18. $35°\,16'$.  19. $75°\,58'$.
20. $90°$.

## Art. 53.  Pages 190–192

1. $(3, 2), (3, -2), (-3, 2), (-3, -2)$.  2. $(2, i), (2, -i), (-2, i), (-2, -i)$.
3. $(3, 1)$.  4. $(2, 3), (-\frac{1}{5}, -\frac{18}{5})$.  5. $(2, -1), (-\frac{142}{59}, \frac{149}{59})$.
6. $(1, 2), (-\frac{11}{5}, \frac{14}{5})$.  7. $(2, -1), (-\frac{53}{2}, -\frac{21}{2})$.  8. $(-2, -2), (-\frac{16}{15}, -\frac{13}{10})$.
9. $(0, 0), (-1, 1)$.  10. $(2, 2), (-2, 2), (-\frac{1}{4}, \frac{1}{4})$.  11. $(0, -1), (2, -3)$.
12. $(5, 2), (-5, -2), (0, i), (0, -i)$.  13. $(\frac{1}{2}, -3), (-\frac{1}{2}, 3), (\frac{3}{2}, -1), (-\frac{3}{2}, 1)$.
14. $(4, 2), (-4, -2)$.
15. $(2, 2), (-2, -2), (-1 + \sqrt{5}, -2 + \sqrt{5}), (-1 - \sqrt{5}, -2 - \sqrt{5})$.
16. $(1, -2), (-1, 2), (\frac{1}{3}\sqrt{3}, -\frac{4}{3}\sqrt{3}), (-\frac{1}{3}\sqrt{3}, \frac{4}{3}\sqrt{3})$.
17. $(-1, 3), (-1, -2), (\frac{1}{3}\sqrt{15}, \frac{1}{3}\sqrt{15}), (-\frac{1}{3}\sqrt{15}, -\frac{1}{3}\sqrt{15})$.
18. $(1, 0), (1, 3), (-\frac{1}{6}, \frac{7}{6})$.  19. $(0, 0), (1, -1), (7, \frac{7}{5})$.
20. $(1, -2), (2, -1)$.  21. $(1, 2)$.  22. $(4, 0), (0, 4)$.  23. $(3, 1)$.
24. $(1, -2, 1), (2, 1, -1)$.  25. $(3, -1, 2), (-3, 1, -2)$.  26. $\pm r\sqrt{m^2 + 1}$.
27. $k^2 = a^2m^2 - b^2$.  28. $a^2 + 2b^2 = c^2$.
29. $(\sqrt{2}, -\sqrt{2}), (-\sqrt{2}, \sqrt{2}), (\frac{11}{85}\sqrt{170}, \frac{1}{85}\sqrt{170}), (-\frac{11}{85}\sqrt{170}, -\frac{1}{85}\sqrt{170})$.
31. $C_1F_2 = C_2F_1$.  32. $(2, 1), (1, 2), (1, -2), (-2, 1)$.  35. $(1, 3), (3, 1)$.
36. 3 in., 5 in.  37. $\frac{6}{5}\sqrt{5}$ in., $\frac{24}{5}\sqrt{5}$ in.  38. $5, 7$.  39. $234$.
40. 6, 8, 24 in.; $11 - \sqrt{89}, 11 + \sqrt{89}, 16$ in.

## Supplementary Exercises, Chapter IX.  Pages 192–193

1. 64 in.  2. 7 in.  3. 54 mph.  4. 40.5 sq. in.  5. $\frac{1}{8}(P^2 - 4D^2)$ sq. in.
7. $\frac{1}{2}, -2, 1 \pm \sqrt{3}\,i, \frac{1}{4}(-1 \pm \sqrt{3}\,i)$.  8. $4$.  9. $-\frac{13}{9}$.  10. $\pm \sqrt{5}$.

**11.** $\pm\frac{5}{3}$.    **12.** $-\frac{15}{4}$.    **13.** $36°\,52'$.    **14.** $75°\,58'$.    **15.** $14°\,29'$.
**16.** $101°\,32'$.    **17.** $(3, 2)$, $(-2, -3)$.    **18.** $(5, 3)$, $(-3, -1)$.
**19.** $(0, 0, 1)$, $(0, 1, 0)$, $(1, 0, 0)$.
**20.** $(1, 2, 2)$, $(2, 1, 2)$, $(-1 + i, -1 - i, -3)$, $(-1 - i, -1 + i, -3)$.

### Art. 54.   Pages 196–197

**1.** $56, 290$.    **2.** $-72, -765$.    **3.** $-2, -84$.    **4.** $2\sqrt{3}, 40\sqrt{3}$.
**5.** $47, 266$.    **6.** $19, -2$.    **7.** $-100, 20$.    **8.** $80, 80$.    **9.** $252, -60$.
**10.** $46$.    **11.** $d = 3$.    **12.** $d = -6$.    **13.** $\frac{95}{2}$.    **14.** $8, 4$.    **15.** $20, -3$.
**16.** $n = (d - 2a_1 \pm \sqrt{d^2 - 4a_1 d + 4a_1^2 + 8ds_n})/2d$.
**19.** $a_n = (-d \pm \sqrt{d^2 - 4a_1 d + 4a_1^2 + 8ds_n})/2$.
**20.** $n = (2a_n + d \pm \sqrt{4a_n^2 + 4a_n d + d^2 - 8ds_n})/2d$.
**25.** $\frac{1}{2}(2n - 1)g$.    **27.** $864$.    **28.** $369$.

### Art. 55.   Pages 199–200

**1.** $768, 1023$.    **2.** $4374, 3280$.    **3.** $\frac{1}{2}, 255$.    **4.** $8, \frac{1}{2}$.    **5.** $729, 2059$.
**6.** $32, 98$.    **7.** $-2 - 2i, -5i$.    **8.** $3, 15 + 9\sqrt{2}$.    **9.** $r = \sqrt{2}$.
**10.** $4, 8 + 8i$.    **11.** $s_n = a_n(1 - r^n)/(1 - r)r^{n-1}$.    **14.** $26\frac{39}{128}$ in.    **15.** $47$ ft.
**16.** $-\frac{1}{2}, -2$.    **18.** $2, 6, 10$; $2, -12, -26$.    **19.** $1, 5, 9$; $1, \frac{5}{9}, \frac{1}{9}$.    **20.** $2$.
**24.** $2, -6, 18, -54$.    **25.** $4, 8, 12, 16$.    **26.** $5, 15, 45, 135$.    **27.** $248$.
**30.** $3, 9, 27$.

### Arts. 56–58.   Pages 206–207

**1.** $3$.    **2.** $\frac{2}{3}$.    **3.** $\frac{9}{2}(\sqrt{3} + 1)$.    **4.** $-1 - \frac{1}{2}\sqrt{2}$.    **5.** $\frac{2}{3} + \frac{1}{6}\sqrt{10}$.
**6.** $\frac{7}{9}$.    **7.** $\frac{29}{99}$.    **8.** $\frac{16}{45}$.    **9.** $\frac{13102}{999}$.    **10.** $\frac{49678}{999}$.    **11.** $\frac{1}{24}$.
**12.** $-\frac{1}{19}$.    **13.** $12, -12$.    **14.** $a$.    **15.** $2xy/(x + y)$.    **17.** $4, 12$.
**19.** $-6, -12$.    **23.** $\frac{1}{4}, -\frac{1}{2}$.

### Supplementary Exercises, Chapter X.   Pages 207–208

**1.** $2$.    **2.** $4(2 + \sqrt{2})$.    **3.** $2\pi$.    **4.** $2\pi(2 + \sqrt{2})$.    **5.** $\frac{1}{3}\sqrt{3}$.

### Art. 61.   Page 215

**1.** $x > 5$.    **2.** $x < 3$.    **3.** $-2 < x < 2$.    **4.** $x < -1$ or $x > 3$.
**5.** $x < -4$ or $x > \frac{1}{3}$.    **6.** $x \neq -3$.    **7.** $-1 < x < \frac{3}{2}$.    **8.** All values.
**9.** $0 < x < 4$.    **10.** $-1 < x < 5$.    **11.** $0 < x < 2$ or $x > 2$.
**12.** $0 < x < \sqrt{2}$ or $x > \sqrt{2}$.    **13.** $x \neq 0$.    **14.** $x \neq -2, x \neq 2$.
**15.** $x > 7$.    **16.** $x < -3$.    **17.** $x \geqq \frac{1}{4}$.    **18.** $x \leqq 4$.    **19.** $x < 2$ or $x > 3$.
**20.** $x < -2$ or $x > \frac{1}{2}$.    **21.** $-2 < x < 0$ or $x > 1$.
**22.** $-3 < x < 0$ or $0 < x < 1$.    **23.** $-\sqrt{3} < x < -\sqrt{2}$ or $\sqrt{2} < x < \sqrt{3}$.
**24.** $x < -1$ or $1 < x < 3$.    **25.** $x < -1$ or $0 < x < 2$.    **26.** $2 < x < \frac{9}{4}$.
**27.** $x > 6$.    **28.** $0 < x < 3$.    **29.** $0 \leqq x < 4$.    **30.** $x > 10$.

### Art. 62.   Page 217

**11.** $0 \leqq x < \pi/4$, $3\pi/4 < x < 5\pi/4$, or $7\pi/4 < x < 2\pi$.
**12.** $0 \leqq x < \pi/6$, $5\pi/6 < x < 7\pi/6$, or $11\pi/6 < x < 2\pi$.

**13.** $\pi < x < 2\pi$.　　**14.** $0 < x < \pi/2$ or $3\pi/2 < x < 2\pi$.

**15.** $0 < x < \pi$ or $7\pi/6 < x < 11\pi/6$.

**16.** $0 \leqq x < \pi/3$, $\pi/2 < x < 3\pi/2$, or $5\pi/3 < x < 2\pi$.

**17.** $\pi/3 < x < \pi$ or $5\pi/3 < x < 2\pi$.　　**18.** $\pi/6 < x < \pi/2$ or $5\pi/6 < x < 3\pi/2$.

**19.** $2\pi/3 < x < \pi$ or $\pi < x < 4\pi/3$.

**20.** $0 < x < \pi/2$, $\pi/2 < x < 3\pi/4$, $\pi < x < 3\pi/2$, or $3\pi/2 < x < 7\pi/4$.

**21.** $\pi/4 < x < \pi/2$ or $5\pi/4 < x < 3\pi/2$.

**22.** $0 \leqq x < \pi/3$ or $5\pi/3 < x < 2\pi$.　　**23.** $0 < x < 2\pi$.　　**24.** No values.

**25.** $\pi/6 < x < \pi/3$ or $7\pi/6 < x < 4\pi/3$.

**26.** $0 \leqq x < \pi/2$, $3\pi/4 \leqq x < 3\pi/2$, or $7\pi/4 \leqq x < 2\pi$.

**27.** $x \neq \pi/2$ and $3\pi/2$.　　**28.** $x \neq 0$ and $\pi$.　　**29.** All values.　　**30.** $x \neq 3\pi/2$.

### Supplementary Exercises, Chapter XI.　Pages 217–218

**1.** $x < -2$, $0 < x < 1$, or $x > 2$.　　**2.** $0 < x < 1$.

**3.** $\pi/2 < x < \pi$ or $3\pi/2 < x < 2\pi$.　　**4.** $0 < x < \pi/2$ or $3\pi/2 < x < 2\pi$.

**5.** $0 < x < \pi/2$ or $\pi < x < 3\pi/2$.　　**6.** $0 \leqq x < \pi/4$.

### Art. 63.　Pages 221–222

**1.** $x = \frac{1}{3}(y - 2)$.　　**2.** $x = \pm\sqrt{y + 1}$.　　**3.** $x = 2 \pm \sqrt{y + 4}$.

**4.** $x = y^2 + 3$.　　**5.** $x = 2/(1 - y)$.　　**6.** $x = 3y/(1 - y)$.

**7.** $x = (y - 4)/(2y - 1)$.　　**8.** $x = \pm\sqrt{(y + 1)/(y - 1)}$.

**9.** $x = 4/(y - 1)^2$.　　**10.** $x = \pm 2y/\sqrt{y^2 - 4}$.　　**11.** All $x$; all $y$.

**12.** All $x$; $y \geqq -1$.　　**13.** All $x$; $y \geqq -4$.　　**14.** $x \geqq 3$; all $y$.

**15.** $x \neq 0$; $y \neq 1$.　　**16.** $x \neq -3$; $y \neq 1$.　　**17.** $x \neq \frac{1}{2}$; $y \neq \frac{1}{2}$.

**18.** $x \neq \pm 1$; $y \leqq -1$ or $y > 1$.　　**19.** $x > 0$; $y \neq 1$.

**20.** $x < -2$ or $x > 2$; $y < -2$ or $y > 2$.　　**34.** $x = (-b \pm \sqrt{b^2 - 4ac + 4ay})/2a$.

### Art. 64.　Pages 225–226

**1.** 0.　　**2.** 0.　　**3.** 0.　　**4.** $\pi/3$.　　**5.** $\pi/3$.　　**6.** $\pi/4$.　　**7.** $-\pi/6$.

**8.** $5\pi/6$.　　**9.** $-\pi/4$.　　**10.** $\frac{1}{2}\sqrt{3}$.　　**11.** $\frac{1}{2}\sqrt{3}$.　　**12.** $\sqrt{2}$.　　**13.** $-\sqrt{3}$.

**14.** $-\frac{1}{2}\sqrt{3}$.　　**15.** $-2$.　　**16.** 1.　　**17.** 0.　　**18.** $-\frac{1}{2}\sqrt{3}$.　　**19.** $\frac{1}{2}\sqrt{3}$.

**20.** 0.　　**21.** $\sqrt{3}$.　　**22.** $-1$.　　**23.** 0.　　**24.** $\frac{1}{16}(\sqrt{105} - 3)$.

**25.** $\frac{1}{16}(3\sqrt{15} - \sqrt{7})$.　　**26.** $\frac{1}{2}$.　　**27.** $-\frac{1}{2}\sqrt{3}$.　　**28.** $\frac{24}{25}$.　　**29.** $\frac{24}{7}$.

**30.** $\frac{1}{10}\sqrt{10}$.　　**31.** $\frac{5}{26}\sqrt{26}$.　　**32.** $-5\pi/12$.　　**33.** $\pi$.　　**34.** 0.403.

**35.** 0.0474.

### Art. 65.　Pages 227–228

**1.** 0.　　**2.** $\frac{1}{2}\sqrt{3}$.　　**3.** $-\frac{1}{3}\sqrt{3}$.　　**4.** $\frac{1}{2}\sqrt{2}$.　　**5.** No solution.　　**6.** 0.

**7.** 0, 1.　　**8.** 0, 1.　　**9.** 0.　　**10.** 0.　　**11.** 0.　　**12.** $\frac{1}{2}$.　　**13.** 0, $\pm 1$.

**14.** 1.　　**15.** 1.　　**16.** 0.　　**17.** 0, 1.　　**18.** $\frac{3}{4}$.　　**19.** $\frac{1}{2}\sqrt{2}$.　　**20.** 0, $\frac{4}{5}$.

### Supplementary Exercises, Chapter XII.　Page 228

**9.** $x = 1 + \sin\frac{1}{2}(y - 3)$; $0 \leqq x \leqq 2$; $3 - \pi \leqq y \leqq 3 + \pi$.

**10.** $x = \frac{1}{2} + \cos(y + 2)$; $0 \leqq x \leqq 1$; $-2 \leqq y \leqq \pi - 2$.

**11.** $x = \sin^2 (y/2); 0 \leqq x \leqq 1; 0 \leqq y \leqq \pi.$

**12.** $x = (\pm\sqrt{9 + 8 \tan^2 y} - 3)/4 \tan y;$ all $x;$ $-\pi < y < \pi.$

**13.** $x = (1 \pm \sqrt{1 - 24 \tan^2 y})/12 \tan y;$ all $x;$ $-\frac{1}{12}\sqrt{6} \leqq \tan y \leqq \frac{1}{12}\sqrt{6}.$

**14.** $x = (\cos y)/\sqrt{5 - 4\sin y};$ $-\frac{1}{2} \leqq x \leqq \frac{1}{2};$ $\pi/6 \leqq y \leqq 5\pi/6.$

**15.** $x = \arcsin(y + 1 - \sqrt{2y + 1}); 0 \leqq x \leqq \pi/2, 0 \leqq y \leqq 1 + \sqrt{2};$
$x = \pi - \arcsin(y + 1 - \sqrt{2y + 1}), \pi/2 \leqq x \leqq \pi, 1 + \sqrt{2} \geqq y \geqq 0.$

### Arts. 66–67.   Pages 231–233

**1.** 500%.   **2.** 13.4%.   **3.** 44%.   **4.** 72.8%.   **5.** 14.7 meters.   **6.** $\sqrt{2}$.
**7.** 25% decrease.   **9.** 1% decrease.   **10.** 13.6% decrease.
**11.** 11.8% increase.   **12.** 38.8% decrease.   **13.** 12.9%.   **14.** $10°31'$.
**15.** 152% increase.   **16.** 23.2%.   **17.** 61.1%.   **18.** 58.7%.   **19.** 7.42%.
**20.** $7°59'$ increase.   **21.** 143,000,000 miles.   **22.** 41.4%.   **24.** 21.5%.
**25.** 18.8% decrease.

### Supplementary Exercises, Chapter XIII.   Page 244

**1.** 1%.   **2.** 3.68% increase.   **3.** 34.5% decrease.   **4.** 32.4% decrease.
**5.** 9.6%.

### Arts. 70–71.   Pages 252–253

**1.** 3.   **2.** 0, 6.   **3.** 3, $-2$.   **4.** 1, $-\frac{3}{5}$.   **5.** $\log 2$.   **6.** $\frac{1}{4}\ln 3$.
**7.** $\ln 2, \ln 3$.   **8.** $\frac{1}{2}\ln(2 + \sqrt{5})$.   **9.** 0.   **10.** $\pm\frac{1}{2}\ln(2 + \sqrt{3})$.
**11.** $x = \frac{1}{2}\ln[(y + \sqrt{y^2 + 4})/2].$   **12.** $x = \pm\ln[(y + \sqrt{y^2 - 4})/2].$
**13.** $x = \ln[(y \pm \sqrt{y^2 - 8})/4].$   **14.** $x = \frac{1}{2}\ln[(y + \sqrt{y^2 + 12})/2].$
**15.** $x = \pm\ln[(1 + \sqrt{1 - y^2})/y].$   **16.** $x = \ln[(1 + \sqrt{1 + y^2})/y].$
**17.** $x = \ln[(y + \sqrt{y^2 + 12y})/2].$   **18.** $x = \frac{1}{2}\ln[(1 + y)/2(1 - y)].$
**19.** $x = 2 + \ln[(y \pm \sqrt{y^2 - 12})/2].$   **20.** $x = 2\ln[(y + \sqrt{y^2 + 8})/4].$
**26.** $x = \ln(y + \sqrt{y^2 + 1}).$   **27.** $x = \frac{1}{2}\ln[(1 + y)/(1 - y)].$
**28.** $x = \frac{1}{2}\ln[(y + 1)/(y - 1)].$   **29.** $x = \pm\ln[(1 + \sqrt{1 - y^2})/y].$
**30.** $x = \ln[(1 \pm \sqrt{1 + y^2})/y].$

### Art. 72.   Page 255

**1.** 46.   **2.** 5, $-2$.   **3.** $3 - \sqrt{10}$.   **4.** $\sqrt{110} - 10$.   **5.** $e$.   **6.** 3.
**7.** 29.   **8.** $\sqrt{7} - 1$.   **9.** $\frac{2}{3}e$.   **10.** 8.   **11.** $y = 10x^2$.
**12.** $y^3 = (x + 2)^2$.   **13.** $y = x^3 e^{2x}$.   **14.** $y = e^{-3x}\cos x$.   **15.** $y = -9x^2$.
**16.** $x = e^{xy}$.   **17.** $2xe^y = 3\cos 2x$.   **18.** $x^3 + y^3 = 3xy$.
**19.** $x^4 - 16y^4 = x^2 y^2$.   **20.** $y = 3e^{-2x}\sin 2x$.   **21.** $x = 2e^y/(e^y + 2)$.
**22.** $x = e^{2y}/(2e^{2y} - 1)$.   **23.** $x = \sqrt{4 + e^y} - 2$.   **24.** $x = \frac{1}{2}(e^y \pm \sqrt{e^{2y} - 3e^y})$.
**25.** $x = \frac{1}{4}(e^y - e^{-y})$.   **26.** $x = \frac{1}{2}(e^y + 4e^{-y})$.   **27.** $x = 2/(e^y + e^{-y})$.
**28.** $x = e^{2y}/(2e^y - 4)$.   **29.** $x = 16e^y/(e^y - 1)^2$.
**30.** $x = 10^y + 2 - \sqrt{4(10^y) + 2}$.

### Art. 73.   Pages 261–262

**1.** 0.2273.   **2.** 3.536.   **3.** 303.5.   **4.** 0.03439.   **5.** 5560.   **6.** 0.3296.

**7.** 700.3. **8.** 126.0. **9.** 6.077. **10.** 23,400. **11.** 2.006. **12.** 1200.
**13.** 498,300,000. **14.** 43.28. **15.** 125.6. **16.** 0.00473. **17.** 0.0576.
**18.** 992.5. **19.** 23,200. **20.** 1330. **21.** $2.99 \times 10^{10}$ cm./sec.
**22.** 0.145 in. **23.** 62.4 lb. **24.** 33.9 ft. **25.** 1.28 sec. **26.** 10.8 lb./in.$^2$
**27.** 64.9 lb./ft.$^3$ **28.** 138 ft./sec. **29.** 944,000 cal. **30.** 8.27 amp.
**31.** 0.0016 sec. **32.** 1.82 ft. **33.** 1.26 ft. **34.** 1.71 ft.$^3$ **35.** 0.582.

### Art. 74. Pages 264–265

**7.** $38° 46'$, $107° 4'$, $34° 10'$. **8.** 228,000. **9.** 183. **10.** 1.15, 0.795.
**11.** 4.17. **12.** 103 ft. **13.** 17.1 ft. **14.** 91.8 ft. **15.** 41.1 ft.
**16.** 30.2 ft. **17.** 35.6. **18.** $52° 35'$. **19.** 102. **20.** 0.859.

### Supplementary Exercises, Chapter XIV. Pages 265–266

**1.** $\ln 7$. **2.** $\ln 2$. **3.** $\ln (1 + 2\sqrt{2})$. **4.** $\sqrt{19} - 1$.
**5.** $\ln (\sqrt{4 + e^2} - 1)$. **6.** $x = \ln [(y + \sqrt{y^2 + 12})/2]$.
**7.** $x = \ln [(y - 1 + \sqrt{9 - 2y + y^2})/4]$. **8.** $x = \frac{1}{9}e^{2y}$.
**9.** $x = \frac{1}{2}(e^y + \sqrt{e^{2y} + 4e^y})$. **10.** $x = \frac{1}{2} \arcsin e^y$. **11.** 30.2 ft.
**12.** 7.39 lb., at angle of $24°$ with 3.75-lb. force. **13.** $93°$. **14.** 3.46 ft.
**15.** 2.34 ft.

### Arts. 75–76. Pages 270–271

**4.** $-2, 4$. **6.** $-2$. **7.** $-23$. **8.** 0. **9.** 0. **10.** 0. **11.** 64.
**12.** 0. **13.** 0. **14.** 0. **15.** 0. **16.** Yes. **17.** No. **18.** Yes.
**19.** Yes. **20.** Yes. **21.** Yes. **22.** Yes. **23.** Yes. **24.** Yes.
**25.** Yes.

### Art. 79. Pages 280–281

**1.** One positive, two complex. **2.** Four complex.
**3.** One negative, two complex. **4.** No positive, one or three negative.
**5.** One positive, four complex. **6.** Zero, four complex.
**7.** One positive, one negative, four complex. **8.** One positive, six complex.
**9.** Six complex. **10.** Four double complex.
**11.** One negative, no or two positive. **12.** One positive, one negative, six complex.
**13.** One positive, one negative, four complex.
**14.** One positive, no or two negative. **15.** No negative; no, two, or four positive.
**16.** Zero and eight complex.

### Art. 80. Page 283

**1.** $-1$. **2.** $\pm 1, -2$. **3.** 0, 3. **4.** $-\frac{1}{2}$. **5.** $\frac{3}{2}$. **6.** None. **7.** $\frac{7}{2}$.
**8.** 2, 2, 4. **9.** $\frac{1}{5}$. **10.** $\frac{1}{4}, \frac{1}{4}, -\frac{1}{4}$. **11.** 3, $-2$. **12.** 1, $\frac{1}{2}, -\frac{2}{3}$. **13.** $\frac{2}{3}$.
**14.** None. **15.** $\pm 1$. **16.** $-4$. **17.** None. **18.** $\pm\frac{1}{2}$. **19.** $\pm\frac{1}{2}$.
**20.** 3.

### Art. 81. Pages 287–288

**1.** 1.414. **2.** 2.646. **3.** $-3.464$. **4.** 2.303. **5.** $-2.414$.
**6.** $-0.5858$. **7.** 1.351. **8.** 2.618. **9.** 2.225. **10.** 1.587.

**11.** $-0.5000 \pm 1.936i$. **12.** $1.000 \pm 2.236i$. **13.** $\pm 0.8165i$.
**14.** $0.5000 \pm 1.323i$. **15.** $-1.000 \pm 1.732i$. **16.** $3\frac{13}{16}$ in. **17.** $5\frac{3}{8}$ in.
**18.** $1\frac{7}{8}$ in. **19.** 11 ft. 3 in. **20.** 0.17365. **21.** 0.93969. **22.** 0.26795.
**23.** 2 ft. 1 in. **24.** 2 ft. 0 in. **25.** 3.20 or 4.71 in.

## Art. 82. Pages 291–292

**1.** $2, -1, -3$. **2.** $-2, \pm 2\sqrt{3}$. **3.** $3, 4, \frac{1}{4}$. **4.** $\sqrt{2}, \sqrt{2}, -2\sqrt{2}$.
**5.** $1, 1, -3, -3$. **6.** $-7, -5, -3, -1$. **7.** $\frac{5}{2}, \frac{5}{4}, \frac{5}{8}$. **8.** $-\frac{1}{2}, -\frac{1}{2}, -\frac{1}{2}, 4$.
**9.** $-10$. **10.** $a = \pm 36, b = \pm 15$. **11.** (a) 0.544; (b) 0.091; (c) 0.010.
**12.** (a) 1.84; (b) 10.99; (c) 101.00. **13.** $m = -A/B$. **15.** $y = 0$.
**16.** $y = \pm 2x$. **17.** $y = x, y = 3x$. **18.** $y = 1, y = \pm x - \frac{1}{2}$.
**19.** $x + y + 1 = 0$. **20.** $y = 8, x + y + 12 = 0, 3x + y = 4$.

## Art. 83. Pages 294–295

**1.** $\pi/2$. **2.** $\pi/3, 3\pi/2, 5\pi/3$. **3.** $0, \pi$. **4.** $7\pi/6, 11\pi/6$.
**5.** $\pi/4, 3\pi/4, 5\pi/4, 7\pi/4$. **6.** $3\pi/2$. **7.** $\pi/3, 5\pi/3$. **8.** No solution.
**9.** 0, 1.231, 5.052. **10.** 0.2527, 2.889. **11.** 0. **12.** 0.6932. **13.** 0.
**14.** No solution. **15.** $-0.6932, -1.099$. **16.** 5. **17.** 2. **18.** 3, 2.676.
**19.** 4. **20.** 2, 2.839. **21.** 1. **22.** 0.4196. **23.** 0, 1. **24.** $\frac{1}{2}$. **25.** 1.

## Supplementary Exercises, Chapter XV. Page 295

**1.** $\pi/6$. **2.** 2.0345. **3.** 0.4055. **4.** 1.238. **5.** $\frac{1}{2}$. **6.** 2.236.
**9.** $k = 0$, quadruple; $k = 2$, double. **11.** $a = -9, b = 4; -1, -3$.

## Art. 84. Pages 298–299

**1.** 20. **2.** 205,200. **3.** 45,600. **4.** 22,050. **5.** 303,600. **6.** 45,540.
**7.** 120. **8.** 325. **9.** 1260. **10.** 12. **11.** 10. **12.** 15. **13.** 3.
**14.** 48. **15.** 130. **16.** 260. **17.** 48. **18.** 72. **19.** 600. **20.** 10,368.
**21.** 30. **22.** 18. **23.** 86,400. **24.** 172,800. **25.** 105.

## Art. 85. Pages 301–302

**1.** 495. **2.** 1485. **3.** 26,400. **4.** $\frac{1}{2}n(n - 1)$. **5.** $\frac{1}{2}n(n - 3)$. **6.** 15.
**7.** $n = 8, r = 4$. **8.** 7920. **9.** 15,102. **10.** 63. **11.** 455. **12.** 91; 13.
**13.** 16,632. **14.** 3780. **15.** 19,008. **16.** 10,395. **17.** 7,484,400.
**18.** $52!/(13!)^4$. **19.** 256. **20.** 70. **21.** 21. **22.** 120. **23.** 20,825.

## Art. 86. Pages 306–307

**1.** $\frac{5}{13}$. **2.** $\frac{7}{10}$. **3.** $\frac{5}{16}$. **4.** $\frac{1}{9}$. **5.** $\frac{2}{9}$. **6.** $\frac{5}{18}$. **7.** $\frac{3}{7}$. **8.** $\frac{7}{13}$.
**9.** $\frac{1}{6}$. **10.** $\frac{4}{9}$. **11.** $\frac{4}{9}$. **12.** $\frac{1}{9}$. **13.** $\frac{2}{7}$. **14.** $\frac{1}{35}$. **15.** $\frac{1}{35}$.
**16.** $\frac{1}{216}$. **17.** $\frac{1}{20825}$. **18.** $\frac{44}{4165}$. **19.** $\frac{92}{833}$. **20.** $\frac{2}{91}$. **21.** $\frac{20}{91}$.
**22.** $\frac{1}{6}$. **23.** $\frac{8}{125}$. **24.** $\frac{8}{225}$. **25.** $\frac{3}{25}$. **26.** $\frac{1}{2}$. **27.** $\frac{37}{63}$. **28.** 0.95.
**29.** $\frac{57}{64}$. **30.** $1 - (1 - p)^n$. **32.** 4, 2, and 1 dollars. **34.** $\frac{16}{31}$.

**1.** 4608.    **2.** $\frac{1}{2}(n+1)(n+2)$.    **3.** 56; 35.    **4.** 604,800.

**5.** $m!(m+1)!/(m-w+1)!$; $m > w-2$.    **6.** $\frac{1}{4}(m^2-m)(n^2-n)$.

**7.** $(m+n-2)!/(m-1)!(n-1)!$    **8.** 0.387.    **9.** $\frac{101}{6664}$.    **10.** 25.

**11.** $(n-1)/(n+3)$.    **12.** $\frac{17}{28}$.    **13.** 3.    **14.** 4.

# Index

Abscissa, 31
Absolute inequalities, 209, 211
Absolute values, 43
  of complex numbers, 162
Addition, 7, 10
  associative, 8
  commutative, 8
  of complex numbers, 163
  of fractions, 12, 13, 23
Algebraic functions, 72
  inverse, 215
  variation of, 233
Algebraic laws, 7, 14
Algebraic quantities, properties of, 7
Amplitude, 162, 240
  fundamental, 170
Angles, 37
  complementary, 52
  functions of, 43
  initial side of, 37
  large, 59
  measurement of, 38, 40
  negative, 37
  of depression, 58
  of elevation, 58
  positive, 37
  terminal side of, 37
  vectorial, 64
Annuity, 200
Antilogarithm, 260
Approximations, 34, 284
Arc, circular, 41
Arccosecant function, 226
Arccosine function, 222
Arccotangent function, 226
Arcsecant function, 226
Arcsine function, 222
Arctangent function, 222
Area, of polygon, 58
  of sector, 41
  of triangle, 58, 147, 264, 265
Argument, 162

Arithmetic progressions, 194
  common difference of, 194
  means of, 195
  sums of, 194
Associative law, 8
Asymptotes, 291, 292
Axes, rectangular, 31
Axis, of imaginaries, 162
  of reals, 162
  polar, 64

Base of logarithmic function, 246
  change of, 248
  common, 248
  natural, 248
Binomial coefficients, 156
Binomial theorem, 153
Braces, 22
Brackets, 22
Briggs's system, 248

Catenary, 251
Characteristic, 258
Circle, inscribed, 265
Circular arc, 41
Circular permutations, 298
Circular system, 38
Classification of functions, 70
Coefficients, binomial, 156
Combinations, 157, 299
Combined variation, 229
Common difference, 194
Common logarithms, 248
Common ratio, 197
Commutative law, of addition, 8
  of multiplication, 8
Complementary angles, 52
Completing the square, 175
Complex fractions, 24
Complex numbers, 160 ff.
  addition of, 163
  amplitude of, 162

Complex numbers, conjugate, 166
  geometric representation of, 162
  modulus of, 162
  polar form of, 162
  product of, 163, 165
  quotient of, 164, 166
  rectangular form of, 162
  roots of, 170
  subtraction of, 163
Complex solutions, 286
Composite numbers, 253
Compound amount, 200
Conditional equations, 69
Conditional inequalities, 209, 212
Conjugate complex numbers, 166
Conjugate complex roots, 272
Constant, 27
  of proportionality, 229
Coordinates, polar, 63
  rectangular, 31
  transformation of, 66
Cosecant function, 44
  of sum or difference, 129
Cosine function, 44
  graph of, 223
  of double angles, 132
  of half angles, 135
  of multiple angles, 134, 169
  of sum or difference, 123, 129
  variation of, 239
Cosine law, 143
Cotangent function, 44
  of sum or difference, 131
Coversed sine function, 47
Critical values, 213

De Moivre's theorem, 167
Decimals, repeating, 204
Defective equations, 85
Defective systems, 116
Degree (algebraic), 71, 74
Degree (angle), 38
Denominator, 8
  lowest common, 23
Dependent equations, 94
  linearly, 96
Dependent events, 303, 304
Dependent variable, 28
Depression, angle of, 58
Descartes's rule, 278

Determinants, 99 ff
  development by minors, 107
  elements of, 99, 101, 103
  of order $n$, 103
  of second order, 99
  of third order, 101
  principal diagonal, 99, 101, 103
  properties, 105–110
  value of, 99, 101, 104
Development by minors, 107
Difference, 12, 13
  of complex numbers, 163
Direct variation, 229
Discriminant, 179
Distributive law, 8
Dividend, 8
Division, 8
  of complex numbers, 164, 165
  of fractions, 13, 23
  synthetic, 268
Divisor, 8
Double angles, 132
Double signs, 20

$e$ (base), 248
Elements of determinants, 99, 101, 103
Elevation, angle of, 58
Ellipse, 292
Empirical probability, 302
Equalities, 69
Equations, conditional, 69
  defective, 85
  dependent, 94, 96
  equivalent, 85
  exponential, 250, 294
  in quadratic form, 181, 184
  incompatible, 94
  inconsistent, 94
  linear, 94, 113
  logarithmic, 253
  quadratic, 174 ff., 292
  rational integral, 267 ff.
  redundant, 85
  solution of, 82, 83
  systems of, 84, 185
  transcendental, 292
  trigonometric, 87, 184, 226, 293
Equivalent equations, 185
Expectation, mathematical, 307

Exponential equations, 250, 294
Exponential functions, 73, 245 ff.
Exponents, 14
    fractional, 15
    negative, 16
    zero, 16
Extraneous solutions, 86

Factor theorem, 268
Factors, 7, 19
Factorials, 104
Factoring, methods of, 19–21
Fibonacci numbers, 159
Fractional functions, 71, 74
Fractional powers, 15, 16
Fractions, 4, 12, 22
    complex, 24
    difference of, 12, 13
    improper, 72
    product of, 13, 23
    proper, 72
    quotient of, 13, 23
    reciprocals of, 13
    sum of, 12, 13, 23
Frequency, 240
Functional notation, 29
Functional variation, 229 ff.
Functions, 27, 28
    algebraic, 72, 219, 233
    classification of, 70
    exponential, 73, 245 ff.
    homogeneous, 74
    hyperbolic, 252, 253
    inverse, 215 ff.
        algebraic, 215
        trigonometric, 73, 222, 226
    irrational, 72
    linear, 93
    logarithmic, 73, 245 ff.
    power, 70, 233, 292
    rational algebraic, 71
        fractional, 71, 74
        integral, 71, 74
        power, 70, 233, 292
    transcendental, 73
    trigonometric, 43 ff., 239
        of large angles, 59
    zeros of, 34, 83
Fundamental amplitude, 170

Geometric progressions, 197
    common ratio of, 197
    means of, 198
    sums of, 197
Geometric representation, of complex
        numbers, 162
    of real numbers, 5
Geometric series, 204
Graphs, of polynomials, 274
    of trigonometric functions, 223, 224
    polar, 65
    rectangular, 32

Half angles, 135
Harmonic progressions, 205
    means of, 205
Haversine function, 47
Homogeneous functions, 74
Homogeneous systems, 114
Hyperbola, 291, 292
Hyperbolic functions, 252, 253

$i$ (imaginary unit), 161
Identities, 69
    trigonometric, 75
Imaginaries, axis of, 162
Imaginary numbers, 161
Imaginary unit, 161
Improper fractions, 72
Incompatible equations, 94
Inconsistent equations, 94
Independent events, 303, 304
Independent variable, 28
Index, 14
Induction, mathematical, 150
Inequalities, 6, 209 ff.
    absolute, 209, 211, 215
    conditional, 209, 212, 215
    trigonometric, 215
Infinite roots, 290
Infinite sequences, 200
Initial side, 37
Inscribed circle, 265
Integers, negative, 4
    positive, 3
Interpolation, 53
Inverse functions, 219 ff.
    algebraic, 219
    trigonometric, 73, 222, 226
Inverse variation, 229

Inversions, 104
Irrational functions, 72
Irrational numbers, 4
Irrational roots, 284

Joint variation, 230

Large angles, functions of, 59
Law of cosines, 143
Law of sines, 142
Law of tangents, 143, 144
Laws, algebraic, 7, 14
Limits, 200
Linear equations, 94, 113
  systems of, 94
Linear functions, 93
Logarithmic computation, 256, 262
Logarithmic equations, 253
Logarithmic functions, 73, 245 ff.
  base of, 246, 248
Logarithmic tables, use of, 259
Lowest common denominator, 23

Mantissa, 258
Mathematical expectation, 307
Mathematical induction, 150
Mathematical probability, 302
Means, arithmetic, 195
  geometric, 198
  harmonic, 205
Mil, 40
Minor, 107
Minute, 38
Modulus, 162
  logarithmic, 260
Mollweide's equations, 149
Multiple angles, 134, 169
Multiple roots, 272
Multiplication, 7
  associative, 8
  commutative, 8
  distributive, 8
  of complex numbers, 163, 165
  of fractions, 12, 13, 23
Mutually exclusive events, 303

Napierian system, 248
Natural system, 248
Negative integers, 4
Negative powers, 16

Non-homogeneous systems, 112
Number systems, 3, 6, 160
Numbers, complex, 160 ff.
  composite, 253
  fractional, 4
  geometric representation, 5, 162
  irrational, 4
  ordering of, 6
  prime, 253
  pure imaginary, 161
  rational, 4
  real, 6
  whole, 3
Numerator, 8

Oblique triangles, 144, 262
  area of, 147, 264
Odds, probable, 303
Ordering of numbers, 6
Ordinate, 31
Origin, 31

Parabola, 179, 292
Parentheses, 12, 22
Pascal's triangle, 157
Period, of sine function, 240
  of tangent function, 242
Permanence, 278
Permutations, 296
  circular, 298
Phase displacement, 240, 242
Polar axis, 64
Polar coordinates, 63
Polar form, 162
Pole, 64
Polygon, area of, 58
  perimeter of, 207
Polynomial, 71, 74
  homogeneous, 74
Positive integers, 3
Power functions, 70, 233, 292
Powers, 14
  fractional, 15
  negative, 16
  zero, 16
Prime numbers, 253
Principal diagonal, 99, 101, 103
Principal values, 223, 224, 226
Probability, 302
  empirical, 302

Probability, mathematical, 302
Product, 7, 8, 9, 10, 11
  of complex numbers, 164, 165
  of fractions, 13, 23
  of functions, 138
Progressions, 194 ff.
  arithmetic, 194
  geometric, 197
  harmonic, 205
Proper fractions, 72
Proportionality constant, 229
Pure imaginary numbers, 161

Quadrants, 32
Quadratic equations, 174 ff., 292
  discriminant of, 179
  in two variables, 185
  number of roots of, 178
  relations between coefficients and
    roots, 177
Quadratic form, equations in, 181, 184
Quadratic formula, 175
Quadratic function of two variables,
    185, 292
  symmetric, 191
Quadratic systems, 186, 191
Quantities, algebraic, 7
Quotient, 8, 10, 12
  of complex numbers, 164, 165
  of fractions, 13, 23

Radian, 38
Radicals, 17
Radicand, 17
Radius vector, 64
Rational functions, 71
  algebraic, 71
  fractional, 71, 74
  graphs, 274
  integral, 71, 74, 267 ff.
  power, 70, 233, 292
Rational numbers, 4
Rational roots, 281
Real numbers, 6
Reals, axis of, 162
Reciprocal, 8
  of a fraction, 13
Rectangular axes, 31
Rectangular coordinates, 31
Rectangular form, 162

Reductio ad absurdum, 4
Reduction, 22
Redundant equations, 85
Redundant systems, 117
Remainder theorem, 268
Repeated trials, 305
Repeating decimals, 204
Right triangles, 51
  area of, 58
Roots, 17, 83, 170
  complex, 286
  extraneous, 86
  infinite, 290
  irrational, 284
  multiple, 272
  of quadratic equations, 177, 179
    equal, 179
  of rational integral equations, 271
    conjugate complex, 272
  rational, 281
  zero, 290
Rule of signs, 278

Secant function, 44
  of sum or difference, 129
Second, 38
Sector, area of, 41
Sequences, infinite, 3, 200
Series, geometric, 204
Sexagesimal system, 38
Signs, of trigonometric functions, 45
  rule of, 278
Simplification, 22
Simultaneous equations, 84, 94
Sine function, 44
  amplitude of, 240
  coversed, 47
  graph of, 223
  of double angles, 132
  of half angles, 135
  of multiple angles, 133, 134, 169
  of sum or difference, 123, 129
  period of, 240
  phase displacement of, 240
  variation of, 239
  versed, 47
Sine law, 141
Solutions, 82, 83
  complex, 286
  extraneous, 86

Solutions, infinite, 290
  irrational, 284
  multiple, 272
  of quadratic equations, 178
  of rational integral equations, 271
  of triangles, 54, 144, 262
  of trigonometric equations, 87, 184,
      226, 293
  rational, 281
  trivial, 114
  zero, 290
Special angles, 47
  functions of, 50
Statistical probability, 302
Subtraction, 7, 11
  of complex numbers, 163
  of fractions, 12, 13
Sum, 7, 8, 12, 13, 23
  of arithmetic progression, 194
  of complex numbers, 163
  of geometric progression, 197
  of geometric series, 204
Sums of functions, 138
Symmetrical quadratic functions, 191
Synthetic division, 268
System, common, 248
  determinant of, 99, 101, 113
  natural, 248
Systems, number, 3, 6, 160
  of equations, 84, 185
    linear, 94, 113
      defective, 116
      homogeneous, 114
      non-homogeneous, 112
      redundant, 117
    quadratic, 186, 191

Tables, logarithmic, use of, 259
  trigonometric, use of, 53
Tangent function, 44
  graph of, 224
  of double angles, 132
  of half angles, 135
  of sum or difference, 129, 130, 131
  period of, 242
  phase displacement of, 242
  variation of, 242
Tangent law, 143, 144
Terminal side, 37
Transcendental equations, 292

Transcendental functions, 73
Transformations, 66, 74
  of coordinates, 66
  trigonometric, 78
Triangle, inscribed circle of, 265
  oblique, 144, 262
    area of, 147, 264, 265
  Pascal's, 157
  right, 51
    area of, 58
Trigonometric equations, 87, 184, 226,
    293
Trigonometric functions, 43 ff., 239
  inverse, 73, 222, 226
Trigonometric identities, 75
Trigonometric inequalities, 215
Trigonometric tables, use of, 53
Trivial solutions, 114

Unity, 8
Unknowns, 70

Values, absolute, 43, 162
  critical, 213
  of determinants, 99, 101, 104
  principal, 223, 224, 226
Variables, 27
  dependent, 28
  independent, 28
Variation, combined, 229
  direct, 229
  functional, 229 ff.
  inverse, 229
  joint, 230
  of algebraic functions, 233
  of sign, 278
  of trigonometric functions, 239
Vectorial angle, 64
Versed sine function, 47
Vinculum, 22

Whole numbers, 3

X-axis, 31

Y-axis, 31

Zero, 8, 10
  of a function, 34, 83, 271, 272, 281,
      284, 286
Zero exponent, 16